FOUNDATIONS
OF PHYSIOLOGICAL
PSYCHOLOGY

HARPER'S PHYSIOLOGICAL PSYCHOLOGY SERIES

UNDER THE EDITORSHIP OF H. PHILIP ZEIGLER

HARPER & ROW, PUBLISHERS

NEW YORK, EVANSTON, AND LONDON

FOUNDATIONS

OF PHYSIOLOGICAL

PSYCHOLOGY

RICHARD F. THOMPSON

ACKNOWLEDGMENTS

(The following publishers and authors are thanked for their permission to reproduce figures from the indicated works. Numbers in parentheses following references refer to the figures in the present text.)

Academic Press Inc., New York

Bureš, J., Petráň, M., and Zachar, J. *Electrophysiological methods in biological research* (2nd ed.). New York: Academic Press, 1962. (3.8)

Doty, R. W., Beck, E. C., and Kooi, K. A. Effect of brain-stem lesions on conditioned responses of cats. *Exper. Neurol.,* 1959, **1,** 360–385. (14.13C)

Eccles, J. C. *The physiology of synapses.* New York: Academic Press, 1964. (7.3D, 7.9A, 7.9B, 7.17)

Eccles, R. M., Kozak, W., and Westerman, R. A. Enhancement of spinal monosynaptic reflex responses after denervation of synergic hind-limb muscles. *Exper. Neurol.,* 1962, **6,** 451–464. (17.13)

Granit, R. Neurophysiology of the retina. Pp. 575–692 in Davson, H. (Ed.) *The eye, 2.* New York: Academic Press, 1962. (10.15A, 10.15B)

Hoyle, G. Neurophysiological studies on "learning" in headless insects. Pp. 203–232 in Treherne, F. E., and Beament, F. W. L. *The physiology of the insect central nervous system.* New York: Academic Press, 1965. (17.8)

Acta Oto-Laryngologica, Uppsala, Sweden

Wersäll, J. Studies on the structure and innervation of the sensory epithelium of the cristae ampullares in the guinea pig. *Acta oto-laryng.*, 1956, Suppl. 126, 1–85. (13.13)

Acta Physiologica Scandinavica Stockholm, Sweden

Granit, R., and Kaada, B. R. Influence of stimulation of central nervous structures on muscle spindles in cat. *Acta physiol. Scand.*, 1952, **27**, 130–160. (13.10, 13.11)

Kaada, B. R. Somato-motor, autonomic and electrocorticographic responses to electrical stimulation of "rhinencephalic" and other structures in primates, cat and dog; study of responses from limbic, sub-callosal, orbito-insular, pyriform and temporal cortex, hippocampus-fornix and amygdala. *Acta physiol. Scand.*, 1951, Suppl. 83, **24**, 1–285. (16.18)

Laursen, A. M. Corpus striatum. *Acta physiol. Scand.*, 1963, Suppl. 211, **59**, 1–106. (13.9)

Ottoson, D. Analysis of the electrical activity of the olfactory epithelium. *Acta physiol. Scand.*, 1956, Suppl. 122, **35**, 1–82. (10.40)

American Association for the Advancement of Science, Washington, D.C.

Bennett, E. L., Diamond, M. C., Krech, D., and Rosenzweig, M. R. Chemical and anatomical plasticity of brain. *Science*, 1964, **146**, No. 3644, 610–619. (Copyright 1964 by the American Association for the Advancement of Science.) (17.2, 17.3)

Davis, H. Enhancement of evoked cortical potentials in humans related to a task requiring a decision. *Science*, 1964, **145**, No. 3628, 182–183. (Copyright 1964 by the American Association for the Advancement of Science.) (15.21B)

Fuster, J. M. Effects of stimulation of brain stem on tachistoscopic perception. *Science*, 1958, **127**, No. 3290, 150. (14.14)

Galambos, R., Sheatz, G., and Vernier, V. Electrophysiological correlates of a conditioned response in cats. *Science*, 1956, **123**, No. 3192, 376–377. (15.24)

Haider, M., Spong, P., and Lindsley, D. B. Attention vigilance and cortical evoked potentials in humans. *Science*, 1964, **145**, No. 3628, 180–182. (Copyright 1964 by the American Association for the Advancement of Science.) (15.21A)

Hernández-Peón, R., Scherrer, H., and Jouvet, M. Modification of electrical activity in cochlear nucleus during "attention" in unanesthetized cats. *Science*, 1956, **123**, No. 3191, 331–332. (15.17)

Rempel, B., and Gibbs, E. L. The berger rhythm in cats. *Science*, 1936, **84**, No. 2180, 334–335. (9.3)

Spong, P., Haider, M., and Lindsley, D. B. Selective attentiveness and cortical evoked responses to visual and auditory stimuli. *Science*, 1965, **148**, No. 3668, 395–397. (Copyright 1965 by the American Association for the Advancement of Science.) (15.22)

Sprague, J. M., Chambers, V. W., and Stellar, E. Attentive, affective and adaptive behavior in the cat. *Science*, 1961, **133**, No. 3447, 165–173. (Copyright 1961 by the American Association for the Advancement of Science.) (14.13D)

The American Institute of Physics, Lancaster, Pennsylvania

Davis, H., Benson, R. W., Covell, W. P., Fernandez, C., Goldstein, R., Katsuki, Y., Legouix, J. P., McAuliffe, D. R., and Tasaki, I. Acoustic trauma in the guinea pig. *J. acoust. Soc. Amer.*, 1953, **25**, 1180–1189. (10.22)

Stevens, S. S., and Davis, H. Psychophysiological acoustics: pitch and loudness. *J. acoust. Soc. Amer.*, 1937, **8**, 1–13. (10.27)

von Békésy, G. The variation of phase along the baselar membrane with sinusoidal vibrations. *J. acoust. Soc. Amer.*, 1947, **19**, 452–460. (10.24)

The American Medical Association, Chicago

Papez, J. W. A proposed mechanism of emotion. *Arch. neurol. Psychiat.*, 1937, **38**, 725–743. (16.1A)

American Physiological Society, Washington, D.C.

Adey, W. R. The sense of smell. Pp. 585–613 in Field, J., et al., *Handbook of physiology, Neurophysiology*, Vol. I, 1959. (10.41)

Anderson, P., Eccles, J. C., and Sears, T. A. Cortically evoked depolarization of primary afferent fibers in the spinal cord. *J. Neurophysiol.*, 1964, **27**, 63–77. (10.44)

Buchwald, J. S., Halas, E. S., and Schramm, S. Progressive changes in efferent unit responses to repeated cutaneous stimulation in spinal cats. *J. Neurophysiol.*, 1965, **28**, 200–215. (17.18, 17.19)

Chamberlain, T. J., Halick, P., and Gerard, R. W. Fixation of experience in the rat spinal cord, *J. Neurophysiol.*, 1963, **26**, 662–673. (17.14)

Chang, H. T. Dendritic potential of the cortical neurone produced by direct electrical stimulation of the cerebral cortex. *J. Neurophysiol.*, 1951, **14**, 1–23. (9.12)

Davis, H. Excitation of auditory receptors. Pp. 565–585 in Field, J., et al., *op. cit.*, Vol. I, 1959. (10.25, 10.26)

Davis, H. Some principles of sensory receptor action. *Physiol. Rev.*, 1961, **41**, 391–416. (10.1)

Diamond, I. T., and Neff, W. D. Ablation of temporal cortex and discrimination of auditory patterns. *J. Neurophysiol.*, 1957, **20**, 300–315. (11.21A, 11.21B)

Doty, R. W. Conditioned reflexes elicited by electrical stimulation of the brain in macaques. *J. Neurophysiol.*, 1965, **28**, 623–640. (15.13)

Field, J., Magoun, H. W., and Hall, V. E. (Eds.) *Handbook of physiology, Neurophysiology*. Washington, D. C.: American Physiological Society, Vol. I. 1959, Vols. II and III, 1960.

Forbes, A., and Morrison, B. R. Cortical response to sensory stimulation under deep barbiturate narcosis. *J. Neurophysiol.*, 1939, **2**, 112–128. (9.11A)

French, G. M., and Harlow, H. F. Variability of delayed-reaction performance in normal and brain-damaged rhesus monkeys. *J. Neurophysiol.*, 1962, **25**, 585–599. (15.9)

Galambos, R., Schwartzkopff, J., and Rupert, A. Microelectrode study of superior olivary nuclei. *Amer. J. Physiol.*, 1959, **197**, 527–536. (10.32)

Gamble, J. E., and Patton, H. D. Pulmonary edema and hemorrhage from preoptic lesions in rats. *Amer. J. Physiol.*, 1953, **172**, 623–631. (3.5B)

Gloor, P. Amygdala. Pp. 1395–1420 in Field, J., et al., *op. cit.*, Vol. II, 1960. (16.14)

Goldring, S., and O'Leary, J. L. Experimentally derived correlates between ECG and steady cortical potential. *J. Neurophysiol.*, 1951, **14**, 275–288. (3.13)

Green, J. D. The hippocampus. Pp. 1373–1389 in Field, J., et al., *op. cit.*, Vol. II, 1960. (16.16)

Green, J. D., and Arduini, A. Hippocampal electrical activity in arousal. *J. Neurophysiol.*, 1954, **17**, 532–557. (16.17)

Harris, G. W. Central control of pituitary secretion. Pp. 1007–1038 in Field, J., et al., *op. cit.*, Vol. II, 1960. (16.12)

Hubel, D. H., and Wiesel, T. N. Receptive fields and functional architecture in two nonstriate visual areas. *J. Neurophysiol.*, 1965, **28**, 229–289. (11.25A, 11.25B)

Huttenlocher, P. R. Evoked and spontaneous activity in single units of medial brain stem during natural sleep and waking. *J. Neurophysiol.*, 1961, **24**, 451–468. (14.11)

Jasper, H. H. Unspecific thalamocortical relations. Pp. 1307–1322 in Field, J., et al., *op. cit.*, Vol. II, 1960. (14.19)

Kuffler, S. W. Discharge patterns and functional organization of mammalian retina. *J. Neurophysiol.*, 1953, **16**, 37–68. (10.15B)

Lindsley, D. B., Schreiner, L. H., and Magoun, H. W. An electromyographic study of spasticity. *J. Neurophysiol.*, 1949, **12**, 197–216. (13.18)

Lloyd, D. P. C. Reflex action in relation to pattern and peripheral source of afferent stimulation. *J. Neurophysiol.*, 1943, **6**, 111–120. (12.7, 12.9)

McCouch, G. P., Austin, G. M., Liu, C. N., and Liu, C. Y. Sprouting as a cause of spasticity. *J. Neurophysiol.,* 1958, **21**, 205–223. (17.10A, 17.10B)

Matthews, P. B. C. Muscle spindles and their motor control. *Physiol. Rev.,* 1964, **44**, 219–228. (12.15, 12.17)

Meyer, D. P., and Woolsey, C. N. Effects of localized cortical destruction on auditory discriminative conditioning in cat. *J. Neurophysiol.,* 1952, **15**, 149–162. (11.8)

Mountcastle, V. B. Modality and topographic properties of single neurons of cat's somatic sensory cortex. *J. Neurophysiol.,* 1957, **20**, 408–434. (9.14)

Mountcastle, V. B., Poggio, G. F., and Werner, G. The relation of thalamic cell response to peripheral stimuli varied over an intensive continuum. *J. Neurophysiol.,* 1963, **26**, 807–834. (10.7, 10.8)

Patton, H. D., and Amassian, V. E. The pyramidal tract: its excitation and function. Pp. 837–861 in Field, J., et al., *op. cit.,* Vol. II, 1960. (13.3A, 13.3B)

Pfaffmann, C. Gustatory nerve impulses in rat, cat and rabbit. *J. Neurophysiol.,* 1955, **18**, 429–440. (10.35)

Porter, R. W., Cavanaugh, E. C., Critchlow, B. V., and Sawyer, C. H. Localized changes in electrical activity of the hypothalamus in estrous cats following vaginal stimulation. *Amer. J. Physiol.,* 1957, **189**, 145–151. (16.8)

Purpura, D. P., and Shofer, R. J. Intracellular recording from thalamic neurons during reticulocortical activation. *J. Neurophysiol.,* 1963, **26**, 494–505. (14.20)

Renshaw, B. Activity in the simplest spinal reflex pathway. *J. Neurophysiol.,* 1940, **3**, 373–387. (12.8)

Rose, J. E., Greenwood, D. D., Goldberg, J. M., and Hind, J. E. Some discharge characteristics of single neurons in the inferior colliculus of the cat. I. Tonotopic organization, relation of spike-counts to tone intensity, and firing patterns of single elements. *J. Neurophysiol.,* 1963, **26**, 294–320. (10.30, 10.31)

Sawyer, C. H. Reproductive behavior. Pp. 1225–1240 in Field, J., et al., *op. cit.,* Vol. II, 1960. (16.8)

Scheibel, M. E., Scheibel, A. B., Mollica, A., and Moruzzi, G. Convergence and interaction of afferent impulses on single units of reticular formation. *J. Neurophysiol.,* 1955, **18**, 309–331. (14.9, 14.10)

Spencer, W. A., Thompson, R. F., and Neilson, D. R. Decrement of ventral root electrotonus and intracellularly recorded PSPs produced by iterated cutaneous afferent volleys. *J. Neurophysiol.,* 1966, **29**, 253–274. (17.22)

Stellar, E. Drive and motivation. Pp. 1501–1527 in Field, J., et al., *op. cit.,* Vol. III, 1960. (16.21)

Thompson, R. F. Function of auditory cortex of cat in frequency discrimination. *J. Neurophysiol.,* 1960, **23**, 321–334. (11.18)

Thompson, R. F., Johnson, R. H., and Hoopes, J. J. Organization of auditory somatic sensory and visual projection to association fields of cerebral cortex in the cat. *J. Neurophysiol.,* 1963, **26**, 343–364. (9.7, 15.4)

Tunturi, A. R. A difference in the representation of auditory signals for the left and right ears in the iso-frequency contours of the right middle ectosylvian cortex of the dog. *Amer. J. Physiol.,* 1952, **168**, 712–727. (11.15)

The American Psychological Association, Washington, D.C.

Duncan, C. P. The retroactive effect of electroshock on learning. *J. comp. physiol. Psychol.,* 1949, **42**, 34–44. (17.23)

Lansing, R., Schwartz, E., and Lindsley, D. B. Reaction time and EEG activation under alerted and non-alerted conditions. *J. exp. Psychol.,* 1959, **58**, 1–7. (14.15)

Teitelbaum, P., and Epstein, A. N. The lateral hypothalamic syndrome. *Psychol. Rev.,* 1962, **69**, 74–90. (16.7)

Thompson, R., and McConnell, F. V. Classical conditioning in the planarian, Dugenia dorotocephala. *J. comp. physiol. Psychol.*, 1955, **48**, 65–68. (17.9)

Thompson, R. F. Role of the cerebral cortex in stimulus generalization. *J. comp. physiol. Psychol.*, 1962, **55**, 279–287. (11.19)

Thompson, R. F., and Shaw, J. A. Behavioral correlates of evoked activity recorded from association areas of the cerebral cortex. *J. comp. physiol. Psychol.*, 1965, **60**, 329–339. (9.10, 15.19)

Thompson, R. F., and Spencer, W. A. Habituation: a model phenomenon for the study of neuronal substrates of behavior. *Psychol. Rev.*, 1966, **173**, 16–43. (17.16, 17.21)

Baillière, Tindall & Cassell Ltd, London

Eisenstein, E. M., and Cohen, M. F. Learning in an isolated prothoracic insect ganglion. *Animal Behav.*, 1965, **13**, 104–108. (17.6, 17.7)

Birkhauser Verlag, Basel, Switzerland

Engberg, I., Lundberg, A., and Ryall, R. W. Reticulospinal inhibition of transmission through interneurons of spinal reflex pathways. *Experientia*, 1965, **21**, 612. (13.16)

Blackwell Scientific Publications Ltd, Oxford, England

Magoun, H. W. The ascending reticular system and wakefulness. Pp. 1–20 in Delafresnaye, J. F. (Ed.) *Brain mechanisms and consciousness*. Oxford: Blackwell, 1954. (14.5)

Brain Books, Chicago

Krieg, W. J. S. *Functional neuroanatomy*. Chicago: Brain Books, 1953. (13.12)

The British Council, London

Whittaker, V. P., and Gray, E. G. The synapse: biology and morphology. *Brit. med. Bull.*, 1962, **18**, 223–228. (7.3B, 7.3C)

Cambridge University Press, Cambridge, England

Caldwell, P. C., and Keynes, R. D. The utilization of phosphate bond energy for sodium extrusion from giant axons. *J. Physiol.*, 1957, **137**, 12–13. (6.16)

Coombs, J. S., Curtis, D. R., and Eccles, J. C. The generation of impulses in motoneurons. *J. Physiol.*, 1957, **139**, 232–249. (7.7, 7.10A)

Coombs, J. S., Eccles, J. C., and Fatt, P. Excitatory synaptic actions in motoneurons. *J. Physiol.*, 1955, **130**, 374–395. (7.8)

Cross, B. A., and Green, J. D. Activity of single neurons in the hypothalamus: effect of osmotic and other stimuli. *J. Physiol.*, 1959, **148**, 554–569. (16.9)

Dow, R. S. The electrical activity of the cerebellum and its functional significance. *J. Physiol.*, 1938, **94**, 67–86. (13.8)

Eccles, J. C., Eccles, R. M., and Magni, F. Central inhibitory action attributable to presynaptic depolarization produced by muscle afferent volleys. *J. Physiol.*, 1961, **159**, 147–166. (7.14)

Eccles, J. C., Krnjević, K., and Miledi, R. Delayed effects of peripheral severance of afferent nerve fibers on the efficacy of their central synapses. *J. Physiol.*, 1959, **145**, 204–220. (17.11)

Eccles, R. M., and Lundberg, A. Integrative pattern of Ia synaptic actions on motoneurons of hip and knee muscles. *J. Physiol.*, 1958, **144**, 271–298. (12.10)

Fatt, P., and Katz, B. An analysis of the end-plate potential recorded with an intracellular electrode. *J. Physiol.*, 1951, **115**, 320–370. (8.5A, 8.5B)

Fatt, P., and Katz, B. Spontaneous threshold activity at motor nerve endings. *J. Physiol.*, 1952, **117**, 109–128. (8.6)

Furshpan, E. J., and Potter, D. C. Transmission at the giant motor synapses of the crayfish. *J. Physiol.*, 1959, **145**, 289–325. (8.10)

Gray, J. A. B., and Sato, M. Properties of the receptor potential in pacinian corpuscles. *J. Physiol.*, 1953, **122**, 610–636. (10.4)

Hamlyn, L. H. The fine structure of the mossy fiber endings in the hippocampus of the rabbit. *J. Anat.*, 1962, **96**, 112–120. (7.3A)

Hodgkin, A. L., and Huxley, A. F. A quantitative description of membrane current and its application to conduction and excitation in nerve. *J. Physiol.*, 1952, **117**, 500–544. (6.14)

Hodgkin, A. L., Huxley, A. F., and Katz, B. Measurements of current-voltage relations in the membrane of the giant axon of *Loligo*. *J. Physiol.*, 1952, **116**, 424–448. (6.11, 6.12)

Hodgkin, A. L., and Katz, B. The effect of sodium ions on the electrical activity of the giant axon of the squid. *J. Physiol.*, 1949, **108**, 37–77. (6.7, 6.10)

Hodgkin, A. L., and Keynes, R. D. Experiments on the injection of substances into squid giant axons by means of a microsyringe. *J. Physiol.*, 1956, **131**, 592–616. (6.2B)

Hubel, D. H., and Wiesel, T. N. Receptive fields, binocular interaction and functional architecture in the cat's visual center. *J. Physiol.*, 1962, **160**, 106–154. (11.23A, 11.23B, 11.23C, 11.24)

Kandel, E. R., and Tauc, L. Mechanism of heterosynaptic facilitation in the giant cell of the abdominal ganglion of *Aplysia depilans*. *J. Physiol.*, 1965, **181**, 1–27. (17.4)

Li, C. L., and Jasper, H. H. Microelectrode studies of the electrical activity of the cerebral cortex in the cat. *J. Physiol.*, 1953, **121**, 117–140. (9.5)

Quilliam, T. A., and Sato, M. The distribution of myelin on nerve fibers from pacinian corpuscles. *J. Physiol.*, 1955, **129**, 167–176. (10.3)

Welker, W. I., and Johnson, J. I. Correlation between nuclear morphology and somato-topic organization in ventro-basal complex of the raccoon's thalamus. *J. Anat.*, 1965, **99**, 761–790. (3.2A)

Young, J. Z. Learning and discrimination in the octopus. *Biol. Rev.*, 1961, **36**, 32–96. (4.23C)

Chatto and Windus Ltd, London

Adrian, E. D. *The basis of sensation, the action of sense organs.* London: Chatto and Windus Ltd, 1928. (10.2)

J. and A. Churchill, Ltd., London

Creutzfeldt, O., and Jung, R. Neuronal discharge in the cat's motor cortex during sleep and arousal. Pp. 131–170 in Wolstenholme, G. E. W., and O'Connor, M. (Eds.) *Ciba Foundation Symposium, The nature of sleep.* London: J. and A. Churchill, 1961. (14.21)

Eccles, J. C. The behavior of nerve cells. Pp. 28–47 in Wolstenholme, G. E. W., and O'Connor, C. M. (Eds.) *Ciba Foundation Symposium, Neurological basis of behavior.* London: Churchill, 1958. (7.12)

Jasper, H. H., Ricci, G., and Doane, B. Patterns of cortical neuronal discharge during conditioned responses in monkeys. Pp. 277–290 in Wolstenholme, G. E. W., and O'Connor, G. M. (Eds.) *Ciba Foundation Symposium, Neurological Basis of behavior.* London: Churchill, 1958. (15.26)

Cold Spring Harbor Laboratory of Quantitative Biology, Cold Spring Harbor, N.Y.

Beidler, L. M. Comparison of gustatory receptors, olfactory receptors, and free nerve endings. Pp. 191–200 in *Sensory receptors.* Cold Spring Harbor, N.Y.: Cold Spring Harbor Lab. of Quant. Biology, 1965, **33**. (10.33)

De Valois, R. L. Analysis and coding of color vision in the primate visual system. Pp. 567–580 in *Sensory receptors.* Cold Spring Harbor, N.Y.: Cold Spring Harbor Lab. of Quant. Biology, 1965, **30**. (10.18)

Young, J. Z. Structures of nerve fibres and synapses in some vertebrates. Pp. 1–6 in *Cold Spring Harbor Sympos. quant. Biol.*, 1936, **4**. (6.3)

Elsevier Publishing Company, Amsterdam

Adrian, E. D. The electrical activity of the mammalian olfactory bulb. *EEG clin. Neurophysiol.*, 1950, **2**, 377–388. (10.42)

Bishop, G. H., and O'Leary, J. L. The effect of polarizing currents on cell potentials and their significance in the interpretation of central nervous activity. *EEG clin. Neurophysiol.*, 1950, **2**, 401–416. (9.16)

Brookhart, J. M., and Zanchetti, A. The relation between electro-cortical waves and responsiveness of the cortical-spinal system. *EEG clin. Neurophysiol.*, 1956, **8**, 427–444. (14.18)

Gerken, G. M., and Neff, W. D. Experimental procedures affecting evoked responses recorded from auditory cortex. *EEG clin. Neurophysiol.*, 1963, **15**, 947–957. (15.25)

Lindsley, D. B., Bowden, J., and Magoun, H. W. Effect upon EEG of acute injury to the brain stem activating system. *EEG clin. Neurophysiol.*, 1949, **1**, 475–486. (14.4, 14.13A)

Moruzzi, G., and Magoun, H. W. Brain stem reticular formation and activation of the EEG. *EEG clin. Neurophysiol.*, 1949, **1**, 455–473. (14.3)

Stohr, P. E., Goldring, S., and O'Leary, J. L. Patterns of unit discharge associated with direct response in monkey and cat. *EEG clin. Neurophysiol.*, 1963, **15**, 882–888. (9.15)

Worden, F. G., and Marsh, J. T. Amplitude changes of auditory potentials evoked at cochlear nuclears during acoustic habituation. *EEG clin. Neurophysiol.*, 1963, **15**, 866–881. (15.16)

Federation of American Societies for Experimental Biology

Acheson, G. H. Physiology of neuro-muscular junctions: chemical aspects. *Fed. Proc.*, 1948, **7**, 447–457. (8.4)

W. H. Freeman and Company, San Francisco

Amoore, J. E., Johnston, J. W., Jr., and Rubin, M. The stereochemical theory of odor. *Sci. Amer.*, 1964, **210**, 42–49. (10.38)

Brazier, M. A. B. The analysis of brain wave. *Sci. Amer.*, 1962, **206**, 142–153. (9.9)

Olds, J. Pleasure centers in the brain. *Sci. Amer.*, 1956, **195**, 105–116. (16.20)

Walter, W. G. The electrical activity of the brain. *Sci. Amer.*, 1954, **190**, 54–63. (9.1)

Charles Griffin & Company Ltd, London

Bain, W. A. A method of demonstrating humoral transmission of the effects of cardiac vagus stimulation in the frog. *Quart. J. exp. Physiol.*, 1932, **22**, 269–274. (8.2)

The Harvey Cushing Society

Adametz, J. H. Rate of recovery of functioning in cats with rostral reticular lesions. *J. Neurosurg.*, 1959, **56**, 85–98. (14.13B)

Hoeber Medical Division, Harper & Row, New York

Galambos, R. Some neural correlates of conditioning and learning. Pp. 120–132 in Ramey, E. R., and O'Doherty, D. S. (Eds.) *Electrical studies on the unanesthetized brain.* New York: Hoeber, 1960. (10.43)

Livingston, R. B. Some brain-stem mechanisms relating to psychosomatic functions. *Psychosom. Med.*, 1955, **17**, 347–354. (16.3)

MacLean, P. D. Psychosomatic disease and the "visceral brain": recent developments bearing on the Papez theory of emotion. *Psychosom. Med.*, 1949, **11**, 338–353. (16.1B)

Hong Kong University Press, Hong Kong

Barker, D. The structure and distribution of muscle receptors. Pp. 227–240 in Barker, D. (Ed.) *Symposium on muscle receptors.* Hong Kong: Hong Kong University Press, 1962. (12.12)

The Johns Hopkins Press, Baltimore

Eccles, J. C. *The physiology of nerve cells.* Baltimore: Johns Hopkins Press, 1957. (7.1B, 7.11, 8.7)

Harris, G. W. The functions of the pituitary stalk. *Bull. Johns Hopkins Hosp.*, 1955, **97**, 358–375. (16.11)

Mountcastle, V. G., and Powell, T. P. S. Neural mechanisms subserving cutaneous sensibility, with special reference to the role of afferent inhibition in sensory perception and discrimination. *Bull. Johns Hopkins Hosp.*, 1959, **105**, 201–232. (11.12)

Poggio, G. F., and Mountcastle, V. G. A study of the functional contributions of the lemniscal and spinothalamic system to somatic sensibility. *Bull. Johns Hopkins Hosp.*, 1960, **106**, 266–316. (10.9)

Woolsey, C. N., and Walzl, E. M. Topical projection of nerve fibers from local regions of the cochlea to the cerebral cortex of the cat. *Bull. Johns Hopkins Hosp.*, 1942, **71**, 315–344. (11.14)

Istituto di Fisiologia, Pisa, Italy

Bizzi, E., and Spencer, A. Enhancement of EEG synchrony in the acute "cerveau isolé." *Arch. Ital. Biol.*, 1962, **100**, 234–247. (14.8)

Rossi, G. F., Favale, E., Hara, T., Giussani, A., and Sacco, G. Research on the nervous mechanisms underlying deep sleep in the cat. *Arch. Ital. Biol.*, 1961, **99**, 270–292. (14.22, 14.23)

L'Académie Royal de Médecine, Brussels

Bremer, F. *Bull. de l'Acad.*, 1937, **2**, 6e serie, 68–86. (14.2)

La Imprenta "Rosgal," Montevideo

Hernández-Peón, R., Sherrer, H., and Jouvet, M. Auditory potentials at cochlear nucleus during acoustic habituation. *Acta neurol. Lat.-Amer.*, 1957, **3**, 144–156. (15.15)

Lea & Febiger, Philadelphia

Kuntz, A. *Textbook of neuroanatomy*, 3rd ed. Philadelphia: Lea & Febiger, 1943. (4.22, 4.23A)

Little, Brown and Company, Boston

Bradley, P. B. The central action of certain drugs in relation to the reticular formation of the brain. Pp. 123–149 in Jasper, H. H. (Ed.) *Reticular formation of the brain.* Boston: Little, Brown, 1958. (14.12)

Penfield, W., and Jasper, H. *Epilepsy and the functional anatomy of the human brain.* Boston: Little, Brown, 1954. (16.1C)

Scheibel, M. E., and Scheibel, A. B. Structural substrates for integrative patterns in the brain stem reticular core. Pp. 31–55 in Jasper, H. H. (Ed.) *Reticular formation of the brain.* Boston: Little, Brown, 1958. (14.17)

McGraw-Hill Book Company, New York

Akert, K. Frontispiece in Warren, J. M., and Akert, K. (Eds.) *The frontal granular cortex and behavior.* New York: McGraw-Hill, 1964. (15.8)

Konorski, J., and Lawicka, W. Analysis of errors by prefrontal animals on the delayed response test. Pp. 271–294 in Warren, J. M., and Akert, K. (Eds.) *The frontal granular cortex and behavior.* New York: McGraw-Hill, 1964. (15.11)

Peele, T. L. *The neuroanatomical basis for clinical neurology,* 2nd ed. New York: McGraw-Hill, 1961. (4.21A, 4.21B, 4.21C, 4.21D)

Pribram, K. H. Interrelations of psychology and the neurological disciplines. Pp. 119–157 in Koch, S. (Ed.) *Psychology: a study of science,* Vol. 4, New York: McGraw-Hill, 1962. (16.15A, 16.15B, 16.15C, 16.15D)

Stamm, J. S. Retardation and facilitation in learning by stimulation of frontal cortex in monkeys. Pp. 102–125 in Warren, J. M., and Akert, K. (Eds.) *The frontal granular cortex and behavior.* New York: McGraw-Hill, 1964. (15.10)

The Macmillan Company, New York

Brazier, M. A. B. *The electrical activity of the nervous system.* New York: Macmillan, 1960. (9.2, 9.4, 9.11)

Penfield, W., and Rasmussen, T. *The cerebral cortex of man.* New York: Macmillan, 1950. (11.11)

Macmillan (Journals) Limited, London

Baker, P. F., Hodgkin, A. L., and Shaw, T. I. Replacement of protoplasm of a giant nerve fibre with artificial solutions. *Nature,* 1961, **190,** 885–887. (6.8)

Chow, K. L., and Hutt, P. J. The "association cortex" of *Macaca mulatta:* a review of recent contributions to its anatomy and functions. *Brain,* 1953, **76,** 625–677. (15.12)

Hodgkin, A. L., and Huxley, A. F. Action potentials recorded from inside nerve fiber. *Nature,* 1939, **144,** 710–711. (6.2A, 6.9)

Horn, G. Electrical activity of the cerebral cortex of the unanesthetized cat during attentive behavior. *Brain,* 1960, **83,** 57–76. (15.18)

Kozak, W., MacFarlane, W. V., and Westerman, R. Long lasting reversible changes in the reflex responses of chronic spinal cats to touch, heat, and cold. *Nature,* 1962, **193,** 171–173. (17.17)

Kozak, W., and Westerman, R. A. Plastic changes of spinal monosynaptic responses from tenotomized muscle in cats. *Nature,* 1961, **189,** 753–755. (17.12)

Sharpless, S., and Jasper, H. Habituation of the arousal reaction. *Brain,* 1956, **79,** 655–680. (15.14)

The Massachusetts Medical Society, Boston

Reichlin, S. Neuroendocrinology. *New Eng. J. Med.,* 1963, **269,** 1182–1191. (16.10)

Masson et Companie

Bremer, F. Cerveau "isolé" et physiologie du sommeil. *Compt. rend. Soc. de Biol.,* 1935, **118,** 1235–1241. (14.2)

Methuen & Co Ltd, London

Sholl, D. A. *The organisation of the cerebral cortex.* London: Methuen, 1956. (3.1C, 3.1D, 11.4, 11.5, 11.6)

The M.I.T. Press, Cambridge, Mass.

Stevens, S. S. The psychophysics of sensory function. Pp. 1–33 in Rosenblith, W. A. (Ed.) *Sensory communication.* Cambridge, Mass: The M.I.T. Press, 1961. (10.45, 10.46, 10.47)

National Research Council of Canada, Ottawa

Jasper, H. H., and Ajmone-Marson, C. *A stereotaxic atlas of the diencephalon of the cat.* Ottawa: National Research Council of Canada, 1954. (3.4)

The New England Journal of Medicine, Boston

Reichlin, S. Neuroendocrinology. *New Engl. J. Med.,* 1963, **269,** 1182–1191. (16.10)

Oliver & Boyd Ltd , London

Clark, W. E. L. *The hypothalamus.* London: Oliver & Boyd, 1938. (16.4)

Ophthalmic Publishing Company, Chicago

MacNichol, E. F., and Svaetichin, G. Electric responses from isolated retina of fishes. *Amer. J. Ophthal.,* 1958, **46**, 26–40. (10.19)

Pergamon Press, New York

Benjamin, R. M. Some thalamic and cortical mechanisms of taste. Pp. 309–330 in Zotterman, Y. (Ed.) *Olfaction and taste.* New York: Pergamon, 1963. (10.36, 10.37)

Brush, F. R., and Levine, S. Adrenocortical activity and avoidance learning as a function of time after avoidance training. *Physiol. Behav.,* 1967 (in press). (16.13)

De Lorenzo, A. L. Studies on the ultrastructure and histophysiology of cell membrane nerve fibers and synaptic functions in chemoreceptors. Pp. 5–18 in Zotterman, Y. (Ed.) *Olfaction and taste.* New York: Pergamon, 1963. (10.39)

Konishi, J., and Zotterman, Y. Taste function in fish. Pp. 215–233 in Zotterman, Y. (Ed.) *Olfaction and taste.* New York: Pergamon, 1963. (3.14)

Pitman Medical Publishing Company, London

MacLean, P. D. Studies on limbic system ("visceral brain") and their bearing on psychosomatic problems. Pp. 101–125 in Witthow, E. D., and Cleghorn, R. A. (Eds.) *Recent developments in psychosomatic medicine.* London: Pitman, 1954. (16.2)

Quartermaster Research and Engineering Command, Chicago

Beidler, L. M. Techniques and methods for research in flavors. Pp. 7–43 in Mitchell, J. H., Leinen, N. J., Mrak, E. M., and Bailey, S. D. (Eds.) Chemistry of natural food flavors. Chicago: Quartermaster Research and Engineering Command, 1957. (10.34)

Rockefeller University Press, New York

Hartline, H. K. The receptive field of the optic nerve fibers. *J. gen. Physiol.,* 1940, **130**, 690–699. (10.15A)

Hubbard, R., and Wald, G. Cis-trans isomers of vitamin A and retinene in the rhodopsin system. *J. gen. Physiol.,* 1952–1953, **36**, 269–315. (10.10)

Lloyd, D. P. C. Post-tetanic potentiation of response in monosynaptic reflex pathways of the spinal cord. *J. gen. Physiol.,* 1949, **33**, 147–170. (12.19)

Lloyd, D. P. C., and Wilson, V. J. Reflex depression in rhythmically active monosynaptic reflex pathways. *J. gen. Physiol.,* 1957, **40**, 409–426. (12.21)

Maturana, W. R., Littvin, J. Y., McCulloch, W. S., and Pitts, W. H. Anatomy and physiology of vision in the frog *(Rana pipiens). J. gen. Physiol.,* 1960, **43**, 129–176. (10.17)

Wald, G., Brown, P. K., and Smith, P. H. Iodopsin. *J. gen. Physiol.,* 1955, **38**, 623–681. (10.11)

The Royal Society, London

Boyd, I. A. The structure and innervation of the nuclear leg muscle fibre system and the nuclear chain muscle fibre system in mammalian muscle spindles. *Phil. Trans. roy. Soc. Series B,* 1962, **245**, 81–136. (12.17)

Eccles, J. C. The nature of central inhibition. *Proc. roy. Soc. Series B,* 1961, **153**, 445–476. (7.13)

Hodgkin, A. L. Ionic movements and electrical activity in giant nerve fibres. *Proc. roy. Soc. Series B,* 1958, **148**, 1–37. (6.13, 6.15, 6.17)

Horridge, G. A. Learning by position by the ventral nerve cord in headless insects. *Proc. roy. Soc. Series B,* 1962, **157**, 33–52. (17.5)

Wycoff, R. W. G., and Young, J. Z. The motoneurone surface. *Proc. roy. Soc. Series B,* 1956, **144**, 440–450. (7.1A)

W. B. Saunders Co., Philadelphia

Gardner, E. *Fundamentals of neurology.* Philadelphia: W. B. Saunders, 1963 (4th ed.). (4.9, 10.14)

Patton, H. D. *The autonomic nervous system.* Pp. 200–233 in Ruch, T. C., and Fulton, J. F. (Eds.) *Medical physiology and biophysics.* Philadelphia: W. B. Saunders, 1960. (8.2)

Patton, H. D. *Reflex regulation of posture and movement.* Pp. 167–198 in Ruch, T. C., and Fulton, J. F. (Eds.) *Medical physiology and biophysics.* Philadelphia: W. B. Saunders, 1960. (12.13)

Patton, H. D. Special properties of nerve trunks and tracks. Pp. 66–95 in Ruch, T. C., and Fulton, J. F. (Eds.) *Medical physiology and biophysics.* Philadelphia: W. B. Saunders, 1960. (6.22)

Ranson, S. W., and Clark, S. L. *The anatomy of the nervous system.* Philadelphia: W. B. Saunders, 1959 (10th ed.). (4.7, 4.14, 4.15, 4.16, 4.17, 4.18, 4.20, 11.3, 13.5, 13.6, 13.14, 13.15)

Woodbury, J. W. Action potential: properties of excitable membranes. Pp. 26–72 in Ruch, T. C., and Patton, H. P. (Eds.) *Physiology and biophysics.* (19th ed.) Philadelphia: W. B. Saunders, 1965. (6.21)

Woodbury, J. W., and Patton, H. D. Action potential; Cable and excitable properties of the cell membrane. Pp. 32–65 in Ruch, T. C., and Fulton, J. F. (Eds.) *Medical physiology and biophysics.* Philadelphia: W. B. Saunders, 1960. (6.18, 6.19)

Springer-Verlag New York Inc., New York

Westbrook, W. H., and McGaugh, J. L. Drug facilitation of latent learning. *Psychopharmacologia,* 1963, **5**, 440–446. (17.24)

Stanford University Press, Stanford, Calif.

Thompson, R. F. The neural basis of stimulus generalization. Pp. 154–178 in Mostofsky, D. J. (Ed.) *Stimulus generalization.* Stanford, Calif.: Stanford Univ. Press, 1965. (11.20)

Charles C Thomas, Springfield, Ill.

Galambos, R. Studies of the auditory system with implanted electrodes. Pp. 137–151 in Rasmussen, G. L., and Windle, W. F. (Eds.) *Neural mechanisms of the auditory and vestibular systems.* Springfield, Ill.: Charles C Thomas, 1960. (9.8, 15.20)

Hind, J. E., Rose, J. E., Davies, P. W., Woolsey, C. N., Benjamin, R. M., Welker, W. S., and Thompson, R. F. Unit activity in the auditory cortex. Pp. 201–210 in Rasmussen, G. L., and Windle, W. F. (Eds.) *Neural mechanisms of the auditory and vestibular systems.* Springfield, Ill.: Charles C Thomas, 1961. (11.16)

Woolsey, C. N. Organization of cortical auditory system: a review and a synthesis. Pp. 165–180 in Rasmussen, G. L., and Windle, W. F. (Eds.) *Neural mechanisms of the auditory and vestibular systems.* Springfield, Ill.: Charles C Thomas, 1960. (11.17)

Universitetets Neurofysiologiske Institut, Copenhagen, Denmark

Buchtal, F., and Kaiser, E. The rheology of the cross-striated muscle fiber, with particular reference to isotonic conditions. *Dan. Biol. Medd.,* 1951, **21** (7), 1–318. (12.2)

University of California Press, Berkeley

Krech, D. The genesis of "hypothesis" in rats. *Univ. Calif. Publ. Psychol.,* 1932, **6**, 45–64. (17.1)

University of Chicago Press, Chicago

Polyak, S. L. *The retina.* Chicago: Univ. of Chicago Press, 1941. (10.12)

Walker, A. E. *The primate thalamus.* Chicago: Univ. of Chicago Press, 1938. (11.7)

University of Nebraska Press, Lincoln

Teitelbaum, P. Disturbances of feeding and drinking behavior after hypothalamic lesions. Pp. 39–65 in Jones, M. R. (Ed.) *Nebraska symposium on motivation.* Lincoln, Nebraska: Univ. of Nebraska Press, 1961. (16.6)

University of Pennsylvania Press, Philadelphia

Erlanger, J., and Gasser, H. S. *Electrical signs of nervous activity.* Philadelphia: Univ. of Penn. Press, 1937. (6.23)

University of Texas Press, Austin

Akert, K. Diencephalon. Pp. 288–310 in Sheer, D. E. (Ed.) *Electrical stimulation of the brain.* Austin: Univ. of Texas Press, 1961. (16.5)

Brady, J. V. Motivational-emotional factors and intracranial self-stimulation. Pp. 413–430 in Sheer, D. E. (Ed.) *Electrical stimulation of the brain.* Austin: Univ. of Texas Press, 1961. (3.16B, 16.19)

Russell, G. V. Interrelationship within the limbia and centrencephalic systems. Pp. 167–181 in Sheer, D. E. (Ed.) *Electrical stimulation of the brain.* Austin: Univ. of Texas Press, 1961. (16.1, 16.2)

Sheatz, G. C. Electrode holders in chronic preparations: A. Multilead techniques for large and small animals. Pp. 45–50 in Sheer, D. E. (Ed.) *Electrical stimulation of the brain.* Austin: Univ. of Texas Press, 1961. (3.16A)

Stevens, S. S., and Volkmann, J. The relation of pitch to frequency: A revised scale. *Am. J. Psychol.,* 1940, **53**, 329–353. (10.20)

The University of Wisconsin Press, Madison. (Copyright 1958 by Regents, Univ. of Wisc.)

Harlow, H. F. Behavioral contributions to interdisciplinary research. Pp. 3–23 in Harlow, H. F., and Woolsey, C. N. (Eds.) *Biological and biochemical bases of behavior.* Madison: Univ. of Wisc. Press, 1958. (15.7)

Meyer, D. R. Some psychological determinants of sparing and loss following damage to the brain. Pp. 173–192 in Harlow, H. F., and Woolsey, C. N. (Eds.) *Biological and biochemical bases of behavior.* Madison: Univ. of Wisc. Press, 1958. (17.25)

Rose, J. E., and Woolsey, C. N. Cortical connections and functional organization of the thalamic auditory system of the cat. Pp. 127–150 in Harlow, H. F., and Woolsey, C. N. (Eds.) *Biological and biochemical bases of behavior.* Madison: Univ. of Wisc. Press, 1958. (3.5A, 11.8)

Woolsey, C. N. Organization of somatic sensory and motor areas of the cerebral cortex. Pp. 63–81 in Harlow, H. F., and Woolsey, C. N. (Eds.) *Biological and biochemical bases of behavior.* Madison: Univ. of Wisc. Press, 1958. (11.9, 11.10)

D. Van Nostrand Co., Inc., Princeton, N.J.

Bartley, S. W. *Vision.* Princeton, N.J.: Van Nostrand, 1941. (10.13)

VEB Gustav Fischer, Jena, Germany

Bierbrodt, E. Der Larvenkopf von *Panorpa communis* L. und seine Verwandlung, mit besonderer Berücksichtigung des Gehirns und der Augen. *Zool Jb. (Anat.),* 1942, **68**, 49–136. (4.23B)

John Wiley & Sons, Inc., New York

Buser, P., and Imbert, M. Sensory projections to the motor cortex in cats: A microelectrode study. Pp. 607–626 in Rosenblith, W. A. (Ed.) *Sensory communication.* New York: Wiley, 1961. (15.5, 15.6)

Davis, H. Psychophysiology of hearing and deafness. Pp. 1116–1142 in Stevens, S. S. (Ed.) *Handbook of experimental psychology.* New York: Wiley, 1951. (10.28)

Katsuki, Y. Neural mechanisms of auditory sensation in cats. Pp. 561–583 in Rosenblith, W. A. (Ed.) *Sensory communication.* New York: Wiley, 1961. (10.29A, 10.29B, 10.29C, 10.29D)

Licklider, J. C. R. Basic correlates of the auditory stimulus. Pp. 985–1039 in Stevens, S. S. (Ed.) *Handbook of experimental psychology.* New York: Wiley, 1951. (10.23)

von Békésy, G., and Rosenblith, W. A. The mechanical properties of the ear. Pp. 1075–1115 in Stevens, S. S. (Ed.) *Handbook of experimental psychology.* New York: Wiley, 1951. (10.21)

The Williams & Wilkins Co., Baltimore

Gasser, H. S. The control of excitation in the nervous system. *Harvey Lectures,* 1937, **32,** 169–193. (9.13)

The Wistar Institute of Anatomy and Biology, Philadelphia

Barnard, J. W., and Woolsey, C. N. A study of localization in the cortico-spinal tracts of monkey and rat. *J. comp. Neurol.,* 1956, **105,** 25–50. (3.2B)

Haggar, R. A., and Barr, U. L. Quantitative data on the size of synaptic and bulbs in the cat's spinal cord. *J. comp. Neurol.,* 1950, **93,** 17–35. (7.2)

Mountcastle, V. G., and Henneman, E. The representation of tactile sensibility in the thalamus of the monkey. *J. comp. Neurol.,* 1952, **97,** 409–431. (10.6)

Pollock, L. J., and Davis, L. The reflex activities of a decerebrate animal. *J. comp. Neurol.,* 1930, **50,** 377–411. (13.17)

Yale University Press, New Haven, Conn.

Granit, R. *Receptors and sensory perception.* New Haven, Conn.: Yale Univ. Press, 1955. (10.16, 12.14)

For Judith,

Kathryn,

and Elizabeth

CONTENTS

PREFACE

Physiological psychology is concerned with the physiological bases of behavior. In the last analysis this means the organization and functions of the brain. This book emphasizes an understanding of the neural processes underlying brain function and behavior. The author has long felt the need for a text that reviews modern neurophysiology in relation to behavior but assumes little or no background knowledge on the part of the student.

The book has been developed and used in preliminary form as a text for a course in neurophysiology and behavior. It can be used either as a basic text or a supplementary reading in both undergraduate and graduate courses in physiological psychology and related fields. A major emphasis is placed on an understanding of basic brain organization and functions. In addition, related topics such as neuroanatomy and neurochemistry are covered in sufficient detail that supplementary texts are not needed. Unusual features include a separate chapter on research methods and techniques, a chapter on the nature of the various electrophysiological measures used in the study of brain activity and behavior, and extensive discussions of areas of current research interest.

The book is divided into four general sections, the first (Chapters 2–5) containing a survey of basic concepts in the physical and biological sciences, including chapters on physics and chemistry, research methods, neuroanatomy, and neurochemistry. The second section (Chapters 6–9) is devoted to basic neurophysiology, the third section (Chapters 10–13) to sensory and motor systems, and the final section (Chapters 14–17) to the integrative aspects of brain function in relation to behavior.

The author is indebted to a great many people. A special vote of thanks is due Ellen Zucker, and also Linda Allison and Mary Meikle; without their help the book would never have been completed. Hilton Smith and Joel Davis also contributed essential help. Sharon Billings, Richard Denney, Susan Keizer and Pamela Parker also assisted. Marilyn Murphy, Donna Moore, and Helen Dickenson typed the manuscript. I am also indebted to the editor of the series, Dr. H. Philip Zeigler, for his untiring and valuable criticisms and suggestions. The authors who have contributed so much by their kind permission for use of their illustrations are acknowledged in the figure legends. Publishers are acknowledged in a list at the front of the book. Finally, I am indebted to the National Institutes of Health (Career Award MH-K-6650 and Research Grant NB-02161) and the National Science Foundation (Research Grant G-15603) for support.

RICHARD F. THOMPSON

FOUNDATIONS
OF PHYSIOLOGICAL
PSYCHOLOGY

CHAPTER I

INTRODUCTION

There are approximately 12 billion nerve cells in the human brain. The number of possible interconnections among the cells in a single human brain is greater than the number of atomic particles that constitute the entire universe. Physiological psychology has as its goal the understanding of how this complicated system functions to produce the almost infinite variety of behavior patterns displayed by organisms. The total history of modern physiological psychology is only about 100 years; systematic study of the electrical and biochemical aspects of brain activity has been in progress for only about 40 years. A great deal more remains to be learned than is now known. Nevertheless, the study of brain activity and behavior is already much too vast a subject to be encompassed in a single book. This volume will review the broad outlines of the field and emphasize recent developments in a variety of areas, ranging from neurochemistry and neurophysiology to psychology, which seem particularly relevant to basic issues in physiological psychology.

A revolution of sorts is currently taking place in physiological psychology. A number of different techniques and approaches have played significant roles in this revolution. Perhaps the most important new method is the microelectrode. This is simply a very small electrode used to record the electrical activity of single nerve cells. Microelectrode studies of nerve fiber and cell body membrane potentials have elucidated mechanisms underlying nerve *action potentials*, the all-or-none discharges conveying information along nerve cell fibers. Nerve cells also exhibit another kind of response to stimulation, which is not an all-or-none discharge. Instead, the size of the voltage generated in the cell depends on how strongly it is activated. These graded potentials add up the various influences acting on the cell continuously in time, much like an analogue computer, and determine whether or not the cell will fire an all-or-none spike discharge along the nerve fiber. An understanding of the nature and significance of these graded electrical responses of nerve cells required microelectrode recording methods. As a result of these developments, the chemical events underlying synaptic transmission (transfer of information from one nerve cell to another) are beginning to be understood. Such knowledge is a necessary prerequisite to basic understanding of the neuronal foundations of complex behaviors like conditioning and learning, motivation, perception, and thinking.

Another area where the microelectrode has played a major role is the traditional common ground of psychology and neurophysiology: the study of sensory processes. Use of the microelectrode has permitted definitive analyses of the patterns of discharge elicited in individual nerve cells at all levels of the brain from receptors to cerebral cortex by sensory stimulation. Some unexpected and striking correspondences have been found between the behavior of individual nerve cells and the behavior of organisms, permitting for perhaps the first time fairly rigorous predictions of behavioral phenomena from neurophysiological data. To give but one example (Lettvin et al., 1959), some nerve cells in the frog eye will respond only to a stimulus that resembles a bug moving with a particular direction and velocity in the frog's visual field!

A technique of great value to the physiological psychologist is the chronic implanted electrode. Electrode wires are positioned in the brain of an anesthetized animal (or man) and permanently fixed to a plug socket. After the animal has recovered from the anesthetic the electrodes can be connected to various devices with no discomfort to the animal. In this way electrical activity can be recorded from various regions of the brain of a normal animal while he is attending, learning, showing motivated behavior, and so on. Alternatively we can electrically stimulate different areas of the brain and observe the effects on the behavior of the animal.

There are many other new approaches to brain function and behavior, both in terms of methods and in terms of ways of thinking about problems, which will be discussed in the course of this book. In the years since the classic texts by Morgan (1943), Morgan and Steller (1950), Hebb (1949), and others we have witnessed discoveries and developments in relation to such problems as ionic mechanisms of the nerve membrane potential, the chemical nature of synaptic transmission, excitation and inhibition of nerve activity, the role of the gamma motor neuron system in the control of posture and movement, the functions of the ascending reticular formation in sleep and alerting, the organization and functions of the limbic system in motivation and emotion, electrical self-stimulation of the brain, changes in brain electrical activity accompanying alterations in behavior, studies of brain chemistry and behavior, and a host of other new and intriguing phenomena relating brain and behavior. To take a specific example, in the late 1940s many authorities held that synaptic transmission was basically electrical in nature. At that time this theory was most strongly championed by Eccles (1946). Since then, Eccles himself has provided the crucial evidence against the electrical theory and has analyzed the chemical mechanisms of synaptic transmission. The Nobel prize in medicine for 1963 was awarded jointly to Eccles, for his work on synaptic transmission, and to Hodgkin and Huxley for their analysis of the nerve membrane potential.

ORGANIZATION OF THE BOOK

This text was written for all students interested in the brain and behavior. An attempt is made to present basic modern knowledge of brain function in a relevant and understandable manner. The book assumes that students will have little or no background in the physical or biological sciences. An introductory college course in biology will be of help, but is not absolutely necessary.

The most difficult problem in writing a book of this sort is the coverage and selection of appropriate material. Where possible, only one or a few experiments and/or theories are discussed to illustrate each point. In most instances hundreds of relevant experiments and discussions exist. However, it was felt that clear illustration by few examples is preferable to extensive but sketchy reviews of the literature. In any event space does not permit the latter. Although every effort was made to avoid bias in favor of any particular theories or observations, the possibility of its occurrence is great when limited numbers of examples are selected. The experimental results that are given are those that seem to be well accepted by the majority of workers in the field. The distinction between agreed-upon experimental data and theories that "explain" the data is emphasized. Appropriate review articles and books are listed at the end of each chapter to give the student easy access to both broad and detailed coverage of the subjects discussed. The recently published three volume series on neurophysiology from the *Handbook of Physiology: Sec. 1, Neurophysiology* (Field, 1959; 1960a; 1960b) is an invaluable source for reviews and critical discussions of all areas of neurophysiology.

The book is divided into four general sections, the first dealing with basic concepts from the physical and biological sciences, the second with basic aspects of nerve function, the third with sensory and motor systems, and the fourth with the more "integrative" aspects of brain-behavior relations. The first section (Chapters 2–5) reviews necessary concepts from physics and chemistry, modern research techniques for the study of brain function and brain-behavior relations, and basic overviews of neuroanatomy and neurochemistry. The second section (Chapters 6–9) discusses basic mechanisms of the nerve membrane potential, electrical and chemical aspects of the synaptic transmission of information from nerve cell to nerve cell, and characteristic patterns of electrical activity recorded from the brain (EEG, evoked response, single cell activity, slow potentials, etc.). The third section emphasizes the sensory and motor aspects of brain function, ranging from the classical sensory systems, which form the neural basis of sensation and perception, through the sensory and motor functions of the cerebral cortex, to the reflex activities of the spinal cord and the various motor systems that form the immediate neural substrates of behavioral responding. The final section (Chapters 14–17) deals with integrative aspects of brain function in relation to behavior. Nonspecific afferent systems (Chapter 14; ascending reticular formation and diffuse thalamic system) are fundamentally related to sleep and arousal. The cerebral cortex (Chapter 15) appear to play an essential role in the elaboration of complex behavior, at least in higher mammals. The limbic system and hypothalamus (Chapter 16) appear to be of particular importance in the emotional and motivational aspects of behavior. The book concludes (Chapter 17) with a discussion of current research on the neural and chemical bases of changes in behavior, ranging from habituation to learning and memory.

In its brief history the study of brain function and behavior has accumulated a vast and complex literature. Nevertheless, the more fundamental and important discoveries can usually be summarized relatively briefly and intelligibly. It is not particularly difficult to understand what is meant by the statement that a nerve cell can transmit information to other nerve cells by releasing small amounts of chemical substances that act on other nerve cells. It is quite a different matter to prove such a statement to everyone's satisfaction. We will discuss selected experiments in sufficient detail so that the student can gain some feeling for the kinds of thinking, experimental maneuvers, and evidence necessary to establish such basic hypotheses.

A BRIEF HISTORY

Historically, physiology and psychology began as one and the same discipline. If the brain can be characterized in any simple way, it is as the anatomical and physiological system controlling behavior. In the nineteenth century the word "mind" was more commonly used than "behavior," but the basic interrelatedness of brain function and psychology was emphasized. Boring (1950) asserts that experimental psychology got its start within experimental physiology during the first half of the nineteenth century. A good example of the relation between physiology and psychology in that period is the work of J. Muller, who formulated the doctrine of "specific nerve energies" in his *Handbook of Human Physiology* (1840). Three of the eight volumes comprising the *Handbook* are concerned primarily with areas that today would be included within psychology. Helmholtz is another illustrative figure. His fundamental work on sensory function, particularly in hearing, straddled psychology and physiology. Throughout his life his writings indicate a strong interest in what are basically psychological problems.

In the middle nineteenth century psychology and physiology began to follow separate paths. The brief historical sketch given below is concerned primarily with the development of physiological psychology, as distinct from physiology. A history of neurophysiology is well beyond the scope of this text (however many of the more recent developments in neurophysiology will be described in the course of the book). The reader can consult the concise and comprehensive history of neurophysiology by Brazier (1959) for a full treatment of the subject. Psychology, with its developing emphasis on the objective measurement and characterization of behavior, plays a unique and important role in the present-day study of brain function.

Boring dates the formal beginning of experimental psychology from the publication of Fechner's book *Elements of Psychophysics* in 1860. This work concerned the fundamental problem of the quantitative relations between the physical world and the organism's responses to it, or as Fechner described it "the exact science of the functional relations ... between body and mind" (Boring, 1950). Weber had earlier noted (1846) that the just noticeable difference in a stimulus bears a constant ratio to the stimulus. Fechner developed this relation into the famous Weber-Fechner law.

$$\text{Response} = K \log \text{Stimulus}$$

where K is simply a numerical constant. For example, in order for a tone to sound twice as loud, the physical intensity must be increased four times. This constituted the first attempt at quantitative characterization and measurement of a psychological variable: sensation.

There were perhaps two major historical traditions that merged in the formation of modern experimental psychology, itself primarily an American development. One was an outgrowth of Fechner's attempt to measure attributes of mind (i.e. relations between stimulus characteristics and responses) and involved such men as Wundt and his student Titchener, who established the tradition in the United States. The other main stream had its origins in the English empirical philosophers, particularly John Locke and John Stuart Mill. They emphasized the necessity for experimental and observational tests of ideas, and the value of the pragmatic approach, i.e. the method that works is the best method to use. This tradition was elaborated in America by such men as William James and John Dewey. Modern experimental psychology represents the coalescence of these two lines; the measurement of psychological variables and an emphasis on pragmatic and empirical methods.

The physiological basis of behavior has always been of interest to psychologists. Wundt's famous text, published in 1874, was entitled *Foundations of*

Physiological Psychology. Titchener considered himself a physiological psychologist. William James, in his *Principles of Psychology* (1890) devotes considerable space to the nervous system. It is somewhat enlightening, incidentally, to see how little our broad understanding of brain function and behavior has developed in the 75 years since James wrote.

Experimental animal psychology had its beginning with Edward Thorndike, who combined both historical traditions, having studied with William James and with James McKeen Cattell, the latter a student of Wundt. In 1898 Thorndike published his quantitative studies on animal learning. Modern physiological psychology as such had its start with Shepherd Franz, a student of Cattell, who used Thorndike's methods of behavior measurement in animals to determine the effects of brain lesions. Franz's major study, published in 1902, was concerned with the functions of the frontal lobes in simple learning tasks.

Karl Lashley, perhaps more than any other psychologist, was responsible for the development of physiological psychology. While he was a student at Johns Hopkins University he worked with Franz and learned his methods. In subsequent years Lashley developed a number of techniques and findings, culminating in his famous 1929 monograph *Brain Mechanisms and Intelligence*. In this work he set out to find the location of "engrams" laid down in the brain during learning. The results of his experiments forced him (and almost everyone else) to abandon the whole idea of localized engrams. Lashley continued active research until his death in 1958 and contributed much to our present knowledge relating brain function and behavior.

There is still another line of development that has had a very considerable impact on modern physiological psychology, namely the work of Pavlov and his many students. Pavlov began his studies of conditioned reflexes in 1903 (cf. Boring, 1950). He worked quite independently of the developing American experimental psychology, and his famous text, *Conditioned Reflexes*, was not available in English until 1927. Thus until the 1930s the mainstream of experimental and physiological psychology was essentially uninfluenced by his work. It is interesting that both traditions developed the same point of view about the importance of objective measurement of behavioral responses, although the kinds of measures used were quite different, Pavlov's classical salivary conditioning technique has been used extensively for many years in the Soviet Union and in certain other European laboratories, but was not widely adopted in America—the more indigenous methods of instrumental and operant conditioning, discrimination training, maze learning, etc., being preferred. However, the experimental findings and theories of the Pavlovian school have played a major role in modern psychology.

The importance of all these techniques for physiological psychology lies in the fact that they are objective, reliable and quantitative measures of behavior. No matter how elegant are the neurophysiological techniques and equipment in an experiment, merely looking at the animal will provide little information about brain function and *behavior*. Hence modern physiological psychology is as much dependent upon the behavioral measures and theoretical analyses developed by experimental psychology as upon the methods, results, and theories of neurophysiology.

In the period from Muller and Helmholtz to Lashley, psychology and neurophysiology were developing more or less independently. It is only in recent years that the two disciplines have recombined. Knowledge and method in both neurophysiology and experimental psychology have developed to the point where the fundamental problems relating brain function and behavior have become potentially solvable.

PHILOSOPHIC ISSUES

The Mind-Body Problem

Interest in the fundamental nature of the mind has probably served as an original motive for more psychologists and neurophysiologists than would care to admit it. If by mind we mean "subjective awareness" the "experience of sensations," "consciousness," and similar phrases, it seems clear that the brain has something to do with the mind. The relation of mind and brain has occupied a central position in philosophy for several thousand years. Sherrington (1950) noted that Aristotle, 2000 years ago, was asking how the mind attached to the body and we are asking that question still.

Modern behaviorism developed in psychology partly as a reaction against an earlier emphasis on the attempt to analyze consciousness by methods of personal introspection. It is often said that behaviorism will not admit the existence of consciousness or the awareness of subjective experience. This is not exactly true. What *is* maintained is that such phenomena cannot be studied directly, but only inferentially through such behavior as verbal reports. It is simply not possible to measure experience directly. We *can* however measure the electrical and chemical activity of the brain and the verbal behavior of people and attempt to relate these.

A recent development in philosophy, logical positivism, with its emphasis on *operational definitions*, has played an important role in modern behaviorism. All that is meant by an operational definition is that a given term or construct must be defined by the operations used to measure it. Intelligence measured by one IQ test is different than intelligence measured by another test. The use of operational definitions in psychology has cleared the field of a vast number of undefined and undefinable words, and has been of great value in physiological psychology. Words like "mind" and "consciousness" have no measurable properties and hence cannot be defined in measurable terms. Human behavior, including verbal behavior, can be measured, and definitions can be established in these terms. Actually, verbal report of "subjective" experience by people is a very useful tool for the student of brain function and behavior. The important and fruitful studies of Wilder Penfield and his group at Montreal (Penfield and Rasmussen, 1950), in which patients described sensations resulting from electrical stimulation of their brain tissue during the course of necessary neurosurgical procedures, are entirely dependent upon such verbal reports. The study of sensory processes could not have developed without the skilled observer who reports that "this tone is louder than that tone" or "this light is more red than the other," and so on. The important point is really not whether terms like consciousness refer to something "real," but rather what kinds of phenomena can be measured and hence studied scientifically. Verbal behavior is eminently within the domain of science.

A number of different positions or theories regarding the mind-body problem have been developed in the history of philosophy. The three most obvious are perhaps: (1) there is only mind, (2) there is only matter, and (3) mind and matter both exist and interact. Descartes, you may recall, suggested that the pineal body in the brain was the locus of interaction between mind and brain. Most philosophers have defined mind as being nonphysical and thus having no physically measurable characteristics. As Ayer has pointed out (1950):

> The physiologist's story is complete in itself. The characters that figure in it are nerve cells, electrical impulses, and so forth. It has no place for an entirely different cast, of sensations, thoughts, feeling. . . . The mind has no position in space—it does not literally make sense to talk of physical signals reaching it. . . . In short the two stories will not mix.

Ayer is emphasizing the notion that there are different levels of discourse. Science deals with measurable events. It cannot treat entities like mind, which are by definition nonmeasurable. Such problems are more properly within the province of philosophy and are dealt with at an entirely different level of analysis than the scientific method permits. By this token, philosophic debates concerning the relation of mind and body will probably never be solved by the sciences of physiology and psychology. What can be accomplished, however, is an ever increasing knowledge of the relations that exist between the behavior of nerve cells and the behavior of organisms, including verbal behavior. As we noted earlier, the fundamental task of physiological psychology is to understand the neurophysiological basis of the behavior of organisms.

Emergent Properties

If a number of elements are combined into a complex system, the system often exhibits properties not exhibited by the elements themselves. Such phenomena are sometimes termed *emergent properties*. A simple example is the combination of hydrogen and oxygen to form water. In the earlier days of chemistry it was simply not possible to predict any of the properties of water— e.g. its physical state as a fluid, its boiling and freezing points, the relation of temperature and density—from knowledge of the physical properties of oxygen and hydrogen. The brain and the behaving organism it controls is a remarkable example of a system exhibiting emergent properties. Individual nerve cells can basically do only one of two things to influence other cells: discharge or not discharge. Yet from the interrelations of these "all-or-none" elements in the brain, the normally functioning organism performs complex responses, exhibits motivation to respond, learns to modify response patterns as a result of experience, writes novels, etc.

There is nothing mystical about the concept of emergent properties. Present-day physics and chemistry, for example, can develop accurate theoretical predictions about the characteristics of water from the properties of hydrogen and oxygen, and a knowledge of the manner in which they interconnect and interact with one another when they form water. Modern knowledge of atomic processes permits a variety of unexpected predictions about "emergent" properties of substances. Similarly, the emergent properties of human behavior are potentially predictable from the behavior of nerve cells and the ways in which they interconnect and interact in the brain.

Intervening Variables

During the 1950s and 1960s experimental psychology developed a large body of data and theory permitting relatively successful predictions of human and animal behavior in a variety of situations. Perhaps because of this success many psychologists feel it is more profitable to study the behavior of intact organisms rather than the behavior of nerve cells. In terms of current results there is no question but that much better predictions of behavior can be made from behavioral data than from physiological information. At least until the late 1960s there were relatively few instances of original behavior predictions from neurophysiological data. However, physiological psychology has reached the point where such predictions are now feasible.

Psychological analysis of behavior has primarily been at what is termed a *molar* level. Gross aspects of behavior such as lever pressing or maze running have been measured and a variety of stimulus variables manipulated. Those interested in developing predictive theories of behavior have treated the organism as a black box. Stimuli go in and responses come out. *Intervening variables* are postulated to act in certain ways within the hypothetical organism. Postulated intervening variables, like drive and habit strength (Hull, 1943), are not held to have any necessary physiological reality. Such approaches have permitted a wide variety of behavioral predictions (cf., Spence, 1960; Brown, 1961; Estes and Atkinson, 1963; etc.).

Physiological psychology, in common with all other aspects of science, utilizes a comparable approach. Physical theories of the atom, molecular bond theory, chromosomal control of heredity, the chemical theory of synaptic transmission, and habit strength are all examples of intervening variables. The major differences among them lie in the extent to which they have been characterized and experimentally tested. Hull, in his molar behavior theory, would have liked to give his postulates physiological referents. In fact one of the postulates is entitled "afferent neural interactions." Too little was known then about neural processes to make this feasible. However, the time is approaching when the predictive value of behavioral intervening variables may well be enriched by casting them in physiological terms. To give only one example, Hebb (1955) suggests that Hullian drive may be localized within the ascending reticular formation. This kind of hypothesis permits a much broader range of predictive interrelations between behavioral and physiological variables.

No one will deny that the brain is the physical substrate of behavior. Nevertheless, a number of psychologists, particularly of the "operant" persuasion, have doubted the value of physiological approaches to behavior. However, Skinner (1963) himself recently emphasized the importance of the physiological analysis of behavior so long as it is directed toward measurable aspects of behavior rather than undefinable constructs like "consciousness" or "mind." It is likely that molar and physiological approaches to behavior will merge in a highly productive fashion in the next few years.

SUGGESTED READINGS

Boring, Edwin G. *A history of experimental psychology.* New York: Appleton-Century-Crofts, 1950.

Brazier, Mary A. B. "The historical development of neurophysiology." Pp. 1–58 in Field, J. (Ed.) *Handbook of physiology. Sec.* 1: *neurophysiology.* Vol. I, Washington, D.C.: American Physiological Society, 1959.

Frank, Philipp. *Philosophy of science.* Englewood Cliffs, N.J.: Prentice-Hall, 1957.

Laslett, Peter (Ed.). *The physical basis of mind.* New York; Macmillan, 1950.

2

PHYSICAL-CHEMICAL FOUNDATIONS

THE interdisciplinary nature of physiological psychology makes it necessary for the student to be acquainted with concepts drawn from a rather wide variety of sciences including physics and chemistry, biophysics, biochemistry, anatomy, physiology and psychology. As far as basic physics and chemistry are concerned, some understanding of the general principles emphasized in introductory college courses is a sufficient basis for an appreciation of most concepts about brain function. This chapter is a brief review of basic physics and chemistry for the reader who has not had such courses, or who may require some review in these areas. Many of the terms and concepts introduced in this section will recur in subsequent chapters and the reader may find it helpful to refer back to this section from time to time as he proceeds through the book.

FUNDAMENTALS OF CHEMISTRY

Physical Chemistry

All substances are made up of various combinations of *atoms*. Atoms, in turn are composed of various combinations of *subatomic particles—electrons, protons,* and *neutrons* being the only subatomic particles that need concern us here. Electrons, protons, and neutrons can be characterized by their mass and electric charge. The electron has a single or "unit" negative charge (see below), the proton has a unit positive charge, and the neutron has no electrical charge. Neutrons and protons have the same mass, but the electron is much lighter, weighing only about one-nineteenhundredth (1/1900) as much. All atoms may be thought of as having a center or *nucleus* of protons and neutrons around which the negatively charged electrons rotate in orbits, much like a miniature solar system (Figure 2.1). This model of the atom, often called the Bohr atom after the Danish physicist Niels Bohr, is of course only an approximate representation. An accurate description in terms of current knowledge would more likely take the form of several volumes of complex equations. However the model is adequate for our purposes, and in fact for most descriptions in chemistry. The use of model systems or theories, incidentally, is fundamental to science, and a number of such theoretical models for nerve membranes, synapses, neural systems, and behavior will be described in this book. It is worth remembering that these models do not differ in principle from the model of the atom we are using here. All such models are theoretical representations of structures and processes which allow us to interrelate a variety of empirical observations and made predictions about the future behavior of the system.

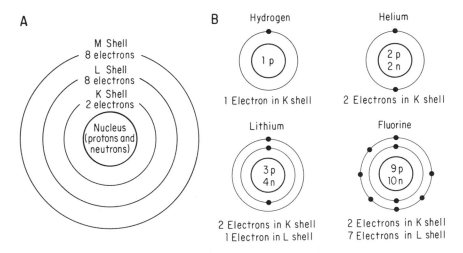

Figure 2.1. **A,** Bohr model of the atom, showing a nucleus composed of protons (positively charged) and neutrons (no charge), and the first three shells of electrons (negatively charged). The number of electrons indicated for each shell is the maximum number the shell can contain. **B,** Examples of small atoms. Note that hydrogen has only one electron and one proton (p), and that the other atoms have equal numbers of protons and electrons, and neutrons (n) in the nucleus as well. Helium is an inert element, but lithium and fluorine are very active—lithium easily giving up an electron and fluorine easily taking an electron.

An atom may have anywhere from one to over one hundred protons in the nucleus. In the normal or "atomic" state the number of electrons rotating around the nucleus always equals the number of protons in the nucleus, so that the positive charge is just balanced by the negative charge and the atom as a whole is neutral. In addition there are usually about as many neutrons in the nucleus as protons. The observable effect of this is to make the atom heavier. In the Bohr model of the atom, electrons orbit in definite paths called *shells* or *energy levels*. Each shell can contain only so many electrons (see Figure 2.1). Thus the first (or K) shell can have only two electrons.

In hydrogen atoms the nucleus consists of only one proton, and there is only one electron outside the nucleus. It lies in the K shell. Helium has two protons in the nucleus and two electrons outside, forming a complete K shell. Lithium is the next element in line with three protons in the nucleus and three electrons outside. Since the K shell can contain only two electrons the third electron must go to the next shell out, the L shell (Figure 2.1). The degree of chemical activity of an atom is related to the number of electrons present in the outermost shell. If the shell is filled the atoms are quite unreactive (helium atoms do not normally react with other atoms, hence it is called an "inert" gas). If there are only one or two electrons in the L shell, for example, which needs eight to be complete, the atoms easily give up these outer electrons and are very reactive. Lithium has only one electron in the outer shell and hence is a very reactive substance. If an atom has all but one of the electrons needed to complete the outer shell it easily "grabs" an electron from other types of atoms to form a complete outer shell, and is thus also very reactive. Fluorine, for example, has seven of the needed eight electrons in the L shell and hence is a highly reactive substance.

The *atomic number* of an atom is the number of protons in its nucleus. An *element* is simply defined as all atoms having the same atomic number, and hence, in the atomic state, the same number of electrons outside. This means that there are the same number of filled electron shells and the same number of electrons in the outermost shell. Since the electron arrangement is the same all such atoms have the same chemical reactivity. Thus all atoms of the element hydrogen have one proton, and an atomic number of 1, all helium atoms have two protons and an atomic number of 2, lithium an atomic number of 3, fluorine an atomic number of 9, and so on. The *atomic weight* of an atom is expressed in terms of the actual weight of the element. Since electrons have negligible weight compared to protons and neutrons, the atomic weight might be expected to be the same as the sum of the protons and neutrons present. However, elements exist in different forms, called *isotopes*, depending on how many neutrons are present. Figure 2.2 shows two isotopes of hydrogen (called hydrogen and deuterium) and two isotopes of helium. The hydrogen naturally present in the atmosphere, in water, and in all other substances containing hydrogen, is a mixture of these isotopes, deterium being present in much smaller amounts than regular hydrogen. The atomic weight of an element is actually the *average* weight of the naturally occurring mixture of isotopes present. For hydrogen the atomic weight is 1.008, reflecting the small percent of deuterium present (each atom of deuterium weighs twice as much as an atom of regular hydrogen). Similarly, the isotope of helium having an extra neutron is present in small quantities, hence the atomic weight of helium is 4.003.

Atoms combine to form the *molecules* making up *compounds* (a compound is a substance composed of like molecules) either by sharing electrons or by taking or giving up electrons. *Valence* refers to the number of electrons an atom must share, give up, or take, in order to form a molecular compound. The rule for valence number is simple: *The valence of an element is determined by the number of electrons needed or given up to yield an atom with a complete outer electron shell.* If electrons are given up the valence is + (since the atoms will then have a net positive charge, there being more protons than electrons), and if they are acquired the valence is − (net negative charge on the atoms). Sodium chloride (common table salt) is a good example of molecular formation (see Figure 2.3). The sodium atom has eleven electrons, two in the inner, (K) shell, eight in the next shell (L) and one left over in the M shell. Since it is much easier to give up one than to take all the additional electrons needed for a stable outer shell, sodium gives up this outer electron when it forms molecular compounds. The valence of sodium is thus said to be +1. Chlorine, on the other hand, has 17 electrons, two in the K shell, 8 in the L and 7 in the next or M shell. Eight are required to form a complete M shell so chlorine accepts one additional electron in forming compounds and has a valence of −1. In combination the

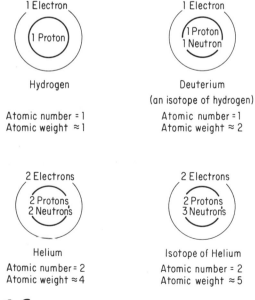

Figure 2.2. Examples of isotopes. Normal hydrogen has no neutrons but deuterium ("heavy" hydrogen) has one neutron. Helium normally has two neutrons but an isotope of helium having three neutrons also exists.

2.2

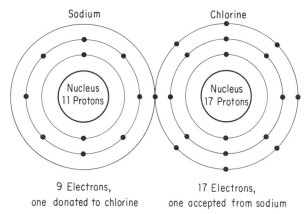

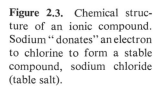

Figure 2.3. Chemical structure of an ionic compound. Sodium "donates" an electron to chlorine to form a stable compound, sodium chloride (table salt).

"extra" electron of sodium is given to chlorine so that each atom now has a complete shell configuration.

There are actually two ways in which electrons are "exchanged" to form molecules. Substances which easily give up or acquire electrons form *ionic bonds*. If sodium chloride is dissolved in water, the sodium and chlorine atoms are present as *ions* (an ion is an atom or molecule having a net negative or positive charge). Thus each sodium ion has one less electron (negative charge) than proton (positive charge) since it gave up one in forming salt, and has a net charge of $+1$. The chloride ions (chlorine atoms in ionic form are called chlor*ide*) each have one extra electron and have net charges of -1. These are written as Na^+ and Cl^-. The solution of sodium chloride in water is called an ionic solution. A water solution of salt really contains very few if any sodium chloride molecules. The sodium ions and chloride ions move about in the water virtually independent of each other, although each small volume of the solution stays electrically neutral. The same is true of solutions of other ionic compounds. All tissues and cells contain and are bathed in weak (i.e. low concentration) ionic solutions having sodium, chloride, potassium, calcium, magnesium and other ions in varying concentrations.

The other type of chemical combination of atoms is called a *covalent* compound. Electrons are neither given up or taken, but shared by both atoms (covalent bonds), resulting in a stable configuration having no net charge. The atoms stick together in a definite spatial arrangement. *Organic* compounds, which in general are molecules containing carbon atoms, are of the covalent type. The carbon atom has six electrons, two in the K shell and 4 in the L shell. Thus the outer shell would have to either give up or take 4 electrons to be complete. In such cases it is easier to share electrons in a covalent configuration (see Figure 2.4).

Since the fluids composing all tissues are ionic solutions, some understanding of their properties is essential. Compounds having ionic bonds form ionic

Carbon (4 electrons in outer L shell)

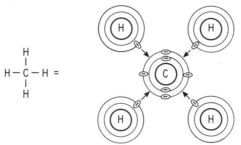

$$H-\overset{\displaystyle H}{\underset{\displaystyle H}{C}}-H =$$

Methane (4 hydrogens share electrons with 1 carbon)

Figure 2.4. The carbon atom and simple organic (covalent) compounds. In methane, four hydrogen atoms share their electrons with a carbon atom, and in carbon tetrofluoride a carbon atom shares its four outer electrons with four fluorine atoms.

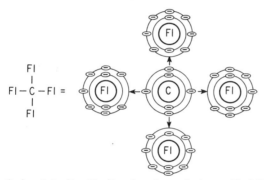

$$Fl-\overset{\displaystyle Fl}{\underset{\displaystyle Fl}{C}}-Fl =$$

Carbon tetrafluoride (1 carbon shares electrons with 4 fluorines)

solutions in water which conduct electric current and are called electrolytes. Covalent compounds such as sugar or alcohol form nonelectrolytic solutions and do not conduct electric current. The simplest measure of the concentration of a solution is the percentage weight of the substance dissolved in the solvent. Physiological saline (same concentration of salt as in blood) is a 0.9 percent solution of salt: 100 grams of the solution contain 0.9 grams of sodium chloride. Another expression of concentration is in terms of the gram-molecular-weight (moles) of substance per liter of solution (at 20° C). The *gram molecular weight* is simply the molecular weight of the substance expressed in grams. The molecular weight in turn is based on the sum of the atomic weights of the atoms making up the molecule. A sodium chloride molecule has a molecular weight equal to that of sodium (≈ 23) plus that of chlorine (≈ 35.5) or 58.5. Thus a 1 mole solution of sodium chloride consists of 58.5 grams of sodium chloride dissolved in 1 liter of solution. Molar concentrations are often symbolized by brackets:

$$[Na^+ + Cl^-]_x$$

where the value of x tells you the molar concentration. For example, $[Na^+ + Cl^-]_{1.5}$ means 1.5 (58.5) = 87.75 grams of salt per liter of solution.

Inorganic chemical compounds may be grouped in four general classes, *oxides, acids, bases,* and *salts.* Oxides are simply compounds containing oxygen, the most common oxide of physiological significance being water. The human body, incidentally, is about 70 percent water, and brain tissue is 80 percent water. Water, as you know, is symbolized by H_2O (it is a covalent compound). The subscript here and in all chemical equations indicates the number of atoms of one element which combine with others to form compounds. *Acids* are special compounds containing hydrogen. In solution the hydrogen is present in the ionic form: H^+. Inorganic acids generally ionize completely in solution to form electrolytes. Organic acids, which are combinations of the hydrogen ion with organic (carbon containing) compounds, dissociate into ionic form only slightly in water and form very weak electrolytes. *Bases* are compounds which form the ion OH^- (this is called the hydroxyl ion) when dissolved in water and are often called hydroxides or alkalis. *Salts,* finally, are combinations of *metal* (positive valence element) ions and negative valence ions, and may be thought of as deriving from acids and bases (by the loss of hydrogen and hydroxyl ions). A typical example is the combination of hydrochloric acid and sodium hydroxide:

Chemical symbols:	HCL	+	NaOH	=	NaCl	+ H_2O
In solution	H^+Cl^-	+	Na^+OH^-	=	Na^+Cl^-	+ H_2O
Common name:	hydrochloric acid	+	sodium hydroxide	=	sodium chloride	+ water
Type of compound:	*acid*	+	*base*	=	*salt*	+ *water*

Thus when solutions of hydrochloric acid and sodium hydroxide are poured together they form salt and water. Most tissue electrolytes are present in the form of salts, some common examples being sodium chloride, sodium bicarbonate, potassium chloride, calcium carbonate, and magnesium chloride.

Any aqueous (i.e. water) solution of chemicals is either acid, alkaline (basic), or neutral. In the chemical reaction given just above, hydrochloric acid is a strongly acid solution. Lemon juice and orange juice are examples of weak acid solutions. Sodium hydroxide (lye) is a strong alkali, or base. Ammonia is an example of a weak base. The solution of salt and water on the right side of the reaction above is neutral. In general aqueous solutions of salts are neither acid nor base but neutral. Water itself is also completely neutral. The degree of acidity or alkalinity of solutions in the body is of considerable physiological significance. Thus blood is always slightly alkaline. If for some reason it loses this alkalinity and becomes neutral or acid, death occurs. On the other hand, gastric juice is a fairly strong acid (mostly hydrochloric acid) solution.

We noted above that acids are characterized by the presence of hydrogen ions, H^+, in solution and bases form the hydroxyl ion, OH^-. A solution containing more H^+ ion than OH^- is acid and one containing more OH^- is basic. In pure water and in any neutral solution the number of each is exactly the same and very small. Because of a property of water, the product of the molar concentration of the H^+ ion with that of the OH^- ion is always 10^{-14} (the reciprocal of one followed by 14 zeros), so that the concentration of OH^- is known if the H^+ concentration is given.

The degree of acidity or alkalinity of any solution is measured by the amount of hydrogen ion present. The index used to indicate the amount of H^+ in a solution is the pH. Actually pH is inversely dependent on the amount of H^+, and is technically defined as being equal to the logarithm of $1/$(molar concentration of H^+). The logarithm is used simply so that the scale will have small numbers. Water or any other neutral solution has a pH of 7. Acid solutions have a pH of less than 7 and bases a pH of more than 7. As examples, blood has a pH of 7.5, gastric juice a pH of 2.0, saline a pH of 6.8, and urine a pH of 6.0. Since blood has a slightly basic or alkaline pH, all fluids of the internal environment are also slightly basic. Complex homeostatic or feedback mechanisms operate to maintain this pH at a constant value (see Chapter 5). Acid solutions like gastric juice and urine are secreted outside the internal environment.

Organic Compounds

All living tissues and cells are formed of organic compounds. All life processes—metabolism, respiration, muscle and nerve activity, etc.—are based upon organic chemical reactions. The number of known organic compounds is vast; we will restrict our discussion to a few compounds and reactions that are of particular significance for physiological processes. Organic compounds are simply covalent compounds containing carbon. Remember that in covalent compounds electrons are neither given up nor acquired, but rather shared. This is illustrated in Figure 2.4, showing the formation of two simple organic compounds, methane (CH_4) and carbon tetrafluoride (CF_4). Carbon has six electrons, two completing the inner of K shell and four in the L shell. Since eight electrons are needed to complete the L shell, carbon would have to give up four electrons or acquire four to form ionic compounds. It is generally not possible for an atom to give up or acquire this many electrons. Hence carbon shares electrons with other substances.

In the case of methane (Figure 2.4), each of the four hydrogen atoms shares its one electron with the carbon atom, and vice versa. As a result of this sharing, each hydrogen atom now shares two electrons, completing the K shell, and the carbon atom shares eight electrons, thus completing its L shell. In combining with hydrogen, which does not hold its electron strongly, carbon behaves somewhat like a negative valence atom (i.e. one which accepts electrons). However when carbon combines with fluorine (Figure 2.4) it acts like a positive valence compound which gives up electrons. The fluorine atom needs one more electron to complete its L shell. Each of four fluorine atoms shares one of the four electrons in the L shell of the carbon atom. Each fluorine atom now shares a complete L shell, and the carbon atom can be viewed as having a smaller share of the eight electrons it is sharing than the fluorines.

Carbon compounds are called covalent because carbon acts simultaneously as an electron donor (positive valence like hydrogen or lithium) and as an electron acceptor (negative valence like fluorine or chlorine). This in turn permits carbon to combine with itself and other atoms to form complicated structures containing chains and rings of atoms and thus an almost infinite variety of compounds. Organic life requires the large variety of compounds made possible by the covalent properties of carbon. Science fiction writers (and scientists) have speculated on the possibility that "silicon life" could also exist. Silicon (a common element in rocks) has fourteen electrons, two in the K shell, eight in the L shell and four in the M shell. Since eight electrons are required to complete the M shell (see Figure 2.1) silicon can share electrons by acting like an electron acceptor or donor, as is the case with carbon. To date, however, no silicon life has been discovered.

The diagrams in Figure 2.4 suggest that carbon compounds are structurally fixed with electrons shared in given positions. Although carbon compounds act in many ways as though this were the case (see discussion of isomers below), it appears, in fact, that it is a kind of dynamic equilibrium, with the shared electrons shuttling back and forth between the two atoms. In writing the structural formulas for organic compounds, a single line is shown for each pair of electrons shared between the carbon atom and other atoms. This line, often called a bond, indicates that one shared electron pair is present. Often carbon will share two electron pairs with another atom or with itself. This is indicated by drawing two parallel lines together, as in the compounds of Figure 2.5. These double lines are called double bonds.

The complex structures of carbon compounds make possible the occurrence of isomers. Isomers are compounds having exactly the same elements present in exactly the same proportions, but in different structural arrangements. Two isomers of butene are shown in Figure 2.5. Both 1-butene and 2-butene have the same composition formula, C_4H_8, but the location of the double bond differs. As a result, the chemical properties of the two form of butene are somewhat different. Isomers are of considerable importance in physiological processes. Many drugs occur in isomeric forms, but only one isomer may be physiologically active. For example, amphetamine ("dexedrine" or "benzedrine") exists as two isomers called d-amphetamine and 1-amphetamine. D-amphetamine has the well known stimulant effects, but 1-amphetamine is inactive. A more physiological example is retinine, a chemical substance in the eye involved in the

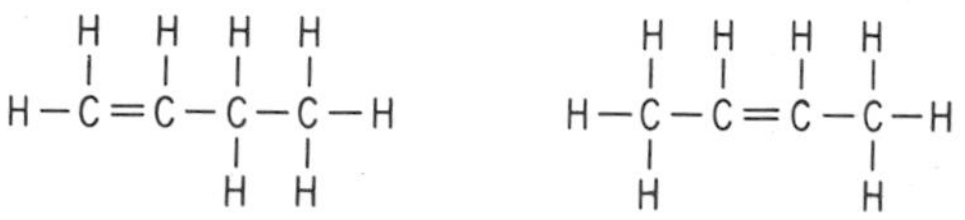

Figure 2.5. Two structural isomers of the organic compound butene. They both have the same elements in the same proportions, but have the double bond in a different location. Their chemical and physical properties are somewhat different.

1-Butene

2-Butene

formation of the light sensitive visual purple of the retina. When visual purple is exposed to light, it breaks down into one isomer of retinine and other substances. The visual purple is later resynthesized from retinine. However the retinine must first be altered to another isomeric form before resynthesis of visual purple can occur. Hence chemical mechanisms in the pigment cells of the retina must act to alter the isomeric form of retinine (see Chapter 10).

Biochemistry

Biochemistry deals with organic compounds and processes characteristic of living tissue. The three basic types of biochemical substances present in living tissue are carbohydrates, lipids and proteins. *Carbohydrates* can be roughly defined as compounds containing only carbon, oxygen and hydrogen, the latter two being in the same proportions as in water (i.e. two atoms of hydrogen for every atom of oxygen). Carbohydrates include such substances as sugars, starches, glycogen, dextrins, and cellulose. Glucose ($C_6H_{12}O_6$) is a sugar of particular significance in metabolism, being the only sugar present in appreciable concentration in the blood. Blood glucose is stored in the liver in the form of glycogen, a complex chain of glucose molecules, and subsequently released into blood as glucose. Glucose is utilized in one form or another by the various body tissues for cellular *metabolism* (production and utilization of energy). Metabolism will be described in more detail in Chapter 5.

Lipids, a general category which includes fats and other related compounds, are usually naturally occurring organic substances which dissolve in "fat-solvents" such as ether or chloroform. Many can be metabolized to serve as energy sources. Carbohydrates can be transformed into fats and so stored in the body. Lipids are of particular interest in neurochemistry in that they constitute about 75 percent of the solids in brain tissue.

Proteins form the basic structural elements of all cells. They may form connective tissue, they may be enzymes, hormones, or oxygen carriers, they participate in muscular contractions, and are associated with the genes. Three-fourths of the dry substance of most tissues is protein. In essence proteins are complex organic compounds containing nitrogen. Most contain sulphur as well. The protein molecule is made up of amino acids. The general structure of amino acids is shown in the top left diagram of Figure 2.6. Characteristic features are the presence of a carboxyl group (COOH) and an amino group (NH_2) tied to the same carbon atom. R stands here for a wide variety of different additional groups also tied to the carbon. These can range from a hydrogen atom (to form glycine) to rather complex structures. The examples shown in Figure 2.6 are three of the simple amino acids (there are a total of about 20 different amino acids commonly found in proteins). Protein molecules are composed of long and complex chains of various amino acids linked together in an order specific to the protein. Insulin, one of the simplest proteins, has a molecular weight of about 12,000 and more complex proteins have molecular weights of well over

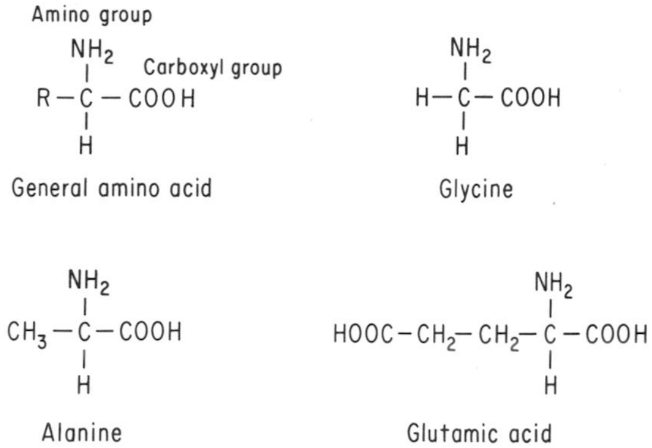

Figure 2.6. The general structural formula for amino acids, and three common examples. Various amino acids are formed by substituting different compounds for " R " in the general formula. Glycine, the simplest, has a hydrogen atom in place of " R."

Amino group

$$NH_2$$
$$R-\underset{\underset{H}{|}}{\overset{\overset{}{|}}{C}}-COOH$$ Carboxyl group

General amino acid

$$NH_2$$
$$H-\underset{\underset{H}{|}}{\overset{\overset{}{|}}{C}}-COOH$$

Glycine

$$NH_2$$
$$CH_3-\underset{\underset{H}{|}}{\overset{\overset{}{|}}{C}}-COOH$$

Alanine

$$NH_2$$
$$HOOC-CH_2-CH_2-\underset{\underset{H}{|}}{\overset{\overset{}{|}}{C}}-COOH$$

Glutamic acid

1,000,000. Since the molecular weights of most amino acids range from about 70 to a few hundred, the number and complexity of possible arrangements of amino acids in proteins is virtually limitless. It has been calculated (Synge, 1943) that for a typical protein with a molecular weight of about 34,000, made up of only 12 different amino acids, there are a total of 10^{300} different possible isomers. If only one molecule of each different isomer existed on earth, the total mass of these protein molecules would be 10^{280} grams. Since the total mass of the earth is only 10^{27} grams, it would appear that many of the possible isomers do not exist.

The percentage composition of the various elements making up proteins (i.e. carbon, hydrogen, oxygen, nitrogen, etc.) is easily determined. However, the actual structural composition remains unknown for virtually all proteins. Even though the amino acids making up a protein can be identified, the sequence of these amino acids and their structural configurations cannot be determined. Consequently, when a substance is labeled a protein, you may take it for granted that it is a long and complex chain of amino acids of unknown sequence.

Enzymes are substances that act as *catalysts* for chemical reactions in living tissues (a catalyst is any substance that changes the speed of a chemical reaction without itself undergoing any permanent chemical change). Enzymes all have the structure of proteins. They are not altered themselves as a result of chemical processes, and need be present only in very small amounts. Most are highly specific, accelerating only one or a few types of biochemical reactions. Their effects are enormous, speeding up some reactions as much as a million times. It is believed that enzymes act by fitting onto the reacting molecules like forms, holding the parts undergoing change in a favorable configuration. Of particular interest in nerve function is the enzyme acetylcholine esterase (AChE), which catylizes the breakdown of acetylcholine (ACh) (see Chapter 5).

Another group of compounds of relevance are the *nucleic acids* and *nucleoproteins*. Nucleoproteins are " conjugated " proteins—a combination of a protein with a complex nonamino acid portion, the nucleic acid. Nucleic acids are made

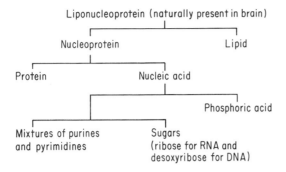

Liponucleoprotein (naturally present in brain)

Nucleoprotein   Lipid

Protein   Nucleic acid

Phosphoric acid

Mixtures of purines   Sugars
and pyrimidines   (ribose for RNA and
desoxyribose for DNA)

Figure 2.7. Chemical breakdown chart illustrating the composition of nucleoproteins. Most nucleoproteins in brain are present as complex liponucleoproteins.

up of basic substances called purines and pyrimidines (ring structures containing carbon and nitrogen; see Figure 2.8) together with phosphoric acid and sugars. Two nucleic acids of particular interest are ribonucleic acid (RNA) and desoxyribonucleic acid (DNA). The chemical breakdown chart shown in Figure 2.7 summarizes the composition of nucleoproteins. In brain they generally occur as liponucleoproteins, which can be broken down into complex lipids and nucleoproteins. The nucleoproteins in turn are composed of proteins, structure unknown, and nucleic acids.

The chemical structures of purine and pyrimidine are illustrated in Figure 2.8 simply to show that they are known; the chemical significance of these structural arrangements is well beyond the scope of this book. In naturally occurring nucleic acids pyrimidine as such does not exist, but a variety of related substances with other elements in place of one or more of the hydrogens, do. These are all termed pyrimidines. In like manner a number of closely related compounds are derived from purine. These substances may have biological importance in

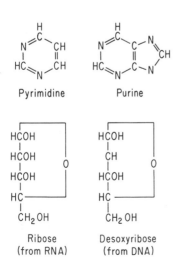

Pyrimidine   Purine

Ribose
(from RNA)

Desoxyribose
(from DNA)

Figure 2.8. Structural formulas for the complex bases (pyrimidine and purine) and sugars (ribose and desoxyribose) that form nucleic acids.

addition to being present in nucleic acids. Thus vitamin B_1 (thiamine) is pyrimidine derivative. Caffeine, found in coffee, tea, and other plants, is a purine. The names of the two major groups of nucleic acids, incidentally, are derived from the sugars present. Desoxyribose nucleic acid (DNA) contains desoxyribose sugar and ribose nucleic acid (RNA) contains ribose sugar. As shown in Figure 2.8, both are pentose or 5-carbon sugars, and their structural formulas are not too different. Nucleic acids, like proteins, are long chains, in this case made up of standard links consisting of phosphoric acid, sugar, and a purine or pyrimidine derivative. Again, an immense variety of structures is possible, this time by the choice of the purine or pyrimidine derivative at each point of the chain.

Naturally occurring nucleoproteins are enormously complex in structure, with molecular weights ranging from about 1,000,000 to over 10,000,000. The nucleic acids appear to be tied together with the protein in complex repeated series. The chromosomes of cells, which contain the genes controlling heredity, are composed largely of DNA. RNA is found both in the cytoplasm and nuclei of cells, and may play specialized roles in nerve cells. Most plant viruses, incidentally, are essentially RNA. The tobacco mosaic virus, perhaps the most familiar to most readers because of the beautiful electron microscope photographs of it that have been published, contains RNA having a molecular weight of 40,000,000. Most animal viruses are a good deal more complex than plant viruses, and contain DNA or both DNA and RNA. In recent years much evidence has accumulated suggesting that RNA is somehow related to activity in nerve cells. It has also been suggested that RNA may have very special functions related to learning. We will discuss this in more detail in Chapters 5 and 17.

ELECTRICITY

Most physiological measures used in psychology and neurophysiology are basically electrical in nature. Voltage and resistance are the two characteristics of living tissue which are commonly measured directly. In this portion of the chapter we will discuss some relevant aspects of electricity.

Recall for a moment the Bohr model of the atom, with positively charged protons in the nucleus and negatively charged electrons spinning around it. Protons and electrons exert forces on one another over and above the forces of gravitational attraction between them. These nongravitational forces are said to be the result of electricity or electric charge. Two like charges repel and two unlike charges attract. The unit charge is arbitrarily labeled negative ($-$) for an electron and positive ($+$) for a proton. All electrons have an identical unit negative charge and all protons have an identical unit positive charge. No charges have ever been observed of smaller magnitude than those of a proton or electron.

In addition to electrical forces between particles, which are dependent only upon the separation of particles, magnetic forces, dependent upon the relative motions of charged particles, are also present. Still another type of force, the nuclear binding force, has been postulated to account for the fact that the protons are all held together in the nucleus in spite of the repulsive electrical forces they exert on one another. We will limit the discussion here to some simple phenomena of electric force.

The *amount* of electric charge on an object is measured in units called coulombs, the letter Q being the symbol for charge. (Note: the units of measurement given here are in the so-called "practical" system; other systems are also in use.) A coulomb is defined as the amount of charge that will repel an equal charge placed one cm away with a force of 1 "dyne" (one dyne is a unit of force in the metric system). In terms of actual amount, one coulomb is the amount of charge carried by about 6×10^{18} electrons.

Potential, or *voltage*, is symbolized by the letter E or V. In an electric field existing around a charged object, the potential at any point is the work per unit charge needed to bring a charged object to that point from a region where no potential field exists. The voltage difference between two points expresses the work needed to move a unit charge from one point to the other. We can write a simple equation from these definitions relating voltage and charge:

$$E = W/Q$$

where W is the work involved.

Current measures the rate of flow of charged particles. If we connect a wire conductor to a source of potential difference such as a battery, electricity flows through the wire. The "free" electrons (i.e. the few electrons in the outer shells of positive valence metal atoms) in a wire actually move along the wire. Each electron moves a short distance and then is stopped by collision with other particles; then is bumped by other electrons and moves again, and so on. The average velocity of the free electrons in the wire is quite slow, about 0.02 cm/sec for a 200-amp current in a thick copper wire. However the flow of electrons is the same everywhere in the wire so the effective propagation of electricity is practically instantaneous. Current is symbolized by the letter I and is measured in amperes, (amps). One amp is defined as a current of one coulomb/sec.

The difference between the relatively slow actual velocity of the electrons as they are bumped along the wire and the nearly instantaneous velocity of electricity in a wire is often somewhat confusing. A good analogy is the flow of water in a garden hose. If a hose is filled with water and connected to a water outlet, water flows out of the hose the instant the outlet is turned on. The actual velocity of the water molecules flowing out from the outlet is very much slower. If the hose were empty, a considerably longer time would be required for the water to flow from the outlet to the end of the hose. When the hose is full of water, turning on the outlet applies pressure to the water and forces it out of the hose. This pressure is actually transmitted at the speed of sound, several hundred meters/sec. The actual rate of flow of the water may only be about 1 meter/sec. In an analogous fashion, the electron "pressure" is transmitted at the speed of light in the wire, even though the actual velocity of the individual electrons is a great deal slower.

In thinking about charge, voltage and current, it is probably easiest to picture an actual flow of electrons. Charge is the number of "additional" electrons present, voltage is the work per unit charge, and current is the rate at which they flow. An analogy is often made with water flow. Charge would then be analogous to the amount of water, voltage to the water pressure, and current would be analogous to the rate at which the water flows.

Conductance and *resistance* are reciprocal terms measuring the ease with which a current is conducted by any given substance. Conductance is dependent upon the availability of free electrons in the substance. Metals are among the best conductors since, as you will recall, metals have one or more electrons in the outer atomic shell, which are readily available as free electrons. Electrolytes also act as conductors by virtue of their charged ions, which conduct electricity in solutions just as electrons do in metal. Many substances, like plastics and glass, have very high electrical resistance and do not act as good conductors. Such substances are called *dielectrics*. Resistance, the reciprocal of conductance, is measured in ohms (which are in units of volts per ampere) and are symbolized by Ω.

The flow of electricity in a resistor may be described exactly in terms of a very simple relationship between voltage (E) in volts, current (I) in amps, and resistance (R) in ohms. This relationship, called Ohm's law, is $E = IR$. Suppose we measure a current of 10 amps through a resistance of 5 ohms. The voltage across the resistance will then be: $E = IR = 10(5) = 50$ volts. If a single resistance is connected across a constant voltage source we can easily calculate the current "drawn" by the resistance. An ordinary light bulb has a resistance of about 100 ohms and thus draws a current from the 110-volt line of about 1 amp. Familiarity with Ohm's law can be very helpful in utilizing electronic equipment and in understanding electrical relations in most electrophysiological experiments.

Let's consider a very few examples. Three simple circuits are shown in Figure 2.9. The symbol ⊣ ⊢ indicates a constant voltage source (battery) and the symbol ⟋\/\/\⟍ indicates a resistance. In A, since the voltage across the battery is constant at 6 volts, the voltage drop across the resistor must also be 6 volts. Since $R = 3$ ohms, the current in the resistor must be $I = E/R = 6/3 = 2$ amps.

In *b*, the total voltage drop across the two resistors (between the two dots) must equal the battery voltage of 6 volts. Since current is the rate of flow it cannot be different at different points along the conductor and hence is the same through both resistors. The total current is $I = E/R = 6/2 + 4 = 6/6 = 1$ amp. For R_1, we now know the resistance and the current and can calculate the voltage drop: $E_1 = IR_1 = 1(2) = 2$ volts. For R_2, $E_2 = IR_2 = 1(4) = 4$ volts. The

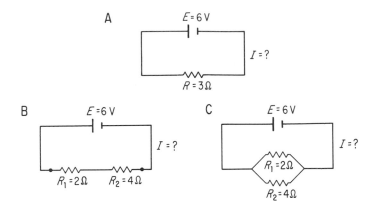

Figure 2.9. A, B, C, Simple electrical circuits illustrating the use of Ohm's law. The two resistors are in *series* in **B** and in *parallel* in **C**.

sum of these two voltage drops equals the total voltage drop of 6 volts. This arrangement of resistors is called a *series* circuit. The total resistance in a series circuit is always the sum of the separate resistance.

$$R_{\text{total}} = R_1 + R_2 + ----$$

In circuit *c*, the two resistances are said to be in *parallel*. The voltage drop across the pair of resistors must equal 6 volts, since it is 6 volts across the battery. If it is 6 volts across the pair of resistors it must be 6 volts across each resistor since the connecting wires have essentially no resistance (the voltage must be everywhere the same along a zero resistance conductor). The current in R_1 is: $I_1 = E/R_1 = 6/2 = 3$ amps and the current in R_2 is: $I_2 = E/R_2 = 6/4 = 1.5$ amps. Consequently the total current across the circuit is $3 + 1.5 = 4.5$ amps. We can also arrive at this by the rule for the total resistance of resistors connected in parallel:

$$\frac{1}{R_{\text{total}}} = \frac{1}{R_1} + \frac{1}{R_2} + ---$$

or

$$R_{\text{total}} = \frac{R_1 R_2 - - -}{R_1 + R_2 + - - - - -}$$

The total resistance in circuit (C) is thus:

$$R = \frac{R_1 R_2}{R_1 + R_2} = \frac{2(4)}{2 + 4} = \frac{8}{6} = 1\frac{1}{3} \text{ ohms}$$

The total current must then be:

$$I = \frac{E}{R} = \frac{6}{1^1/_3} = 6\left(\frac{3}{4}\right) = 4.5 \text{ amps}$$

Another common electrical device is the *condenser*. Physically, a condenser consists of two plates of conducting material separated by a dielectric like silicone or glass, and is symbolized as ⊣⊢. The general function of a condenser is to store charge. Charge is applied to a condenser by connecting a current source such as a battery to the two metal plates. When the battery is connected electrons begin to flow. As electrons leave one side of the battery and accumulate on the condenser plate connected to that side of the battery, they repel electrons (like charges repel) from the other plate, which flow to the other side of the battery. Since electrons cannot actually cross the insulating material between the two plates of the condenser, the amount of charge that can build up on the condenser is limited. The actual amount is determined by the physical characteristics of the condenser (i.e. the sizes of the plates, thickness of dielectric, etc.).

A large amount of charge can be transferred to a condenser by a relatively small difference in potential. You can convince yourself of this by connecting a condenser across the terminals of a 6-volt automobile battery briefly. When the terminals of the condenser are then shorted a high current discharge occurs. The amount of charge a condenser can store is measured in *farads*: transfer of 1 coulomb per volt of potential difference equals 1 farad. Most condensers transfer relatively much less than 1 farad of charge and are described in terms of microfarads (μF), i.e. millionths of a farad. In electronic equipment it is also convenient to utilize a unit called the picofarad (pF) which is 10^{-12} farad.

A condenser requires a certain length of time to build up full charge. The time course of charging (and discharging) follows an *exponential function*. Examples of charge and discharge curves are shown in Figure 2.10. For the mathematically inclined reader, the charging curve has the equation:

$$q = Q(1 - E^{-t/RC})$$

where q is the actual charge at any time, Q the final maximum charge, E is related to the dielectric characteristics of the particular material of which the condenser is made, C the actual capacitance of the particular condenser, and R the circuit resistance in series with the condenser. The nonmathematical reader needs to remember that such exponential equations relating various processes to

Figure 2.10.   Charge and discharge curves for a condenser. When charge is applied, it builds up in an exponential curve. The time constant is the time at which about 2/3 of the full charge is developed, (t_{RC}).

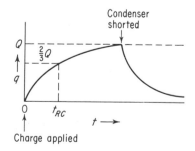

time simply mean that the *rate* of a given process is inversely proportional to how much of the process has already occurred.

In any given circuit the rate of charge or discharge thus depends not only on the capacitance of the condenser but also on the value of whatever resistance is in series with it. From the equation given above it can be shown that about 2/3 of the final charge will be built up in *RC* seconds. In other words, for any condenser and series resistance, we can calculate how much time in seconds is required to develop 2/3 of full charge by simply multiplying the capacitance of the condenser (*C*, in farads) and the resistance of the series resistor (*R* in ohms). This *RC* time is called the *time constant*. Thus if the condenser is $1\mu F$ (10^{-6} farads) and the series resistor 1,000,000 ohms, the time constant will be:

$$RC = 10^{-6}(10^{6}) = 1 \text{ sec}$$

Two thirds of the charge will be built up on one second.

The time constant or discharge time of a condenser is important both in terms of electrophysiological characteristics of tissues, and in terms of electronic apparatus. As we will see later (Chapters 6 and 7) the nerve cell membrane acts in part like a condenser, with a time constant determining the rate at which charge can build up or decay across it. A good example of the use of the condenser time constant in electronics is the electronic timer. By placing variable resistors in series with condensers, the discharge time can be adjusted to almost any time interval from microseconds to seconds. Current can be turned on or off by a tube or transistor when the voltage applied to a portion of it by the condenser builds up or discharges down to a given level.

Alternating Current

So far in our review of electricity we have dealt with circuits involving steady or constant voltage sources such as batteries. This kind of current is called *direct current* (dc). In dc sources the potential at one terminal is always positive and the other negative (see Figure 2.11). In alternating current (ac) sources the

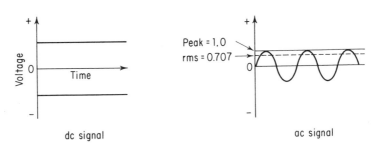

Figure 2.11.   Voltage *vs* time graphs of direct current (dc) and alternating current (ac) electrical signals. Ac voltage alternates from positive to negative. The amplitude of ac voltage is often expressed as the root-mean-square (rms) value, which is 0.707 of the maximum voltage.

potential at each terminal alternates from positive to negative (see Figure 2.11). The ordinary wall outlet current alternates at a rate of 60 cps, a given terminal being positive and then negative 60 times each second. In alternating current the charges move back and forth in the conductor. The increase or decrease in current follows a *sine wave*, which increases rapidly from the neutral level, then flattens out and decreases through zero to the negative level, and so on (Figure 2.11).

In practice, alternating current may often be treated as if it is a steady-state dc current. Thus to analyze resistors and other applications of Ohm's law, we simply treat ac current as if it were dc current. Voltage measurement of an ac signal is usually given as a kind of average called the "root-mean square" (rms). For sine waves the rms value amounts to 0.707 of the maximum value. The ordinary house voltage is rated as having an rms value of 110, but the maximum is actually 155 volts. Most physiological signals are ac in that they vary from positive to negative over time, although not usually in a simple sine wave fashion. However in some kinds of measurements, dc signals are also important. The major difference in practice concerns the type of *amplifier* used. Ac and dc amplifiers differ considerably in construction, although both accomplish the same thing—increase of voltage amplitude from the small levels of physiological signals to levels that will operate galvanometers or oscilloscopes.

Magnetism

If current is passed along a conducting wire, an *electromagnetic* field is set up in the space around the wire. Conversely, if a wire is moved through a magnetic field a current is generated in the wire. The reasons for these phenomena are complex, depending upon subatomic characteristics of matter such as electron "spin," but the basic observations of magnetism are familiar to everyone. The interrelations of current and electromagnetic field form the basis of such devices as the *transformer* and the *galvanometer*.

The transformer consists simply of two adjacent coils of wire, often wound around a metal core. A simple transformer is indicated in Figure 2.12. When current begins to flow through one of the coils a magnetic field is generated. As this field develops, it "crosses" the other coil and induces a voltage in it (moving a magnetic field across a wire has the same voltage inducing effect as moving the wire through a magnetic field). The voltage induced in the second coil (secondary) by the first (primary) is in the same proportion as the ratio of turns in the two coils. If the primary coil has 100 turns and the secondary 1000 turns, the development of a 10-volt potential in the primary yields 100 volts in the secondary. Current induced is inversely proportional; if the 10-volt primary has a current of 10 amps, the 100-volt output of the secondary would be only 1 amp. A transformer will not work if a dc current is applied across the primary. The magnetic field must *cross* the wire of the secondary coil in order to reduce current in it. With a steady potential in the primary, the magnetic

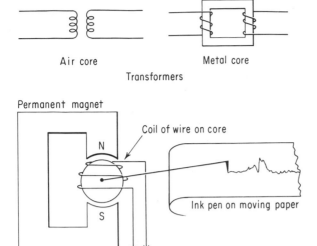

Air core   Metal core

Transformers

Permanent magnet

Coil of wire on core

N

S

Ink pen on moving paper

To unknown current source

Recording galvanometer

Figure 2.12. *Above.* Examples of transformers. Current flow in one coil induces current flow in the other coil. *Below.* Application of current induction used in the galvanometer. When current flows in the coil, it sets up an electromagnetic field that interacts with the magnetic field of the permanent magnet to cause partial rotation of the coil. This moves the pen fastened to the coil to produce a written record of the movement.

field is stationary and hence does not move across the secondary coil. Current must increase and decrease (i.e. be alternating) through the primary coil to induce current in the secondary coil.

Electronic Recording Devices

The galvanometer, which forms the basis of a variety of electrical measuring devices such as the voltmeter, ohmmeter, ammeter, and EEG recorder, is a simple application of the principle of electromagnetic induction of current (see Figure 2.12). A coil is suspended in the magnetic field of a strong stationary magnet. Current in the coil generates a field that interacts with the permanent field to cause partial rotation of the coil. The indicator needle (or ink pen or other recorder) is so set that amount of deflection on the dial is directly proportional to amount of current.

To use a galvanometer as an *ammeter*, it is simply placed in series with the circuit whose current is to be measured (Figure 2.13). Remember the current is constant in a series circuit and the same through each element of the circuit. Hence the current through the ammeter will be the same as the current through the circuit that you wish to measure. However, the current through the circuit and ammeter is determined by the total resistance of the circuit plus the ammeter (i.e. $E = IR$, $I = E/R$). If the ammeter has an appreciable resistance of its own, it would increase the total resistance and hence decrease the current flow (series resistances add, remember). In other words, introducing the measuring instrument into the circuit could change the circuit. This is avoided by placing a very low "shunt" resistance in parallel with the galvanometer coil. The total resistance of the ammeter can thus be made very low relative to the resistance of the circuit whose current you wish to measure. This results in a fixed division or fractionation of the current through the galvanometer coil and shunt resistance. The galvanometer is calibrated to read amps in terms of this fraction so that the indicator dial shows the actual current through the circuit. To summarize, the ammeter is a galvanometer having a low shunt resistance across the coil. The unit is placed in series with the circuit whose current is to be measured.

When using a galvanometer as a *voltmeter*, it must be connected in parallel with the element whose voltage is to be measured (Figure 2.13). The voltage across both will then be the same (see above). To avoid drawing much current from the element measured, a large resistance is placed in series with the coil. The galvanometer actually registers current, but is calibrated in terms of voltage using Ohm's law. Thus if the total resistance of the coil and series resistor is 100,000 ohms, and the galvanometer is calibrated to read 1/1000 amp (1 milliamp) full scale, the full scale voltage reading will be $E = IR = (1/1000)$ $(100,000) = 100$ volts. The same galvanometer is usually employed both as an ammeter and a voltmeter by switching from low resistance parallel shunt to the high resistance series resistor, and placing the unit in series or parallel with the circuit to be measured.

The *ohmmeter* is really just an application of voltage measurement. The galvanometer and a series resistance are placed in series with a battery of known voltage and the unknown resistance connected as indicated (Figure 2.13). The

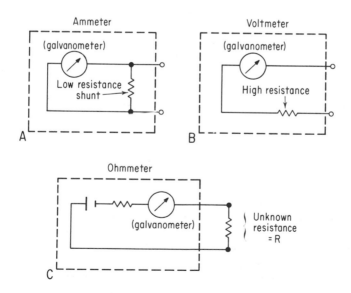

Figure 2.13. Applications of the galvanometer to measure **A**, current (ammeter); **B**, voltage (voltmeter); and **C**, resistance (ohmmeter). See text.

total current is proportional to the total resistance and the meter, which registers current, is calibrated in ohms. If the battery voltage is 10 volts and the total resistance of the meter and its series resistor is 100 ohms, the measured current will be

$$I = E/R = \frac{10}{100} + R$$

If R is zero, i.e. a good conductor, I will equal 0.1 amps and the meter calibrated to read zero ohms. If R is 900 ohms, I will equal 10/1000 or 0.01 amps and the meter will read 900, and so on.

In EEG recording devices utilizing a moving coil, the coil of the galvanometer is fastened to a pen which writes out the amount of current on moving paper (see Figure 2.12). The electroencephalograph amplifier is actually connected to the subject as a voltmeter (i.e. in parallel with the source of voltage) so that the record written on the paper is a tracing of the voltage output over time.

Physiological recording display systems usually employ either an inkwriting EEG or polygraph (using galvanometer), or an oscilloscope. The galvanometer has one major disadvantage; the mechanical coil system has mass, and hence inertia, and cannot follow fast fluctuations in potential. The oscilloscope obviates this difficulty by using an "electron beam," which has essentially no inertia, as the moving component. The cathode ray tube in the oscilloscope emits a stream of electrons which cause phosphorescence when they strike the target face of the tube, providing visual displays analogous to those on a TV tube. A diagram of a cathode ray oscilloscope is shown in Figure 2.14. The basic features include an electron source (a heated cathode which emits electrons) and two sets of deflecting plates. Since electrons are charged particles, they will be deflected when they pass a pair of plates that are generating an

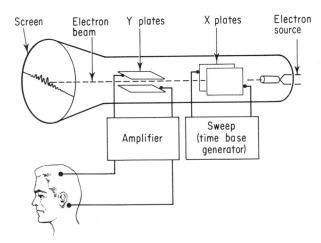

Figure 2.14. Basic operation of the oscilloscope. The electron beam is moved across the 'scope face by the X plates, and the incoming signal (here a human EEG) is displayed as vertical deflections produced by the Y plates.

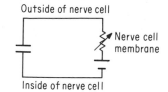

Figure 2.15. Electrical model of nerve membrane function. When the membrane conducts activity the variable resistor (symbolized by) briefly decreases, resulting in current flow.

electrical field. This is accomplished simply by putting a voltage across the two plates. The X plates (Figure 2.14) determine the "sweep speed," the rate at which the electron beam moves from left to right across the tube face. The sweep generator places preselected voltages across the X plates. In an inkwriter, incidentally, "sweep speed" is determined by how fast the paper moves under the galvanometer pen. The Y plates of an oscilloscope function as does the galvanometer pen of an inkwriter. The biological signal to be recorded (human EEG in Figure 2.14) is amplified and placed across the Y plates. The extent to which the electron beam is deflected in a vertical direction is determined by the voltage across the Y plates. The net result of the actions of the X and Y plates is to display a voltage-time line representing the recorded neural activity on the face of the oscilloscope tube. These oscilloscope displays are usually photographed on film for permanent records. With the advent of computors and "FM" (frequency modulated) tape recorders it has become possible to record physiological signals directly on tape, convert them to digitalized information in the form of sequences of numbers, and store these numbers in a computor for various kinds of analyses and subsequent displays. We will discuss these various physiological recording systems in more detail in the next chapter.

The simple principles of electricity reviewed above should provide adequate background to understand most research involving electrical stimulation and recording. Cell membranes of brain, muscle and gland tissue generate the voltages recorded in such experiments. These membranes have measurable resistance, capacitance, current flow, and voltage associated with their activity. In addition to providing an understanding of experimental procedures and results, simple electrical principles can be used to construct theoretical models of complex physiological processes. These theoretical models are similar in principle to the Bohr model of the atom; they tie together a great many observations and permit prediction of new observations. One example is sufficient here. The nerve cell membrane is an enormously complex system which conducts information. The basic functioning of the membrane can however be represented by the circuit shown in Figure 2.15. This simple circuit, involving a battery, a variable resistor and a condenser, can serve to predict many properties of the nerve cell membrane. Normally the membrane resistance (variable resistor in Figure 2.15) is very high, and there is a potential difference (indicated by the battery in Figure 2.15) across it. Since it acts more or less like a condenser, the potential difference remains constant. When neural activity is conducted along the membrane, the resistance becomes very low for a short period of time, current flows, and the high resistance is then reestablished. We will examine these phenomena in much more detail in Chapters 6 and 7.

SUGGESTED READINGS

Any introductory college texts on chemistry and physics.

Aronson, M. H. *Electronic circuitry for instruments and equipment.* Pittsburgh: Instruments Publishing Company, 1953.

3

RESEARCH TECHNIQUES

The four fields of science which are perhaps most relevant to physiological psychology are anatomy, chemistry, physiology (particularly electrophysiology), and experimental psychology. Anatomy provides methods for the analysis of neural structures, electrophysiology has developed techniques for the study of the electrical activity of the nervous system, and chemistry furnishes procedures used to analyze the chemical composition of biological tissues. Finally, experimental psychology provides the methods for analyzing behavior that make the study of physiological correlates of behavior possible. It is necessary for the student to have some understanding of research techniques and concepts in these areas to appreciate research in physiological psychology. This chapter brings together the basic aspects of such techniques and concepts to serve as background for the experimental findings and theories given in the remainder of the book. Although nerve activity is a physico-chemical process, most of our information about neurophysiology is based upon electrical recording of neural activity. Such techniques are somewhat specialized, and probably not familiar to most readers. Consequently they will be emphasized here. The student may find it useful to review portions of this material in conjunction with subsequent chapters, and other texts in the field.

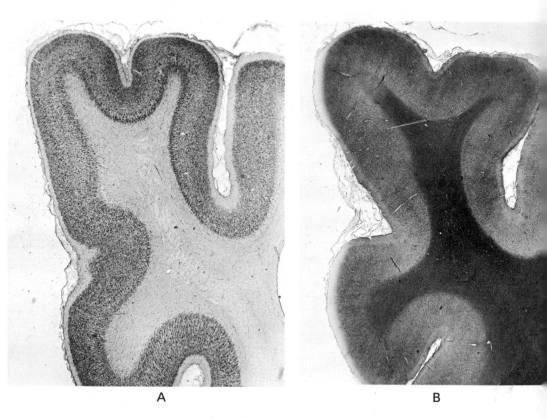

                        A   B

Figure 3.1.   Sections of brain tissue (cerebral cortex) stained by various methods. **A,** Nissl method stains only cell bodies. **B,** Weil method stains only myelinated fibers. **C,** Reduced silver method stains all nerve cell bodies and fibers, but does not stain glial cells or axon sheaths. (From Sholl, 1956.) **D,** Golgi method stains only a few nerve cells, but stains all portions of them. (From Sholl, 1956)

ANATOMICAL METHODS

A wide variety of procedures have been developed for the study of structural characteristics of the nervous system. These procedures range from gross anatomical dissection of the entire brain, through microscopic analysis of the histology of thin tissue slices to electron microscopy of minute portions of individual nerve cells. We will review briefly the standard methods used, particularly for microscopic study of tissue characteristics (see McClung, 1929; Gatenby and Beams, 1950).

Gross anatomy is the naming and describing of the structural aspects of organs that can be seen with the unaided eye. Historically this was naturally

C

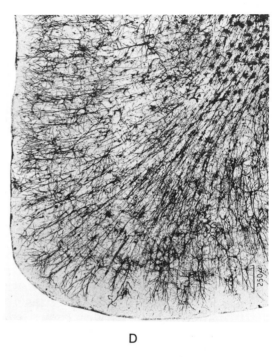

D

the earliest branch of neuroanatomy to develop. While gross anatomy is a necessary starting point (agreed-upon names for structures are a prerequisite for further study), its value as an analytic method is somewhat limited. This is particularly true for the nervous system, where the most important structural characteristic is interconnections among fibers that are too small to be visible without a microscope. A large variety of *histological* (study of tissues) procedures have been developed for microscopic analysis of the nervous system. These in turn can be subdivided into descriptive methods used with normal tissues and analytic methods used to trace fiber connections. Use of the electron microscope to study very fine details of nerve cells is perhaps the most recent development in the analysis of structural features of the nervous system.

When a thin slice of untreated brain tissue is viewed in a microscope little can be seen other than a complex jumble of cellular elements. The appearance and nature of neural tissue seen through a microscope depends entirely upon the techniques used to prepare the tissues, particularly the stains used. Common elements in all procedures include an initial *fixing* of tissue by formalin or alcohol to preserve the structural features, *hardening* of the tissue by freezing, or by impregnation with paraffin or celloidin, and *sectioning* or slicing of the hardened tissue with a *microtome*. The microtome is merely a calibrated knife blade which permits cutting tissue slices of a given thickness, usually ranging between 20 and 100 microns. After sectioning, tissue slices are *stained* with a variety of chemical agents to bring out different aspects of the tissue. If we stained all cells and fibers including all the nonneural *glia* cells in a given section of brain tissue it would be difficult to see details of organization. Consequently stains have been developed that show only cell bodies, only fibers or portions of fibers, only a few cells, but these in their entirety, or all nerve cells but not glia cells.

The selective stains that show only portions of the nerve cell do so because the chemicals used have special affinities for certain structural-chemical aspects of the cell. Thus a cell body stain might stain nucleoproteins, which are found only in the cell body; a fiber stain might stain only the fatty myelin sheaths surrounding the axon fibers; and so on. The four staining methods listed immediately below are examples of selective stains. These methods are used for descriptive microscopic study of normal neural tissue.

Nissl methods are used to stain only *cell bodies*. The dyes used, such as cresyl violet or toluidine blue, selectively stain nucleoproteins in the nucleus and other structures of the cell body. An example of a section of brain tissue prepared by the Nissl method is shown in Figure 3.1A. Different regions of brain can be characterized in terms of the sizes and distributions of the nerve cell bodies (see Chapter 11).

Weigert or *Weil* methods are used to stain fiber processes. Actually they stain the fatty tissue composing the *myelin sheaths* (the outer layers of most nerve fibers). This method is excellent for large fiber tracts but of limited value in areas containing cell bodies since most fibers lose their myelin sheaths prior to termination. An example of the Weil stain in shown in Figure 3.1B.

Reduced silver methods take advantage of the fact that nerve cell bodies and processes have a special affinity for silver. *All nerve cell bodies and processes* (but not glia cells) are stained by these methods. After treatment with silver the tissue is placed in substances that reduce the silver, so that the final appearance of cells and processes ranges from yellow to brown or black (see Figure 3.1C).

Golgi methods are used to stain *only a few cells* in a section of tissue, but *all* portions of these nerve cells are stained. Consequently it is possible to see the detailed structures of these few cells very clearly (see Figure 3.1D).

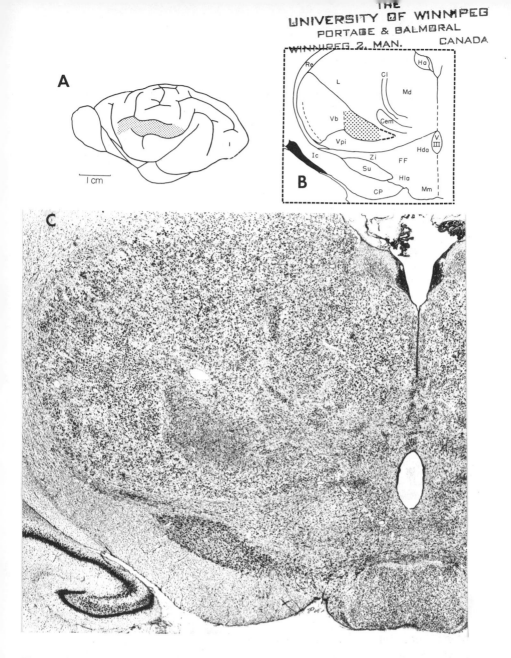

Figure 3.2.A Retrograde degeneration in the head area of the thalamic ventrobasal nuclear complex of the raccoon. Nissl method. Thionin stain. **A,** Cortical lesion. Dotted portion indicates head region of somatic sensory neocortex (SM I). This region was ablated and degeneration in the thalamus was studied. **B,** Diagram of coronal section of left thalamus of same animal to indicate region of degeneration (stippled) in head portion of ventrobasal nuclear complex. **C,** Photomicrograph of section shown in **B,** indicating region of degeneration. Note gliosis and absence of large nerve cell bodies in head region as compared with adjacent Vb regions. Abbreviations: Ha, habenula; Su, subthalamic nucleus; Re, reticular nuclei; Md, Mediodorsal nuclei; Hda, Hla, hypothalamus; Mm, mammilary bodies; CP, cerebral peduncle; IC, internal capsule; Zi, zona incerta; FF, Fields of Forel. (From Welker and Johnson, 1965)

DEGENERATION TECHNIQUES

The methods listed above are all used with normal brain tissue. A variety of modifications of these techniques have been developed to trace neural pathways and interconnections. These procedures are based on the fact that nerve cells in the central nervous system usually degenerate and die if they are damaged. In such analytic studies circumscribed lesions are placed in the nucleus or fiber tract to be traced, time allowed for degeneration to occur and the animal sacrificed for histological analysis. The processes of degeneration commonly take days or weeks. During this period physical-chemical changes occur in the

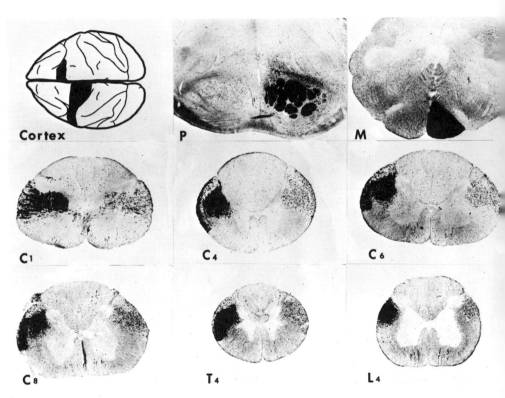

Figure 3.2.B Degeneration of fibers in the cortico-spinal tract of the monkey. Marchi method for staining fibers. The precentral motor cortex has been completely ablated on the left side and a smaller lesion has been made in Area 6 of the right side. Fiber degeneration may be traced in successive sections through the Pons (P), Medulla (M), and spinal cord (Cervical, Thoracic, Lumbar). Since the corticospinal tract decussates (crosses) at the level of the pyramids (M), stippling in succeeding sections is heaviest on the right side. However, the existence of an uncrossed lateral cortico-spinal tract is indicated by the presence of degenerating fibers on the left side of the spinal sections. (The lesion of Area 6 on the right side caused no degeneration in the spinal cord.) (From Barnard and Woolsey, 1956)

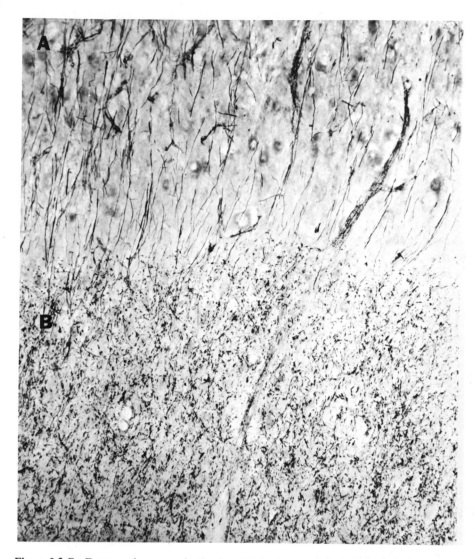

Figure 3.2.C Degenerating axons in the dorsal lateral geniculate nucleus of the cat. Nauta technique. **A**, normal; **B**, degenerated. Degeneration was produced by removal of the left eye 11 days before death. The lateral geniculate body is a laminated structure, and a few normal axons are visible in the lamina in the upper half of the structure. The small dark circular bodies are nerve cells. (From R. Guillery, University of Wisconsin, Dept. of Anatomy. Unpublished figure)

nerve cell, both in its gross appearance and in its affinity for various stains. Consequently special procedures can be used for differentially staining degenerating fibers and cell bodies.

If a nerve axon fiber is cut, two types of degeneration occur: retrograde or proximal, and prograde or distal. In retrograde degeneration the nerve cell body gradually changes appearance, exhibiting what is called *chromatolysis*. During this process the Nissl granules (particles in the cell body composed mostly of RNA nucleoproteins) gradually break up and disappear. If the cut axon is in a peripheral nerve, such as the axon from a spinal motor neuron, chromatolysis develops and then stops as the nerve regenerates a new axon. If the cut axon is within the central nervous system, the cell body usually degenerates completely and disappears. After total degeneration, a number of small nonneural glia cells proliferate in the region of degeneration. Standard Nissl methods are used to study retrograde degeneration. Both the dissolution of Nissl granules during chromatolysis and the cell bodies of the glia cell that develop can be seen. An example of retrograde degeneration is shown in Figure 3.2A.

When a nerve axon fiber is cut the distal portion of the fiber severed from the cell body always degenerates. During degeneration the fatty myelin sheath surrounding the severed axon condenses into droplets of chemically altered substance. This degenerating myelin can be differentially stained using a variation of the Weigert myelin stain called the *Marchi* method. The tissue is first treated with potassium dichromate, which prevents normal myelin from staining. When it is then treated by the standard Weigert method, only the degenerating myelin sheaths stain. An example of the Marchi method is shown in Figure 3.2B.

The Marchi procedure is limited to fibers that have myelin sheaths. Unfortunately, the small terminal portions of axons do not have myelin, so the actual endings of the axon on other nerve cells cannot be determined. Very specialized techniques such as the *Nauta* method have been developed to stain the degenerating small unmyelinated terminals (*terminal boutons*). The Nauta technique is a modification of the reduced silver method which selectively stains degenerating terminals. An example is shown in Figure 3.2C. All of the methods described above are limited to the cell bodies or fiber processes of damaged or destroyed cells. In rare instances it has been possible to demonstrate *transneural* degeneration (Minkowski, 1920) where alterations actually appeared in other cells that received connections from the damaged cells.

LESION TECHNIQUES

The general procedures involved in brain lesion studies are very simple. Following damage to the nervous system, changes in the behavior of the organism or in the activity of the remaining portions of the brain are measured. In animal studies every effort is made to produce exactly defined and reproducible lesions. In addition, clinical and experimental studies of humans with various types of accidental damage to the nervous system have provided much valuable information (see Teuber, 1960). However, it is generally quite difficult to determine the extent of the damage in humans. Most brains (hopefully) never come to autopsy in the course of an experiment. Even in animal studies it is extraordinarily difficult to produce the same lesion reliably.

The rationale underlying interpretations of the effects of brain lesions is much more complex than might appear at first glance. Suppose we remove a portion of the brain, and the animal can no longer perform a certain behavioral task. We will quickly get involved in logical difficulties if we assume that the removed portion was the brain "center" necessary for this task. It might be involved in the motor performance of the task; it might be a part of the visual nervous system necessary to provide cues for the task; it might be a part of a system regulating motivation; perhaps it is involved in the general level of attention or arousal of the animal, and so on. A great deal of additional experimentation is needed before it can be concluded that this region is the one and only necessary "center" for the task. In general it has not been possible to make such simple and clear-cut statements about functions of various portions of the nervous system. Nevertheless, lesion studies have provided much of our current information on the roles of various neural structures in behavior. As Sholl (1956) has noted, Lashley's studies on the functions of the cerebral center are examples of "brilliant use of the lesion method." We will discuss some of his experiments in a later chapter.

In general there are two different types of lesion procedures: *chronic* lesions, in which the lesion is produced under surgically sterile conditions and the animal allowed to recover, and *acute* lesions, in which the effects of the lesion are studied immediately and the animal sacrificed. Chronic lesion animals are most typically used in studies involving long term postoperative behavioral testing of the animal, whereas acute lesion animals (often called "preparations") are most often used to study the effects of lesion on electrical and chemical activity of the remaining portions of the nervous system. Often the effects of a lesion are not themselves studied, but rather the lesion is used to produce a convenient preparation for study. Thus if we wished to look at the reflex activity of the spinal cord, we would first cut the spinal cord above the region of interest (perhaps where it joins the brain) in order to study the cord in the absence of the controlling influences normally exerted by the brain.

Some of the more generally used methods of removing or inactivating tissue will be discussed here, including transection, surface ablation, depth destruction and reversible lesion.

Transection of the spinal cord or brainstem yields "simplified" preparations that can be further studied without anesthetics. For spinal cord, after the animal is anesthetized the cord is exposed dorsally. The cord may either be cut, or crushed by an extradural thread passed around it and tied. If sterile technique and careful postoperative care are used, animals with isolated posterior spinal cord can be maintained chronically for long term study of spinal reflexes (Dykman and Shurrager, 1956; Kellogg et al., 1947). The results of studies obtained from the neurally isolated spinal cord must, of course, be interpreted with some caution in relation to the functioning of the spinal cord in the intact animal. Nevertheless we can determine what the organization and activities of the spinal cord are in the absence of influences from the brain.

When the spinal cord is cut at the point where it joins the brain, the activity of the entire spinal cord can be studied. In addition, we can study the electrical activity of the brain in the absence of all input from the body (excepting the head) with such a transection. The brain end of this preparation is called the *encéphale isolé* (Bremer, 1935). Even though the animal can no longer move, the brain exhibits a pattern of sleeping and waking electrical activity, and is a convenient preparation for the study of many types of electrical and chemical processes.

Transection of the brainstem at the level of the superior colliculus yields the *cerveau isolé* first described by Bremer (1935). If the portion of the CNS below the level of transection is to be studied, the transection may be made by aspiration and all brain tissue anterior to the section removed. If an island of hypothalamus and pituitary is left, such animals can be maintained chronically for long periods of time (Bard and Macht, 1958). If the anterior portion of the brain is to be studied transection is done by spatula. The anterior portion contains only the olfactory and visual systems, has no pain input, and exhibits permanent "EEG sleep."

Ablation of cerebral cortex is best accomplished by subpial aspiration, using weak suction and small pipettes. It is often important to make restricted

Figure 3.3. Photograph of a portion of cat skull held in a stereotaxic machine. The electrode is held in a carrier that can be moved over the skull in a rectangular coordinate system and lowered into the brain by a micromanipulator.

lesions with bordering tissue intact. Using proper suction and pipettes it is possible to achieve this with little damage to underlying white matter and minimal bleeding. It is important in lesion studies to use sterile surgical technique in order to avoid uncontrollable enlargement of lesion by infection.

Depth lesions involve placement of lesion electrodes using a standard *stereotaxic machine*, first introduced by Horsley and Clarke (1908). The major purpose of the stereotaxic machine is to place an electrode wire or tube at a given location in the depths of the brain. If you simply pushed a wire into the brain by hand, you would have no idea where the tip was going. The stereotaxic machine holds the animal's head in a fixed position and permits the insertion of electrodes at locations having a known relation to the skull. A photograph of a cat skull held in position in a stereotaxic machine is shown in Figure 3.3. (Anesthetics are always used when inserting the animal in the head holder.) The animal's head is held rigidly in position by ear bars inserted in the external ear canals, bars pressing down on the infraorbital bone ridges under the eyes and bars pressing upward against the upper teeth. A calibrated framework fastened to the head holder carries one or more electrode holders.

Stereotaxic machines are calibrated in rectangular or, less commonly, polar coordinates. This is done by mapping the anatomical locations of all brain structures for a "standard" animal placed in position in the holder. Stereotaxic atlases prepared in this manner give enlarged cross sections at 1-mm intervals throughout the brain together with the stereotaxic coordinates. Any place in the brain can be described and localized by the set of three rectangular coordinates. The basic measuring point is the ear bars. As noted above, these are inserted in the ear canals. All brain positions can be located in terms of how far in front or behind the ear bars they are, how far above the ear bars they are, and how far to the side of the head midline they are. All stereotaxic atlases give numbers for each brain section that refer to these measurements.

A plate taken from a stereotaxic atlas of a cat (Jasper and Ajmone-Marsan, 1954) is shown in Figure 3.4. This is a section through the thalamus, a large collection of nerve cell nuclei (collections of cell bodies) lying in the depths of the cerebrum (see Chapter 4). The drawing illustrates the appearance of the thalamus of the cat at frontal plane 6. It was drawn from photomicrographs of the appropriate brain sections (which are also shown in the atlas, stained both for cell bodies and fiber tracts). The drawing indicates the cell nuclei and fiber bundles. The various cell nuclei are labeled. Note that the drawing has a set of coordinate numbers along the side and top, and the label "Fr. 6.0" below. The latter stands for "frontal plane 6" and means that the section was taken exactly 6 millimeters anterior to (in front of) the ear bars. The numbers along the top starting from 0 in the middle of the drawing refer to number of millimeters to the left of the midline (center point of the head). The numbers along the left tell you height above "stereotaxic zero" in millimeters. Stereotaxic zero for this atlas is exactly 1 centimeter above an imaginary line connecting the two ear bars.

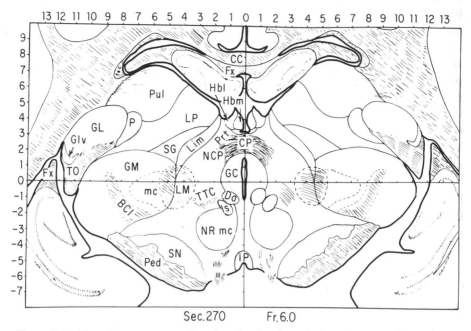

Figure 3.4. Plate from a stereotaxic atlas showing frontal plane 6. Photomicrographs of tissue sections through the thalamus were used to make the atlas drawing. The atlas gives the dorsal-ventral and medial-lateral coordinates in millimeters. Frontal plane 6 is six mm anterior to the ear bars. Note that the zero-zero point on frontal plane 6 is in the central canal. Most of the labeled structures are portions of the thalamus. Some of the abbreviations are: GL, lateral geniculate body; GM, medial geniculate body; Pul, pulvinar nucleus; LP, lateral posterior nucleus; NR, red nucleus; Ped, cerebral peduncle; CC, corpus callosum. (From Jasper and Ajmone-Marsan, 1954)

In using a stereotaxic machine, the electrode is calibrated before the animal's head is placed in position. The two ear bars are pushed together so their tips just about touch in the midline. The electrode tip is moved by the rectangular, millimeter-scaled manipulators until it touches the point where the two ear bar tips come together. The electrode tip is now at frontal plane zero, midline zero, and 10 mm below horizontal zero. The actual numbers on the electrode manipulators are read and converted to these coordinates. After the animal's head is placed in position, the electrode can then be placed in any location in the brain using atlas maps like that shown in Figure 3.4.

Suppose we wished to make a depth lesion in the *lateral geniculate body*. This structure relays visual information from the eye to the visual area of the cerebral cortex. In the drawing of Figure 3.4, GL refers to lateral geniculate body, which lies between 8 and 12 mm to the left of the midline and between 2 and 4 mm above stereotaxic zero. If we wish to place our electrode in the center of GL we first move it anteriorly until it is 6 mm in front of the ear bars (the drawing is of frontal plane 6), and then move it 10 mm to the left of the midline.

We then plunge it down into the brain until it is 3 mm above stereotaxic zero (i.e. 13 mm above the ear bars). It should now lie in the center of the lateral geniculate body. With a sensory relay structure like this it is easy to check location of the electrode. If it is in the lateral geniculate body it will record a burst of electrical activity from the nucleus in response to a flash of light delivered to the eye.

There is always some degree of error in placing electrodes stereotaxically. small errors in calibration and adjustment of the machine are common. Furthermore no two brains are exactly alike. Consequently, the placement of the electrode and lesion must be verified histologically. The brain is perfused, fixed, sectioned, and appropriately stained, and the electrode track located on the sections. Photomicrographs showing sections of brain with electrode tracks and depth lesions are given in Figure 3.5.

Surprisingly enough, it is usually possible to come within a millimeter or so of any locus in the brain using the stereotaxic method. Interanimal variability of skull and brain dimensions is relatively small for most species. Standard stereotaxic atlases are available for a number of species (Bureš et al., 1962; deGroot, 1959; Emmers and Akert, 1963; Jasper and Ajmone-Marson, 1954; Jimenez-Castellanos, 1949; Massopust, 1961; Olszewski, 1952; Russell, 1961b; Snider and Lee, 1961; Snider and Neimar, 1961; Zeman and Innes, 1963).

For depth lesions, monopolar (single) or bipolar (double) electrodes insulated except for several millimeters at the tips are stereotaxically inserted. Since depth lesions are usually produced by running fairly strong electric current through the tissue, wires are commonly used. Steel wires are preferred because of their strength and good conducting properties. When a strong current flows through the electrodes, it will tend to destroy brain tissue everywhere that the wire is in contact with the tissue. Consequently it is necessary to insulate all but the tips of the electrodes. Tissue will be destroyed only in the region of the uninsulated tips, permitting a discrete and localized lesion. The size of the lesion will depend upon the length of uninsulated electrode tip, the type and intensity of the current, and the length of time the current is allowed to flow.

Two general types of electric current are used to make depth lesions in the brain. One method, called *electrolytic*, uses a source of dc current such as a battery. When sufficiently strong current flows, the tissue near the electrodes is destroyed. In electrolytic lesions, the current consists of ions moving out from one electrode in to the other. The brain acts as an electrolyte (see Chapter 2). With sufficient movement of ions, the brain tissue is destroyed. The other method employs a very high frequency alternating current (RF or radio frequency method). When high frequency current flows through a medium having appreciable resistance, like brain tissue, heat is generated. With sufficiently high current intensity the heat developed destroys brain tissue in the region of the electrodes. Recent evidence suggests that electrolytic lesions may tend to produce unwanted side effects such as abnormal activity in bordering structures resulting from deposit of metallic ions (Reynolds, 1963a, b). The RF method

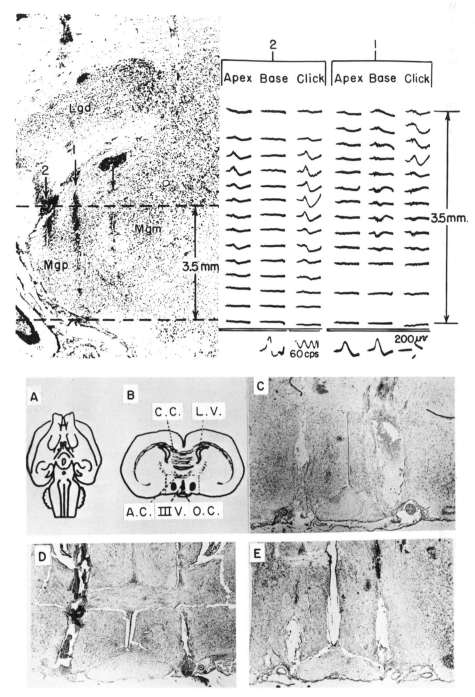

Figure 3.5. *Above:* photograph of a section of brain tissue containing electrode tracks. Arrows indicate paths of electrodes. Evoked responses (shown on right) were recorded from the medial geniculate body (Mgp, the auditory relay nucleus of the thalamus) by an electrode in tracts marked 1 and 2 (shown on left) in response to electrical stimulation of the apex and base of the cochlea and to clicks. (From Rose and Woolsey, 1958) *Below:* photograph of a section of brain tissue containing depth lesions. **A**, a ventral view of the brain. **B**, cross section through the site of the lesion. **C**, **D**, and **E**, successive sections through the site of the lesion, showing electrode tracks and lesions. (From Gamble and Patton, 1953)

would seem to be somewhat preferable, and inexpensive RF units are commercially available.

Brain lesions have been made by a variety of other techniques, most of which require rather specialized equipment. Depth lesions can be produced by beaming several x-ray units to a common focus, by beaming ultrasonic sound waves to a common point, or by injecting a poison like alcohol through a small needle inserted in the brain. Cortical lesions can be produced by implanting a small pellet of a radioactive isotope (Harlow, 1958). An ingenious method for controlled destruction of one or more *layers* of cortex using a cyclotron beam has also been developed (Rose et al., 1961).

Because of the uncertainties attendant upon any lesion procedure, histological study of the tissue to determine the extent of tissue damage is usually necessary. A spirited defense for "no histology" has been presented (Meyer, 1958) and the position would seem to have considerable merit if the hypothesis to be tested does not relate structure and function in any detail. Consistent behavioral alterations as a result of a standardized lesion procedure speak for themselves. However, if correlations between structure and function are desired, histology is necessary.

Several methods for producing *reversible* lesions have recently been developed. These have the advantage of producing no permanent trauma, and permit repeated study of the animal in the normal and "lesion" conditions. The long known phenomenon of *spreading depression*, a temporary inactivation of cortical neurons as a result of trauma (see Marshall's comprehensive review, 1959) has been utilized by Bureš and Buresova (1963). Small amounts of salt solutions (e.g. KCl) are injected on the cortex with a permanently implanted cannula (tube), or a piece of filter paper soaked in the solution is placed on the cortex. The entire cortical hemisphere may be inactivated for 20 minutes or more. Reversible cooling can also be used. For surface structures such as cortex, a metal plate can be substituted for skull and dry ice placed briefly on the plate. For depth, a V-tube is implanted and compressed gas is allowed to expand through the tube, resulting in cooling. The approximate extent of the cooling effect can be estimated by calculation. Still another method is to stimulate brain tissue with an alternating current of such characteristics that it temporarily inactivates the tissue.

CHEMICAL METHODS

Three general types of preparations are commonly employed in chemical studies of the brain. The *in vivo* methods analyze chemical processes occurring in the intact, normally functioning brain. *In vitro* methods involve the study of portions of brain tissue such as slices maintained in a solution providing all the necessary nutrients and oxygen. This type of preparation is of course to some degree artificial; nevertheless, some neuronal functions do continue *in vitro*.

The third method, which might be called *processed tissue*, involves grinding up neural tissue to analyze its chemical composition. All of these methods provide complementary but sometimes mutually exclusive types of information. Thus it is difficult to determine the chemical composition of brain without removing it; however the kinds of chemical processes occurring in intact brain may not occur in brain tissue that has been removed, particularly if it has been ground up in preparation for chemical analyses.

In Vivo Methods

Over-all measurements of such processes as brain oxygen consumption and metabolic exchange can be made by sampling blood from the large arteries and veins as it enters and leaves the brain. The normal values of such processes and the alterations produced by various physiological and behavioral states have been studied in this fashion (cf. Chapter 5 and Kety, 1955). Alternatively, chemical factors may be studied in localized regions of brain using specialized methods for measurement of pH, oxygen tension, and so on (Tower, 1958).

Direct injection or perfusion of compounds into brain tissue has been widely used. Thus if a substance is believed to act as a synaptic *transmitter* agent (see Chapter 8) it should cause increased neural activity. Alternatively, specific chemical *inhibitors* that prevent a given chemical reaction would be expected to decrease activity. A further elaboration is the use of a substance to "inhibit an inhibitor." Thus if acetylcholine (ACh) is believed involved, an enzyme called acetylcholine esterase (AChE), which breaks down ACh, can be inhibited by a substance called eserine. Injection of eserine should lead to increased or prolonged activity. Perhaps the ultimate refinement is a process called *electrophoretic* injection whereby substances can be injected inside single nerve cells. If a very small micropipette is inserted inside a cell, a weak current through the pipette will result in a flow of ions out into the cell (the current itself is of course the flow of ions). For studies of biochemical factors in regional brain activity and behavior, (i.e. endocrine functions of the hypothalamus is sexual behavior), microinjection of small amounts of substance through a permanently implanted cannula is used.

In Vitro Methods

TISSUE SLICES. This preparation has some advantages over the *in vivo* methods, since the influence of many physiological and chemical variables can be studied in isolation (McIlwain, 1959). Thus the effect of electrical stimulation on tissue respiration and energy consumption may be assessed by measuring changes of oxygen and chemical substances. A good deal of information about biochemical processes involved in energy consumption and utilization as well as an increased understanding of many drug effects has been derived from tissue slice studies. However, substances which might occur in the blood in the intact brain are not present, nor is the electrical activity of the slice in any sense normal.

Processed Tissue Methods

Study of the chemical composition of neural tissue has generally been done on whole brain and is somewhat removed from chemical analysis of specific types of nerve cells or neural functions. When evaluating the finding of such studies, it should be kept in mind that more than half of all the cells in brain tissue are not nerve cells but glia cells, which do not conduct impulses and presumably serve only supportive and nutritional functions. Neural and glial cells are thoroughly intermingled in brain tissue and generally cannot be separated out, even by the most discrete dissections. Peripheral nerve fibers have glia and are surrounded by connective tissue layers which cannot be fully removed. Consequently any chemical analysis of neural tissue is really an analysis of nerve cells plus other kinds of cells.

Typically, the brain is removed and "fixed" as rapidly as possible. *Fixing* here means stopping all chemical processes and preserving all substances intact. For study of certain structural features fixing speed is not crucial, but many important substances are extremely labile, and can alter in the first few seconds after death. Early studies of brain chemistry often gave inaccurate results due to slow fixing procedures. A common method today is whole body immersion in liquid nitrogen. For smaller animals this will freeze brain tissue in two seconds (Stone, 1938). For animals larger than the rat it is usually necessary to anesthetize the animal (this introduces other complications) and expose the region of brain to be frozen.

After brain tissue has been frozen it is homogenized and treated by a variety of standard biochemical extraction procedures. Different solvents are used to dissolve different types of chemicals and further fix them for study. Organic solvents such as alcohol or acetone will dissolve lipids and amines, after which lipids can be separated by other solvents, and so on. Different portions of ground cells can be separated by centrifugation; heavier portions "sediment" (move to the bottom of the container) sooner during spinning. Thus the DNA containing nuclei sediment out when spun at 1000 gravities for 10 minutes, but the RNA fraction requires 100,000 gravities for 30 minutes to sediment (McIlwain and Rodnight, 1962).

These general procedures of fixing and extraction are also used for specific *assays*. Instead of attempting to determine the composition of brain tissue, the investigator may wish to assay the presence and concentration of a particular compound such as acetylcholine, which might play a special role in neural activity. If the nuclear portion is believed to contain the substance, this portion is separated by centrifugation and treated with specific solvents or reacted with compounds that remove only acetycholine. Microassays of very discrete regions of brain tissue, e.g. rat visual cortex, can be done in this manner by dissecting the desired piece from the frozen brain and then running it through these procedures.

Another general biochemical method involves the use of radioactive tracers.

If a compound is believed to be involved and incorporated in certain neural structures or processes, it can often be "tagged" with radioactive elements such as phosphorous 32 or carbon 14. This is done by replacing the normal atoms with radioactive atoms in some of the molecules of the compound. The substance is then injected in the bloodstream or brain. If the neural tissue or substance in question utilizes the compound it will take up some of the radioactive atoms. If the neural tissue is then placed in a radio-activity counter the relative number of radioactive atoms incorporated can be measured. Both the amount of the compound utilized and the rate at which it is utilized can be determined in this way.

ELECTRICAL RECORDING

A wide variety of techniques are used to record electrical activity from the nervous system. The type of information obtained in a given experiment depends in large part on the techniques used to obtain it. Our discussion here will emphasize the nature of the information available from different techniques, the assumptions and limitations involved in interpreting the data, and general problems of technique. Practical details of procedure are available in several reference volumes (Sheer, 1961; Bureš et al., 1962; Sidowski, 1966).

Most experiments in which electrical activity is recorded have measured voltage changes over time (some experimenters have also measured current or impedance as well). Basically, the records obtained are voltage-time tracings, i.e. changes in the amplitude of the signal voltage over time. A sampling of the various types of electrical records commonly obtained from the nervous system is indicated in Figure 3.6. Although these responses appear very different from one another they share one thing in common: they are all graphs relating voltage amplitude to time. Two fundamentally different types of neural activity commonly measured are averaged responses of large populations of nerve fibers or cells, and activity of single cells (the terms "unit" or "single unit" are often used to refer to the latter). Records from populations of cells are obtained using large or "gross" (usually greater than 0.1 mm) electrodes, whereas single cell activity is commonly measured with very small "microelectrodes." Figure 3.6 illustrates gross recordings of evoked responses, spontaneous EEG activity, peripheral nerve responses, and "massed unit" activity. Microelectrode recordings are shown for extracellularly recorded discharges of single nerve cells and intracellularly recorded responses of single nerve cells. If you compare the voltage calibration scales to the left of each tracing you will see that the responses may range from 100 microvolts to 100 millivolts. Amplitudes of different types of electrical activity may differ by as much as a factor of 1000. The time scales range from a few milliseconds (F) to several minutes (D) for the responses. In spite of the marked differences, all the records of Figure 3.6 are simply voltage-time graphs, as noted above. Very different types of information about neural activity are provided by these various measures, and rather different types of electrodes and recording equipment are needed to obtain them.

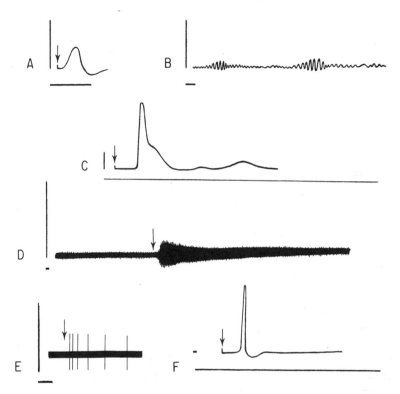

Figure 3.6.   Examples of various types of electrical activity recorded from the nervous system. All of these are schematic drawings of voltage (ordinate) *vs* time (abscissa) tracings. Voltage calibrations are indicated by the vertical line to the left of each graph. This line always represents 1 millivolt (1 mV). Note that the response in **D** is very much less than 1 mV, but response **F** is very much greater than 1 mV. Time calibrations are given by the horizontal line under each graph. The length of the line always represents 50 milliseconds (50 msec). Note that the response in **C** is much shorter than 50 msec, but the response in **D** is much longer than 50 msec. Stimulus onsets are shown by arrows. **A**, gross evoked "primary" response recorded from the cerebral cortex to a sudden peripheral stimulus such as a click, skin shock, or light flash. Positive up. **B**, spontaneous ongoing EEG activity recorded from the scalp. Negative up. **C**, gross response of a peripheral nerve to shock stimulation given some distance away from the recording site. Negative up. **D**, unit hash activity recorded grossly from a peripheral nerve. This example illustrates the type of response seen in a taste nerve when a taste solution is placed on the tongue. The thickened baseline indicates a greater number of single fiber discharges. **E**, extracellular microelectrode recordings of the discharges of a single nerve cell. Note that all spikes have approximately the same amplitude. Positive up. **F**, intracellular microelectrode recording of a spike discharge of a single nerve cell. Note that the amplitude is approximately 100 mV, in contrast to the 0.5 mV extracellularly recorded spikes of **E**. Positive up.

The convention (or rather the lack of convention) used to display voltage *vs* time tracings of brain activity is always a source of confusion to the student. When a physicist or electrical engineer draws a plot of voltage against time he uses the convention of "positive up." Calling the zero or ground level the baseline, when the voltage becomes positive, he draws it as rising up above the baseline on the graph. When it goes negative from zero, he draws it below the baseline. Many neurophysiologists use this convention; they show positive brain voltages as being above the baseline and negative voltages as being below. However, even more neurophysiologists use just the opposite convention! They show positive brain voltages as going below the baseline and negative voltages as going above. The reasons for these conflicting conventions are largely historical. Early experimenters who worked with EEG used the negative up convention, and it has persisted, particularly in the field of EEG studies. Because of the two opposite conventions, it is always necessary to state which convention is used in a given experiment. Examples are shown in Figure 3.7 illustrating a gross evoked response recorded from the auditory portion of the cerebral cortex to a click stimulus. In A the response is shown using the "positive up" convention. The major component of this type of evoked cortical sensory response is a positive deflection. In B the same response is shown using the "negative up" convention. Remember that this is the very same voltage time tracing as that in A, displaying a large positive deflection. The only difference is that the positive is indicated as down rather than up. Many types of recording devices today have switches that permit the voltage-time display to be shown using either convention. Remember that whenever you look at a record of neural activity you must find out which convention is used before you can interpret the response. In this text we will indicate the recording convention in the figure legend. Figures 3.8 and 3.9 are further illustrations. The spontaneous EEG activity in Figure 3.8 is recorded negative up, but the evoked responses of Figure 3.9 are recorded positive up.

Common features of all electrophysiological recording experiments include: recording *electrodes* (wires, plates, wicks, pipettes, etc.) placed in tissue under

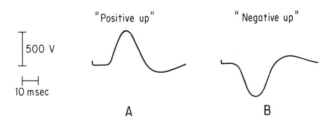

Figure 3.7. Examples of a gross evoked response recorded from the auditory cortex of the cat to a click stimulus, using the two recording conventions. It is the same response in both cases but is displayed as positive voltage up or negative voltage up.

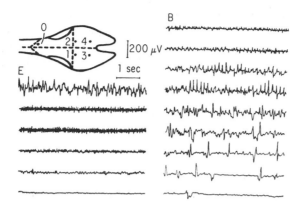

Figure 3.8.   EEG recorded from the cerebral cortex of the rat during the induction of anesthesia using ether (E—tracings on the left) or barbiturate (B—tracings on the right). The top tracing in each represents activity at the beginning of anesthesia and the bottom tracings were during very deep anesthesia. Note that the EEG activity appears to be totally different with the two anesthetics. The insert above shows the top view of the rat skull; all recordings were taken between electrodes 1 and 3 (i.e. from the top of the skull somewhat to the left of the midline). Negative up. (From Bureš, Petráň, and Zachar, 1962)

study in a particular arrangement, *amplifiers* that increase the voltage picked up by the electrodes, and *write-out systems* that provide a permanent record of the voltage changes over time. The most commonly used types of electrodes and amplifiers employed for studying various aspects of neural activity are described below.

There are two different types of write-out devices, the ink writer or polygraph and the oscilloscope. The basic principles of operation of the oscilloscope were described in Chapter 2. It can respond to any range of frequencies and can handle physiological signals of almost any duration. The response displayed on an oscilloscope tube is usually photographed either on film or paper. The display of an oscilloscope is a voltage-time line and it appears as would a single

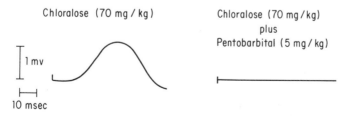

Figure 3.9.   Effect of barbiturate on the evoked nonspecific "association" response recorded from the cerebral cortex to peripheral sensory stimulation. This response is present in certain regions of the cortex in the unanesthetized and chloralose anesthetized animal (left drawing) but is totally abolished by small doses of barbiturates (right drawing). Positive up.

line across a TV tube face. Signals of different duration are handled by changing the sweep speed of the voltage-time tracing, which is actually produced by a point of light (electron beam) traveling across the tube face. The only drawbacks to oscilloscope recording are unavailability of inexpensive multiple channel units, and the lack of immediate write out when photographic transcribing is done. The ordinary EEG inkwriter using galvanometers with ink pens (see Chapter 2) does have several recording channels and an immediate display. Its great drawback is the lack of high-frequency response due to the mechanical impedance of the galvanometer pens. Most units do not record accurately above about 70 cps and thus do not properly display fast or sharply peaked activity. Recently developed optical oscillograph write-out systems can record up to 3000 cps—enough for most physiological recording.

Most of our electrophysiological information about the nervous system has been obtained in what are called *acute* experiments. Typically, the animal is anesthetized, the neural tissue to be studied is exposed, and neural activity is recorded while the animal is still anesthetized. At the end of such an experiment, which may last as long as several days and nights, the animal is "sacrificed" (i.e. killed, usually by an overdose of anesthetic), and the portion of tissue studied is preserved for various anatomical control procedures.

Many different types of anesthetics have been employed in electrophysiological studies. Barbiturates such as sodium pentobarbital ("Nembutal") and sodium pentothal are widely used. They have several advantages: since they are available in solution form they are easy to administer by injection (in animals this is usually done by injecting the anesthetic directly into the abdominal cavity), there is no danger of explosion, there is a large safety factor in that a great deal more of the drug is required to produce death than is necessary to obtain a surgical level of anesthesia, and the effects of the initial dose may last for several hours. It is not too difficult to maintain the animal at a given depth of anesthesia using barbiturates. Ether, on the other hand, must be administered by some type of breathing device, is explosive, has a low safety factor, and has a much shorter duration of action. This last characteristic, incidently, is a decided advantage if you wish to use some type of preparation other than ether in the actual experiment. Other anesthetics, such as chloralose, dial, urethane, or mixtures of these, are widely used. They are administered in solution form, and tend to produce a more responsive nervous system than do the barbiturates.

A type of "anesthetized" preparation can be achieved by transection of the brain stem (the "*cerveau isolé*" described above). The transection is typically carried out using ether anesthesia and the animal allowed to recover from the ether. Since all pain input to the brain occurs below the level of transection, no pain activation can reach the cerebrum, which remains permanently asleep. It is assumed that the brain stem below the level of the transection does not appreciate pain as such. Consequently, if you wish to study systems that lie entirely above the transection (e.g. primary visual pathways), this can be done without the use of any further anesthetics following transection.

The kind of anesthetic used in a given experiment poses very complex problems of interpretation. In many cases the type of activity recorded from a given structure in the brain is entirely dependent on the particular type of anesthetic employed. This unfortunate difficulty is illustrated in Figure 3.8. Spontaneous ongoing gross EEG activity is recorded from the surface of the brain of the rat for increasing doses of ether on the left and for a barbiturate on the right. There appears to be no similarity at all in the EEG activity with the two different anesthetics, except in the bottom tracing where the brain is depressed to the point that no activity at all occurs. To take another example, a type of nonspecific evoked "association" response can be recorded from certain regions of the cerebral cortex in the chloralosed animal. However, when a very small dose of a barbiturate is added, these responses vanish (Figure 3.9). Consequently generalizations based on electrical activity recorded from the brain using a particular anesthetic must always be viewed with great caution.

One solution to the problem of anesthetic effects has been to work with the unanesthetized but paralyzed animal. Ether is used for the initial surgery and the animal is then shifted to a local anesthetic such as procaine in combination with muscular paralyzing agents like curare. This method has serious ethical and practical difficulties, and is *not recommended* for the beginner. Since the animal is paralyzed, he cannot *respond* to painful stimuli. It is easy to become careless about repeatedly applying local anesthetics on cut tissues and pressure points, particularly if the animal is in a stereotaxic head holder. One method that seems to eliminate pain involves section of the fifth cranial nerve (see Chapter 4) which carries essentially all pain input from the face and head. This can be done as a part of the surgical procedures involved in exposing the brain prior to the experiment. The fact that a paralyzed animal cannot breath presents still another problem, The animal must be artificially respirated with an adequate mixture of moisturized oxygen and carbon dioxide.

The difficulties noted above in using the paralyzed but unanesthetized animal were primarily concerned with the ethical problems of avoiding suffering. Another serious problem with such preparations is the obvious fact that they are paralyzed. For physiological psychologists whose major interests are in the relations between neural and behavioral variables, such preparations are clearly of limited value. The paralyzed animal cannot behave. One solution to this difficulty has been to implant electrodes permanently in the brain. These *chronic* (i.e. long term or permanent) preparations make possible repeated study and observation of neural activity in the normal behaving animal. Methods used for chronic study of neural activity will be discussed further below.

Populations Responses: Spontaneous and Evoked Gross Activity Recorded from Brain Structures

Any type of procedure that involves recording the activity of more than a single nerve cell or fiber may be said to record or sample the response of a

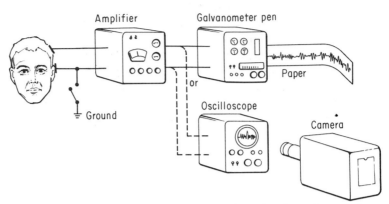

Figure 3.10. Block diagram of EEG recording system. The active electrode comes from scalp and the indifferent from a neutral point such as the ear. If the ground switch is open, the recording is "double ended." However, if the switch is closed to short the indifferent electrode to ground, the recording is "single ended." The amplified response can be recorded on an ink writing galvanometer or displayed and photographed on an oscilloscope.

population of cells. Such procedures are often called "gross" recordings. The general experimental setup for recording gross voltage changes from the brain is shown in Figure 3.10. The diagram actually illustrates the arrangement that is used for recording ongoing EEG (electroencephalographic) activity from the scalp of a human. One wire, the *active* electrode, is placed on the scalp over the brain, and the other wire, the *indifferent* electrode, is placed on a presumably neutral point like the ear. Electrical activity recorded by the electrodes is amplified and recorded on a write-out system of some type. In acute experiments on an anesthetized animal, the scalp and skull are removed and the active electrode is placed directly on the surface of the brain. If a structure in the depth of the brain is being studied, the wire is simply pushed through the brain to it, using a stereotaxic machine to place the electrode accurately. The gross evoked response is recorded in exactly the same manner. The major difference is that the evoked response is evoked by giving a sudden stimulus, either a peripheral sensory stimulus or an electrical stimulus to some portion of the nervous system. Evoked activity is usually only recorded for from 50 to 200 milliseconds following the stimulus. Spontaneous EEG activity on the other hand may be recorded for any length of time. For examples of both spontaneous EEG activity and gross evoked responses see Figures 3.8 and 3.9.

Electrodes

"Gross" electrodes are usually wires which either come in direct contact with tissue or are connected to it by an electrolytic fluid. For scalp electrodes, paste containing an electrolyte such as potassium chloride (KCl) is used to make good contact with the scalp. When recording from the depth or surface of the brain, stainless steel wires insulated to the recording tip are commonly employed. The insulation used is generally an enamel which can be painted or baked on the wire. If an uninsulated wire were simply stuck in the brain, you would record electrical activity at every place where brain tissue contacted the wire; hence you could not localize the region of the brain where the activity occurred. However, if the wire is insulated to the tip, you know that the activity is being picked up only from the uninsulated tip portion of the electrode. We will discuss particular kinds and types of recording electrodes further when we consider the procedures involved in implanting permanent or chronic recording electrodes.

Recording Methods

The configuration or pattern of arrangement of the recording electrodes markedly influences the form and meaning of the gross response obtained. The general type of physical phenomenon involved in gross electrode recording is called *volume conduction*. Voltage changes measured in brain tissue are the result of many different configurations of current flow. A given origin of current flow is called a "source" and the place to which it flows is called a "sink." The location of the source and sink determine the pattern of potential change and the amount of current flow determines the amplitude of the potential change recorded. The body may be thought of as a conducting pool of saline containing many "source-sinks" of current flow. The current density and voltage amplitude are maximum at the source-sink and fall off exponentially with distance, except for distortions introduced by blood vessels, large nerve tracts, etc. This means that at least in theory recordings from any point will permit detection of activity from all source-sinks in the body. In practice this commonly introduces difficulties—electrical activity from the heart (EKG) is often picked up as a signal by brain electrodes or by electrodes recording the activity of skin sweat glands (GSR).

A few of the various kinds of results that can be obtained from a current source-sink and associated potential field in the brain are illustrated in the much-simplified schematic diagram of Figure 3.11. Suppose that a potential field is generated by current flow in the cerebral cortex underlying the surface electrode A. Recording from the surface by electrode A against a distant indifferent electrode (I) is called *monopolar* recording. It is assumed that the indifferent electrode is at an electrically neutral point of the body such as skin or muscle. If these two electrodes go to a differential or push-pull amplifier (see below) they are called a push-pull input. If the indifferent is connected to earth ground as well, to insure electrical neutrality, they are called a "single-ended" input. The amplifier records the potential difference between A and I. If we assume that the current flow simply builds up and then decays, the recorded evoked response might look like that shown for A-I. If we recorded from B

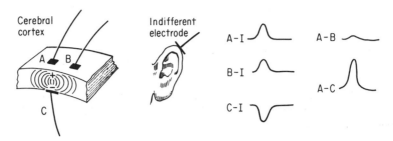

Figure 3.11. Volume conduction effects in evoked response recording. The potential field is assumed to be generated in the cortex. The maximum potential difference is recorded across the field (**A-C**) and the minimum potential difference by two adjacent electrodes on the same side of the field (**A-B**). Upward deflections indicate positive potentials at the first electrode relative to the second. (**A, B,** and **C** are brain recording sites and **I** is an indifferent site.)

against I, the active electrode would be somewhat further away and a slightly smaller response is seen (B-I). If we now cross the source-sink and record from C to I the potential will have reversed its sign, but may be of comparable magnitude (C-I).

If instead of recording against the distant indifferent we now record *bipolarly* from two electrodes in the active field, the amplifier still displays the difference between the two electrodes. If we are recording between A and B, although the field is large at both, the difference between the two is small and a very small potential is displayed (A-B). Finally, if we record the across source-sink, we get a very large potential which is the algebraic sum of the difference between the two points (A-C). Monopolar recording (A-I, B-I, C-I) gives the exact amplitude of the potential at a given point relative to the indifferent, but gives only approximate location of the source-sink. Bipolar recording (A-B, A-C) gives better information about the location of a potential gradient, and hence of the source-sink, but does not permit measurement of amplitude at either point alone. For these reasons a combination of monopolar and bipolar recording will usually provide the greatest amount of information. In human EEG recordings, where depth electrodes are not used, a number of electrodes are placed on the scalp and the differences between many or all possible pairs are recorded. Sources of abnormal activity can be roughly localized by a kind of triangulation procedure.

Amplifiers

Physiological recording amplifiers are of two general sorts: Ac and dc. Ac amplifiers are used in most experiments where gross EEG or evoked activity is studied. Electrical activity of brain and body structures is not itself dc or ac, but rather exhibits voltage changes ranging from many seconds for one "cycle" to 2000 cps or more. An ac amplifier will record changes only as slow as a few seconds per cycle but has essentially no upper limit of frequency response

(10,000 cycles is probably high enough to record all physiological responses). The ac amplifier usually has a resistance-capacity coupled input, which means that incoming signals go through a condenser connected to ground. If a steady dc input is applied to the amplifier, the output of the amplifier decreases exponentially to zero as the input voltage establishes a charge on the condenser.

The time required for the amplitude to fall to one-third its initial value is called the *time constant* of the amplifier Most physiological ac amplifiers have a selection of condenser inputs, which permit recording of a wide range of frequencies. This can be a great advantage. Radio and TV signals are high frequency and show up as " hash, " but can be eliminated by cutting out high-frequency inputs. Most electrical activity of brain and body structures recorded by gross electrodes ranges from 1 cps to several hundred cps and is adequately handled by an ordinary ac amplifier. The amplitudes of physiological signals range from about one millionth of a volt (1 microvolt = $1\mu V$) to one-tenth of a volt (100 millivolts = 100 mV). Recording and write-out systems usually need signals in the volt range to operate, so physiological amplifiers must be capable of high " gain " or amplification.

The voltage changes measured in spontaneous or evoked gross activity are generated by large populations of cells, ranging from hundreds to millions depending on the neural structures involved. It used to be thought that such grossly recorded population responses were simply the sum or average of all the all-or-none spike discharges fired by the nerve cells. This is in fact the case when recordings are taken from peripheral nerves or from large fiber tracts in the brain. However, most gross recordings from the brain are obtained from regions like the cerebral cortex, which are composed of cell bodies and small fiber processes, particularly dendrites. It is now known that cell bodies and dendrites generate a quite different kind of electrical activity which is *graded* in amplitude, rather than all-or-none, and which may or may not result in spike discharges. Such graded responses may reflect either excitatory or inhibitory activity in the nerve cell. It is this graded activity which is now believed to be the major source of grossly recorded brain voltages. We will explore these graded processes in considerable detail in the later chapters (see especially Chapter 6–9). For now it is only necessary to remember that grossly recorded brain activity in large part reflects these graded electrical processes. In general it is not possible to determine whether the gross activity recorded reflects excitatory processes, inhibitory processes, or combinations of these. We usually cannot determine what the individual nerve cells are doing in gross population recordings.

Population Responses: The Nerve Action Potential

The most traditional demonstration of neural activity in elementary physiology courses is the gross nerve action potential. Frog nerve is commonly used because it remains in a relatively normal functional state for several hours after it has been removed from the animal. The experimental arrangement for studying the nerve response is shown in Figure 3.12. The cut piece of frog nerve is laid on a series of uninsulated wires (usually of platinum or silver) in a moist chamber. Two of the wires at one end are used to stimulate the nerve electrically and two wires at the other end are connected to a recording device, usually a cathode-ray oscilloscope.

When a brief supra-threshold electrical pulse is delivered to the nerve through the stimulating electrodes, an action potential develops and travels along the nerve to the recording electrodes. As the activity crosses one recording electrode, the potential shifts in one direction away from the zero point; when activity crosses the other recording electrode, the potential shifts in the other direction. Such a response is called *biphasic* (changes both above and below the baseline). Unfortunately, the amount of neural activity producing the response cannot be directly related to the size of the biphasic response. The two deflections may overlap partially and tend to cancel each other. However, if the nerve is crushed over the recording electrode furthest away from the stimulating electrode, a *monophasic* response (shift in only one direction away from the baseline) is recorded. In monophasic recordings of gross nerve responses, the size of the

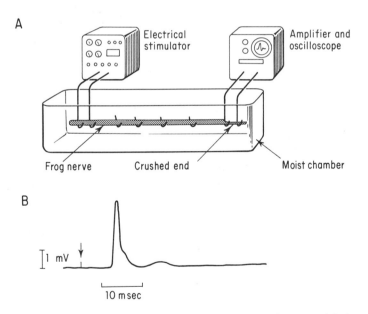

Figure 3.12.   A, experimental arrangement for recording the nerve action potential. A portion of an excised frog peripheral nerve is laid on a series of electrodes in a moist chamber. The response is recorded from one end of the nerve; usually the nerve is crushed over the electrode at the end. **B,** the monophasic nerve action potential recorded in the experiment shown in **A** following electrical stimulation of the nerve. Negative up. Arrow (stimulus artefact) indicates onset of stimulation.

response (or more correctly the total area under the response) is directly related to the amount of neural activity. The reasons why this is so are somewhat complicated; they will be discussed further in Chapter 6. An example of a monophasic nerve action potential recording is shown in Figure 3.12.

Population Responses: Slow Potentials

The study of brain voltages which change slowly in time, over periods of seconds or minutes rather than milliseconds, is relatively recent. The brain does exhibit slowly shifting potentials both spontaneously and in response to many types of stimulation. However, rather specialized recording equipment is necessary to measure such changes accurately. Slowly changing voltages are often called dc potentials, implying that a fixed direct current source analogous to that generated by a battery is being measured. While such steady dc or "standing" potentials do exist (there is a relatively constant dc voltage from the surface to the depth of the brain) most brain potentials do change in time. The term slow potential is thus a more accurate description.

Slow potentials cannot be recorded by the usual ac-coupled physiological amplifier. As noted earlier, if a dc voltage is applied to such an amplifier, the output of the amplifier will quickly drop to zero because of the condenser coupling to ground in the input. Consequently, a dc amplifier must be used to record slow potentials. Dc amplifiers are very much more complicated than ac-coupled amplifiers, and until recent times were not commercially available. Even relatively well-designed modern dc amplifiers often have "drift" problems. Drift simply means that the calibrated voltage level of the amplifier will change over time in an unpredictable fashion. In ac amplifiers the ground level or zero potential is always seen because of the condenser short to ground on the input. However, the dc amplifier cannot compare input to ground and must maintain an absolute voltage measurement. If this distinction does not seem very meaningful to you, think of ac amplifiers as measuring a relative voltage and dc amplifiers as measuring an absolute voltage level. Most dc amplifiers tend to drift away from calibration and must frequently be recalibrated.

An even more difficult problem in slow potential recordings concerns the recording electrodes. Whenever wires are inserted in ionic solutions such as body fluids, an electrolytic potential is generated (see Chapter 2). Such potentials are called *junction* potentials; they are generated at the junction between the wire and the solution. Junction potentials are dc and may be as high as several volts. A slow potential generated by the brain, on the other hand, may reach only 100 microvolts or less. Consequently, the junction potential, which is completely unrelated to brain activity, may be one-hundred-thousand times greater than the brain activity. Since a dc amplifier amplifies both types of potentials, the brain signals will be completely washed out.

These junction potentials are no problem if an ac amplifier is used, as in the study of EEG or evoked activity described above. Because the junction potential is a steady dc level, the condenser coupled amplifier "ignores" it and amplifies only the more rapidly changing signals. Rather specialized electrode systems can be used to minimize junction potentials. Perhaps the most common are the silver-silver chloride electrode and the mercury calomel electrode. In the former, silver wire is "chlorided," i.e. coated with silver chloride. When such an electrode is placed on neural tissue, the silver chloride coat contacts the chloride containing ionic solution of the tissue. The calomel electrode is similar except that mercury is used instead of silver. Under these conditions (for reasons well beyond the level of this text) only very small junction potentials are generated. Such electrode systems are called *nonpolarizable* electrodes.

An example of an evoked slow potential recorded with nonpolarizable electrodes and a dc amplifier is shown in Figure 3.13A. This is the type of evoked activity recorded from the visual area of the cerebral cortex in response to a light flash (see Goldring and O'Leary, 1959). Note that there is first a rapidly changing positive evoked response that lasts about 30 milliseconds, followed by a slower negative potential, a still slower positive potential, and finally a slow negative potential. The entire response complex lasts about 1 second. In Figure 3.13B the *same* response is shown as it would look if recorded by a regular ac amplifier. The initial fast positive component appears the same, but the subsequent slower components are either much distorted or completely lost. Remember that this is the same response being recorded in both cases. The ac amplifier loses slower potentials. They are still being generated by the brain but the recording system is not reproducing them. Although the neural mechanisms which generate the slow potentials of the brain are not well understood, it is clear from their long time course that they do not represent summed spike discharges, but rather some type of slow graded population response of nerve cells (and possibly other types of cells as well).

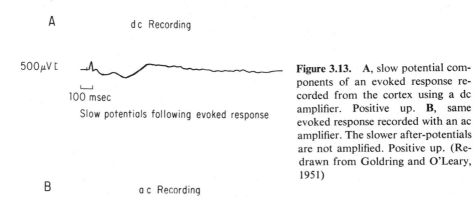

A   d c Recording

500 μV

100 msec

Slow potentials following evoked response

B   a c Recording

Figure 3.13. A, slow potential components of an evoked response recorded from the cortex using a dc amplifier. Positive up. B, same evoked response recorded with an ac amplifier. The slower after-potentials are not amplified. Positive up. (Redrawn from Goldring and O'Leary, 1951)

Population Responses: Massed Unit Discharges

One of the major limitations in recording gross evoked responses is that a very sudden stimulus is required to "drive" an evoked response. For example a sudden loud sound such as a click or a hand clap will produce a clear evoked response on the auditory cortex. However, an ongoing tone, music, or a voice speaking, will result in no gross evoked activity at the cortex. This is because an evoked response reflects the summed activity of many elements acting at the same time. Ongoing stimuli cannot activate the cells at the same time. Instead, cells are activated in an irregular and asynchronous manner in time. Since sudden sensory stimuli are not common in our world, the gross evoked response is a relatively artificial response, or at the very least one which occurs infrequently. Irregular activity of the nerve cells would seem to be the rule and synchronous evoked activity the exception.

The measures of evoked neural activity we have discussed so far have all been over all summed responses from a large population of cells in response to sudden stimuli. The gross evoked responses and slow potentials both reflect graded responses of nerve cells, and the nerve action potential is the sum of a great many all-or-none spike discharges firing at about the same time in the nerve. One major difference between the summed-spike discharges of the nerve fiber and graded responses of nerve cells is the time course of the response. Spike discharges last less than a millisecond, but graded responses may last up to a second or more. If we were to stick a small wire, say of about 0.1-mm diameter, into a region of the brain containing nerve cell bodies such as the cerebral cortex and record evoked activity we could see both the summed graded evoked potentials, and many very small fast nerve spike discharges superimposed on the slower potentials. By changing the condenser coupling of the amplifier we can "filter out" the slower graded potentials and record only the spikes. If the spikes all occurred at about the same time we would see a response that closely resembles the gross nerve action potential. However, if the spikes occurred less synchronous in time, the response might appear more like intermittent "hash" on the base line. Such a response is shown in Figure 3.14A. This hash response is an example of massed unit discharges. Since many cells are firing spikes at irregular intervals, the density of the hash is a measure of the amount of cellular spike activity. In this instance the hash response is recorded from a taste nerve of a Carp to the application of human saliva to the olfactory receptors (Konishi and Zotterman, 1963). The same technique can be used to record massed asynchronous spike discharges from any neural tissue.

Direct measurement of the amount of hash in a massed unit discharge record is rather difficult. However, it is possible to convert this record to one which does directly and accurately reflect the amount of spike activity (see Beidler, 1953; Pfaffman, 1955). The technique used involves *integration* of the irregular spike discharges. (Integration is a mathematical procedure that in this application amounts to adding together all the spike activity to yield a total response

A   Hash response of nerve

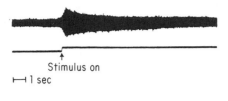

Stimulus on

⊢—⊣ 1 sec

B   Integrated hash response

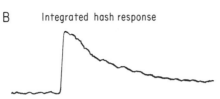

Figure 3.14. **A,** unit hash response recorded grossly from taste nerve of a fish following application of a taste solution to peripheral taste receptors. **B,** electronic integration of the response of **A** produces an integrated tracing whose height is proportional to the amount of unit activity (i.e. thickness of baseline) in the nerve. (Redrawn from Konishi and Zotterman, 1963)

measure). Fortunately, there are relatively simple electronic circuits that will perform operations comparable to integration for us. The integrated record of the hash response of Figure 3.14A is shown in Figure 3.14B. The height of the integrated record is proportional to the amount of spike activity in the original hash record. Examples of integrated massed unit discharges are shown in Figure 3.14B. The massed unit discharge method, incidently, is about the only technique that can be used to record population measures of nerve activity following taste stimulation. Natural taste stimuli are not sufficiently sudden to yield gross nerve action potentials. The individual nerve fibers respond at different times so no synchronous gross response results.

The massed unit discharge technique would seem to have many advantages as a population measure of nerve cell activity. It is the only population measure that permits recording of all-or-none spike discharges from many nerve cells which are not firing synchronously in time (as is often the case with nerve cells of the normal behaving organism). In view of this it is somewhat surprising that the technique has had relatively limited use. There would seem to be a great many potentially valuable applications of the method that have not yet been explored.

Single Cell Responses: Microelectrode Recording

The methods of recording neural activity described above yield measures of the overall response of populations of neurons. Such gross recording techniques do not usually permit us to identify particular cells, or to determine whether the behavior of the individual cells tend to be excitatory, inhibitory, or a combination of these. Gross methods are most useful for demonstrating functional connections, and for interrelations of regional activity with stimulus or behavior conditions. Analysis in terms of what the nerve cells are actually doing is generally not possible with gross methods. The development of microelectrode techniques for recording the activity of single nerve cells has added an important new dimension to the study of brain and behavior. These procedures permit analysis of the exact conditions which will excite or inhibit the activity of a given nerve cell, and can provide information about the synaptic processes involved. There are two basically different types of microelectrode techniques: extracellular recording and intracellular recording. The extracellular method involves placing a microelectrode near a cell, but outside the cell, and recording all-or-none spike discharges of the cell. Intracellular recording, on the other hand, involves penetrating the cell membrane with the microelectrode and recording the potential difference across the cell membrane from the inside of the cell to the outside. The extracellular method has perhaps provided more relevant kinds of information for the physiological psychologist. However, intracellular recording methods are beginning to be applied to problems that are essentially behavioral in nature.

Extracellular Recording

Perhaps the first use of microelectrodes, per se, was by Ling and Gerard (1949) although activity of single nerve fibers had been studied much earlier (e.g. Adrian and Bronk, 1929). The basic technique has not altered greatly since. A very small electrode is plunged blindly into the neural tissue and poked about until a single cell response is obtained. To record the isolated extracellular response of a single cell, uncomplicated by activity of other cells, an electrode tip of 10 μ (0:01 mm) or less is usually required. A large variety of such electrodes have been used, the most common types being sharpened wire needles or finely drawn glass pipettes filled with conducting materials or solutions. Such microelectrodes have a very high resistance, ranging from about one-hundred-thousand ohms to several million ohms, and cannot be used directly with ordinary physiological amplifiers. These amplifiers simply cannot record electrical activity through a microelectrode having such a very high resistance. Furthermore, ordinary amplifiers generate small currents, called grid currents, which tend to flow out of the input to the amplifier and hence through the electrode to the tissue. Such currents present no problem when gross electrodes (i.e. large wires) are used to record population responses, because the current density is very small. However, with an electrode having a tip not much larger than one micron, the current flow from the amplifier can quickly polarize the tip of the microelectrode and render it useless. Consequently, a very specialized type of preamplifier has to be used between the microelectrode and the regular amplifier. This is called a *negative capacitance*, or *unity gain*, or *cathode follower* preamplifier. In effect, it (1) tends to compensate for the high resistance of the recording electrode, and (2) has a negative feedback circuit which always balances out the grid current from the regular amplifier to the microelectrode in such a way that virtually no current flows at the recording tip.

The signal recorded by an extracellular microelectrode is a monophasic or biphasic spike of less than one millisecond duration (see Figure 3.15A). There are two basic problems of technique involved in microelectrode recording. The first of these concerns the identification or demonstration that activity is being recorded from only one cell rather than from several cells. This is usually done on the basis of the height of the recorded spike response. A given nerve cell under stable conditions will always generate a spike of about the same height. In the third record of Figure 3.15A, two different spike heights are shown. If both of these spikes are found consistently, either as a result of stimulation or due to spontaneous activity, it can be assumed that two different cells are generating spikes. The grossly recorded slow waves described above, incidentally, may also be recorded by the microelectrode. The spikes that are being recorded will then be superimposed upon the evoked potential. Since in microelectrode recording we are primarily interested in the individual spike discharges of cells it is common practice to filter out the slow waves and display the spikes on the level baseline, as in Figure 3.15A.

The second basic problem regarding microelectrode recording has to do with the extent to which the cell has been damaged by the microelectrode. There appears to be no universally adopted solution to this problem. Perhaps the most operational demonstration that a given cell is undamaged lies in the duration of time it will continue to show spike activity. If the cell continues to

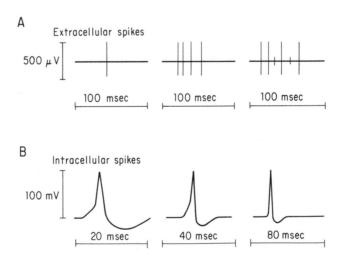

Figure 3.15.   **A,** the typical appearance of extracellularly recorded single nerve cell discharges. A given cell, if not injured, always has about the same spike height. The third record shows activity of two different cells. Positive up. **B,** typical appearance of an intracellularly recorded single nerve cell discharge. Note that the amplitude of the response is nearly 200 times greater than the extra cellularlyrecorded response (see amplitude calibrations). Positive up. (Schematic drawings.)

fire in response to stimulation for a period of an hour or more it is probably safe to assume that it is relatively undamaged. A badly damaged cell will characteristically fire with a very high discharge frequency for a short period of time and then cease entirely. Some investigators have used the polarities of the spike as an indication of freedom from damage. Thus, if the spike response is primarily negative, or biphasic with first a negative and then a positive deflection, it may be assumed to be in good condition. It is not always possible, incidentally, to differentiate between a spike recorded from a nerve cell body and a spike generated by a nerve fiber.

Several technical problems make microelectrode recording a rather more difficult procedure than gross recording. Mechanical control of the microelectrode movement must be precise: sudden advance or backlash of a few microns is enough to kill the cell being studied. Ordinary electrode manipulators are not adequate; special micromanipulators must be used. Movement of the animal is a constant problem, even in acute anesthetized preparations. Two general types of strategy have been massive head-holders and microdrives with large mechanical impedance, or very light units attached to the animal. The latter type has obvious utility in chronic recording studies. Another source of movement lies in brain pulsations due to respiration and heart beat. An easy solution is a plastic plate with a small center hole for the electrode which is placed on the brain surface. If recording is from cortical cells, such a restraining device may interfere with blood supply. A more elaborate method is a saline filled sealed chamber attached to the skull, with a microdrive mounted on it (Davies, 1956). For chronic recording, the microdrive unit is cemented to the skull to form an airtight seal.

Extracellularly recorded unit response data may be transcribed in a variety of ways. The most common method is to photograph the oscilloscope tracing. Alternatively, the output of the high-gain differential amplifier can be fed into any ordinary tape recorder (a frequency response range of 20 cps to 5,000 cps is sufficient to record spike discharges). Subsequently the taped data can be fed into an oscilloscope for photography or an electronic counter to count spikes. This latter approach is becoming increasingly popular. Such electronic counters not only count the number of spikes in response to a given stimulus, but also the time between spikes, and can thus provide rather complete information about the time pattern of spike discharges of the cell being studied. Extracellular microelectrode recording provides information about whether a cell does or does not fire an all-or-none spike discharge under the conditions of study. The method does not allow you to measure a population response of many cells at the same time, nor does it allow you to measure with any accuracy the graded potentials generated by the cell body and dendrites. However, it does provide complete information about the firing or nonfiring of the cell. Since the spike discharge is the only mechanism whereby a given nerve cell can conduct activity to other nerve cells, this might well be regarded as a basic datum of the nervous system.

Intracellular Recording

Intracellular microelectrode recording involves a good many rather specialized problems. Glass pipettes of less than 1-micron tip diameter must be used, in conjunction with a dc recording system. The cell membrane must be penetrated without serious injury, and the cell held impaled. This is usually only possible for a few minutes. Intracellular recording does not seem very feasible at present in the normal behaving animal.

An electrode inside a nerve cell records the potential across the cell membrane relative to a distant indifferent electrode. In an inactive cell the resting membrane potential across the cell membrane will be about −70 mV. During the spike discharge the membrane potential shifts briefly in the positive direction by about 100 mV (one tenth of a volt). The occurrence of a spike discharge can be recorded equally well extracellularly. The power of the intracellular method is that it permits recording of the graded potentials leading up to spike discharge or failure of spike discharge in a cell. These potentials are brief shifts in the level of the resting membrane potential which range in value from 1 to 15 mV or more. The spike discharge threshold of a cell is a few millivolts positive to the resting level. Excitatory synaptic activity causes a brief positive shift in membrane potential, with a spike if discharge level is reached. Inhibitory activity causes a brief negative shift in the membrane potential, thus moving the potential level further away from discharge threshold (see Figure 3.15B).

It is in measurement of the postsynaptic potential shifts of the cell membrane that the analytic power of intracellular recording lies. If an extracellular recording demonstrates that a given stimulus causes a cell to stop firing, for example, this could be due to changes in cells prior to the cell in question, or to synaptic inhibitory activity on the cell. Intracellular recording will demonstrate which possibility has occurred. Illustrations of intracellularly recorded single cell responses are shown in Figure 3.15B. We will spend a good bit of time in subsequent chapters discussing results of studies devoted to intracellular analysis of nerve activity. This method has elucidated a number of the fundamental mechanisms involved in the control of nerve cell behavior.

It must be remembered that the type of recording technique used in a given experiment depends upon the hypothesis to be tested and the kinds of measurements required. Gross electrode recording of evoked responses provides a measure of sorts of the behavior of a population of cells, but does not tell you what the individual cells are doing. Extracellular microelectrode recording will give you the latter kind of information, but will not tell you what the population of cells is doing. Intracellular recordings from single cells will provide information about the underlying graded responses of the cell but again may not provide information about population responses. All of these types of information are different and to a degree complementary indices of neural activity.

Chronic Recording

We noted earlier that the majority of analytic studies measuring electrical activity of the brain have used some type of anesthetic or immobilization procedure. For the psychologist interested in relating brain activity to behavior, such an approach has obvious limitations. The problems of primary interest to psychologists, such as learning, motivation, attention, etc. require measurement of behavioral variables. In recent years a number of techniques have been developed for recording electrical activity of the nervous system from the normal waking animal using chronically (i.e. permanently) implanted electrodes (see Sheer, 1961; Sidowski, 1966).

The basic considerations regarding type of electrical information obtained from the nervous system as a function of the techniques used to record it do not differ with chronic recording. Most of the special problems relating to chronic recording have to do with methods of permanently implanting an electrode array in such a way that it will permit repeated measure of electrical activity in a convenient and relatively trouble-free manner. Typically, electrode wires are inserted into the appropriate regions of the brain and fastened to a plug fixed to the skull. When the experiment is to be run the animal is simply plugged into the recording equipment and data is collected. In general, neither animals nor humans have voiced any particular complaints about discomfort resulting from permanently implanted electrodes and plugs (see Ramey and O'Doherty, 1960).

A wide variety of electrode materials have been tried as chronic implants, including copper, silver, silverchloride, stainless steel, platinum, tungsten, and molybdenum (Sheatz, 1961). An even wider variety of insulating compounds have been employed. In terms of absence of tissue reaction over long periods of time, it appears that the most satisfactory electrode wire material is stainless steel. The type of insulating material seems relatively unimportant since none of them appears to react with tissue. Recording electrodes may be monopolar, or bipolar, they may be used to record from the depths, or from the surface of the cortex, or all combinations of these. In using depth electrodes, the stereotaxic method is employed to place the electrode tip accurately. There are a few particular requirements for stereotaxic technique in implanting chronic electrodes. First, sterile technique is advisable. It is somewhat disheartening to complete a long series of experiments with negative results only to find large regions of infection surrounding the electrodes. If animals are to be run in experiments involving auditory stimulation particular care must be used. The standard ear bar of the stereotaxic head holder breaks the ear drum when it is inserted. In fact the slight crunch of the tympanic membrane is usually the best cue that the ear bar is properly seated. Special ear bars may be obtained which do not rupture the tympanic membrane.

Since most chronic implanted electrodes are rigidly fixed, electrode localization at the time of implantation must be as precise as possible. In many instances

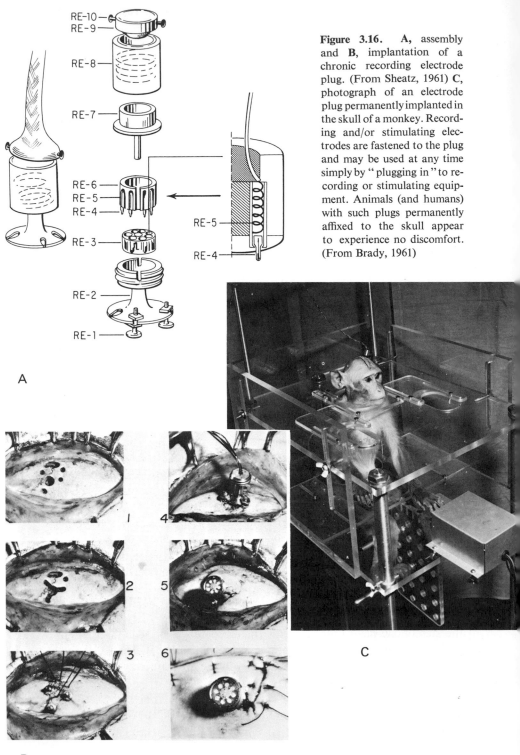

RE-10
RE-9
RE-8
RE-7
RE-6
RE-5
RE-4
RE-3
RE-2
RE-1

RE-5
RE-4

A

B

C

Figure 3.16. **A,** assembly and **B,** implantation of a chronic recording electrode plug. (From Sheatz, 1961) **C,** photograph of an electrode plug permanently implanted in the skull of a monkey. Recording and/or stimulating electrodes are fastened to the plug and may be used at any time simply by " plugging in " to recording or stimulating equipment. Animals (and humans) with such plugs permanently affixed to the skull appear to experience no discomfort. (From Brady, 1961)

the structure that you wish to study may be responsive to peripheral stimulation under the conditions of anesthesia you were using for the implantation. Thus, if you are aiming for a structure that responds to light flash, you can monitor activity in response to light flash while the electrode is being positioned. In spite of such controls, histological reconstruction of the exact position of the electrode tip in the brain must be done at the completion of the experiment to insure that your localization is accurate.

A large variety of techniques have been devised for chronic implantation of depth and surface electrode arrays. Every investigator has developed his own particular methodological details. Approaches range in complexity from steel needles or nails pounded into the skull to a 610 electrode array imbedded in a plastic skull substitute casting (cf. Lilly, 1958a). The obvious common features required from an implantation of electrodes are rigid fixation of electrodes to the skull, good contact of electrode to the tissue and a noise-free and convenient method of plugging in the electrode to recording and stimulating equipment. The most common method used is to insert the electrode wires or plates either in the depths of the brain or on the surface of the cortex, and then lead wires to a plug over the center of the skull. The wires are soldered to the plug contacts at the time of implantation. The plug and wires may be fastened directly to the skull with metal cement or a kind of metal pedestal arrangement may be screwed to the skull with the electrode held above (see Figure 3.16). This latter method (Sheatz, 1961) permits the scalp to be tightly closed around the pedestal, where as the other method usually requires that a good deal of dental cement be built up around the plug, resulting in a large permanent opening in the scalp. This tends to increase the chances of infection.

Gross electrical activity recorded from the brain of the normal waking animal does present some specialized problems. The amplitude of evoked activity in the normal animal is a good deal lower than in the anesthetized animal. Furthermore, there is a good deal of spontaneous "background" activity, which tends to swamp out the response being studied. Another way of stating this is to say that signal-to-noise ratio is low; the signal you are interested in recording is buried in background electrical noise and may be very difficult to see. Several different solutions have been used to improve the signal-to-noise ratio. Perhaps the simplest is to employ one of the less expensive *online* average response computers (an online device is one that operates on the data directly as it is being obtained) such as the computer of average transients (CAT) or the Enhancetron. These devices average the evoked electrical activity following each stimulus. Activity that is randomly fluctuating in time will tend in the long run to cancel out. A signal which is always present, even though very small, will become relatively much clearer. The most serious limitation of this method is that you cannot measure individual responses, but must take averages of 20 or more responses in order to obtain clear signals. If your experiment involves the study of signals which may change over time as a function of trials, the change you are interested in studying will be washed out by the averaging procedure. A very high-powered but expensive solution is to convert each signal to the kind of information that can be entered in a large digital computer and then program the computer to analyze the data in whatever manner you wish. In general, if you are recording gross activity that is generated in a fairly localized region of the brain, a bipolar electrode recording across the field of activity will tend to increase the signal and decrease background or spontaneous noise not generated in the same region. Reference back to Figure 3.11 should clarify the situation for you. Bipolar recording across the field gives the maximum evoked response.

A number of control problems are particularly important in experiments in which electrical activity is chronically recorded from the brain. First, responses of the unanesthetized animal are highly variable and must be analyzed statistically if changes relative to behavioral variables are to be illustrated. Second, a number of nonrelevant factors may operate to change response amplitude over time. Tissue reactions, growth of scar tissue, regrowth of dura over the cortex, deterioration of the electrode tips, loose connections, etc. may all result in progressive changes in response amplitude. Such changes could easily correlate by accident with behavioral changes that may have occurred in the experiment.

Electrical Activity of Non-neural Structures

Electrophysiological recording methods are also employed for the measurement of activity from a variety of non-neural structures. The measures most widely used in physiological psychology have been of sweat gland activity, muscle activity, and heartbeat. A variety of other kinds of responses have also been recorded, such as the electrical activity of the retina (electro-retinogram) and the electrical activity of the cochlea (cochlear microphonic). However, they are rather specifically concerned with particular receptor processes and will not be discussed here (see Chapter 11). Excellent discussions of these and many other measures are available elsewhere (Stevens, 1951; Sidowski, 1966).

SWEAT GLANDS. Measurement of the galvanic skin response (GSR) resulting from activity of sweat glands has long been the favorite index of autonomic (i.e., emotional) activity for psychologists. Two general methods have been used to record the GSR: the Féré (or resistance) technique in which skin resistance is measured by an ohmmeter, and the Tarchanoff (or potential) procedures in which the electrical potential accompanying sweat gland activity is recorded directly (see Figure 3.17). Activity of skin sweat glands, particularly those in the palms, can be increased or decreased by a variety of stimuli and conditions. When the glands are active, sweat is extruded, skin resistance decreases, and concommitant voltage changes occur. Contrary to what might be expected, the skin resistance drop is *not* due to the presence of sweat on the skin surface. Most authorities now seem to agree that the resistance changes are the result of electrochemical activity in the sweat gland cells (Wang, 1958; 1964).

In the Féré procedure, electrodes are placed on the palm and back of the hand and the resistance measured by sending a small current through the skin,

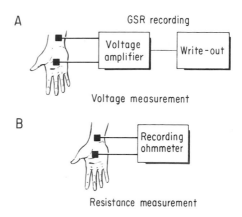

Figure 3.17. Examples of the voltage (A) and resistance (B) methods of recording the galvanic skin reflex (GSR). In the voltage method the voltage generated by the sweat glands is simply amplified and recorded, as in the case of the EEG. In the resistance method the change in resistance of the palm during the GSR is measured with an ohmmeter by passing a small current through the skin.

using an ohmmeter application of the galvanometer (see Chapter 2). Both slow changes in basal resistance level and sudden changes can be recorded in this fashion. However, since the rapid changes in response to stimulation are superimposed upon a shifting base resistance level, it is difficult to compare response magnitudes. Standard methods today commonly use a percentage measure or a conductance measure (the reciprocal of the resistance). Although much less widely used, the potential measurement method (Tarchanoff) is probably better for rapid changes. Modern physiological amplifiers make it possible to measure brief, small changes in the voltage output of the skin independently of the basal skin resistance level.

MUSCLE.   Electrical recording of muscle activity does not differ in principle from neural recording. To record the ongoing electromyogram (EMG), steel needles are inserted in the muscle or plates placed on the skin overlying the muscle, and the signal fed to an ordinary ac amplifier and oscilloscope or ink writer (see Figure 3.10). Commercial EEG units can be used directly. Spike discharges of single muscle fibers may quite easily be recorded using a sharp needle insulated to the tip, or fine wires run through small hypodermic needles. Such needles can be inserted through the skin to muscles relatively painlessly. It is worth remembering that the EMG measures electrical activity associated with changes in muscle tension and not muscle tension directly. There is not always a close relationship, and tension is best measured more directly using mechanical measuring devices.

HEART.   Electrical activity associated with the heart is commonly measured by placing plate electrodes on the skin surface of arms, legs, and/or chest so that recording is done across the heart. The resulting voltage charges are amplified and recorded in the same manner as in EEG and EKG techniques (see Figure 3.10). The electrocardiogram (EKG) so recorded is an excellent illustration of volume conduction: EKG potentials are generated in the heart muscle proper, but can be recorded from almost any two widely separated points of the body.

The detailed form of the EKG record provides a great deal of information about activity of different regions of the heart and their temporal sequence. Any standard physiology text can be consulted for details. Such information, per se, is usually of less interest to the psychologist than overall heart *rate*. A special type of electronic device called a *cardiotachometer* can be used in conjunction with direct recording to provide a write out in terms of heart rate. Such devices simply count the frequencies of the largest voltage change associated with the heart beat (the " R wave "), and display a signal whose amplitude is proportional to the time between successive heart beats.

The study of these and other non-neural electrical measures involves considerable logical and procedural problems, particularly in the intact human. See Lacey (1956) and Lacey and Lacey (1962) for comprehensive discussions.

ELECTRICAL STIMULATION

Most of what has been said about recording electrode systems holds for electrical stimulation as well. Stainless steel wires insulated to their tips are commonly used. Stereotaxic methods are employed for depth placement. It will be recalled that monopolar electrodes record activity from a wider region than bipolar electrodes (Figure 3.11). In like manner, monopolar stimulating electrodes activate a wider region of tissue than bipolar electrodes. In Figure 3.11 assume we are stimulating rather than recording and measuring current flow between different pairings of electrodes. A very localized current flow will occur between A and B but a more wide-spread and diffuse current will flow between A and I.

There is considerable controversy over the parameters of the electrical stimulus to be preferred. Lilly (1961) maintains that only one rather complex waveform is noninjurious when used over long periods of time. Many other investigators use a simple 60 cps stimulus requiring only a door bell transformer and a resistor (Olds and Milner, 1954; Miller et al., 1961). The latter is certainly satisfactory if stimulation is done in the acute or short-term chronic animal. There is unanimous agreement on two extreme types of current to be avoided: dc and rf. These, remember, are the two ways of making *lesions* in the CNS. A simple statement about proper frequency and intensity characteristic for electrical stimuli is not possible; different conditions often yield completely opposite effects.

In many instances it is desirable to isolate the animal and the stimulus pulse from the ground side of the stimulating equipment. If concomitant electrical recording is done, this is essential to avoid blocking the recording amplifier by the electrical stimulus. A variety of devices ranging from simple transformers to complex radio frequency units are available for *stimulus isolation*. In addition to isolation it is common to monitor the stimulus current during stimulation. This can be done by placing a low resistance in series with the output of the stimulus isolation unit. The current flow through the resistor, and hence the animal, can be calculated using Ohm's law. As an exercise, suppose the animal resistance is large, the series resistor is 10 ohms and the measured voltage drop across the resistor is 1/100 of a volt (i.e. 10 mV). What would the current flow be?

Electrode localization is a crucial problem in stimulation and recording studies (see the excellent discussion of electrode localization by Akert and Welker, 1961). Locating the electrode tip histologically is not the same thing as locating the effective site of stimulation. The activated structure producing a behavioral effect may be several millimeters away from the electrode tip, but have a much lower electrical response threshold than closer structures. Localization of "reward" areas of the brain in electrical self-stimulation experiments is a good example. Initially, the septal area was believed to be a region of strong reward, but more recent evidence indicates that it is in fact neutral (Olds, 1962).

BEHAVIORAL PROCEDURES

The many techniques described in this chapter are used by physiological psychologists and neurophysiologists in their attempt to relate physiological processes to changes in the *behavior* of organisms. A wide range of methods for the measurement of behavior have been developed (cf. Stevens, 1951; Woodworth and Scholsberg, 1954; Sidowski, 1966). Behavioral concepts and techniques must be understood and utilized with as much care as physiological procedures. Thus, if you were to record many indices of brain activity using elaborate electronic instrumentation, merely looking at the animal's behavior would be of little or no help. The study of animal behavior has progressed to such a degree in psychology that very subtle questions can successfully be asked of animals. For example in the nineteenth century the effects of removing various brain structures on sensory discrimination and learning abilities were determined by simply observing the animal in a "free-field" situation. With the development of conditioned response methods it became possible to train an animal to respond to the occurrence of any effective stimulus. Discrimination learning procedures allow the animal to compare a variety of stimuli. Operant conditioning methods have developed to the point where an animal can be trained and tested on a large variety of complex discriminations quite rapidly. Such methods are in widespread use today for the study of effects of brain lesions, results of electrical stimulation, drug influences on behavior, changes in brain activity during learning, and a host of other applications in physiological psychology.

Careful and *appropriate* control procedures, use of standardized testing techniques, sufficiently large group of animals, and proper statistical analyses are all necessary aspects of behavioral procedures in experiments attempting to relate changes in brain activity to changes in behavior. To illustrate the importance of careful behavior control procedures, let us consider two kinds of experiments concerned with recording evoked neural activity in the normal animal: habituation and conditioning. Examples of inadequately controlled experiments in these areas are unfortunately all too numerous. Habituation refers to a decrease in response amplitude resulting from repeated stimulation. There are many reports of habituation of neural evoked responses to repeated sounds. Most of these did not attempt to control head position in the sound field. Recent evidence indicates that head position determines effective intensity of sound, which in turn determines amplitude of evoked response. When such variables are controlled, there appears to be little or no evidence of evoked response habituation (Marsh, Worden, and Hicks, 1962; Worden and Marsh, 1963).

Many experiments have been concerned with conditioned or learned changes in brain evoked responses. A frequent procedure is to measure the amplitude of a neural response evoked in the cerebral cortex to a repeated sound. If the sound is then paired with shock, or other unpleasant stimulus, the amplitude of the evoked response is commonly reported to increase. In ordinary learning or conditioning experiments, it is customary to run a *backward* or *random control group* in which the unconditioned stimulus (i.e. shock) and the conditioned stimulus (i.e. sound) are both presented but not paired together. If the evoked response to the sound also increases in the backward control group, this demonstrates that *sensitization* or *pseudoconditioning* rather than learning has occurred in the "conditioned" group. The development of learning is crucially dependent on the pairing of the conditioned and unconditioned stimuli. Unfortunately, in most studies of "conditioned" changes in neural evoked responses the appropriate backward control (i.e. sensitization) procedures have not been run. When they have been employed, it appears that the evoked response changes in the backward group may be just as great as in the conditioning group (Gerkin and Neff, 1963). Merely because a change in brain activity occurs simultaneously with the development of the conditioned response does not demonstrate that it is necessarily related to the *learning* aspects of the experiment. A control group given the stimuli separately, where behavioral conditioning does not develop, might well exhibit precisely the same change in brain activity. Clearly any change in neural activity correlated with behavioral alterations might be of interest; however, a number of control procedures are necessary to determine just what aspects of the behavioral situation (i.e. learning, sensitization, alerting, pseudo-conditioning, etc.) are *relevant* to the neural changes (see Hilgard and Marquis, 1940).

Suggested readings

Bureš, J., Petráň, M., & Zachar, J. *Electrophysiological methods in biological research.* (2nd ed.) New York: Academic Press, 1962.

McIlwain, H., & Rodnight, R. *Practical neurochemistry.* Boston: Little, Brown, 1962.

Sidowski, J. B. (Ed.) *Experimental methods and instrumentation in psychology.* New York: McGraw-Hill, 1966.

Stevens, S. S. (Ed.) *Handbook of experimental psychology.* New York: Wiley, 1951.

4

BASIC
NEUROANATOMY

Neuroanatomy is traditionally considered a very difficult subject. Since the brain is undoubtedly the most complex of all biological structures, this is perhaps to be expected. However a number of simple principles can be described which lead to a relatively uncomplicated over-all view of the anatomical relationships of the central nervous system. In this chapter emphasis is placed on such a general overview of the brain. Additional details of brain organization will be described in subsequent chapters dealing with particular regions and functions.

Anatomists have developed a number of standardized directional terms to indicate the relative locations of structures. While these terms may seem unfamiliar and perhaps unnecessarily complicated at first, they have the advantage of being unambiguous. In essence all these terms tell us is whether a given piece of the brain is at the top or bottom, front or back, or middle or side of the brain, and from what direction it is viewed. Figure 4.1 summarizes most of these terms. *Dorsal* refers to the back, *ventral* to the front, *medial* is toward the middle, and *lateral* to either side. The head end is termed *anterior, cephalic,* or *rostral,* and the tail end is referred to as being *caudal* or *posterior.* One common source of confusion

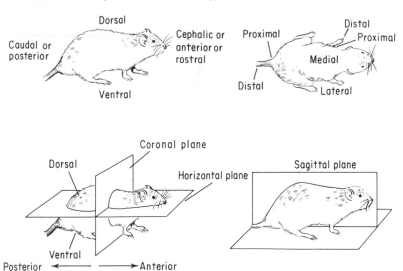

Figure 4.1. Anatomical terminology used to describe position and location in reference to the axes of the body.

has to do with the terms dorsal and ventral. In a four-legged animal such as the frog, rat, or cat, dorsal refers to the back of the animal and the top of the head. As seen in Figure 4.1, the top of the rat's head is a continuous extension of the back of the animal. However in two-legged animals like man the top of the head is at right angles to the back of the body. Rather than switch terms (so that the back of the human head would be called dorsal and the top anterior) anatomists have chosen to put a right angle bend in the directions. This allows us to use the same directional terms for all brains, be they rat or human. As indicated in Figure 4.2, the top of the human brain is termed dorsal, the bottom ventral, the back posterior, and the front anterior, just as with the rat, even though the human brain is at a right angle to the body axis.

A special set of terms is used to describe the connectional relationships between brain and body structures, or between different places in the brain. To take a concrete example, a region on the left side of the brain (the motor area of the cerebral cortex) is involved in the control of movement of the right arm and leg. This functional connection is from one side to the other and is called *contralateral*. However, a portion of the motor cortex on each side controls movements of muscles on both sides of the face. Such functional connections of both sides with both sides are termed *bilateral*. Finally, if we wish to refer only to the connections of the left side of the motor cortex to the left face muscles, we would refer to the interconnections as *ipsilateral*. The term *unilateral* is used to indicate one side of the brain (i.e. a unilateral lesion is on one side only). To summarize, functional relations between opposite sides are contralateral, between both sides are bilateral, and to the same side are ipsilateral.

All biological structures are three-dimensional. As you will remember from geometry, three axes, coordinates, or planes, all at right angles to one another, are necessary to localize any point in a three dimensional object. The positions of the three localizing planes used in neuroanatomy are shown in Figures 4.1 and 4.2. These planes are placed in relation to an imaginary line running through the animal or brain from posterior to anterior, a line perpendicular to this from dorsal to ventral, and a third line running from lateral to medial perpendicular to the others. The plane surface passing through the posterior-anterior line of the animal or brain from dorsal to ventral is called a *sagittal* plane (Figures 4.1 and 4.2). One bisecting the animal into two symmetric halves is termed *mid-sagittal*. If another plane parallel to the long axis of the animal is passed through the animal at right angles to a sagittal plane, thus dividing the animal into dorsal and ventral portions, it is called a *horizontal* plane. A third plane at right angles to the other two, dividing the animal into anterior and posterior portions, is called a *frontal* or *coronal* plane.

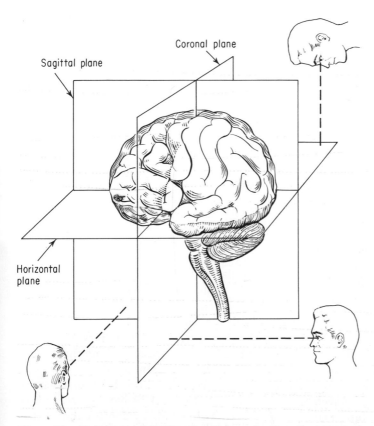

Figure 4.2.   Definitions of the directional planes for the primate brain.

When a brain is sectioned into pieces or slices for anatomical study, the slices are usually made in one of the three anatomical planes. However, even if you know that a section was made, for example, in the coronal plane (perpendicular to the posterior-anterior axis) there would still be ambiguity. The locations of structures in the section would depend on whether you are looking at the section from behind or in front of the animal. Conventions have been adopted to eliminate this ambiguity. As indicated in Figure 4.2, a coronal section is always viewed from behind the animal, i.e. you look anteriorly at the section from a posterior position. In this way structures on the right side of the brain are on the right side of the section. The sagittal plane is usually viewed so that the front or anterior end of the brain is on the left. The horizontal plane is viewed from above, so that structures on the left side of the brain are on the left side of the section. These relationships are all illustrated in Figure 4.2, together with outline sketches of sections through the brain taken in the three planes. Occasionally sections may be cut at oblique angles (so that they do not lie in any of the standard planes) or the angle of view may not correspond to the conventions noted above. These exceptions are always noted and described.

It is necessary to begin with a few simple definitions. The *brain* refers to the enlarged collection of cells and fibers inside the skull at the head end of an animal: It becomes the *spinal cord* as it leaves the skull. The *central nervous system* (CNS) includes both the brain and the spinal cord and is composed of nerve cell bodies and their characteristic fiber processes, nonneural glia cells, and a variety of other types of cells making up blood vessels, membranes, etc. A complete cell with its cell body and fibers is called *neuron*. The word *nerve* refers to a collection of nerve fibers (not including the cell bodies). Collections of nerve cell bodies are called *nuclei* if they are inside the CNS and *nerves* outside. *Grey matter* consists of cell bodies and small fibers, and *white matter* is made up of tracts of larger fibers covered with fatty *myelin sheaths*. They are so-called because in fresh brain they have these respective colors. The CNS is *bilaterally symmetrical* in that most structures are duplicated on the two sides. A number of CNS systems are *crossed*, so that neural structures on the left are functionally related to body structures on the right and vice versa.

A typical nerve cell has several characteristic features. The cell shown in Figure 4.3A is a common type having a relatively long fiber. The main *cell body* contains the cell nucleus and is referred to as the *soma*. It has many short fibers extending out from it called *dendrites*, which serve to receive activity from adjacent cells and conduct this activity to the cell body. The long fiber transmitting activity to other neurons or to *effectors* (muscles and glands) is called the *axon*. Actually, if the axon is stimulated it will conduct in both directions; however impulses can cross the interconnections between nerve cells (*synapses*) in only one direction, from the axon of one cell to the cell body or fibers of another. Larger axons such as the one shown in Figure 4.3A have a surrounding myelin sheath of fatty material interrupted at intervals by constrictions called *nodes of Ranvier*. The initial portion of the axon is unmyelinated as it leaves the cell body, and is called the *axon hillock*. The presynaptic *axon terminals* at the distal end are typically fine and unmyelinated as they branch and terminate in close apposition to other neurons.

The cell shown in Figure 4.3A is a spinal motor neuron which has its cell body in the spinal cord and sends its axon out of the nervous system to the

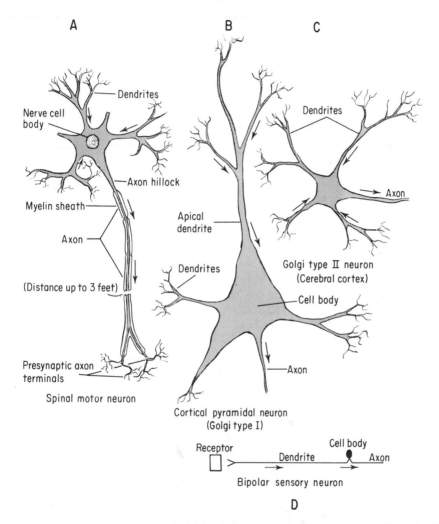

Figure 4.3. A, a "typical" neuron (spinal motor neuron). Dendrites conduct information to the cell body, and the axon conducts from the cell body to other nerve cells or muscle fibers (spinal motor neurons connect to muscle cells). **B-D,** several common types of neurons. The *cortical pyramidal neuron* has both short dendrites and a long apical dendrite extending up through the cerebral cortex. The *Golgi type II* neuron has short dendritic processes. The *bipolar sensory neuron* has a specialized shape, with the "dendrite" and axon forming one continuous fiber from receptor to CNS.

peripheral striated muscle it innervates (controls). The cortical pyramidal cell, in Figure 4.3B, is somewhat similar in structure in that it sends a long axon down from the cerebral cortex of the brain. This axon may extend down to the posterior end of the spinal cord (a considerable distance, particularly in animals like the whale or giraffe). Since all of the energy producing activities of a neuron take place in the cell body, a neuron with a very long axon must manufacture considerable energy to supply the axon. Consequently such cells have large cell bodies. The giant Betz cells of the motor cortex, which have the largest cell bodies in the human brain, are of the cortical pyramidal type. The cortical pyramidal cell lies fairly deep in the cortex (about 1.8 mm below the surface) and sends one large dendrite, the *apical* dendrite, up to the surface of the cortex. The apical dendrite, like all other dendrites, serves to receive information from other nerve cells.

The Golgi type II neuron (Figure 4.3C) is fairly typical of *interneurons*. It usually has a relatively short axon and serves as an interconnecting link between other neurons in the nervous system. The bipolar sensory neuron shown in Figure 4.3D is typical of many sensory neurons. The dendrite has become a long nerver fiber that conducts information from sensory receptors to the central nervous system. The cell body typically lies quite close to the CNS. The dendrite and axon may form a single nerve fiber, with the cell body offset to the side (as in sensory nerves from the skin), or the cell body may simply form an enlarged

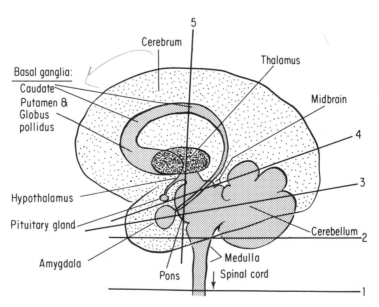

Figure 4.4. Generalized drawing of the primate brain showing the major structures of the cerebrum and brain stem overlaid by the cerebral cortex (transparent). Numbered lines through the brain refer to locations of cross sections shown in later figures.

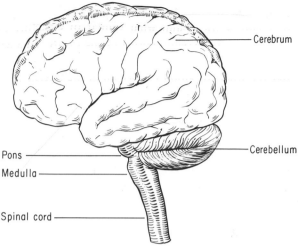

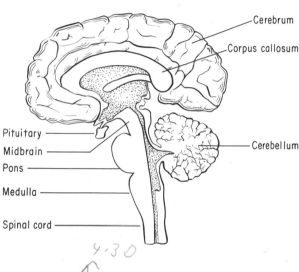

Figure 4.5. Drawings of lateral and medial views of the human brain. The lower drawing shows the midsaggital plane.

portion of the continuous fiber (as in the auditory or vestibular nerves). To summarize, sensory input nerves are bipolar, interneurons are often of the Golgi type II, and output neurons are of the pyramidal or motor type. There are a variety of other rather specialized neuron forms in the brain not shown in Figure 4.3.

A schematized drawing of a generalized primate brain (facing left) and spinal cord is shown in Figure 4.4. More realistic views of the brain are shown in Figure 4.5. Most of the spinal cord is omitted. The lightly shaded *cerebrum* overlies brain stem structures, as does the *cerebellum.* The posterior portion of the brain stem is called the *medulla;* the portion just above it with an enlarged ventral region is the *pons,* with the cerebellum overlying it, and the upper portion of the brain stem is called the *midbrain* (or *mesencephalon*). Above or anterior to the brain stem are the *thalamus* and *hypothalamus*, and the structures of the cerebrum, including the *cerebral cortex, basal ganglia,* and *rhinencephalon.*

The numbered lines in Figure 4.4 refer to sections cut through the CNS at the indicated positions. As we discuss each region of the CNS we will show a diagram of the cross-sectional appearance of the brain taken from the approximate location of the appropriate line. These lines are all coronal sections taken at right angles to the anterior-posterior axis of the CNS. As we mentioned above, the human brain bends at a right angle. Consequently coronal sections shift through a 90° angle from spinal cord to cerebrum in order to remain perpendicular to the anterior-posterior axis. Perhaps the easiest way to keep this clear is to think of the brain as simply an enlarged portion of the tube-shaped spinal cord. As it enlarges in embryological development the tube bends in a right angle in the region of the midbrain and the very large cerebrum grows out around the tube-like core. We will discuss this in more detail later in the chapter when we consider the embryological development of the brain.

Neuroanatomists have subdivided the brain into five general regions ranging from the *myelencephalon* (medulla) to the *telencephalon* (cerebrum). While these terms are not as commonly used as are specific structural names like cerebrum or cerebellum, they do have certain advantages. All vertebrate brains can be so subdivided, even though particular structures may not correspond in different species. The five subdivisions and the various structures they include are listed in Table 4.1.

TABLE 4.1.   GENERAL SUBDIVISIONS OF THE BRAIN

General Division	Major Structures Included
Myelencephalon	Medulla
Metencephalon	Pons Cerebellum
Mesencephalon	Midbrain
Diencephalon	Hypothalamus Pituitary gland Optic tracts Subthalamus Thalamus
Telencephalon	Cerebral hemispheres Basal ganglia Olfactory bulb and tracts

The organization of the CNS is best understood in terms of the groupings of cell bodies, and the fiber tracts interconnecting them. We will examine this organization in somewhat general terms here and in more detail in subsequent chapters. There are a few simple principles that help to convey an over-all impression of the system. In the spinal cord, cell bodies forming nuclei lie in the central core, and are surrounded by fiber tracts. Those tracts travelling the farthest tend to lie more toward the outside, while short tracts lie closer to the central core. This generalization tends to hold for the pons and medulla as well. However in the cerebellum and cerebrum the outside covering is composed of cell bodies in a layer about 2 mm thick, which surrounds the more centrally lying fiber tracts. In each case a number of nuclei are buried within the central core region; the thalamus and basal ganglia within the cerebrum and the cerebellar nuclei within the cerebellum.

Interactions among nerve cells occur only in the vicinity of cell bodies, where axon terminals *synapse* on the cell bodies, dendrites, or other axon terminals. The synapse, incidentally, is not an actual connection but rather a close approximation to one, the space between the axon terminal *bouton* (ending) from one cell and the cell body of the other cell being about 200 Å (see Chapter 7). Thus the grey matter, consisting of cell bodies forming the nuclei and cerebral cortices, is the site of neuronal interactions. White matter is made up of fibers which simply connect different regions of grey matter. Throughout the spinal cord and brain stem, cell bodies and fibers concerned with sensory input tend to lie dorsally, and those concerned with motor output tend to lie ventrally.

Peripheral Nerves

The nerves lying outside the spinal cord are termed *peripheral*. Throughout most of their length in the body they are *mixed*, that is, they contain both incoming sensory (*afferent*) fibers carrying information from receptors of skin, muscle and joints to the spinal cord, and outgoing (*efferent*) motor fibers conveying activity from the spinal cord and brainstem motor neurons to muscle fibers. The diagram of Figure 4.6 illustrates this arrangement in a cross section view cut through the spinal cord at right angles to it (Section 1 in Figure 4.4). The motor nerve fibers have their cell bodies in the ventral part of the central grey matter within the cord (called the *ventral horn*). Their axons go out through the ventral root, which contains *only* motor fibers, and then together with afferent fibers form mixed nerves, which travel to various body structures. As they approach the regions where they terminate, the motor and sensory fibers again separate and go to their appropriate locations. The sensory or afferent nerve fibers are somewhat different from the motor nerves, having their cell bodies in a series of separate ganglia called *dorsal root ganglia*. Sensory fibers are activated by peripheral receptors (i.e. touch, pain, temperature, pressure, joint movement, etc.) and convey information to the spinal cord.

The anterior-posterior arrangement of the peripheral nerves and spinal roots is called *segmental*. That is, spinal roots and nerves innervating a given level of body structures come from a given level of the spinal cord. The skin region

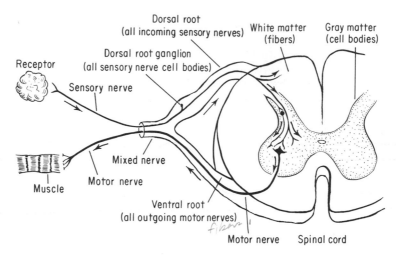

Figure 4.6. Spinal organization of peripheral nerves. Sensory input fibers connect directly or indirectly with motor output neurons, or travel to other regions of the spinal cord and brain.

innervated by one dorsal root is called a *dermatome*. For example, there are 12 spinal roots from the thoracic (chest) regions of the spinal cord. The skin of the body trunk and a portion of the arm has 12 corresponding regions of innervation (dermatomes). These 12 dermatomes are shown in Figure 4.7, even numbers on the left and odd numbers on the right. Actually all 12 are of course found on both sides, They are separated in the figure to emphasize the very considerable *overlap* of dermatomes. As you can see, most skin regions have input to at least two dorsal roots, and some regions (e.g. nipples) share three dermatomes.

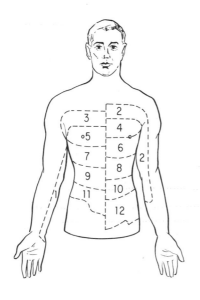

Figure 4.7. Dermatomes of the human thoracic region. Numbers refer to the dorsal roots innervating the indicated skin regions. Alternate roots are shown on the two sides for clarity; both sides of the body are actually innervated by each pair of dorsal roots. Note the considerable overlap of innervation; e.g. the nipple is innervated by three roots (numbers 4, 5 and 6). (From Ranson and Clark, 1959)

Autonomic Nerve Fibres

The nerves we have just described are often called *somatic* nerves because they innervate the striated skeletal musculature (i.e. somatic or body muscles), as opposed to the *autonomic* nerve fibers concerned with structures such as smooth muscle, heart muscle, and those glands involved in autonomic aspects of responding, such as lacrimation, sweating, activity of stomach and heart, etc., commonly related to "emotional" behavior. There are two divisions of the autonomic system: the sympathetic or thoracicolumbar, and the parasympathetic or craniosacral, which have somewhat different connections.

The arrangement of the *sympathetic* fibers is illustrated in Figure 4.8. The *preganglionic* motor fibers have the cell bodies in the lateral portion of the grey matter in the cord and run out through the ventral root and a brief portion of the mixed nerve to the *sympathetic ganglia*. These form a connected chain which runs parallel to the spinal cord but lies outside the spinal bony vertebrae. In the sympathetic ganglia these preganglionic fibers synapse on post ganglionic nerves that course out directly or through the mixed nerves to activate various autonomic structures. The afferent nerve fibers from pain and pressure receptors in the autonomic organs have the same general organization as do somatic afferent fibers, in that their cell bodies are found in the dorsal root ganglia. However, they do pass through (but *not* synapse in) the sympathetic ganglia. Both sensory and preganglionic motor sympathetic fibers may pass up or down along the chain of autonomic ganglia before coursing out to body structures.

The *parasympathetic* division has a somewhat different type of organization (see Figure 4.8). The preganglionic motor fibers come out through cranial nerves (see below) which come directly from the brain, or sacral nerves at the caudal end of the spinal cord, and travel to ganglia located near the target organs which they innervate. They synapse there on short post-ganglionic neurons that connect to the organs. Thus the parasympathetic and sympathetic portions of the autonomic system come from different regions of the CNS and have their ganglia in different locations. Often the functions of the two systems are opposite. Activation of the sympathetic system causes contraction of arteries, acceleration of the heart, inhibition of contraction and secretion of the stomach, dilation of pupils, etc., whereas activation of the parasympathetic system causes dilation of arteries, inhibition of the heart, contractions and secretion of stomach, constriction of pupils, etc. These different effects are the basis for the commonly accepted generalization that the sympathetic system functions to mobilize the resources of the body for emergencies, whereas the parasympathetic system tends to conserve and store bodily resources. Thus, in a sudden emergency or stress a person will experience increased heart beat, inhibition of stomach activity, widening of the pupils, and so on. Such conservative functions as digestion, on the other hand, will be carried on in the intervals between stresses. A final point of difference between the two portions concerns the chemicals mediating synaptic transmission in the ganglia. The nature of these chemical transmitters, and the

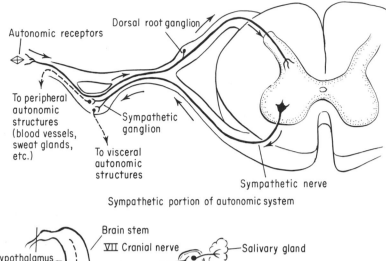

Sympathetic portion of autonomic system

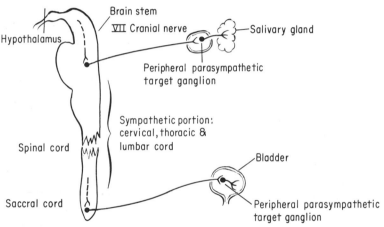

Parasympathetic portion of autonomic system

Figure 4.8. Spinal organization of the autonomic system. The *sympathetic portion* includes autonomic motor neurons of most of the spinal cord, which relay in the sympathetic ganglia. From here postganglionic fibers innervate various autonomic structures. Sympathetic sensory fibers have their cell bodies in the dorsal root ganglia. The *parasympathetic portion* involves autonomic motor neurons from the cranial nerve nuclei and sacral spinal cord. These go directly to the target organs and synapse on local target ganglia. Short postganglionic fibers innervate the target organs.

more detailed organization of the peripheral autonomic system will be examined in Chapter 8. Many different regions of the brain can activate these two portions of the autonomic system. A number of these CNS regions have been linked together descriptively as the *limbic system* and will be discussed in more detail in Chapter 16.

Figure 4.9 illustrates the gross anatomical arrangement of the peripheral nerves, dorsal and ventral roots of the cord, the autonomic ganglia, and the

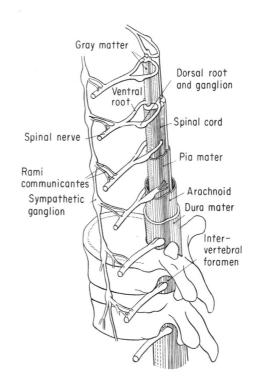

Gray matter

Dorsal root
and ganglion

Ventral
root

Spinal cord

Spinal nerve

Pia mater

Rami
communicantes

Sympathetic
ganglion

Arachnoid

Dura mater

Inter-
vertebral
foramen

Figure 4.9. Gross relations of spinal cord, dorsal and ventral roots, sympathetic ganglia, associated membranes (pia, arachnoid, and dura), and bony vertebrae. (From Gardner, 1963)

spinal cord, together with its long vertebral covering, and the *dura, arachnoid* and *pia* membranes covering it. In summary, remember that motor fibers have their cell bodies in the ventral (somatic) or lateral (autonomic) regions of the grey matter in the cord and run out to muscles or autonomic ganglia. The sensory fibers have their cell bodies in the dorsal root ganglia and enter the spinal cord, to convey information from receptors either directly to motor neurons (in reflexes) or to more central regions of the CNS for "processing".

Cranial Nerves

The cranial nerves are not really different in principle from the spinal nerves, except that they enter and leave the *brain* rather than the spinal cord. Table 4.2 lists the 12 nerves and some of their characteristics. Probably those of greater interest to the psychologist are the optic (II) and the auditory (VIII), conveying information from receptors of the eye and ear. If you wish to remember the names of the twelve in sequence, the following rhyme may help:

I	II	III	IV	V
On	*Old*	*Olumpus'*	*Towering*	*Top*

A	Fat	Armed	Girl	Vends	Snowy	Hops
VI	VII	VIII	IX	X	XI	XII

Spinal Cord

Two general categories of activity are handled by the spinal cord. *Spinal reflexes* are muscular and autonomic responses to bodily stimuli which occur even after the spinal cord is severed from the brain, as in a paraplegic accident victim. In addition a wide variety of *supraspinal* activity is channelled through the spinal cord. The cerebral cortex and other brain structures controlling movement of the body convey activity down the spinal cord to motor neurons, and all bodily sensations are conveyed up the spinal cord to the brain. Analogous sensory and motor relations for the head are handled directly by the cranial nerves and brain (see Table 4.2).

TABLE 4.2.   THE CRANIAL NERVES

Number	Name	Functions	Origin or End in the Brain
I	Olfactory	(s) Smell	Cerebral hemispheres (ventral part)
II	Optic	(s) Vision	Thalamus
III	Oculomotor	(m) Eye movement	Midbrain
IV	Trochlear	(m) Eye movement	Midbrain
V	Trigeminal	(m) Masticatory movements	Midbrain and pons
		(s) Sensitivity of face and tongue	Medulla
VI	Abducens	(m) Eye movement	Medulla
VII	Facial	(m) Facial movement	Medulla
VIII	Auditory vestibular	(s) Hearing	Medulla
		(s) Balance	
IX	Glossopharyngeal	(s) Tongue and (m) pharynx	Medulla
X	Vagus	(s) Heart, blood (m) vessels, viscera	Medulla
XI	Spinal accessory	(m) Neck muscles and viscera	Medulla
XII	Hypoglossal	(m) Tongue muscles	Medulla

A schematic cross section of the spinal cord is shown in Figure 4.10. The incoming dorsal root fibers and the outgoing ventral root fibers separate each half of the cord into dorsal, lateral, and ventral regions of white matter. Remember that white matter is composed simply of nerve fibers. The locations of some of the more important spinal pathways are shown in Figure 4.10. Note that the dorsal region of white matter is almost entirely taken up by ascending fibers conveying sensory information to nuclei of the lower brain stem, whereas

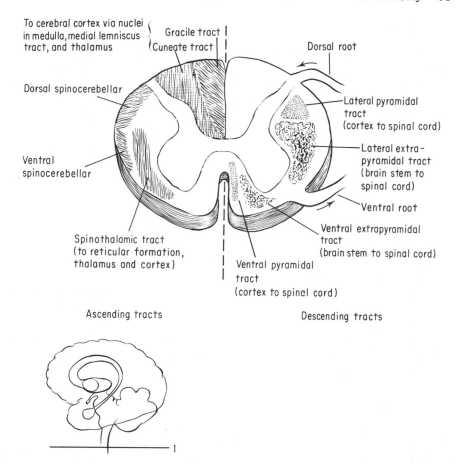

To cerebral cortex via nuclei
in medulla, medial lemniscus
tract, and thalamus

Gracile tract
Cuneate tract

Dorsal root

Dorsal spinocerebellar

Lateral pyramidal
tract
(cortex to spinal cord)

Lateral extra-
pyramidal tract
(brain stem to
spinal cord)

Ventral
spinocerebellar

Ventral root

Ventral extrapyramidal
tract
(brain stem to spinal cord)

Spinothalamic tract
(to reticular formation,
thalamus and cortex)

Ventral pyramidal
tract
(cortex to spinal cord)

Ascending tracts

Descending tracts

Figure 4.10. Major ascending and descending tracts of spinal cord. Both are present on *both sides* of the cord; they are separated here to aid visualization. Ascending tracts are of three basic types: the dorsal columns (gracile and cuneate tracts) of the lemniscal system, lateral tracts to the cerebellum, and the spinothalamic tract. There are two basic types of descending pathways, pyramidal tract fibers from the cerebral cortex, and extrapyramidal fibers from the cortex and brain stem. Small inset shows level of section as in Figure 4.4.

the dorsal half of the lateral portion is taken up almost entirely by descending (motor or efferent) fiber systems. As noted previously, it is evident that the pathways traveling furthest tend to lie most peripherally in the white matter. There are a number of short "association" fibers interconnecting various regions of the spinal cord that are not shown in Figure 4.10. These fibers tend to lie along the borders of the grey matter.

The descending fiber systems all terminate in some fashion upon the various types of motor neurons in the cord. As we will see later, different tracts tend to exert somewhat different types of influences on movement. For the present, we need simply distinguish between the *pyramidal* tract fibers, coming mostly from cerebral cortex and forming the lateral and ventral cortico-spinal tracts, and the *extrapyramidal* fibers comprising the other tracts.

Insofar as ascending systems are concerned, the spinothalamic tract conveys information about temperature, pain and diffuse touch and pressure from body surfaces and viscera. In contrast to the spinothalamic system, the cuneate and gracile tracts, often called the dorsal column system, convey to the brain detailed information about light touch, pressure, and the sense of position and movement. As their name implies, the dorsal and ventral spinocerebellar tracts project to the cerebellum.

The grey matter of the cord (Figure 4.11) contains nerve cell bodies whose axons may connect to closely adjacent cells, others whose axons make up descending and ascending fiber tracts, and the motor neurons whose axons go out to muscles and autonomic ganglia. The larger cells of the dorsal portion are sensory in function, relaying incoming information from sensory receptors. The intermediate and lateral cells of moderate size are autonomic motor neurons, and the large cells of the ventral region (some having cell bodies as large as 0.1 mm) are the somatic motor neurons activating peripheral skeletal musculature. Scattered in and among these groups of larger neurons are small and medium sized neurons, some of which are "associative" and interconnect neurons at a given level, and others of which may send axons up or down the cord for short distances.

The sensory and motor systems of the cord will be examined in greater detail in later chapters. We will consider only a few examples here to illustrate some general principles of organization of this region.

ASCENDING FIBER SYSTEMS.   The "wiring diagrams" for general aspects of these systems are shown in Figure 4.12. The gracile and cuneate tracts, mediating light touch and position sense, are composed of first order or primary sensory

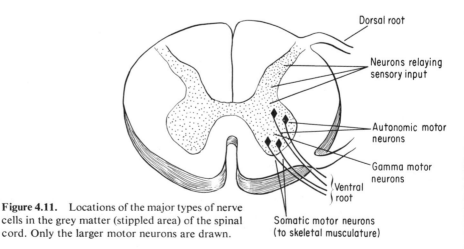

Figure 4.11.   Locations of the major types of nerve cells in the grey matter (stippled area) of the spinal cord. Only the larger motor neurons are drawn.

Dorsal root

Neurons relaying sensory input

Autonomic motor neurons

Gamma motor neurons

Ventral root

Somatic motor neurons (to skeletal musculature)

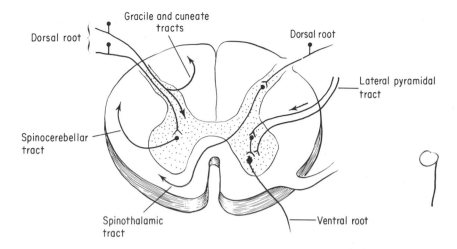

Figure 4.12. Diagrams of a few spinal pathways. Fibers forming the gracile and cuneate tracts are continuations of the incoming sensory nerves. Spinocerebellar tracts involve one synapse, and spinothalamic tract fibers involve one synapse and cross to the opposite side of the cord. Descending pyramidal tract fibers synapse directly or indirectly on motor neurons.

neurons. They are the axons of the afferent nerve fibers that have their cell bodies outside the CNS in the dorsal root ganglia. These axons enter the cord, turn and ascend in the gracile and cuneate tracts all the way to the lower brain stem, where they synapse on secondary neurons in the gracile and cuneate nuclei. From here they *cross* to the opposite side of the brain stem and ascend to higher relays. Thus for these tracts, the first synapse is in the brain rather than the spinal cord, and they cross in the brain. Crossing is a general principle of CNS organization: in most cases incoming information from the left side of the body ends up in structures on the right side of the brain, and vice versa. The same holds true for descending motor fibers.

Fibers of the spinothalamic tract mediate pain, temperature, pressure and general contact sense. Incoming sensory neurons with cell bodies in the dorsal root ganglia synapse on secondary neurons in the dorsal portion of the dorsal grey matter of the cord. These neurons in turn send axons *across* to the opposite side of the cord which turn and ascend in the spinothalamic tract.

DESCENDING FIBER SYSTEMS. The most prominent descending system is the lateral corticospinal tract, containing pyramidal fibers from the cerebral cortex. These fibers cross to the opposite side of the brain in the lower brain stem (*pyramidal decussation*) and descend from this region to synapse directly or indirectly upon the larger motor neurons of the ventral "horn", i.e. the ventral portion of the ventral grey. Both a direct connection and an indirect connection involving one interneuron are shown in Figure 4.12. In lower mammals there is always at least one interneuron interposed between the descending pyramidal fiber and the spinal motor neuron. The direct connection from pyramidal fiber to spinal motor neuron is found only in man and primates. This probably reflects the greater elaboration of the pyramidal system and its increasingly important role in the control of movement in higher mammals.

REFLEX CONNECTIONS.   The reflex connections of the cord are omitted in the diagram of Figure 4.12 for simplicity (see Chapter 12 for discussion of spinal reflexes). Some incoming sensory fibers synapse directly on motor neurons to form *monosynaptic* reflexes such as the stretch reflex. These reflexes consist of an incoming fiber and an outgoing neuron with only one synapse interposed in the CNS. Still others synapse on intermediate neurons, which in turn synapse on motor neurons to form *polysynaptic* reflexes such as flexion, crossed extension, and scratch reflexes. Several intermediate synapses may be involved in the more complex reflexes.

Brain Stem

The term *brain stem* technically refers to everything between the spinal cord and the cerebral and cerebellar cortices. The major subdivisions, going from cord to cortex, are *medulla, pons, midbrain, thalamus or diencephalon,* and the *basal ganglia.* More often than not "brain stem" is used to mean only the medulla, pons, and midbrain. Actually these three structures appear as a somewhat enlarged continuation of the tubular shaped spinal cord, and contain a

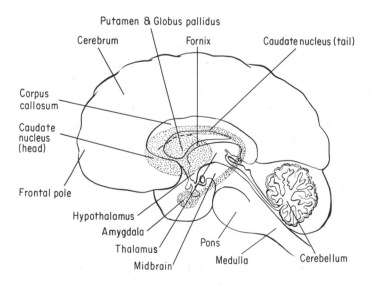

Basal ganglia =

Figure 4.13.   Outline drawing of the brain showing the approximate internal locations of the basal ganglia within the cerebral hemisphere.

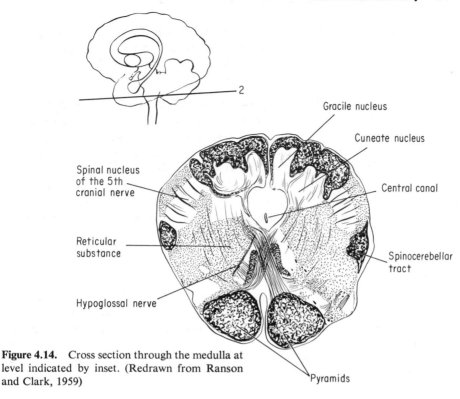

Gracile nucleus

Cuneate nucleus

Spinal nucleus
of the 5th
cranial nerve

Central canal

Reticular
substance

Spinocerebellar
tract

Hypoglossal nerve

Pyramids

Figure 4.14. Cross section through the medulla at level indicated by inset. (Redrawn from Ranson and Clark, 1959)

large number of nuclei and fiber tracts. The pons is overlaid ventrally by large fiber bundles giving it its characteristic appearance and name (i.e. bridge).

A sketch of the appearance of the brain stem including the thalamus and hypothalamus in a sagittal section, is shown in Figure 4.13. The figure also illustrates the relation of the brain stem to cerebral cortex and cerebellum.

The *medulla* is the continuation of the spinal cord in the brain and contains all the ascending and descending fiber tracts interconnecting brain and spinal cord, together with a number of important nerve cell nuclei. The majority of the cranial nerves have their entrances and exits from the medulla and the bordering region of the medulla and pons. Several of the cranial nerve nuclei are found entirely or in part in the medulla (the 5th nerve nucleus, for example, extends from the midbrain to the spinal cord). In addition, several "vital" autonomic nuclei concerned with respiration, heart action, and gastrointestinal function are located in the medulla. A cross section of the medulla is sketched in Figure 4.14.

The brain stem reticular formation has extremely important functions which have only recently been appreciated. Anatomically it is a complex mixture of cell bodies, fibers and nuclei extending from the spinal cord to the thalamus, generally occupying a somewhat ventral location in the brain stem. The two major aspects of reticular function concern descending influences on spinal and cranial motor neurons and ascending influences on thalamus, cortex, and other structures. Stimulation of descending portions of the reticular formation may result either in decreases (inhibition) or increases (facilitation) in the activity of the motor neurons controlling the skeletal musculature. This aspect of reticular functioning, incidentally, is included within the *extrapyramidal* system (see basal ganglia, below). In a classic paper Moruzzi and Magoun (1949) demonstrated that stimulation of the *ascending reticular formation* resulted in an *arousal response* of the EEG, a pattern of low voltage fast cortical activity characteristic of the waking animal. Destruction of the midbrain reticular formation tends to yield a sleeping or stuporous animal (Lindsley et al., 1949). The ascending reticular formation thus appears crucially involved in the control of sleeping and waking. It also seems to play a fundamental role in behavioral alerting or "attention" (Lindsley, 1958). We will consider the organization and functions of this extremely important system in more detail in a subsequent chapter (Chapter 14).

The *pons* is the upward continuation of the brain stem, and contains ascending and descending fiber tracts and many additional nuclei. A very large bundle

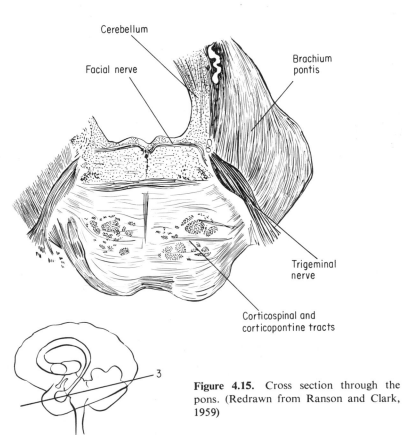

Cerebellum

Facial nerve

Brachium pontis

Trigeminal nerve

Corticospinal and corticopontine tracts

Figure 4.15. Cross section through the pons. (Redrawn from Ranson and Clark, 1959)

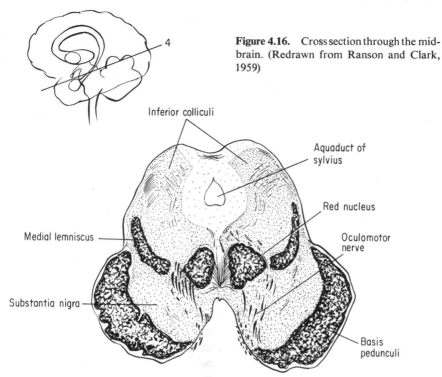

Figure 4.16. Cross section through the midbrain. (Redrawn from Ranson and Clark, 1959)

Inferior colliculi

Aquaduct of sylvius

Red nucleus

Medial lemniscus

Oculomotor nerve

Substantia nigra

Basis pedunculi

of transverse fibers lies on the ventral aspect of the pons. These bundles interconnect the brain stem and cerebellum, as well as containing the pyramidal fibers going from cortex to spinal cord. Several cranial nerve nuclei, including the main motor nucleus of the 5th nerve, the nucleus of the 7th nerve and nuclei controlling salivation are found in the pons. These nuclei play a major role in feeding and in facial expression. In addition, higher order relays for the auditory system, neurons which act to inhibit and facilitate spinal motor neurons and additional respiratory nuclei are found in the pons. A cross section through the pons is shown in Figure 4.15.

The *midbrain* (mesencephalon) is the most anterior extension of the brain stem that still maintains the basic tubular structure of the spinal cord. It merges anteriorly into the thalamus and hypothalamus. The dorsal portion of the midbrain (the *tectum*) contains two pair of important relay nuclei for the visual and auditory systems called the superior and inferior colliculi. These nuclei appear as four bumps on the dorsal surface of the midbrain (see Figure 4.10). The ventral portion of the midbrain (the tegmentum) contains nuclei for the 3rd and 4th cranial nerves, which control eye movement, all of the ascending and descending tracts interconnecting the upper and lower portions of the brain, and the rostral portion of the reticular formation. A large nucleus called the *red nucleus* is found here, as is a collection of heavily pigmented cells, *substantia nigra*. A cross section through the midbrain is shown in Figure 4.16.

The medulla, pons, and midbrain developed early in the course of evolution and are surprisingly uniform in structure and organization from fish to man. There are of course some variations among species. Lower vertebrates such as the shark or frog, who have little cerebral cortex, have essentially no pyramidal tract, fewer ventral fiber bundles on the pons, etc. A general principle of neural organization states that the size and complexity of a structure is related to the behavioral importance of that structure. In fish, where there is no cerebral cortex, the superior and inferior colliculi are the important centers of seeing and hearing, and are relatively large. Among mammals, the bat, for example, has a much enlarged inferior colliculus (auditory relay nucleus) correlated with its extensive use of auditory information. As you may know, the bat employs a system much like " sonar." It emits very high frequency sound pulses and determines the location of objects in space by the echo sounds of the reflected pulses. A number of clues about possible functions of brain structures have been obtained by use of this principle of relating size of structure to behavioral importance.

In summary, the brain stem contains all fiber systems interconnecting higher brain structures and spinal cord; it also contains the cranial nerves and their nuclei (except for the olfactory and optic nerves), nuclei subserving vital functions, emotional expression, and many higher order nuclei concerned with various sensory modalities. When all brain tissue above the midbrain is removed in an animal such as the cat, it can still exhibit an amazing variety of behavior. Such preparations will live for long periods, can walk, vocalize, eat, sleep, exhibit some components of emotional expression, and may even be capable of very limited "learning" (Bard and Macht, 1958).

Cerebellum

The cerebellum is a phylogenetically old structure and was probably the first to be specialized for sensory-motor coordination. It overlies the pons (see Figure 4.13) and typically presents a very much convoluted appearance, having a large number of lobules· separated by fissures. As in the cerebral cortex, the nerve cell bodies form a surface layer about 2 mm thick which covers the underlying white matter and cerebellar nuclei. Histologically (i.e. in terms of organization of nerve cells) the cerebellar cortex presents a remarkably similar appearance everywhere, in contrast to structures like the cerebral cortex, which exhibit marked regional characteristics. The general schematic arrangement of the cerebellum is indicated in Figure 4.13.

The cortex and underlying nuclei of the cerebellum receive connections from the vestibular system, from spinal sensory fibers, from the auditory and visual systems, from various regions of the cerebral cortex, and from the reticular formation. It sends efferent fibers to the thalamus, reticular formation and several other brain stem structures. Although it is probably involved in a number of other functions as well, the cerebellum is primarily concerned with the regulation of motor coordination. Removal of the cerebellum produces a characteristic *syndrome* (i.e. set of symptoms) of jerky, incoordinated movement. We will examine the functions of the cerebellum in greater detail in a later chapter (Chapter 13).

Thalamus

The thalamus is a large grouping of nuclei located just anterior and dorsal to the midbrain. In gross appearance it is shaped somewhat like small footballs, one within each cerebral hemisphere. A rough sketch of its location within the hemisphere is presented in Figure 4.13, and a cross section through the thalamus is given in Figure 4.17.

The many nuclei of the thalamus have been differentiated and named in terms of several different sets of criteria, including histological appearance, anatomical location and connections. Perhaps the simplest classification is in terms of input and output connections. The three classes are *sensory relay* nuclei, *association* nuclei, and *intrinsic* nuclei. Sensory relay nuclei receive projections from specific ascending sensory pathways and in turn project to specific sensory regions of the cerebral cortex. The major nuclei of this class are the *lateral geniculate body*, receiving visual fibers and relaying to the visual cortex, the *medial geniculate body*, receiving auditory projections and relaying to the

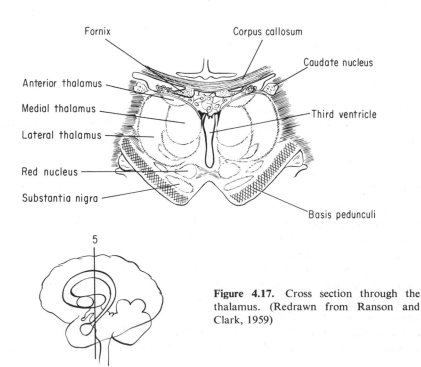

Figure 4.17. Cross section through the thalamus. (Redrawn from Ranson and Clark, 1959)

auditory cortex, the *ventrobasal nuclear complex*, receiving projections from the somatic sensory system and projecting to the somatic sensory cortex, and the *lateral ventral* nucleus, receiving fibers from the cerebellum and relaying to the motor areas of the cerebral cortex. If the cerebral cortex is removed, all of these nuclei degenerate completely. This is an example of *retrograde degeneration*, since the cell bodies in the thalamus degenerate after the axon terminals in the cortex are destroyed.

The association nuclei also project to the cerebral cortex, and degenerate completely after removal of the cortex. However, these nuclei do not receive direct projections from ascending pathways, and they project to "association" areas of the cerebral cortex rather than to specific sensory regions. The most important association nuclei are the *dorsomedial nucleus*, projecting to the frontal cortex, and the *pulvinar* and *lateral posterior* nuclei, which project to posterior association areas of the cortex.

Finally, the intrinsic nuclei are often classified as midline and intralaminar on the basis of anatomical location. These nuclei do not project to the cerebral cortex (at least not to the neocortex). They remain virtually intact following total removal of all cerebral neocortex. The intrinsic nuclei have interconnections with other thalamic regions, with the reticular formation, and with various structures of the *limbic* system (see below). They appear to play a significant role in the regulation of spontaneous EEG activity in the cortex (see Jasper, 1960) and are sometimes viewed as comprising a "diffuse thalamic system."

It should be emphasized that the thalamus is an extremely complex structure. We have named only a few of the major nuclei in the thalamus and given a general overview of their connections. Thalamic nuclei projecting rostrally to the cortex also appear to receive projections *from* the cortex, and many project caudally as well. A great deal remains to be learned about the organization and functions of the thalamic nuclei, particularly the association and intrinsic groups. The sensory relay group may be thought of as *relatively* simple relay stations transmitting sensory information from lower regions to the cerebral cortex.

Hypothalamus

The term "hypothalamus" refers to a grouping of small nuclei that lie generally in the ventral portion of the cerebrum at the junction of the midbrain and thalamus. It is not possible to convey a clear appreciation of their rather complicated spatial layout from diagrams. The various nuclei lie along the base of the third ventricle and are contiguous with the pituitary gland. A schematic sketch of a sagittal section along the floor of the third ventricle and base of the skull indicates a few of the general relations (Figure 4.18). The pituitary gland (*hypophysis*) is actually innervated by neurons from the hypothalamus. In recent years these hypothalamic-hypophysial interrelationships have been found to be of crucial importance in the neural regulation of endocrine gland functions. It

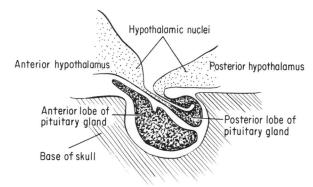

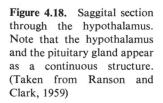

Figure 4.18. Saggital section through the hypothalamus. Note that the hypothalamus and the pituitary gland appear as a continuous structure. (Taken from Ranson and Clark, 1959)

is difficult to stress sufficiently the importance of the very minute nuclei composing the hypothalamus. They are crucially involved in eating, sexual behavior, drinking, sleeping, temperature regulation, and emotional behavior generally. The hypothalamus is the major central brain structure concerned with the functions of the autonomic nervous system, particularly with its sympathetic division.

The hypothalamus interconnects with many regions of the brain. A number of these structures, including *paleocortex* (old cortex), portions of the *rhinencephalon* (nosebrain), the *hippocampus*, the septal area and the hypothalamus itself, are viewed by many anatomists as comprising an integrated network of structures called the *limbic system*. Many of these structures seem to be involved in aspects of behavior such as emotion, motivation, and reinforcement. We will devote a separate chapter (Chapter 16) to the organization and functions of the limbic system.

Basal Ganglia

These are a group of large nuclei (ganglia is really a misnomer) lying in the central regions of the cerebral hemispheres. They partially surround the thalamus and are themselves enclosed by the cerebral cortex and cerebral white matter. The major nuclei commonly included are the *caudate nucleus*, the *putamen*, and the *globus pallidus*. Figure 4.4 illustrates the spatial distribution of these nuclei in relation to the thalamus and cerebrum. The amygdala, sometimes included as well, has quite different connections and probably different functions from the other nuclei of the basal ganglia and is usually grouped in the limbic system (see Chapter 16). The remaining nuclei, collectively termed the *corpus striatum*, appear to play a role in the control of movement and form the major part of the *extrapyramidal motor system*. They have connections with the cortex, thalamus, hypothalamus, reticular formation, portions of the midbrain, and the spinal cord. It should be noted that the *substantia nigra* and *red nucleus* of the midbrain, which are usually included in the extrapyramidal motor system, also have connections with the corpus striatum.

The basal ganglia seem to be involved in motor activity and certainly have indirect connections with motor neurons. However the specific functions they subserve remain a mystery. Animals display no particular motor dysfunctions after ablation of the basal ganglia (Peele, 1954). In man, clinical evidence suggests that damage to the extrapyramidal system may produce two syndromes, *hypertonia* (an incressed muscle tone which tends to restrict bodily movements and facial expression), and abnormal repetitive movements. We will discuss the extrapyramidal system in more detail in Chapter 13.

Cerebral Cortex

The cerebral cortex, a mantle of cells covering the cerebrum, has traditionally been the brain structure of greatest interest to psychologists. It is the most recent neural system to develop in the course of evolution, and is markedly enlarged in primates, especially man. Of the approximately 12 billion neurons in the human brain, 9 billion are found in the cortex. In contrast, fish have no cerebral cortex, amphibians only a very rudimentary and scanty cortex, and reptiles and birds a small and poorly developed cortex. Much of the cerebral

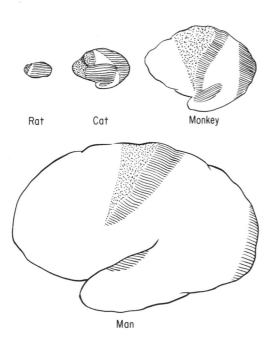

Rat   Cat   Monkey

Figure 4.19. Approximate scale drawings of the cerebral hemispheres of four mammals. Note both the increase in size and relative increase in amount of "association" cortex.

Man

▦ = Motor areas

▤ = Sensory areas

▭ = Association areas

cortex in these lower forms is *paleo*—or *archicortex*, having close interrelation-ships with the more primitive olfactory and limbic systems. It is only in mammals that the neocortex becomes elaborated.

All incoming sensory systems project to the cortex, each to a specific region. Efferent or motor systems controlling the activity of cranial and spinal motor neurons arise in other regions of the cortex. Interestingly enough, the basic organization of the cortical sensory and motor areas does not appear to differ markedly from rat to man. However, as one ascends the mammalian scale of evolution, the relative amount of "association" cortex (cortex that is neither sensory nor motor and has often been assumed to be involved in higher or more complex behavioral functions) increases strikingly. Rough scale drawings of the cerebral cortex of rat, cat, monkey, and man are shown in Figure 4.19. Note both the remarkable increase in absolute brain size and the increase in relative amount of association cortex. Man, incidentally, does not have the largest brain. Porpoise, whale and elephant all have larger brain masses, although the packing density of cells may be less. We will examine the structure and functions of the cerebral cortex in detail in Chapter 11.

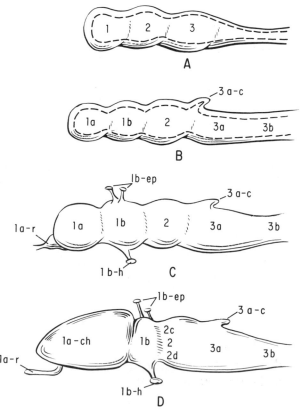

Figure 4.20. Embryological de-velopment of the primitive verte-brate brain. **A**, first stage, side view, cavity indicated by dots; **B**, second stage; **C**, third stage; **D**, fourth stage. 1, prosencephalon; 1a, telencephalon; 1 a-r, rhinen-cephalon; 1 a-ch, cerebral hemi-sphere; 1b, diencephalon; 1 b-ep, epithalamus; 1 b-h, hypophysis; 2, mesencephalon; 2c, optic lobes; 2d, cerebral peduncle; 3a, met-encephalon; 3 a-c, cerebellum; 3b, myelencephalon. (Redrawn from Ranson and Clark, 1959)

Comparative and Developmental Aspects of the Vertebrate Brain

A fundamental biological principle is summarized in the phrase " ontogony recapitulates phylogony." This simply means that in embryological development the individual organism passes through many of the forms that comprise its evolutionary history. As the novelist Aldous Huxley (1928), put it, "something that has been a single cell, a cluster of cells, a little sac of tissue, a kind of worm, a potential fish with gills, . . . would one day become a man." This principle is clearly illustrated by the developing human nervous system.

Drawings showing some of the embryological stages of the more primitive and generalized vertebrate brain are presented in Figure 4.20. In all vertebrates the CNS begins as a relatively straight tube. In the earliest stage of differentiation three enlargements which will become the forebrain, midbrain, and hindbrain, develop at the head end (Figure 4.20A). At the next stage (Figure 4.20B) the forebrain divides to form the telencephalon and diencephalon, and the cerebellum begins to grow out. In the third stage (Figure 4.20C) the rhinencephalon

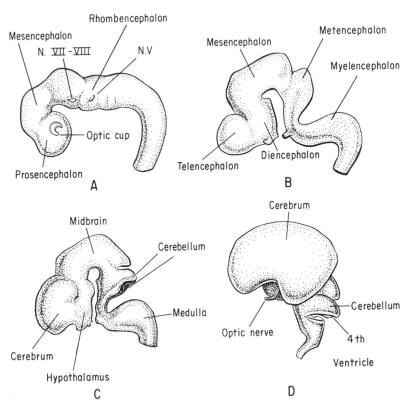

Figure 4.21. Embryological development of the human brain. **A**, 5 mm embryo; **B**, 11 mm embryo; **C**, 15 mm embryo; **D**, 53 mm embryo. (Redrawn from Peele, 1954)

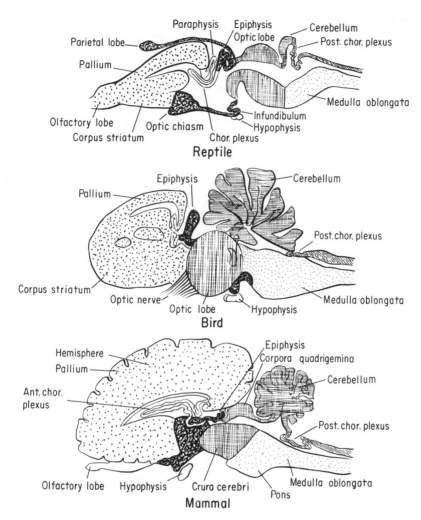

Figure 4.22.   Comparison of reptile, bird, and generalized mammal brains (drawings of sagittal sections; all brains facing left). (Taken from Kuntz, 1943)

develops, the pituitary gland and related neural structures appear, and the pons and medulla begin to differentiate. Finally, in the fourth stage (in brains having cerebral hemispheres) the cerebrum grows out and overlays the diencephalon, and the cerebellum enlarges. Through these stages of development essentially all vertebrate brains that have cerebral hemispheres are quite similar. In fact, it is only relatively late in the development of the embryo that the brains of such divergent species as pig and man are easily distinguished.

Some of the developmental stages of the human brain are illustrated in Figure 4.21. The brain of the 5-mm embryo (Figure 4.21A) resembles the first

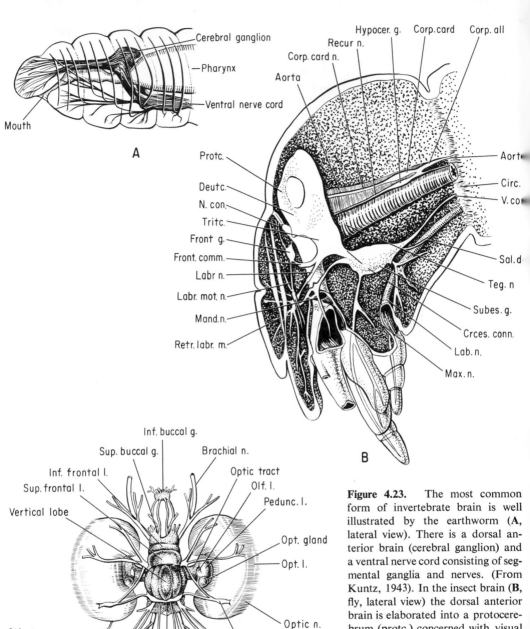

A

Cerebral ganglion
Pharynx
Ventral nerve cord
Mouth

B

Hypocer. g.　Corp. card　Corp. all
Recur n.
Corp. card n.
Aorta
Protc.
Deutc.
N. con.
Tritc.
Front g.
Front. comm.
Labr n.
Labr. mot. n.
Mand. n.
Retr. labr. m.

Aorta
Circ.
V. co
Sal. d
Teg. n
Subes. g.
Crces. conn.
Lab. n.
Max. n.

C

Inf. buccal g.
Sup. buccal g.　Brachial n.
Inf. frontal l.　Optic tract
Sup. frontal l.　Olf. l.
Vertical lobe　Pedunc. l.
Opt. gland
Opt. l.
Optic n.
Olfactory n.
Head retractor n.
Pallial n.　Post. sup. ophth. g.
Stomatogastric n.　Subesophageal g.
Post. basal l.

Figure 4.23. The most common form of invertebrate brain is well illustrated by the earthworm (**A**, lateral view). There is a dorsal anterior brain (cerebral ganglion) and a ventral nerve cord consisting of segmental ganglia and nerves. (From Kuntz, 1943). In the insect brain (**B**, fly, lateral view) the dorsal anterior brain is elaborated into a protocerebrum (protc.) concerned with visual input and the more complex aspects of behavior, a deutocerebrum (deutc.) and a tritocerebrum (tritc.). The subesophogeal ganglion (subes g.) is the anterior portion of the ventral nerve cord. (From Bierbrodt, 1942). In the octopus (**C**, dorsal view) a series of lobes have developed, e.g. optic lobes (opt. l.), inferior and superior frontal lobes (inf. and sup. frontal l.), a vertical lobe, basal lobes, etc. (From Young, 1961)

stage shown in the previous figure. Note, however, that even at this early stage there is a right angle bend at the midbrain. By the time the embryo is 11 mm long (Figure 4.21B) the brain shows the five general subdivisions, and is beginning to fold back upon itself. This would correspond roughly to stage three. By 15 mm the cerebrum is beginning to grow out, as is the cerebellum (Figure 2.21C). Finally, the brain of the 53 mm embryo (Figure 4.21D) shows a marked similarity to the adult brain, although the cerebellum has not yet grown out over the midbrain.

A sampling of vertebrate brains is shown in Figure 4.22. The reptile brain shows considerable similarity to the generalized primitive brain of Figure 4.20. The pallium of the reptilian brain is the precursor of the cerebral hemisphere. The bird brain does have a modest cerebrum, but much of the cortex is paleo- (i.e. old) rather than neocortex. The generalized mammalian brain illustrates the massive development of the cerebral hemisphere.

The Invertebrate Nervous System

The multiplicity of one-celled animals attests to the fact that a nervous system is not necessary for adaptive behavior. Such organisms as amoeba, paramecium, and vorticella exhibit a wide variety of responses to stimulation (see Maier and Schneirla, 1935) even though they have no nerve cells to conduct information. Specialized conduction does not seem necessary when both input and output are handled by the same cell. The simplest multicellular animals such as the sponge have no nervous system but are able to respond to stimulation. However the behavior of the sponge is somewhat limited in variety. A nervous system (cells specialized for conducting activation or information) does seem necessary for any degree of behavioral complexity in multicellular organisms. The simplest type of nervous system is the *nerve net*, found in coelenterates such as the sea anemone or jellyfish. These nets are diffuse arrangements of nerve cells and fibers interconnecting receptors and muscles. The nerve net is not structurally continuous; there are synapses between nerve cells. However, there appears to be no particular organization to the nerve net; it is spatially diffuse and conducts information in a very diffuse manner.

Worms exhibit the first centralized nervous system. A drawing of the earthworm brain, Figure 4.23A, shows both a central neural core (nerve cord) and a "brain," or at least an enlarged head end to the nerve cord. The specialization of the anterior end of the worm for feeding and exploring is reflected in this early precurser of the brain. The brain and nerve cord of the earthworm are essentially a series of ganglia, having input fibers, interneurons, and output fibers. Both the input and output are organized into nerves. The bulk of the input is from sensory receptors at the head end and most of the output tends to go in a posterior direction from the head end. The nervous system of the worm illustrates the basic plan elaborated in the vertebrate CNS.

Nervous systems of the more advanced invertebrates exhibit a wide variety of forms. Organisms that are bilaterally symmetric like insects tend to have the same fundamental neural organization as does the worm, whereas radially symmetric animals like the octopus have a series of interconnected head ganglia. The brains of an insect and an octopus are shown in Figure 4.23B and 4.23C. Higher invertebrates like the more advanced insects and molluscs are capable of a wide variety of complex behavior patterns, and will exhibit rapid and effective learning under appropriate conditions. The reader may consult Maier and Schneirla (1935) and the recent and comprehensive text by Bullock and Horridge (1961) for extensive discussions of both the neural and behavioral characteristics of invertebrates. Analysis of the neural and biochemical corre-lates of invertebrate behavior is an active and extensive area of physiological psychology today.

Suggested readings

Gardner, E. *Fundamentals of neurology*. Philadelphia: Saunders, 1952.

Peele, T. L. *The neuroanatomical basis for clinical neurology*. New York: McGraw-Hill, 1954.

Ranson, S. W., & Clark, S. L. *The anatomy of the nervous system*. Philadelphia: Saunders, 1953.

5

BASIC
NEUROCHEMISTRY

Experimental study of relations between brain chemistry and behavior has only begun in the past few years. Some of the more intriguing current discoveries and theories in physiological psychology are concerned with possible chemical bases of learning and other behavior phenomena. Recent developments in neurophysiology suggest that most interactions between nerve cells (i.e. synaptic transmission, see Chapter 7) are basically chemical in nature. The long and sometimes heated controversy over whether synaptic transmission is chemical or electrical appears to have been resolved in favor of chemical mechanisms, at least for the mammalian nervous system (we will examine this evidence in some detail in Chapter 8). Since the interactions among neurons are chemical, it is reasonable to assume that chemical processes play a fundamental role in learning and other types of behavioral change. An understanding of current research in chemistry and behavior presupposes some knowledge of basic neurochemistry. In this chapter we will review those aspects of neurochemistry most relevant to considerations of neural activity and behavior. Relations of neurochemistry and behavior will be discussed in more detail in Chapter 17.

Cellular composition of brain tissue

The chemical composition of whole brain tissue, indicated in Tables 5.1 and 5.2, is representative of values given in most texts. These determinations are made by taking whole brain, or grey matter *vs* white matter, and treating it as a uniform homogeneous tissue to be ground up and analyzed. Unfortunately if any single feature characterizes brain it is the high degree of organization and *lack* of homogeneity of the cellular elements. There are many different types of nerve cells and fiber processes organized into structurally distinct nuclei and fiber tracts of various sorts. Most of the unique characteristics of brain are obliterated by treating it as a uniform " bag of chemicals." Perhaps the greatest source of confounding in the analysis of whole brain tissue is the fact that the majority of cellular elements in brain are not even nerve cells. Ninety percent of the cells in the brain are *glial* cells and only 10 percent are nerve cells (Nurnberger 1958). Glial cells themselves come in a variety of shapes and forms; they closely invest and surround nerve cell bodies and fiber processes. If a stained section of brain tissue is viewed under a light microscope, the relatively large nerve cell bodies appear to be separated by rather extensive extracellular spaces. However, electron microscope studies have shown that there is essentially no extracellular space; it is filled up with glial cells (De Robertis and Gerschenfeld, 1961). On the basis of histological characteristics glial cells have often been considered as connective tissue, serving the same general kind of supportive function as connective tissue in most other organs. Recent evidence suggests that they may play much more crucial and direct nutritive and regulatory roles in nerve function (see Hydén and Lange, 1962).

Glial cells and nerve cells differ markedly from one another in many structural and chemical features. Glial cells tend to be smaller than nerve cells; although 90 percent of brain cells are glia, they account for only about 50 percent of brain weight (see Giacobini, 1964). The RNA (ribose nucleic acid) content of glial cells is only about one-tenth that of nerve cells and its composition differs in the two types of cells (Hydén and Pigon, 1960; Egyhazi and Hydén, 1961). Neurons appear to have higher cellular respiration than glia (see Giacobini, 1964). Glia exhibit contractile movements and neurons do not (Chang and Hild, 1959).

Certain enzyme systems are strikingly different in the two types of cells. Thus the glia contain about 60 times as much carboanhydrase (an enzyme that facilitates the formation of carbonic acid from carbon dioxide) as nerve cells. Two different enzymes can facilitate the breakdown of acetylcholine (ACh), a substance believed by many to be associated with some types of synaptic transmission in the brain. One of these enzymes, so-called "true" acetylcholine esterase (AChE), rapidly breaks down ACh and only ACh. The other, "pseudo" or "serum" choline esterase (ChE), breaks down ACh and a variety of other substances. In the brain, only true AChE is found in nerve cells and ChE is found in glia.

In the brief discussion of the chemical composition of brain given below, it is well to keep in mind that much of the data refer to the chemical composition of neurons and glial cells analyzed together.

CHEMICAL COMPOSITION OF BRAIN TISSUE

Whole brain tissue has some rather striking differences from other types of tissue in its over-all chemical composition. Table 5.1 compares some typical values of the major constituents of mammalian brain and muscle. Brain has significantly more lipid (fatty substances) and less protein than muscle and most other organs.

TABLE 5.1.   APPROXIMATE COMPOSITION OF BRAIN AND MUSCLE

Component	Skeletal Muscle (percent)	Whole Brain (percent)
Water	75	78
Lipids	4	10
Protein	18	8
Carbohydrate	1	1
Inorganic salts	1	1
Other	3–5	2

NOTE: These values do not take into account variations that occur for different animals, different ages, different regions of the brain, and neural *vs* nonneural cellular elements of the brain. (Based on McIlwain, 1959.)

There are also differences between the chemical composition of grey and white matter. As indicated in Table 2, grey matter has a good deal more water and less lipid. Spinal cord and peripheral nerve have about the same relative composition as white matter, except that nerve has more protein (15 percent) and somewhat less water.

TABLE 5.2.   APPROXIMATE COMPONENTS OF BRAIN

Substance	White Matter (percent)	Grey Matter (percent)
Water	70	83
Lipid	19	7
Protein	8	8
Other	2	2

NOTE: These values do not take into account variations that occur for different animals, different ages, different regions of the brain, and neural *vs* nonneural cellular elements of the brain. (Based on McIlwain, 1955.)

In Table 5.2 the "other" category includes such essential substances as glucose and glycogen, amino acids, electrolytes, etc., which are not stored to any appreciable extent in brain tissue (liver, by contrast, is about 5 percent stored glycogen). Most of the water is contained within cells of the nervous system, only about 15 percent being in the cerebrospinal fluid and extracellular regions.

If grey and white matter constituents are averaged together, more than half the *dry* weight of the brain is composed of lipids. However, simple fats (triglycerides) are present only in very low concentration in the brain. The three major groupings of lipids in brain tissue are *cholesterol, phospholipids* and *glycolipids*. The cholesterol is normally present as "free" cholesterol (i.e. not bound together with other substances) as much of it is associated with the fatty sheaths (*myelin*) that cover nerve fibers. The most rapid build up of cholesterol content in human brain tissue occurs during the first year of life when myelinization is proceeding most rapidly. Phospholipids are simply compounds containing diglycerides and phosphoric esters and the glycolipids contain fatty acids, sugar, and other substances. These compounds are also found to predominate in the myelin sheaths of nerve fibers. Many of the brain lipids exist in combination with proteins.

Most remaining dry weight of brain tissue is protein. Much of this occurs in complex compounds containing both protein and lipid, some of which are unique to brain. You may recall that proteins are simply long chains of amino acids hooked up in certain sequences. The configurations of protein molecules are such that regions may have accessible side chains of functional groups permitting hook-up with other compounds. With some exceptions, protein molecules in solution generally exhibit a net negative charge, which as we will see later has implications for maintenance of cell membrane potentials (Chapter 7). The complex protein and lipid substances of brain have been classified in terms of whether they behave chemically as proteins or lipids. The *lipoproteins* (which behave like proteins) contain about 75 percent of the protein in these lipid-protein complexes and the *proteolipids* the remaining 25 percent. Many different proteins are of course present as proteins in the brain as well.

Nerve cells contain nucleoproteins common to all cells, the two general types being *desoxypentose nucleic acid* (DNA) and *ribose nucleic acid* (RNA) (see Chapter 2). The latter often exists in the form of liponucleoprotein. It is now fairly well established that DNA, which occurs exclusively in the cell nucleus, is associated with the chromosomal elements and is concerned with cell division. It is less subject to the influences of cellular metabolism or environmental factors than is RNA. RNA molecules, on the other hand, are associated with the nucleolus and Nissl bodies (ribosomes or microsomes) and are markedly affected by metabolic and environmental factors. Perhaps partly for this reason, it has recently been suggested that RNA may play a role in learning (Hydén, 1959).

Inorganic salts, which form about 1 percent of brain weight (see Table 5.1) are the *electrolytes*, which are present in ionic form in brain tissue. The major electrolytes are sodium (Na^+), potassium (K^+) and chloride (Cl^-), with smaller

amounts of calcium (Ca^{++}), magnesium (Mg^{++}) and others. You may remember that in an ordinary ionic solution, the number of $+$ and $-$ charges
balances out. If brain tissue is simply analyzed as a whole, the total cations
(positively charged ions like Na^+ and K^+) are present in considerable excess of
the chloride anion (Cl^-). The difference is made up with negatively charged
protein, lipid and other organic ions.

The distributions of electrolytes are markedly different inside and outside
nerve cells, and these differential concentrations play a major role in the nerve
membrane potential. This will be discussed in detail in Chapter 6, but for now
it is only necessary to remember that sodium is in much greater concentration
outside cells and potassium inside cells. The negatively charged proteins and
lipids are for the most part inside cells, and are too large to diffuse through cell
membrane. The small ions of the inorganic electrolytes (e.g. Na^+, K^+, Cl^-) are
able to diffuse through cell membranes, but are maintained at the *net* differential
distributions inside and outside cells noted above.

BLOOD-BRAIN BARRIER

Before considering the chemical properties of brain metabolism and neural
function, it is necessary to make some mention of a rather unique system termed
the *blood-brain barrier* (or barriers). Early experimenters noted that when vital
tissue dyes were injected systemically (i.e. into the blood stream) most tissues of
the body rapidly became stained, but brain and spinal cord tissue did not
(Ehrlich, 1885). Subsequent studies have shown the same differential distribution
for a wide variety of compounds (Tschirgi, 1950). In effect a special barrier
exists between blood vessels and brain tissue, which sequesters the brain and
prevents the diffusion of some substances from blood plasma to brain. Such a
barrier is not found for other organs. There is no unanimity of opinion among
authorities regarding the anatomical locus of the barrier. Some identify it with
the special membrane of glial cells (the perivascular glial membrane of Held)
that surrounds all blood vessels of the nervous system (Tschirgi, 1952), and
others identify it with the endothelial cells lining the blood vessels (Tower, 1958).
Nevertheless, it is localized somewhere between blood plasma and nerve cells.
In general terms the blood-brain barrier may be viewed as a safety device for
maintenance of a more stable chemical environment for neurons. It is certainly
true that the organism is uniquely dependent on a normally functioning brain.
If brain were at the mercy of every fluctuation in plasma constituents, normal
function would be much harder to maintain. The mechanisms of the barrier
are not fully understood, but its empirical operation has been well characterized. There is no barrier to water or gases such as oxygen and carbon dioxide.
Many lipid soluble compounds such as anesthetics pass freely. However many
electrolytes such as sodium and potassium apparently have long delays in
crossing, as do a number of other substances.

When studying the central effects of any compound, the action of the blood-brain barrier must be considered. One example will suffice. A substance called *serotonin* (to be discussed at greater length later in the chapter) occurs naturally in brain and is believed by some to be of considerable importance in brain function. Serotonin (technically 5-hydroxytryptamine, also referred to as 5 HT—see Figure 5.5) does produce some symptoms when administered. However, these are all due to peripheral actions; it does not cross the blood-brain barrier. On the other hand, its immediate precursor (substance from which it is formed), 5-hydroxytryptophan (also called 5 HTP) freely crosses the blood-brain barrier and is then converted to serotonin in brain tissue (Udenfriend, Weissbach, and Bogdanski, 1957). Thus in order to study the central effects of serotonin, it is necessary to administer its precursor, 5 HTP, rather than serotonin itself. In all studies of supposed effects of administered substances on the central nervous system it is first necessary to show that they can cross the blood-brain barriers. The blood-brain barriers, incidentally, can be bypassed in experimental procedures by direct injection of substances into the cerebrospinal fluid.

METABOLISM

Metabolism is a general term which refers to all chemical processes in the body related to the production and utilization of energy. Considerable amounts of energy are used continuously by all living organisms, even under conditions of minimal activity. This energy is available to the organism only in the form of chemical energy, obtained from foods. When foods are ingested they are broken down into component substances by the processes of digestion and transported to all cells via the bloodstream. The most common food substance carried by the blood is glucose, a sugar derived from natural carbohydrates. The processes of metabolism, whereby glucose and other compounds are broken down to form energy, occur separately in all individual cells of the body. Each cell contains a complete metabolic "factory" for the production of energy.

All natural food substances can be grouped in one of three general categories: carbohydrates, fats, or proteins (see Chapter 2). These are all derived from plant foods, which in turn are formed by photosynthesis from water, carbon dioxide and sunlight, by nitrogen fixation, etc. In the course of metabolism, natural food substances are ultimately broken down into water and carbon dioxide, which are excreted to recycle through the whole chain of events again, and into energy in a form available for biological processes. The initial energy for metabolism, sunlight, is measured in units of heat energy: *calories* (one calory is the amount of heat necessary to raise one gram of water from 15° C to 16° C). The overall chemical reaction of photosynthesis can be described as follows.

$$6\,CO_2 \; + \; 6\,H_2O \; + \; 686{,}000\ \text{calories} \; \rightarrow \; C_2H_{12}O_6 \; + \; 6\,O_2$$

(6 mols of* carbon dioxide)	(6 mols of water)	(free energy from the sun)	(1 mol of carbohydrate)	(6 mols of oxygen)

low energy substance   high energy substance

Thus a great deal of energy is potentially available from the high-energy carbo-hydrate. A surprisingly large percentage of this energy is reclaimed by the organism during metabolism.

Chemical or biological energy is also measured in terms of calories (or more commonly in kilocalories, 1 kcal = 1000 calories). The total potential chemical energy available in foodstuffs can be measured simply by burning them (i.e. oxidation, see Chapter 2) in a special apparatus called a combustion calorimeter. Typical values from such studies for a gram of substance are: carbohydrate, 4.2 kcal; protein, 5.6 kcal; fats, 9.5 kcal. The amount of energy used from these substances during metabolism in the body is: carbohydrate, 4.1 kcal; protein, 4.1 kcal; and fats, 9.15 kcal. Metabolism thus utilizes most of the energy in foodstuffs. Actually, however, only about 55 percent of this energy is made available (in the form of ATP, see below) for biological processes.

The energy obtained from foods during metabolism takes one of two forms, direct heat energy used to maintain body temperature, or metabolic energy used as fuel for all of the ongoing processes of living cells (muscle contractions, nerve activity, gland secretions, kidney function, etc.). A very special group of com-pounds containing phosphorous (P) serve as the agents for transfering energy from metabolism of foods to ongoing biological processes. Starting with simple inorganic phosphates (H_3PO_4), organic compounds that have very high energy chemical bonds are built up (see Figure 5.1). One particular compound, called *adenosine triphosphate* (ATP), serves as the direct and immediate energy source for essentially all energy used by the organism. If not directly used, the energy in ATP may be transferred to another substance, *phosphocreatine*, and stored until needed. A schematic of the over-all processes is shown in Figure 5.1. As foodstuffs are broken down during metabolism, the energy is mobilized so that inorganic phosphates are converted to high energy organic phosphates such as ATP. These substances in turn provide the energy for biological processes (ATP immediately and phosphocreatine indirectly). Each mole of ATP provides a very substantial amount of biological energy in the course of its total break-down, about 16,500 calories.

Metabolic processes are differentiated in terms of whether or not oxygen is used. Those pathways requiring oxygen are called *aerobic*, and those not re-quiring oxygen are called *anaerobic* (without air). Ultimately, metabolism in vertebrates does involve the utilization of oxygen, particularly in the Krebs cycle (see below and Figure 5.2). However metabolism may be completely anaerobic in bacteria. The utilization of oxygen in metabolism is the cellular

* See Chapter 2 for definition of mol.

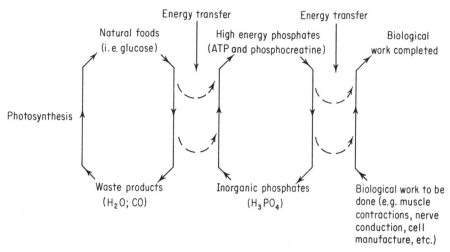

Figure 5.1. Basic energy exchanges in metabolism. Plants manufacture natural foods from water, carbon dioxide, and sunlight, by photosynthesis, nitrogen, fixation, etc. These foods are broken down to water and carbon dioxide during metabolism, and the energy released transforms inorganic phosphates to high energy substance like ATP. ATP in turn is the immediate source of energy for biological work, and is broken down again to inorganic phosphates.

definition of *respiration*. Physiologically speaking, respiration of course includes reference to breathing air, absorption of oxygen in the blood, oxygen transport to cells, and its use there. However, in discussing cellular metabolism, respiration refers specifically to the utilization of oxygen and release of carbon dioxide in cells.

Essentially all metabolism in brain is aerobic. However, in muscle tissue anaerobic metabolism can yield a significant amount of energy for relatively short periods of time. Thus after a runner sprints a short distance at maximum speed, he is just beginning to breath heavily. Deep breathing develops after the run and lasts for several minutes. During the short sprint much of the muscular energy comes from anaerobic metabolism. However this builds up an "oxygen debt" that must then be repaid by increased aerobic metabolism.

A general schematic of the pathways involved in the metabolism of carbohydrates and glucose is indicated in Figure 5.2. Dotted line arrows represent anaerobic pathways and solid line arrows aerobic pathways. The portion below the heavy dashed line is the aerobic pathway termed the Krebs cycle (also the citric acid cycle or the tricarboxylic acid cycle). Carbohydrates and glucose are broken down in a long series of steps to form pyruvic acid. This is accomplished either through aerobic or anaerobic pathways. At this point the anaerobic pathway proceeds from pyruvic acid to lactic acid, which remains in tissues and blood (after a sprint the muscle and blood levels of lactic acid are much elevated). If oxygen is available, lactic acid can be converted back to pyruvic acid. This step accounts in part for deep breathing after a sprint; the oxygen debt is being paid off. Again, it must be emphasized that this anaerobic metabolism does *not* occur in brain. The pathway from pyruvic acid to acetyl-CoA and around the Krebs cycle is aerobic. It is in this cycle that most of the energy is made available for biological processes. The broad arrows indicate the reactions along the cycle where high energy ATP is directly or indirectly formed. The numbers in parentheses show the relative or net contribution from each reaction (actually the number of high energy phosphate bonds per molecule of substance).

It was noted above that one mol of carbohydrate contained 686,000 calories of energy (from photosynthesis). Approximately 55 percent of this energy is made available for biological processes by the Krebs cycle. Anaerobic metabolism accounts for less than 10 percent of the energy. The Krebs cycle is the major source of biological free energy in higher organisms.

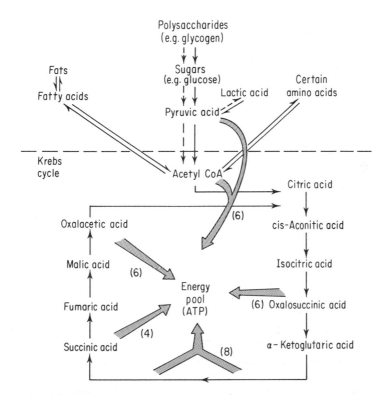

Figure 5.2. General schema of metabolism. Carbohydrates are broken down to form acetyl CoA, either by aerobic (solid arrows) or anaerobic (dotted arrows) pathways. The pathway below the dashed line, the Krebs cycle, is aerobic and is the major source of biological energy. Numbers next to the broad arrows indicate the number of high energy phosphate bonds (i.e. ATP) formed by each step in the Krebs cycle. Proteins and fats may be interconverted to acetyl CoA and enter the Krebs cycle.

We have discussed carbohydrate metabolism, particularly the Krebs cycle, in some detail. In addition to being the major source of biological energy, it is essentially the *only* source of energy available for brain tissue. As noted below, protein and fat substances are also metabolized to yield energy, and may in turn enter into the Krebs cycle. However, the only metabolic energy source that can freely cross the blood-brain barrier and hence be utilized by brain cells to form ATP is glucose. The metabolic pathway shown in Figure 5.2 is the only energy-producing pathway of significance for the brain.

Fats and proteins participate in a variety of metabolic pathways to provide energy in other tissues (in fact fats are twice as good a source of energy as carbohydrates). Complex natural fats are broken down into their component fatty acids (see Chapter 2), which may be stored or utilized as energy sources. Proteins are broken down into their constituent amino acids (see Chapter 2), which enter into a multiplicity of metabolic reactions. Widespread interconversions of fats, carbohydrates, and proteins occur. Fatty acids and amino acids can both form Acetyl CoA and enter into the Krebs cycle. Other amino acids can enter at various points along the Krebs cycle. Many of the intervening reactions are reversible, hence carbohydrates and proteins can be converted to fats, fats to proteins, etc. However, the human body is unable to manufacture about a dozen different amino acids and three fatty acids. These essential substances must be obtained from natural food sources or severe deficiency sympttons will develop.

A number of details have been omitted in our brief discussion of metabolism. Vitamins, for example, serve as essential enzymes which participate in the reactions shown in Figure 5.2. In the absence of necessary vitamins the reactions cannot take place. Many other enzymes and series of reactions are also involved in various aspects of metabolism. It is hoped that this simplified review of metabolism will provide a framework of sorts for subsequent discussions. Perhaps the most important point to remember is that essentially all processes of cells (including nerve cells) require energy. This energy is immediately available in the form of ATP, most of which is generated in the Krebs cycle, the aerobic pathway of carbohydrates and glucose (Figure 5.2).

Brain tissue is exclusively dependent upon oxidative metabolism of glucose (i.e. Krebs cycle) for energy. For this reason brain is somewhat unique among organ systems in being critically and very sensitively dependent upon blood levels of oxygen and glucose. Most tissues store energy producing substances such as glycogen and fats, which can be utilized on demand. In contrast, only about 0–1 percent of brain weight is in the form of glycogen, far too little to maintain function. The energy requirements of brain tissue are remarkably constant. It has been estimated that the *additional* energy required for 1 hour of intense "mental effort" can be supplied by one half of a peanut, and most of this is probably attributable to associated increases in muscle tension. Brain metabolism requires oxygen, and the only energy substance available for oxidation is glucose. Associated measurements of oxygen and glucose levels in blood sampled upon entering and leaving the brain in humans demonstrates that essentially all the oxygen utilized by brain can be accounted for by oxidative metabolism of glucose (i.e. Krebs cycle) (McIlwain, 1959).

If oxygen were withheld from the brain, the total oxygen of the blood in the brain together with all oxygen dissolved in brain tissue at any one time would be completely consumed in about 10 seconds! Furthermore, although brain is about 2.5 percent of body weight, 25 percent of all oxygen used by the body is consumed in the brain under basal metabolic conditions (i.e. when resting). This inordinate demand for oxygen is also reflected in the fact that brain received 15 percent of the total blood supply. In summary, then, brain has a high metabolic rate and its metabolism is almost entirely restricted to oxidative utilization of glucose. These factors emphasize the extreme dependence of neural tissue on stable and adequate supplies of oxygen and glucose, and account for the fact that brain function is far more rapidly and profoundly depressed than other organ systems by such conditions as diabetic hypoglycemia and anoxia.

A number of metabolic processes involving lipids and proteins occur in brain tissue. In the case of lipids, interactions with glucose metabolism occur in the neonate, where anaerobic metabolism is involved in the building of myelin. There is considerable turnover of lipid materials in the adult brain, and it appears that lipids in the central nervous system are synthesized there. In terms of cellular proteins, RNA has rapid turnover rates but DNA does not (see below) (McIlwain, 1959). Glutamic and aspartic acids and their derivatives account for the bulk of amino acid metabolism.

In addition to providing descriptions of energy production and utilization, the study of metabolism has greatly increased our understanding of many forms of neural and behavioral defects. Vitamin deficiencies with their profound general effects on behavior are familiar to everyone. A strikingly clear example of a metabolic "lesion" is the relatively rare hereditary disease *phenylketonuria*. This is characterized by severe mental retardation and the excretion of a simple organic compound, *phenylpyruvic acid*, in the urine. It has been demonstrated that these symptoms result from abnormal metabolism of one of the naturally occurring amino acids, *phenylalanine*, which is present in many protein foods. Normally phenylalanine is converted to another amino acid, tyrosine, in the liver. However, in individuals suffering from phenylketonuria this conversion does not take place. Instead, the phenylalanine blood and tissue levels increase and the phenylalanine metabolism is diverted to phenylpyruvic acid and phenyllactic acid. These in turn result in toxic effects on the CNS.

It has often been assumed that phenylpyruvic acid is itself a toxic substance. However, recent evidence suggests that the symptoms of phenylketonuria may instead be due to abnormally low tissue levels of serotonin (Woolley and van der Hoeven, 1964a, 1964b). It appears that excess phenylpyruvic and phenyllactic acids inhibit the enzymes that normally synthesize serotonin. In animal studies Woolley and van der Hoeven have shown that the impaired learning ability of mice made phenylketonuric by excessive feeding of phenylalanine and tyrosine from birth can be completely prevented by concomitant administration of 5 HTP (the precursor of serotonin). Thus the behavioral symptoms associated with phenylketonuria may be the result of low brain serotonin rather than of any direct toxic actions of phenylpyruvic acid. That serotonin is the crucial factor was suggested by giving another group of mice reserpine. This depletes tissue stores of serotonin without forming phenylpyruvic or phenyllactic acid. The reserpine group was as deficient as the phenylalanine-plus-tyrosine-fed groups (Woolley and van der Hoeven, 1964b).

The metabolic abnormality in phenylketonuria appears due to a single defective gene. Given this understanding of the disease, remarkably successful preventive therapy has been possible. The presence of phenylpyruvic acid in the urine can be determined by relatively simple biological assay methods now given routinely to newborn infants. If infants with phenylketonuria are placed on a special phenylalanine-free diet, all abnormal symptoms are permanently reversed and the disease does not develop (Armstrong and Tyler, 1955).

CHEMICAL ASPECTS OF NEURAL ACTIVITY

Evidence to be considered later (Chapters 7 and 8) overwhelmingly favors the hypothesis that transmission of information from nerve cell to nerve cell across the synapse is chemical in nature, at least for the mammalian nervous system. Nevertheless there is only one synaptic junction in the central nervous system where the chemical agent, in this case acetylcholine, has been established beyond reasonable doubt, and this is a rather specialized synapse of the spinal cord. Acetycholine is also the transmitter (i.e. chemical agent acting at the synapse) at the neuromuscular junction and at the preganglionic synapses of autonomic ganglia. However, there are several other substances of particular interest in the CNS whose chemistry is to some degree understood, including serotonin, glutamic acid, adrenalin and noradrenalin, and RNA.

Acetylcholine

The main features of acetylcholine (ACh) metabolism are schematized in Figure 5.3, together with the chemical structure of ACh. It is presumed that ACh is present in nerve cells in the bound form (i.e. in association with other substances) and when released or utilized, changes to the free or unbound form shown in Figure 5.3. Thus at the neuromuscular junction it crosses the synaptic space as free ACh and combines with chemical substances on the muscle fiber to produce activation of the fiber. Acetylcholine esterase (AChE) is present in nerve cells and rapidly breaks down ACh into acetate and choline, which can then recycle. There is some evidence indicating that bound ACh may be manufactured in the cell body, at least in spinal motor neurons (which send axons to form the neuromuscular junctions), and then flows down the axon to be released at the terminals.

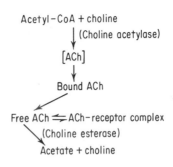

Figure 5.3. *Above*, structural formula for acetylcholine (ACh). *Below*, metabolic pathway for ACh. ACh is stored in the bound form and converted to the free form when it is released as a transmitter at the neuromuscular junctions.

At present, ACh is the most likely candidate for an excitatory synaptic transmitter substance in the CNS. Nachmansohn (1955) has perhaps been the most vigorous proponent of such a view, and has further suggested that it may be essential in nerve conduction as well. There is overwhelming evidence that acetylcholine has *something* to do with neural activity in the CNS, but with the exception of the one specialized synapse in the spinal cord mentioned above (see Chapter 8) direct evidence for its role in synaptic transmission is lacking. The indirect evidence is as follows. (1) ACh is found in essentially all neural tissue as is its inactivating enzyme, AChE, (2) it is in much higher concentrations in grey matter (where synapses and cell bodies occur) than in white matter, (3) choline acetylase, the enzyme that synthesizes ACh, is also found in neural tissue, (4) in brain tissue, all true AChE is in nerve cells whereas the non-specific ChE is found in glial cells, (5) the bound ACh content of brain is inversely related to activity in the intact animal—the highest levels occurring during anesthesia and sleep and lowest during emotional excitement and convulsions (Richter and Crossland, 1949) (this is consistent with the idea that ACh is stored in bound form and released in free form during activity, as noted above), (6) electrical stimulation of brain tissue slices depletes bound ACh but increases free ACh (Rowsell, 1954), (7) injection of very small amounts of ACh in the immediate vicinity of nerve cells causes increases in neural activity (McIlwain, 1959), and (8) injection of substances like eserine, which inactivate cholinesterase (so that free ACh is not broken down), produce similar effects to injection of ACh (McIlwain, 1957). All this can be summarized by stating that ACh increases neural activity, and neural activity results in increased amounts of free ACh and decreased amounts of bound ACh. Such evidence may appear to form a rather good case for ACh being an excitatory transmitter substance. However, the direct evidence required to prove that a substance is a transmitter is rather more complex, and will be discussed in greater detail in the chapter on synaptic transmitter substances (Chapter 8).

Serotonin (5-Hydroxytryptamine, also 5 HT)

This relatively simple compound is derived from a naturally occurring amino acid called tryptophan. It is found in many portions of the CNS, with maximal concentration in the region of the hypothalamus (Pletscher, Shore, and Brodie, 1956). The metabolism of serotonin is shown in Figure 5.4 (Tower, 1958). Direct injection of serotonin has been said to have a marked "tranquilizing" effect on behavior. We noted earlier that if serotonin is administered systemically it will not cross the blood-brain barrier. However, its immediate precursor, 5 HTP, crosses freely and is converted to serotonin in brain tissue. Unfortunately 5 HTP causes such severe diarrhea that any possible central effects cannot be determined. Still another compound, a synthetic antiserotonin agent called BAS, inhibits the peripheral actions of 5 HTP on intestinal motility. Woolley attempted to evaluate the central effects of serotonin by giving 5 HTP after protective administration of BAS to a group of psychotic patients (Woolley, 1958). The drugs were of no therapeutic value.

The potent tranquilizer reserpine (the active component of *Rauwolfia*) is believed to act by mobilizing stored serotonin (Shore, Silver and Brodie, 1955). Thus after doses of reserpine, brain serotonin is rapidly depleted with a concomitant increase in the urinary excretion of 5-hydroxyindole acetic acid, the end product of serotonin metabolism (see Figure 5.4). A much smaller dosage of reserpine is needed to mobilize brain serotonin than that required for mobilization from other body stores. Of further interest is the fact that lysergic acid diethylamine (LSD-25) is both a potent inhibitor of serotonin activity (as measured by intestinal mobility) and an extremely potent "psychotomimetic" drug, producing hallucinations, delusions and bizarre behavior in doses as small as 1 μg/kg (Shore, Silver, and Brodie, 1955). Brodie and Shore (1957) have

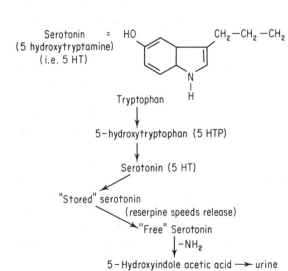

Figure 5.4. *Above*, structural formula for serotonin. (5-hydroxytryptamine; 5HT). *Below*, metabolism of serotonin. The amino acid tryptophan is converted to a stored or bound form of serotonin. When released, serotonin is converted to the free form.

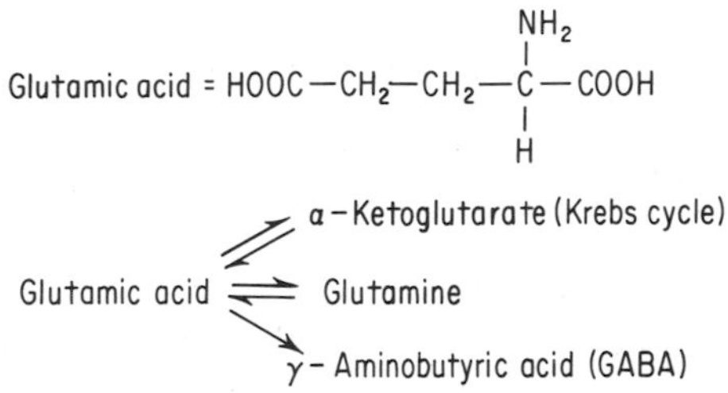

$$\text{Glutamic acid} = HOOC-CH_2-CH_2-\overset{\overset{\displaystyle NH_2}{|}}{\underset{\underset{\displaystyle H}{|}}{C}}-COOH$$

Figure 5.5. *Above*, structural formula of the naturally occurring amino acid, glutamic acid. *Below*, several conversions of glutamic acid.

$$\text{Glutamic acid} \rightleftharpoons \begin{array}{l} a-\text{Ketoglutarate (Krebs cycle)} \\ \text{Glutamine} \\ \gamma-\text{Aminobutyric acid (GABA)} \end{array}$$

suggested that serotonin may be a transmitter substance in at least a portion of the central autonomic nervous system (i.e. the hypothalamus).

Detailed evidence is lacking for the specific roles of serotonin, and there are seemingly contradictory findings. Thus certain substituted forms of LSD (where small changes in the molecule have been made) will inhibit serotonin activity but have no psychological effects; other forms are just the opposite, having potent psychotomimetic effects but not acting as inhibitors of serotonin activity, etc. (Cerletti and Rithlin, 1955). Nevertheless, as was the case for acetylcholine, it seems clear that serotonin has *something* to do with neural activity.

Glutamic Acid

This naturally occurring amino acid has already been mentioned as accounting for a large percent of the free amino acid composition of brain tissue. The metabolism of glutamic acid is indicated in Figure 5.5. Glutamic acid as a source of energy is metabolized through the route of alpha-ketoglutaric acid which enters into the Krebs cycle, yielding ATP. The other route, through gamma-amino butyric acid (GABA), is of particular interest. GABA has a widespread distribution in neural tissue and has been demonstrated to be a specific inhibitory transmitter substance for the stretch receptor neurons of the crayfish (Kuffler and Edwards, 1958). There has been much speculation about its playing a comparable role in mammalian neural tissue (Purpura and Grundfest, 1956), and it has been shown to depress neural activity (Florey and McLennan, 1955). However, direct evidence at present indicates that it is *not* a specific inhibitory transmitter substance in the mammalian nervous system (see Chapter 8).

Glutamic acid came into prominence a few years ago as a possible factor in mental retardation. Several studies (e.g. Zimmerman et al., 1946) reported that injection of glutamic acid increases the intelligence of mentally retarded patients. This seemed reasonable in as much as it was known than *in vitro* brain tissue slices can metabolize glutamic acid. However, the supposed central effects of glutamic acid were subsequently dismissed because the substance did not appear to cross the blood-brain barrier (Schwerin et al., 1950). Actually it seems that glutamic acid will cross the blood-brain barrier but the brain concentration of the amino acid is not elevated, even following large systemic doses. It is apparently broken down as rapidly as it crosses the barrier. The reported effects of glutamic acid in mental retardation may have been due to inadequate control procedures (i.e. if the same IQ test is given twice in succession the patient usually scores higher the second time; nonglutamic acid control patients given the test twice have usually not been run in these experiments). Alternatively, peripheral "side effects" of glutamic acid injection such as the increase in blood adrenalin level could be responsible for the effects. It is still possible that increased metabolism of glutamic acid in brain may be a factor as well.

Ribose Nucleic Acids

The ribose nucleic acids (RNA) have also been implicated in neural activity. It should be remembered, incidentally, that nucleic acids are often present as lipoproteins, (i.e. bound together with lipids and proteins) rather than in the "free" form (Hydén, 1955). Studies with radioactive phosphorous indicate a rapid turnover of RNA in contrast to DNA (Findlay et al., 1953). As nerve cells proceed through various stages of growth and development the relative amounts of DNA and RNA change. In young cells DNA predominates; but in adult cells the RNA predominates (Caspersson, 1950). During regeneration of nerve fibers, very high concentrations of RNA are found in the cell body (Hydén, 1955).

In a number of studies Hydén and co-workers (Hydén, 1955, 1959) have demonstrated changes in RNA content of nerve cells during conditions of activity. Intense muscular effort causes decreases in the RNA content of spinal motor neurons with up to 72 hours required for recovery. Intense sound stimulation yields an initial loss followed by an increase in RNA in auditory nerve cells. In studies of rabbit spinal motor neuron RNA content during stimulation, increases were found for 5 minutes followed by subsequent decreases. Riesen (1961) summarized considerable evidence indicating that dark rearing of animals is accompanied by marked reduction in RNA content of retinal cells in the eye. This is at least partially reversible upon subsequent exposure to light. Thus RNA content of nerve cells is extremely labile and appears associated with degree of neural activity. Hydén interprets this to indicate a vigorous protein production mediated by RNA (1955).

Other Compounds

A variety of other naturally occurring substances have been suggested as playing specific roles in CNS function. *Adrenalin* (epinephrine) and *noradrenalin* (norepinephrine), particularly the latter, have been implicated in hypothalamic function (Vogt, 1954). Noradrenalin is the transmitter substance mediating postganglionic sympathetic transmission to effector organs. Adrenalin has very marked effects on CNS activity. However, it appears that adrenalin is not directly released to any substantial degree with the brain (Tower, 1958). Instead, it is released into the bloodstream from the adrenal glands following adequate chemical or neural stimulation of them (more specifically, from the medullary portion of the adrenal glands). Adrenalin thus exerts its actions via the general circulation rather than acting directly as a central transmitting agent. Glutamic acid, you may recall, stimulates such a release of adrenalin. The major symptons resulting from systemic (into the blood stream) administration of adrenalin or noradrenalin, such as increased heart rate and blood pressure, are due to direct peripheral action on the target organs of the sympathetic system. Neither adrenalin nor noradrenalin crosses the blood-brain barrier, except to a small extent in the hypothalamus (Weil-Malherbe et al., 1961). Interestingly, direct administration of noradrenalin to the CNS via the cerebrospinal fluid may result in sleep or anesthesia (McIlwain, 1959). *Histamine*, which is formed *in vivo* from the naturally occurring amino acid histidine, is also present in brain tissue. A variety of other substances, some derived from known metabolites and others as yet unidentified, may well play important roles in synaptic transmission and other aspects of neural function (see Crossland, 1957).

Homeostasis

The chemical reactions described above, and for that matter all activities of living cells, take place in a remarkably constant environment. No matter what the temperature is outside the warm-blooded organism, the temperature of the *internal environment* is constant. Similarly the pH of the blood is always about 7.4; a shift toward acidity would result in death. The level of glucose in the blood is also of importance; too low a level can result in coma, as occurs with diabetes. These are just a few examples of processes that are maintained at fixed levels or within restricted ranges in the organism. The nineteenth century French physiologist Claude Bernard was perhaps the first to emphasize the critical importance of a stable internal environment: " La Fixité du milieu intérieur est la condition de la vie libre."

A number of complex physiological and biochemical mechanisms exist to maintain the constancy of the internal environment. Most of these are examples of a general principle of control systems called *homeostasis*. This term was coined by the American physiologist Walter Cannon, and refers to any process that alters a given condition, and as a result initiates other reactions that tend to reestablish the initial condition. Homeostasis is by no means unique to biological systems. One of the simplest homeostats is the thermostat. When room temperature drops, the thermostat closes the contact that turns on the furnace. When room temperature increases, the contact is opened and the furnace is turned off. Room temperature is thus maintained at a relatively constant level. This type of control in which any reaction initiates a counter-reaction, has also been termed inverse or negative feedback. In recent years much progress has been made in our understanding of complex homeostatic or feedback regulatory mechanisms. This is in part due to the development of more general conceptual and mathematical treatments such as "Cybernetics" which include consideration of both biological and physical homeostatic feedback systems. In subsequent chapters we will discuss a number of neural control systems which exhibit homeostatic control properties. Perhaps the most important point to keep in mind here is the remarkable sensitivity and reliability of the general physiological and biochemical homeostatic mechanisms that maintain the constant internal environment.

It is evident that chemicals are among the most potent means of altering behavior. Anesthetics, tranquilizers, energizers, excitants, depressants, psychotomimetics, paralyzing agents, and other drugs all have extremely powerful effects on the behavior of organisms. The mechanisms of action of most drugs are unknown; the effects have been empirically established. There are some intriguing interrelationships, such as those between serotonin, reserpine and LSD (see above); but how such substances actually effect the behavior of neurons, and hence of organisms, remains to be determined. The neuronal basis of action is at least partially understood for a few compounds, e.g. paralyzing agents like curare and convulsive drugs like strychnine, and will be discussed in later chapters. We have limited our discussion of neurochemistry in this chapter to the more important naturally occurring substances. Any attempt to survey all chemical actions on the nervous system would require several volumes on biochemistry, neurochemistry, and pharmacology. The student is urged to consult such texts as West and Todd (1961), Sourkes (1962), and Goodman and Gilman (1966) for details.

The neurochemical foundations of behavior are currently the subject of widespread interest and research activities. A number of different areas are being emphasized, including the study of endocrine gland secretions, hypothalamic-pituitary relations, metabolic functions and malfunctions, relation of ACh and AChE to learning, role of RNA in learning, etc. In addition to these investigations of naturally occurring compounds, the whole new field of *psychopharmacology*, the study of drug effects on behavior, has developed. We will consider neuroendocrine relations in Chapter 16, and discuss current research on neurochemistry and learning in more detail in Chapter 17.

Suggested readings

Goodman, L. S., & Gilman, A. *The pharmacological basis of therapeutics* (3rd ed.) New York: Macmillan, 1965.

McIlwain, H. *Biochemistry and the central nervous system* (2nd ed.) Boston: Little,Brown, 1959.

Sourkes, T. L. *Biochemistry of mental disease.* New York: Hoeber, 1962.

West, E. S., & Todd, W. R. *Textbook of biochemistry* (3rd ed.) New York: Macmillan, 1961.

6

THE
NERVE
MEMBRANE
POTENTIAL

It was established at about the beginning of the twentieth century that the nerve cell is the basic functional unit of the nervous system. Activity is initiated in a given neuron and conducted out along the nerve axon (the long fiber of the cell) to other cells. Activity is transferred from one nerve cell to another at the synapse, the close functional "connection" between the small terminal fiber of the axon and another nerve cell. The two basic processes of the nervous system are thus conduction of activity along fibers and transfer of activity at synapses. We will consider the conduction of information along the nerve fiber in this chapter, and examine transmission of information across synapses in the following two chapters.

A large variety of physical and chemical processes occur in the nerve cell, both when it is conducting information and when it is at rest. Oxygen is consumed, carbon dioxide and heat are given off and energy substances are metabolized, various biochemical substances are formed and altered, and so on. These processes occur in nerve cells and all other types of cells. However, the neuron is a specialized cell designed to conduct information, and a number of unique physical-chemical phenomena appear to be associated with this specialized activity. It has been known for many years that nerve conduction involves a variety of *electrical* processes. The active nerve cell generates voltages large enough to be easily measurable. There are also metabolic processes relative to nerve activity but these are considerably more difficult to measure directly. Furthermore, the electrical events of nerve activity are perhaps the most fundamental aspect of the mechanism involved in transmission of information along the nerve fiber. For these reasons, physiologists have focused their attention upon what Erlanger and Gasser have called "the electrical signs of nervous activity."

It has been known for a good many years that there are two types of electrical events associated with nerve fibers. When a nerve is at rest, and not conducting information, there is a steady *resting membrane potential*. If we could measure the voltage across the resting nerve cell membrane (the structure that forms the boundary between the inside and outside of the neuron) we would find that it is nearly one-tenth of a volt. Early measurements of the resting potential were obtained simply by crushing one end of a large nerve (bundle of nerve fibers) or a muscle and recording the so called "injury potential," the voltage difference between intact and crushed portions of the tissue. These measures were inaccurate, but they did demonstrate the existence of a steady potential difference. The resting membrane potential, incidentally, is not unique to nerve cells; most living biological cells maintain a voltage difference across the cell membrane.

In addition to the resting potential, nerve cells also exhibit the *propagated action potential*. When a nerve cell is activated, a change in voltage develops and travels along the axon. This action potential is not simply an electrical current that flows down the axon. Currents in wires can propagate at close to the speed of light (186,000 miles/sec); the action potential travels down the axon at a very much slower speed (a few feet/sec). Electric currents are, of course, involved in the action potential, but the actual sequence of events is much more complicated, involving movements of various ions across the nerve membrane.

The diagram in Figure 6.1 illustrates an idealized experiment for measuring both the resting and action potentials of a nerve fiber. The record from R_1 is shown as a simple measure of the voltage changes recorded over time. When both electrodes of R_1 are outside the nerve fiber, and the fiber is resting, the voltage measured is zero. When one electrode of R_1 is pushed through the membrane, the voltage suddenly shifts to about -70 mV (measured now across the membrane from inside to outside), and remains stable. This is the resting membrane potential. If the nerve is now stimulated at S so that an action potential develops and travels down the fiber, the action potential will be recorded at R_1 as a rapid and reversible shift in the membrane potential. For a given fiber the height of the action potential is constant along the fiber (provided that characteristics of the fiber such as size do not change); regardless of where we put S to stimulate the nerve the action potential would have the same appearance. Further, it travels at a constant velocity along the fiber.

The idealized experiment illustrated in Figure 6.1 has only been accomplished in recent years. The typical nerve fiber of the mammalian nervous system is

Figure 6.1. Idealized experiment for measuring the resting membrane potential and the action potential of a nerve fiber. The graph shows the voltage changes over time measured by the recording device, R_1. At the beginning of the graph both electrodes are resting on the outside surface of the membrane and the potential difference is zero. At the point where the voltage drops from zero to -70 mV, one electrode (arrow head) has been pushed through the membrane; the steady -70 mV potential recorded across the membrane is the *resting potential*. After an electrical stimulus is given at some other point (S), a nerve *action potential* develops, travels along the nerve, and is recorded at R_1.

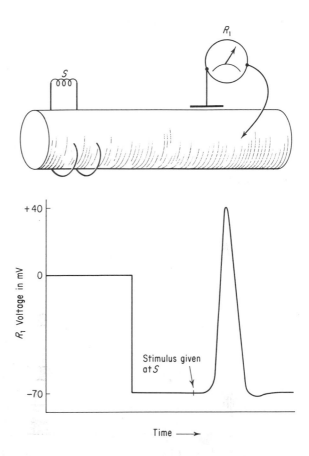

extremely small, the largest being only a few microns in diameter. Until about 1950, when the recording microelectrode having a tip diameter of less than 1 micron was developed, it was simply not possible to measure nerve membrane potentials directly in mammalian nerve fibers. In addition to their very small size, mammalian nerve cells are extremely fragile, and are usually found in complex networks or fiber bundles. Consequently a single fiber cannot be dissected out and still remain functionally normal. However, experimental analysis of the nerve membrane potential began in the late 1930s and was virtually completed by 1950, thanks to a very fortunate biological " accident." Certain invertebrates have giant single nerve axons that are both very large (up to 1 mm diameter) and very sturdy. J. Z. Young discovered the existence of the giant axon of the squid in 1936. By 1937 Cole and Curtis were studying the electrical characteristics of the squid giant axon at Woods Hole. A young English physiologist, A. L. Hodgkin, who had previously worked on the much smaller giant axon of the shore crab, spent the summer of 1938 at Woods Hole with Cole and Curtis. He returned to England and began a long term research program on nervous conduction in the giant squid axon, in collaboration with Huxley, Katz, Keynes, and others, at the laboratory of Marine Biology in Plymouth, England. In recognition of the importance and the significance of their work, Hodgkin and Huxley were awarded the Nobel Prize in 1963. Most of the material presented in this chapter is based on their research.

Use of the squid giant axon to study nerve transmission is an outstanding example of the "model system" approach to complex biological problems. While sharing the common property of conducting information, the giant fiber has many advantages for the experimenter. In addition to being large, it is exceedingly strong; it will remain functional for hours after it has been removed from the squid and placed in a solution of sea water. A photomicrograph of a section of squid axon is shown in Figure 6.2. When first removed from the squid, the single nerve fiber is surrounded by connective tissue, which can be dissected away leaving the isolated single fiber intact. This preparation is perhaps one of the closest approximations to a true single biological membrane yet found in nature. The membrane appears to be about $50 - 100$ Å (1 Å $= 10^{-2}$ mm) thick. Because of its size, and the fact that there is no connective tissue surrounding it, many types of studies on the functions and characteristics of the membrane

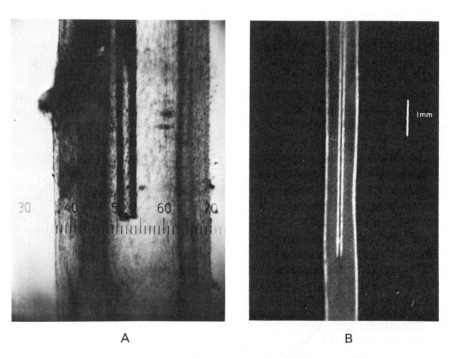

A   B

Figure 6.2. **A,** photomicrograph of recording electrode inside a squid giant axon. The axon is the clear space surrounding the electrode wire. (From Hodgkin and Huxley, 1939) **B,** lower power photomicrograph showing a 0.1-mm glass tube inside a single giant axon. (From Hodgkin and Keynes, 1956)

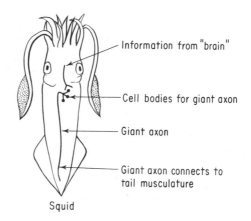

Figure 6.3.   Drawing of Squid showing approximate location of the giant axon in the body wall. (After Young, 1936)

can easily be conducted. The material inside the membrane, the *axoplasm*, can be squeezed out like toothpaste and studied chemically. In fact the membrane will still function if all the interior axoplasm is squeezed out and replaced with saline! A wire can be inserted inside the fiber for a considerable distance and the potential across the membrane measured. Both the external and internal concentrations of the various chemicals and ions can be altered or replaced with other chemicals. Finally, the squid giant axon fulfills perhaps the most important requirement of the model biological system: the mechanisms underlying resting and action potentials of the squid axon appear to be essentially the same as those of the mammalian nerve cell.

The location of the squid giant axon is diagramed in Figure 6.3. It appears to serve as a mechanism for rapid conduction of information from various receptors to the body musculature. Squids can swim backwards at high speeds by taking water into a large cavity and squirting out a jet through a funnel in front of the animal. The giant nerve fibers run in the body wall and supply the muscles that expel water from the mantle cavity. Stimuli activating receptors of the head end such as the eyes can thus produce rapid movement of the animal resulting in attack or escape. This function was well demonstrated in an early experiment by Hodgkin and Huxley. They were recording from the fiber in an anesthetized squid, but had not disconnected the nerve from the body muscles. When they first stimulated the nerve, the animal gave a powerful flip and smashed their recording electrode. The somewhat safer method of recording now in use involves tying a segment of nerve at both ends and removing it from the squid to a bath of sea water (the body fluids of the squid have about the same salt concentration as present day sea water, a good deal higher than in mammals).

THE RESTING NERVE MEMBRANE POTENTIAL

The experiment illustrated in Figure 6.1 indicates that the resting membrane potential of the squid giant axon was about -70 mV. This was recorded by R_1

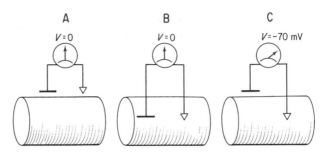

Figure 6.4. Experimental demonstration that the nerve membrane resting potential occurs across the membrane itself. **A,** two electrodes at any locations outside the resting nerve membrane always record a zero potential difference. **B,** two electrodes at any locations within the nerve fiber always record a zero potential difference. **C,** one electrode outside and one inside the fiber in any location always record the full resting membrane potential of approximately −70 mV.

when one electrode was outside the membrane and the other inside. When both electrodes are placed outside on the surface of the membrane as in Figure 6.4A, no potential difference exists between the electrodes, and the measured voltage will be zero (so long as the membrane is not conducting action potentials). If both recording electrodes are inside the membrane in any two locations, as in 6.4B, the measured voltage will also be zero. The potential level of the axoplasm inside the membrane is said to be *isopotential*, i.e. the same everywhere. It is only when we record across the membrane from inside to outside that a steady potential can be recorded. Since all locations outside the membrane are isopotential, and all locations inside are isopotential, the potential must be generated across the membrane itself. This is further demonstrated in experiments in which the interior axoplasm is squeezed out and replaced by saline having comparable ionic composition. The potential still exists across the membrane. The membrane itself has a high electrical resistivity at about 1000 ohm-cm^2, in contrast to low values of 30 and 20 ohm-cm^2 for axoplasm and external fluid respectively (Cole and Hodgkin, 1939).

The existence of a steady potential difference across the nerve membrane may seem puzzling. There are no obvious batteries or other sources of current flow, and yet a steady potential exists. As a matter of fact, such a membrane potential is a necessary result of basic physical-chemical processes and is characteristic of all *semipermeable* membranes separating different ionic solutions. Semipermeable means that some molecules can pass through the membrane and others cannot, usually depending upon the size of the molecule. Most semipermeable membranes apparently are filled with small holes that go through the membrane. These holes are of such size that shall molecules can pass through fairly easily while larger molecules cannot (see Figure 6.5).

A simple model system illustrates the point well. Ordinary sausage casing (the thin skin covering sausage) is a good example of a semipermeable membrane. If we fill a sausage casing with skim milk and place it in a solution of salt water, as shown in Figure 6.5, a potential difference (voltage) will develop across the casing from the milk to the salt water. The potential will be the same everywhere inside the skim milk, and the same everywhere outside in the salt water. The potential difference will exist only across the casing membrane. A clear

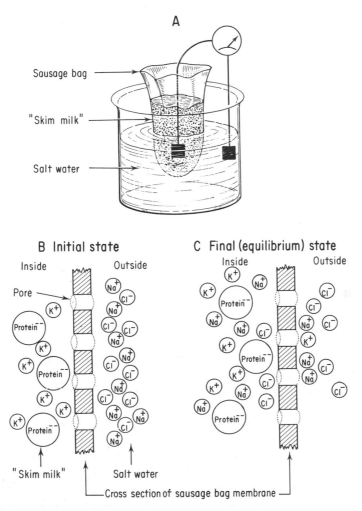

Figure 6.5.   The "skim milk" model of the nerve membrane resting potential. A steady potential difference develops from the skim milk to the salt water (**A**). When the bag of "skim milk" (containing potassium instead of calcium) is first placed in salt water it contains only protein and potassium ions (**B**). Small ions like potassium, sodium, and chloride can pass freely through the holes, and redistribute inside and outside the membrane in the final equilibrium state (**C**). Protein molecules are too large to cross the membrane and remain inside.

understanding of why this potential develops is essential in order to understand the basis of the nerve membrane potential.

By changing the composition of the skim milk somewhat we can make the model system of 6.5A very similar to a nerve fiber. Skim milk is composed mostly of water, and contains the calcium salt of a protein called casein. In addition, there are some fats, sugar, and various ions such as sodium and chloride. As far as the membrane potential is concerned, we can ignore everything except the calcium salt of casein. Like most proteins, casein molecules tend to act as though they have a net negative charge (i.e. to attract positive ions; see Chapter 5). This is balanced in milk by the positively charged calcium ions. We could write the salt as: Ca^{++} (casien)$^{--}$. The double negative charge of the casein is balanced by the double positive charge for the calcium ion (the calcium ion has a valence of 2; see Chapter 2), so the skim milk has no net charge; it is electrically neutral. The axoplasm inside the nerve fiber also contains various negatively charged protein molecules, but balances these by potassium ion (K^+) rather than calcium. Therefore, in our model of Figure 6.5A, let us substitute potassium for calcium; balancing out the negative charge of casein with K^+ ions. The altered "skim milk" in the bag is now a water solution of the potassium salt of casein: K_2^+ (casein)$^{--}$ (the subscript "2" after K indicates that two potassium ions, each having a valence of one, are required to balance the double negative charge of each casein molecule; see Chapter 2).

When the sausage bag containing potassium ions and casein molecules is first placed in the salt water, the solution inside the bag has only K^+ and casein^{--} ions in it and the solution outside has only Na^+ and Cl^- (Figure 6.5B). The bag membrane is semipermeable; it is filled with small holes. These holes are large enough to allow the small ions, K^+, Na^+, and Cl^-, to pass through the membrane freely. However, the casein^{--} molecules are too large and cannot pass through the holes. Consequently K^+, Na^+, and Cl^- pass back and forth from inside to outside but the casein remains inside (see Figure 6.5B).

Whenever an ion exists in differential concentrations across a semipermeable membrane, it tends to pass through the membrane until the concentrations are equal on both sides. Consequently the initial movements in Figures 6.5B are K^+ *out* and Na^+ and Cl^- *in*. If there were no protein molecules inside the bag (suppose instead it were a solution of potassium chloride, K^+ Cl^-), all molecules would redistribute themselves until they were in equal concentrations inside and outside. However, since the casein molecules are too large to pass through the membrane, and must remain inside, the other ions cannot redistribute themselves equally on both sides. Since the net ionic charges tend to balance out both inside and outside the membrane, there is a tendency for K^+ to move out and Na^+ to move in. This together with a tendency of each small ion to be equally distributed inside and outside the membrane, results in unequal distribution of the small ions (Figure 6.5C). It is the unequal distribution of these ions that results in membrane potential. The net concentrations of the small ions inside and outside the membrane soon reach *equilibrium*. This simply means that there is no longer any change in the ion concentration. In actual fact, the ions are always moving in and out to some extent; however the *net* concentrations remain the same so the system is said to be in equilibrium.

If the "permeant" ions (i.e. those than can pass through the membrane) did not carry electric charge, their flow would result solely from their random thermal motion. Since, on the average, this motion would be the same for a given type of ion just inside and one just outside the membrane, the condition of no net flow would be satisfied only if the concentration of this ion were identical on both sides of the membrane. If the concentration of each type of ion (sodium, chloride and potassium) were the same on both sides of the membrane then the total concentration of electric charge carried by each would also be equal on either side of the membrane. However, inside the sausage casing, there would be a contribution to the total charge by the negative casein ions, which would be absent on the outside. Thus, the skim milk and bathing solution could not both be electrically neutral, and the deviation from neutrality would approximately the charge carried by the casein. This amount of unneutralized charge would be immense, and the assumed equality of ion concentrations would lead to the absurd conclusion that one cubic centimeter of the solution would carry as much charge as a thunder cloud.

There are, therefore, strong electric forces acting to prevent the separation of charges of opposite sign. They oppose the random movements that would tend to equalize the concentrations of the individual permeant ions. These electrical forces are so strong that at equilibrium the bulk of both the skim milk and the bathing solutions are electrically neutral. This means that the potassium in the bag is more concentrated than in the bathing solution, and the chloride less than in the bathing solution. The random ionic dance can significantly change the neutrality of layers of solution only a few angstrom units on either side of the membrane. This layer on the inside contains more negative casein and chloride ions, and fewer positive potassium and sodium ions than the same amount of skim milk further inside the bag. Also, the equivalent layer outside the sausage casing has an excess of potassium and sodium ions and is depleted in chloride ions compared to the rest of the bathing solution. The negatively charged layer on the inside and the positively charged layer on the outside generate the potential difference across the membrane (see Figure 6.5C).

The model we've examined produces a membrane potential without requiring a continuing expenditure of energy. Once such a semipermeable membrane with immobile protein ions on one side is set up, the system rapidly reaches the equilibrium state described. Since there is then no further net flow of anything, no power must be supplied from chemical or metabolic sources to maintain the potential. In this sense the system is passive. In such a passive system, the voltage calculated from each permeant ion concentration inside and outside ought to be the same, and would equal the measured membrane potential.

As indicated in Figure 6.5C, most of the K^+ ions are inside the membrane at the equilibrium condition. Because of this unequal distribution, there is a strong tendency for the K^+ ions to move outwards from the more concentrated solution inside the bag. This is countered by the distribution of ionic charges on both sides of the membrane. The same tends to occur for Na^+ ions. For chloride ions, Cl^-, the situation tends to be reversed. More of them remain outside (since all the negatively charged casein molecules are on the inside) and have a tendency to move in, which is also countered by the total distribution of ionic charges. To summarize, potential across the membrane is the end result of the tendency of all ions to be equally concentrated on both sides and the counter-tendency of the net distributions of ionic charges to equalize.

If it is still unclear to you just why these unequal distributions of ions across a semipermeable membrane result in a constant potential difference (voltage) across the membrane, it is perhaps best to simply "take it on faith." The proof that this will occur and the method for calculating the actual value of the membrane potential can be derived from basic first principles of physics, namely the laws of thermodynamics. The actual mathematical derivations involve a good bit of calculus, and are beyond the scope of this book. However, the final equation relating membrane voltage to ion concentrations on both sides of the membrane is quite simple, and extremely important for an understanding of the nerve membrane potential.

The equation used to calculate the membrane potential is called the *Nernst equation* and has the following form:

$$V = k \log \frac{[x]_o}{[x]_i}$$

where V is the voltage across the membrane, $[x]_o$ is the concentration of a given ion outside the membrane and $[x]_i$ is the concentration of the same ion inside the membrane. It is important to remember that this equation can be used for only one ion at a time. We could calculate the voltage on the basis of K^+ inside and K^+ outside, or Cl^- inside and Cl^- outside, and so on. Furthermore, it holds only for ions that can pass through the membrane; we could not use the concentration of casein inside and outside (all inside and none outside) because it cannot cross the membrane. The log term in the equation given above, incidentally, is simply the logarithm to the base 10. The value of the constant, k, depends upon a great many factors such as the temperature of the solution, the number of charges on the ions, the units of measurement, characteristics of the ions, and so on. However, it can be evaluated prior to an experiment and simply plugged into the equation as a number.

The voltage calculated by the Nernst equation may be called a *passive* voltage. The word "passive" is used to mean that according to "simple" laws from physics, the ions of potassium, sodium, and chloride should distribute themselves in such a way as to balance out the unequal distribution of protein ions. Remember that the protein ions are inside the membrane sac, are too large to pass through the membrane, and are predominantly negatively charged.

Thus more positive (potassium and sodium) ions should tend to be inside and more negative (chloride) ions should be outside. When the distribution of ions has reached equilibrium (i.e. a stable point where there is no longer any net change in ionic concentrations) a net voltage difference across the membrane will occur. If we now measure the concentration of an ion inside and outside the membrane, the Nernst equation will predict correctly the voltage drop across the membrane. This calculation may be done separately for each ion (e.g. for potassium, for sodium, for chloride, etc.). If the distribution is passive, the calculated voltage based on each ion concentration inside and outside ought to be the same, and will equal the measured voltage across the membrane.

Let us perform the experiment illustrated in Figure 6.5 and measure the final concentrations of potassium ions inside and outside the membrane. Suppose that the measurements showed a concentration of about 400 millimoles of K^+/kg of water inside and a concentration of about 20 millimoles of K^+/kg of water outside. Assume that the constant, k, has a numerical value of 58 for the conditions of the experiment, and the units are so adjusted that the results will give calculated voltages in terms of millivolts:

$$V = k \log \frac{[K^+]_o}{[K^+]_i}$$

$$V = 58 \log \left[\frac{20}{400} \right] = 58 \log (0.05) = 58 \, (-1.3)$$

$$V = -75 \text{ mV}$$

The potential across the membrane should be -75 mV. The minus sign here simply means that the potential inside the sausage bag is 75 millivolts negative relative to the outside solution.

If we have done our experiment and our calculations correctly, the actual measured voltage across the membrane will also be -75 mV. If we were to do the calculations over again using concentrations of sodium or chloride ions, we would obtain the same results: voltage across the membrane from inside to outside would be -75 mV. This is the passive membrane potential resulting from unequal distributions of ions across a semipermeable membrane.

Bernstein's Hypothesis of the Nerve Membrane Potential

In 1902 Bernstein first suggested that the resting membrane potential was primarily the result of concentrations of potassium ions inside and outside the nerve fiber. His theory was essentially the same as the discussion given above for the "skim milk" model of Figure 6.5. In other words, he assumed that the nerve membrane was freely permeable to K^+ ions only, and that the actual resting membrane potential level was entirely dependent upon concentrations of potassium ions. The actual concentrations of the more common ions inside and outside the squid giant axon are illustrated in Figure 6.6. Note that potassium is

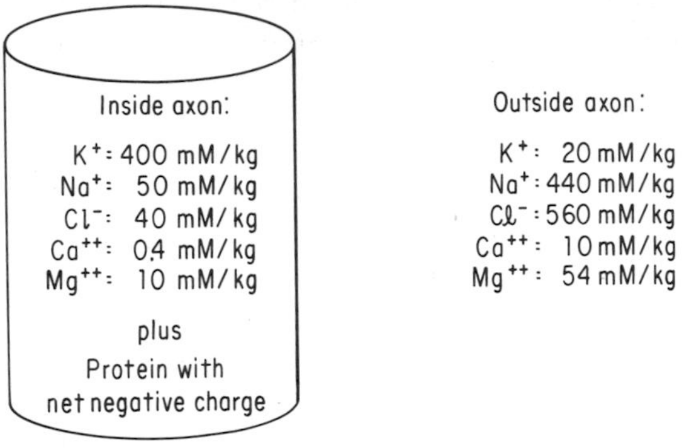

Inside axon:

K$^+$: 400 mM/kg
Na$^+$: 50 mM/kg
Cl$^-$: 40 mM/kg
Ca^{++}: 0.4 mM/kg
Mg^{++}: 10 mM/kg

plus
Protein with
net negative charge

Outside axon:

K$^+$: 20 mM/kg
Na$^+$: 440 mM/kg
Cl$^-$: 560 mM/kg
Ca^{++}: 10 mM/kg
Mg^{++}: 54 mM/kg

Figure 6.6. Concentrations of small ions inside and outside the squid giant axon; expressed in terms of millimoles (mM) per kilogram (kg) of axoplasm or extracellular fluid. (Hodgkin, 1958)

very much more concentrated inside the axon than outside the axon. In fact the values we selected for potassium concentrations inside and outside the sausage bag in the "skim milk" model of Figure 6.5 were the same as those measured for the squid giant axon. As shown above, when we plug these values of potassium concentrations into the Nernst equation we obtain a predicted value of about −75 mV for the nerve membrane potential. The measured value of the squid giant axon potential is about −70 mV (inside negative to outside). The agreement between measured and predicted values is quite close. The slight discrepancy of about 5 mV might be due to various measurement errors. However, more recent evidence suggests that there may be other factors such as a very slight resistance to K$^+$ passage across the membrane or a deviation from the passive nature of the equilibrium, which would account for the difference. We will return to this point later.

The fact that observed values of the membrane potential and those calculated from K$^+$ ion concentrations agree very closely does not of course constitute definitive proof that Bernstein's hypothesis is true. The correspondence could be fortuitous. If the resting membrane potential is in fact a passive potential resulting from the concentration of K$^+$ ions inside and outside the nerve fiber, then the *membrane potential should change in a predictable fashion as external or internal K$^+$ ion concentration is changed.* Changes in the concentration of other ions, however, should *not* alter the resting membrane potential. Some years ago Curtis and Code (1942) showed that increasing the external potassium ion concentration (normally very low, remember) caused a corresponding reduction in the membrane potential of the squid giant axon. Hodgkin and Katz (1949) calculated the values of the membrane potential predicted by the Nernst equation for the various external K$^+$ concentrations used by Curtis and Cole. The comparison of Curtis and Cole's measurements with the theoretical predictions by Hodgkin and Katz is shown in Figure 6.7. The agreement is extremely good. Thus the actual value of the membrane potential is determined by the relative concentrations of K$^+$ ions inside and outside the membrane, as predicted by the Nernst equation for a passive membrane.

It could be argued (although perhaps not very convincingly) that the experiment just described depended upon an abnormally high external concentration of K^+, which might be "poisoning" the axon. In a recent experiment by Baker, Hodgkin, and Shaw (1961) the internal concentration of K^+ ions was varied. This was accomplished by the rather bold maneuver of squeezing out all of the internal axoplasm from a squid giant axon, and replacing the axoplasm with ionic solutions containing varying amounts of K^+ ions. If the ionic composition of the replacing solution is comparable to that of the axoplasm, incidentally, the nerve will function normally for a period of several hours. The results of the experiment are shown in Figure 6.8. As predicted by the Nernst equation, the membrane potential varied directly with the internal concentration of K^+ ions. The external concentration of K^+ ions was held constant at a low value. Consequently, the membrane potential appears to be completely dependent upon the internal and external concentrations of potassium ions, just as predicted from the Nernst equation for a passive membrane. A final and rather important point concerns the possible role of the other positive ion, sodium, in maintaining the resting potential. Hodgkin and Katz (1949) showed that varying the external concentration of sodium ions has *no effect* on the resting nerve potential.

The most important evidence favoring Bernstein's hypothesis for the resting membrane potential was summarized above. There are several other lines of evidence provided by the very elegant experiments of Hodgkin and his colleagues. To give just one example, Bernstein's hypothesis requires that the high internal concentration of K^+ ions represents *free* K^+ ions. If the internal potassium were chemically bound to protein or other molecules it could not participate freely

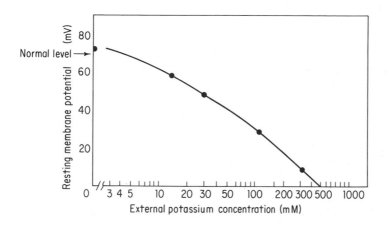

Figure 6.7. Effect of increasing the external potassium ion concentration on the resting membrane potential. As the concentration is increased above normal level the resting membrane potential decreases. Dots represent the original data of Curtis and Cole (1942) and the smooth curve the expected relationship calculated by Hodgkin and Katz (1949) using the Nernst equation. (Redrawn from Hodgkin and Katz, 1949)

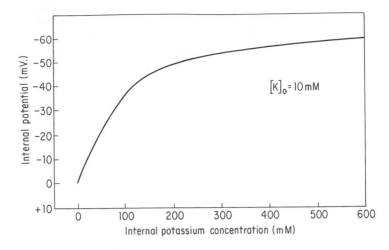

Figure 6.8. Effect of decreasing the internal potassium ion concentration on the resting membrane potential. As the concentration is reduced below normal the membrane potential decreases. (Redrawn from Baker, Hodgkin, and Shaw, 1961)

in the exchange across the membrane. Hodgkin and Keynes (1953) were able to test this possibility by an ingenious use of the radioactive tracer technique. Potassium ions were irradiated in an atomic reactor and altered to a radioactive isotope of potassium. This radioactive potassium was introduced into a squid axon and the axon placed in a magnetic field. Ions in solution will normally move in a magnetic field with a velocity determined by such factors as the charge on the ion and on the size of the ion. For a given magnetic field it is possible to calculate the velocity at which free K^+ ions will move. However, if potassium is chemically bound to other substances inside the axon, it will move more slowly. The rate of movement of the radioactive K^+ ions along the axon was measured by a radioactive counter. Movement of K^+ ions measured in this way was found to agree closely with the rate of movement calculated for free K^+ ions in solution. Consequently, K^+ ions exist in free ionic form inside the axon.

   In discussing our "skim milk" model, we stated that the membrane potential can be predicted equally well by the differential distribution of any type of ions. In the model, the membrane potential of -75 mV was calculated for K^+ ions, but it would also have been -75 mV if we had used the external and internal concentrations of Na^+ or Cl^- ions. In a passive system, all ions that can cross the membrane distribute themselves so as to yield the same membrane potential as calculated by the Nernst equation. Figure 6.6 indicated that the internal and external concentrations of Na^+ and Cl^- ions are quite different than those of K^+. Can the squid axon membrane potential of about -70 mV be predicted equally well from these ions? The answer appears to be yes for chloride, but very definitely no for sodium. Table 6.1 compares the actual membrane potential of about -70 mV with the calculated membrane potential for each type of ion using the Nernst equation. The differential concentration of K^+ ions and of Cl^- ions both predict the actual membrane potential rather closely. However, the predicted membrane potential based on sodium ion concentration is $+50$ mV. This discrepancy could hardly be worse, and clearly indicates that Na^+ is not passively distributed across the membrane.

The very low concentration of Na^+ ions inside the membrane suggests that the membrane is not permeable to sodium. In the resting state (i.e. in the absence of nerve action potentials) this appears to be very nearly the case. A barrier of some type seems to prevent Na^+ ions from flowing in along their concentration gradients (i.e. from the high external concentration to the low internal concentration), even though the actual membrane potential would encourage such an exchange. The nature of the apparent barrier to the influx of the Na^+ ions across the membrane is not well understood. Measurements using radioactive sodium indicate that some Na^+ ions do "leak" into the resting nerve membrane and are subsequently extruded. We will consider this further when we discuss the "sodium pump" below.

TABLE 6.1. COMPARISON OF ACTUAL AND CALCU-
LATED (FROM NERNST EQUATION) MEMBRANE POTENTIAL

| | Membrane potential in millivolts (mV) | | |
Ion	Predicted from Nernst equation	Measured	Discrepancy
K^+	≈ -75	-70	$\approx \quad 5$
Cl^-	≈ -75	-70	$\approx \quad 5$
Na^+	$\approx +50$	-70	≈ 110

THE NERVE MEMBRANE ACTION POTENTIAL

An example of a propagated action potential recorded from the squid giant axon is shown in Figure 6.9. This was obtained in a type of experiment illustrated in Figure 6.1, where a stimulus is applied at one portion of the axon, and changes in the potential across the membrane recorded at another locus on the fiber. In Figure 6.9, the stimulus marker indicates the time when a stimulus was applied; the time, about 1 msec, between the stimulus and the onset of the response is the time required for the action potential to travel from the stimulating electrodes to the recording electrodes. Remember that the action potential is propagated (i.e. travels) down the axon at a fixed and relatively slow speed (several meters/sec) and is nondecremental; wherever it is recorded along the nerve it has the same

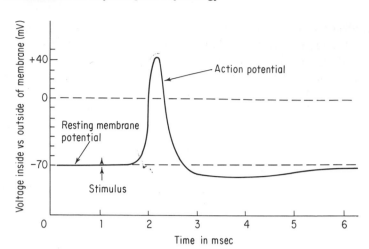

Figure 6.9. The action potential in response to electrical stimulation recorded across the membrane of a squid giant axon. Note that the response peak overshoots the point of electrical neutrality. (Redrawn from Hodgkin and Huxley, 1939)

amplitude. The propagated action potential is not itself directional, incidentally. If a nerve fiber is stimulated at a given point, action potentials will develop at that point and travel out along the fiber in both directions from the stimulus site. As you will learn in the next chapter, directionality of conduction in the nervous system is the result of one-way transmission across the synaptic interconnections between cells. In his early theoretical analysis of the nerve membrane potential, Bernstein developed an explanation for the action potential. He hypothesized that the membrane barrier normally preventing free exchange of ions breaks down and permits a free exchange of all types of ions. If this were the case, it could be shown by use of the Nernst equation that the action potential ought to rise only to about the zero membrane potential level (i.e. until there is no differential potential across the membrane). Direct measurements of the amplitude of the action potential were first obtained in 1939, by Curtis and Cole in the U.S.A. and Hodgkin and Huxley in England. Figure 6.9 is taken from the study by Hodgkin and Huxley. As seen, the maximum height of the action potential rises some 40 to 50 mV *above* the zero membrane potential level. The resting potential is normally 70 mV negative inside the membrane relative to the neutral outside value. During the action potential it does not merely shift to zero, but the inside actually becomes 40 to 50 mV positive to the outside. This positive overshoot of the action potential constitutes a major flaw in Bernstein's theory.

The Sodium Hypothesis of the Nerve Action Potential

In 1947, Hodgkin, Katz, and Huxley worked out a new hypothesis to account for the nerve action potential, based on the exchange of sodium ion across the nerve membrane. They postulated that the membrane becomes *selectively* permeable to Na^+ ions during the initial large positive "spike" of the action potential. The major difference between this hypothesis and Bernstein's is that Bernstein assumed a brief permeability to all ions, whereas Hodgkin assumed a brief permeability only to sodium ions. If other ions remain at the same internal and external concentration and do not suddenly flow across the membrane, then the amplitude of the action potential ought to be precisely predictable from the differential concentration of sodium that exists inside and outside the membrane when the axon is not conducting action potentials. In other words, if the membrane becomes freely permeable to sodium for a brief time, Na^+ ions will flow into the axon from a region of high concentration outside to the low concentration inside. This flow of Na^+ ions will attempt to reach the equilibrium distribution produced by the Nernst equation for sodium. As we noted earlier, the predicted membrane potential, based on the resting distribution of Na^+ ions, was about + 50 mV, *the potential level reached by the action potential* (see Figure 6.9). Application of the Nernst equation for Na^+ ion distributions, remember, predicts a membrane potential of about 120 mV positive to the actual resting potential. The total height of the action potential is 120 mV. The correspondence between the predicted and observed amplitudes of the action potential is essentially perfect if it is assumed that the membrane becomes briefly permeable only to sodium ions.

There is now a large array of evidence favoring the sodium hypothesis for the nerve action potential. Perhaps one of the most obvious experiments is to change the external concentration of Na^+ ions. Remember that the external concentration of Na^+ is normally very high. If the action potential is completely dependent upon a differential distribution inside and outside the membrane, reducing the external Na^+ ion concentration ought to reduce the amplitude of the action potential. The amount of reduction in the action potential ought to be predicted by the Nernst equation for the reduced external Na^+ concentration. As illustrated in Figure 6.10, this is just what Hodgkin and

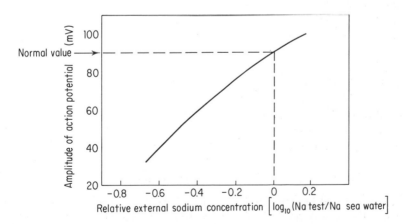

Figure 6.10. Effect of varying the external sodium concentration on the amplitude of the nerve action potential. (Redrawn from Hodgkin and Katz, 1949)

Katz (1949) found. Furthermore, if the external Na^+ concentration is made higher than normal, the action potential is higher than normal (portion of the curve in Figure 6.10 to the right of the dashed lines). As Hodgkin notes, the latter finding is particularly satisfying because it would seem most unlikely that the amplitude of the action potential could be increased above normal value by an abnormal solution if in fact the external Na^+ ion concentration were not the crucial factor.

As we noted earlier, changing the external concentration of Na^+ has no significant effect on the *resting* membrane potential. In a complementary fashion, altering the external concentration of potassium ions has *no effect* on the amplitude of the positive action potential (Hodgkin and Katz, 1949). In recent experiments, using the method of squeezing out the axoplasm from the axon and replacing it with ionic solutions, it has been shown that the action potential is also decreased in a predictable manner if the internal concentration of Na^+ ions is increased, thus reducing the net differential concentration of Na^+ across the membrane (Baker, Hodgkin, and Shaw, 1961). All evidence is thus consistent with the sodium hypothesis for the nerve action potential. During the action potential the membrane barrier that normally keeps Na^+ ions out breaks down briefly and allows Na^+ ions to enter freely. This flow of Na^+ ions into the membrane is the current which generates the propagated nerve action potential.

The large positive response of the nerve action potential is often referred to as *depolarization*. The resting membrane potential is polarized at a level of about -70 mV inside to outside. This polarized level is taken as the reference level when referring to shifts in the membrane potential. If you will examine the action potential of Figure 6.9, you will note that following the large positive response a small but longer-lasting increased negativity of the membrane occurs. This can be termed a *hyperpolarization* since the membrane becomes even more negatively polarized than it is at rest. Hodgkin and colleagues hypothesized that this after-hyperpolarization was the result of a slower outward flow of K^+ ions across the membrane following the initial rapid influx of Na^+ ions that produced the initial large depolarization.

You may recall that there was a slight discrepancy of about 5 mV between the actual resting membrane potential level of -70 mV and the level predicted by the Nernst equation based on the distributions of K^+ ions of about -75 mV. This could be accounted for if we assume that normally the membrane has a very small barrier (i.e. low resistance) to the passage of K^+ ions. If that barrier were to break down for a time following the positive action potential, then the membrane potential would seek the equilibrium value for K^+, which would be about 5 mV more negative than the normal resting level. As you can see in Figure 6.9 this appears to be just what happens. Consistent with this hypothesis is the fact that varying the external potassium ion concentration (which remember does not change the positive action potential) does alter the amplitude of the after-hyperpolarization in a predictable fashion. In fact the amplitude of the hyperpolarization is even more sensitive to changes in K^+ ion concentration than is the resting membrane potential, an observation to be expected if the hyperpolarization does in fact result from a *movement* of K^+ ions across the membrane.

We have summarized a good deal of evidence which suggests rather strongly that the large positive action potential is the result of a rapid influx of Na^+ ions and that the subsequent hyperpolarization represents a slower outward movement of K^+ ions. However, all the evidence is indirect, resulting from calculations based on the Nernst equation and from variations of the Na^+ and K^+ ion concentrations inside and outside the membrane. In addition, there are two major types of direct evidence favoring the hypothesis. One line of evidence comes from actual measurement of the exchanges of radioactively labeled ions across the membrane, and the other is based on direct measurements of the current flows generating the action potential, using an ingenious procedure called the *voltage clamp.*

Before describing these experiments, it might be worth while to review briefly the sequence of events hypothesized to occur during the action potential. It is particularly important to keep in mind the difference between current flow and voltage or potential. The resting membrane voltage or potential of -70 mV is due mostly to the distribution of potassium ions inside and outside the membrane. There is no current flow generating the resting membrane potential. It is quite analogous to a charged condenser; the voltage difference exists across the plates, but no current flows as long as the two plates are not connected together. The nerve action potential is the voltage change measured at a given point of the nerve membrane as the propagated action potential passes along the nerve membrane. These voltage changes are produced by current flows. The currents themselves are movements of ions: the inward current of Na^+ ions produces the large and rapid positive component and the outward current of K^+ ions produces the slower and smaller negative potential. Normally the resistance of the membrane to Na^+ ions is extremely high. However, during the positive portion of the action potential it drops to nearly zero. In addition, there is some resistance to K^+ ions which drops to nearly zero during the negative afterpotential. During the action potential the resistance, the current, and the voltage are all changing at the same time.

Measurements of the inward movement of sodium ions and the outward movement of potassium ions during action potentials in the squid axon were made by Keynes (Keynes, 1951a, 1951b; Keynes and Lewis, 1951). The technique involves measurement of the changes in the internal and external concentrations of radioactively labeled sodium and potassium ions following a series of nerve action potentials. Such experiments require rapid and repeated stimulation of the axon. Changes in ion concentrations produced by a single action potential are much too small to be measured. However, the average number of ions crossing the membrane for each action potential can be calculated from overall data based on many action potentials. It appears that from 3 to 4×10^{-12}

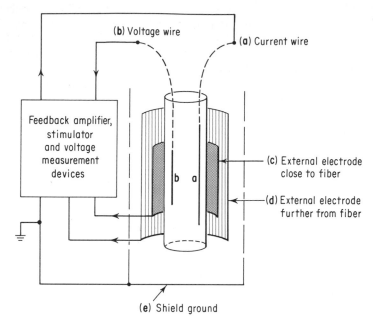

Figure 6.11. The voltage clamp method of measuring current flows across the giant axon during an action potential. Changes in the membrane potential are measured using a voltage electrode (**b**). When the voltage changes, a counter current is sent through the membrane from (**a**) to (**c**) by the feedback amplifier. The amplitude of this current is directly proportioned to the amplitude of ionic currents flowing across the membrane. (Redrawn from Hodgkin, Huxley, and Katz, 1952)

mole* of Na^+ and K^+ ions cross the membrane during each impulse. This amounts to about 20,000 sodium ions and potassium ions crossing each square micron of membrane surface. Theoretical calculations indicate that this degree of ion movement or current is ample to produce the measured action potential.

Measurement of ion flows by radioactive labeling requires that the axon be stimulated hundreds of times. Ideally, one would like to have direct measurements of the current flows that occur during a single action potential. This was accomplished by Hodgkin, Huxley, and Katz in 1949, using the *voltage clamp* technique. As you may recall, the nerve membrane can be represented by an electrical circuit containing a resistor, a condenser, and a battery (Chapter 2). Such simple electrical circuits can usually be analyzed by Ohm's law ($E = IR$). If the values of two terms are known, such as the voltage and the resistance, the current can be calculated. However, as we pointed out above, during the nerve

---

* NOTE: Mole = gram molecule. The quantity of a pure substance comprised by 1 g molecular weight of it. One mole of any substance contains 6.023×10^{23} molecules (Avogadro's number). (See Chapter 2)

membrane action potential all three quantities are changing at the same time. The voltage clamp technique fixes or clamps the membrane voltage at a given level and does not allow it to vary. Hence current can be measured directly.

The voltage clamp is illustrated in Figure 6.11. Two wires are inserted inside the giant axon. The potential across the membrane, recorded from the voltage wire (b) and the external electrode (c), is continuously monitored. It is electronically compared with the voltage the experimenter wishes to maintain across the membrane, and any deviations from equality are immediately corrected by changing the current that is made to flow between the current wire (a) and the ground electrode (e) by the feedback amplifier. An instant after the membrane potential is forced to jump from the resting voltage to some other steady potential, the total ionic current through the portion of the membrane exposed in the measuring section can be determined by the potential difference it produces between electrodes (c) and (d). Since this section of the membrane participates synchronously in all changes in potential and current flow, the technique provides information in a simpler form than could be obtained during a propagated action potential. For voltage clamps decreasing or reversing the resting membrane potential, the membrane resistance seems to go through a sequence of changes quite similar to those postulated during an action potential. The advantages of the clamp permit quantitative data to be obtained for conditions under the investigator's control.

In effect, the voltage clamp allows the membrane potential to be held fixed at any level, prevents the development of an action potential, and allows the current flow to be measured following a stimulus. Normally, of course, the electrical stimulus pulse would produce an action potential. However, the clamp technique permits determination of the current flows that would have occurred

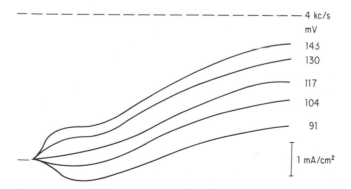

Figure 6.12. Current measurements taken from the axon membrane by the voltage clamp following different applied voltages. Numbers at the right indicate the level of the clamping voltage. Deflections below the baseline at the extreme left indicate inward current flow and deflections above the baseline indicate outward current flow. (Redrawn from Hodgkin, Huxley, and Katz, 1952)

had the membrane not been clamped. If the clamp technique still seems some-what opaque to you, simply remember that it is a method allowing quantitative determination of the actual current flows that occur during the action potential. By varying the clamp it is possible to determine the direction and extent of the ionic flow across the membrane for a variety of conditions.

Examples of current measurements obtained with the voltage clamp are shown in Figure 6.12. The tracings represent measured current flows during a maintained voltage pulse. The number to the right of each tracing indicates the voltage level at which the membrane was clamped relative to the resting potential. Thus the 91 mV clamp means that the membrane potential is clamped at 91 mV positive relative to the resting potential level. This is still somewhat negative to the actual maximum positive amplitude of the action potential, which in this experiment is 117 mV. Deflections below the baseline mean inward current and deflections above the baseline indicate outward current. During the first milli-second following the stimulus, the current flows in for clamps below 117 mV and out for clamps above 117 mV. There is no flow for the 117 mV clamp. In other words, when a membrane is held at the sodium equilibrium potential of 117 mV above resting level, there is no sodium flow. If it is held below that level, Na$^+$ ions flow in to reach equilibrium, and if it is held above that level, Na$^+$ ions flow out to reach equilibrium.

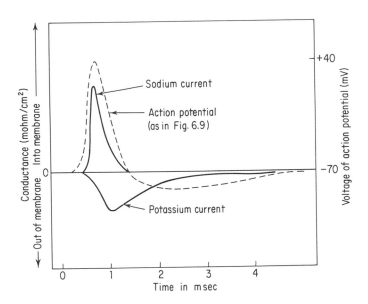

Figure 6.13. Actual ionic currents associated with the voltage changes of the nerve action potential. Solid lines show the inward sodium current and the outward potassium current, actually expressed in terms of changes in the conductance of the membrane of these ions (left ordinate). The dotted line is the voltage change of the action potential (right ordinate). (Redrawn from Hodgkin, 1958)

The sodium and potassium ion contributions to the measured current flow were determined by using the voltage clamp technique in experiments in which concentrations of these ions were varied. Thus it was possible to make direct measurements of the Na^+ current and the K^+ current during the clamp and hence to calculate the currents that produce the nerve-membrane action potential. The time courses of these currents are indicated in Figure 6.13. The heavy lines actually indicate changes in the conductance of the nerve membrane for Na^+ ions and K^+ ions. Sodium ions flow into the axon for a brief period of time, and K^+ ions flow outward for a longer period of time. The sum of these currents produces the action potential. The membrane potential shown in Figure 6.13, incidentally, is not simply the algebraic sum of the sodium and potassium conductances. They are actually plotted in terms of conductance, the opposite of resistance, and the action potential is plotted as a voltage change. The voltage change is the *result* of these current flows. They are all shown together in the diagram to emphasize this point.

By making a few minimal assumptions Hodgkin and Huxley (1952a; 1952b; 1952c) were able to derive differential equations predicting the exact form of the measured membrane action potential for a variety of conditions. These equations are based on the Na^+ and K^+ ionic currents measured in the voltage clamp experiments. Examples of the comparison between predicted and obtained action potentials are shown in Figure 6.14. The normal membrane potential is plotted for a fairly slow time base in Figure 6.14A. The initial portion of this potential is indicated in Figure 6.14B using a much faster time base. In both cases the correspondence between obtained and predicted responses is virtually perfect. In Figure 6.14C the over-all net conductance changes are illustrated. The obtained curve is from the initial measurements of Cole and Curtis (1939). Again the correspondence is close. Finally, Figure 6.14D compares obtained and predicted responses following " anode break " excitation. Here the membrane potential is held more negative than the normal resting level by an anodal (inward flowing) current and then released. Following release an action potential develops. Note the small late after-positivity in both the predicted and obtained curves.

The comparisons of Figure 6.14 were given to illustrate the very considerable power and precision of the mathematical theory for the nerve membrane potential developed by Hodgkin and Huxley. Similar close correspondences between theoretical and actual responses were demonstrated for a variety of other nerve membrane phenomena. There are also some intriguing theoretical predictions that have yet to be tested. The equations developed by Hodgkin and Huxley are exceedingly difficult to solve. In fact exact solutions had to await development of modern highspeed computers. It is interesting to note that Huxley developed approximate numerical solutions for the predicted curves obtained in Figure 6.14. It took weeks to calculate the predicted form of a single propagated action potential. Huxley's solutions have subsequently been verified by computers.

A relatively simple electrical model of the nerve membrane potential can serve to illustrate the various characteristics and processes postulated by Hodgkin and Huxley's theory (Figure 6.15). The nerve membrane has a given capacitance (about 1 microfarad/cm^2) indicated by the condensor (C). The sodium battery (V_{Na}) represents the tendency for Na$^+$ ions to enter the axon and the potassium battery (V_K) the tendency for K$^+$ ions to leave the axon. Each of these has a variable resistance associated with it, which changes during the action potential. The conductance curves shown in Figure 6.14 for Na$^+$ and K$^+$ describe the actual changes in these resistors during the action potential. In

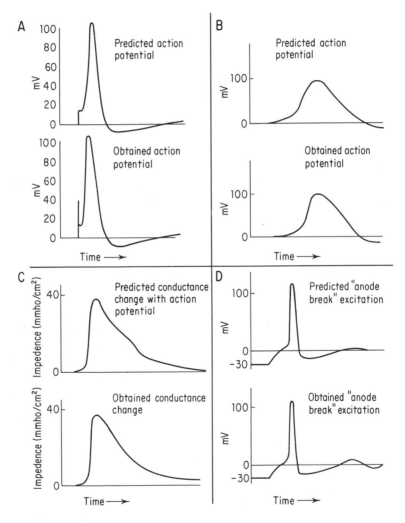

Figure 6.14.   A, B, & D. Comparisons of obtained action potentials and theoretical potentials predicted by the Hodgkin-Huxley theory for a variety of conditions of temperature and activation. **C** shows predicted and obtained conductance changes. (Redrawn from Hodgkin and Huxley, 1952)

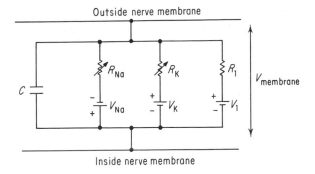

Figure 6.15. Electrical model of the nerve membrane permitting prediction of resting and action potentials. It contains sodium, potassium, and "leakage" batteries (V_{Na}, V_K, V_1) and associated variable resistances, and a condenser C. (Redrawn from Hodgkin, 1958)

addition, there is a small leakage battery (V_1) and an associated leakage resistance (R_1) that obeys Ohm's law and remains constant during the action potential.

The "Sodium Pump"

It was necessary to postulate a membrane barrier keeping out Na^+ ions to account for the very high external concentration of Na^+ ions that exists in spite of the strong equilibrium tendency of Na^+ ions to have a much greater concentration inside. Although the net differential concentration of Na^+ ions across the membrane remains relatively constant, there is a slow but steady leakage of Na^+ ions into the axon. Furthermore, every time an action potential occurs, a certain number of Na^+ ions flow into the membrane. However, over a long period of time, the Na^+ concentration does not increase inside the axon. Radioactive tracer studies have shown that there is a slow but steady extrusion or "secretion" of Na^+ ions out of the axon (Caldwell and Keynes, 1957; Caldwell, Hodgkin, Keynes, and Shaw, 1960).

The secretion of Na^+ ions out of cells against the concentration gradient (which would favor Na^+ leaking in) has been known to occur for some time. It was apparently first suggested by Dean (1941) that this secretion is the result of an active *sodium pump* that pushes out Na^+ ions against the concentration gradient. Since the pump operates against the concentration gradient it should require a considerable amount of metabolic energy. As described earlier (Chapter 5) biological energy is stored in the form of ATP. There are several chemicals that act as metabolic poisons, destroying the energy producing system. One such poison is cyanide. If Na^+ is in fact pumped out of the membrane by an *active* process of extrusion, then cyanide should stop the pump and Na^+ should no longer be extruded. Further, injection of ATP inside the fiber after cyanide poisoning ought to "start up" the pump again briefly. The results of an experiment using radioactively labeled ions to test these deductions are shown in Figure 6.16 (Caldwell and Keynes, 1957). As you can see, cyanide stops the output of Na^+, ATP gives a brief rise in Na^+ output, and removal of cyanide allows the pump to return Na^+ output to resting level. Both predictions are completely

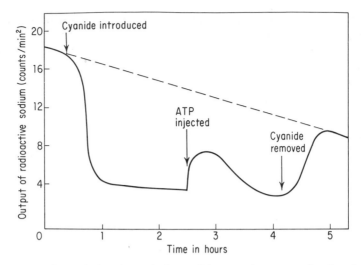

Figure 6.16.   The effects of altered metabolic conditions on the output of sodium by a squid axon (the "sodium pump"). When the metabolic poison, cyanide, is introduced, activity ceases. Adding ATP provides a brief source of energy permitting the pump to act for a while. When the cyanide is inactivated, the pump returns to normal operation. (Redrawn from Caldwell and Keynes, 1957)

verified. The slight steady decline in Na$^+$ output seen in Figure 6.16, incidentally, is due to the fact that the excised fiber is slowly "dying."

There appears also to be a "potassium pump" operating in an analogous manner to the sodium pump. Potassium ions tend to leak out of the resting axon, and flow out down their slight concentration gradient (see Figure 6.13) during action potentials. It seems that K$^+$ ions are "secreted" *into* the cell by an active process, just as sodium ions are secreted out. In fact, there is some evidence suggesting that sodium and potassium pumps are coupled together (Hodgkin, 1958).

It is often said that the sodium (and potassium) pump is merely an hypothesis and has not yet been shown to exist. This is not quite the case. Evidence such as that of Figure 6.16 would seem to demonstrate rather conclusively that sodium ions are secreted out of the axon by an active biological process requiring metabolic energy. It is the *nature* of the pump mechanism that remains highly speculative, not its existence. The activity of the pump is much too little to account for the extreme differential concentrations of Na$^+$ ions inside and outside the axon. A barrier must be postulated to account for this. However the pump does seem to take care of the Na$^+$ that leaks in or enters during the action potential, and the K$^+$ that flows out. The actual amount of ion exchange occurring during an action potential, incidentally, is very small. Hodgkin (1964) has estimated that about one-millionth of the internal potassium flows out of an axon during a single action potential. Hence, an axon can fire many thousands of times before the ionic "drain" becomes noticeable. Since most axons rest a good deal more than they fire, the sodium pump is able to keep the ionic "battery" charged. In contrast to the substantial metabolic requirements of the sodium pump, the processes involved in the development of the action potential (i.e. breakdown of the barrier keeping Na^+ ions out) require virtually no metabolic energy.

A summary description and diagram of the nerve membrane potential given by Hodgkin (1958, pp. 32–33) can hardly be improved upon for clarity:

There are two quite distinct systems in a nerve fibre. On the one hand, there is a secretory mechanism [i.e. sodium pump] which builds up concentration differences by absorbing potassium and ejecting sodium. In parallel with this system are the special channels, which allow sodium and potassium ions to move at varying rates down their concentration gradients. There are a number of differences between the two systems. Metabolic inhibitors affect the secretory system but, at all events in giant nerve fibres, seem to have little effect on the system controlling permeability. Changes in membrane potential or changes in external calcium concentrations have a large effect on permeability, but do not seem to have much effect on the secretory system. . . . For these reasons the two systems have been drawn in Figure [6.17] as physically separate. This conclusion may have to be revised when more direct information is forthcoming; on present evidence it seems to be the most satisfactory inference from experiment.

Figure [6.17] provides a convenient opportunity for summarizing the role of sodium and potassium ions in the conduction of nervous impulses. To begin with, the fibre is in its resting condition with a large potential difference across the membrane. The sodium permeability is very low so that only a trickle of ions enters the fibre; this trickle is dealt with by the pump which keeps the fibre in a steady state. When the nerve conducts an impulse the channels open up, allowing first sodium ions and then potassium ions to move down their concentration gradients. These movements generate the action potential and the fibre pays by accumulating sodium and losing

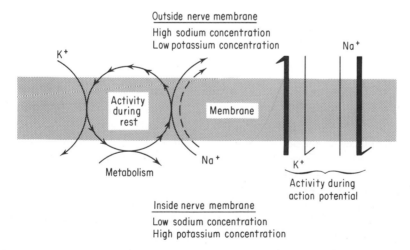

Figure 6.17.   Schematic diagram of the ionic mechanisms for resting and action potentials of the nerve membrane. The "pumps" are shown on the left and the rapid exchanges during activity are shown on the right. (Redrawn from Hodgkin, 1958)

potassium. After activity, the original state is restored by the cyclical process which uses metabolic energy to eject sodium and absorb potassium.

The whole mechanism seems admirably designed for a system in which information is conveyed as a series of brief impulses spaced at widely varying intervals. The ionic concentration differences allow electrical energy to be dissipated at a high rate. If the nerve has to handle a large number of impulses in a short time it can run into debt by accumulating sodium and losing potassium. However, sooner or later the debt must be paid off, and this can be done during the periods of rest which alternate with these of more intense activity.

The Propagated Nerve Action Potential

We have described the ionic events that occur during the nerve action potential in some detail. However, we have not yet discussed how an impulse is initiated in a nerve fiber by an electrical stimulus nor how it is propagated along the fiber. Many of the classical phenomena of the nerve action potential discussed in the older texts, such as the all-or-none law, absolute and relative refractory periods, anodal block, etc., are dependent upon these aspects of nerve activity.

It is very important to distinguish clearly between (1) the actual movements of Na^+ and K^+ ions across the membrane during the action potential, and (2) the flow of current in the nerve fiber when a brief electrical pulse is applied to the fiber. You may remember from our discussion of electricity in Chapter 2 that current flow (or more correctly current, since current means a flow of electrons) in a conducting medium is virtually instantaneous. However, when a condenser is connected to a battery it may take considerable time for sufficient charge to collect on the condenser plates to bring them to the potential of the battery. This delay occurs because the maximum current (rate of charge) from a battery is limited. By the same token, when an electrical pulse is applied to a nerve fiber, or for that matter to any conducting medium, current flows instantaneously. This current flow has certain effects on the nerve membrane, which develop more slowly in time. With an appropriate stimulus the membrane barrier to Na^+ ions will break down and an action potential will develop and travel along the axon. The initial current that is conducted through the nerve prior to the development of the action potential is often referred to as *electrotonus*.

The current distribution developed across a nerve membrane by an externally applied source of current is shown in Figures 6.18, 6.21. Two leads from a battery are simply placed on the outside of a nerve fiber. Current flows from the *anode* to *cathode* of the battery. Considerable current flows between the electrodes through the conducting medium outside the membrane. In addition, current flows across the membrane, into the fiber at the anode and out of the fiber at the cathode. The current density is greatest where the anode and cathode contact the membrane, and falls off exponentially away from them. Remember that the resting nerve membrane is negative inside relative to outside. Hence movement of current out of the membrane at the cathode will tend to move the membrane potential toward zero, i.e. *depolarize* it. At the anode the inward current will tend to *hyperpolarize* the membrane. Consequently, when a nerve action potential

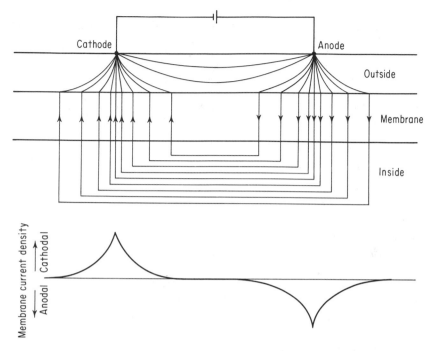

Figure 6.18. Current distribution developed across a nerve membrane by an externally applied source of current. Current flows in at the anode and out at the cathode. (Redrawn from Woodbury and Patton, 1960)

is initiated it will develop at the cathode. Conversely it will tend to be prevented from developing at the anode (so-called "anodal block").

The most crucial factor in the development of a nerve action potential is the membrane barrier *threshold*. The level of the resting nerve membrane potential is determined by the differential distribution of K^+ ions. Sodium ions are kept out by a selective barrier in the membrane. The membrane potential itself is not the barrier; however, the existence of the barrier is dependent upon the level of the membrane potential. The membrane barrier has a threshold that is a few millivolts positive to the resting potential level. If the membrane potential is shifted a bit toward zero from its resting value of -70 mV the barrier keeping Na^+ out against its concentration gradient breaks down and the action potential develops. The actual time course of the barrier breakdown during an action potential was indicated in Figure 6.13. The brief change in sodium conductance represents the reversible barrier breakdown for Na^+ ions. In addition a slower breakdown of the much smaller barrier to K^+ ions occurs, which produces the negative after-potential.

The membrane barrier breaks down initially at the cathode following an electrical stimulus (Figure 6.18). Once the action potential develops, current flows in at the place on the membrane where the action potential occurs, and

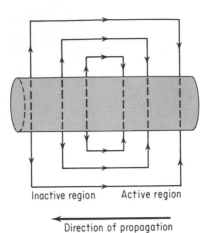

Figure 6.19.   Current flow during the propagation of an impulse along an unmyelinated nerve fiber.

Inactive region   Active region

Direction of propagation

flows out at a more distant region. This is illustrated in Figure 6.19. The current flowing out at the inactive region tends to depolarize the membrane potential level, just as occurred at the cathode of the applied stimulus in Figure 6.18. When the outward current flow is sufficient to reach barrier threshold, the membrane barrier to Na$^+$ breaks down and the action potential develops at the previously inactive region. This is the mechanism whereby an action potential is propagated down the nerve fiber. The propagation is a continuous process in nonmyelinated fibers such as the giant axon. Outward current density decreases continuously from the region of maximum flow (Figure 6.19). As noted earlier, if an electrical stimulus is applied to the middle of an axon, action potentials will develop and travel out the axon in both directions away from the stimulus site.

If a point on a nerve fiber is electrically stimulated immediately after an action potential has occurred, the fiber will not respond no matter how strong the stimulus. This brief time period of about 1 msec is called the *absolute refractory period*. Immediately following this period an action potential can be initiated but it requires a much stronger than normal stimulus current. This time period, called the *relative refractory period*, lasts several msec. These refractory phenomena are easily explained in terms of the membrane resistance to Na$^+$ and K$^+$ ion flows. Immediately following the period during increased Na$^+$ conductance of the action potential (Figure 6.13) and Na$^+$ conductance of the membrane apparently becomes zero for about 1 msec, hence the absolute refractory period. Following this the sodium conductance is less than would normally occur for a few msec. During the absolute refractory period there is also an increased outward conductance of K$^+$ ions, which hyperpolarizes the membrane (Figure 6.13), thus further increasing the membrane threshold to a depolarizing stimulus. The relative refractory period is the result of the decreased inward Na$^+$ conductance and the increased outward K$^+$ conductance.

The action potential of a single nerve fiber is all-or-none; its amplitude and velocity of conduction down the axon are independent of the stimulus strength.

This fact is obvious in view of the ionic mechanisms involved in nerve activity. When the membrane barrier is broken down the amplitude of the action potential is dependent upon the differential distribution of Na^+ ions inside and outside the membrane. The velocity depends on such factors as the size of the axon, presence or absence of myelin, temperature, etc. Once initiated, the characteristics of the action potential are determined by the intrinsic characteristics of the nerve fiber and are independent of the stimulus. In an ordinary peripheral nerve, composed of many different fibers, the amplitude of the gross nerve response recorded from the whole nerve by large wire electrodes grows as the strength of the stimulus to the nerve increases. This is often confusing to the student since it is clearly not an all-or-none effect. Each fiber in the nerve is firing in an all-or-none fashion; however different fibers have different thresholds. Most peripheral nerves are composed of various sized fibers having quite a range of diameters. The discharge threshold of a fiber to an externally applied electrical stimulus tends to be inversely proportional to the fiber diameter. The large fibers in the nerve fire to weak stimuli but a very much stronger stimulus is needed to activate all fibers. As we will see later, the amplitude of the gross nerve action potential is directly related to the number of fibers firing. Hence the gross nerve action potential, which reflects the summed total activity of all the active nerve fibers, grows in amplitude with stimulus strength over quite a range of stimulus values, even though each fiber in the nerve obeys the all-or-none law.

Saltatory conduction

Most nerve axons in vertebrates are surrounded individually by a covering of fatty material termed by the *myelin sheath* (the squid giant axon, remember, has no such covering). This sheath begins a short distance away from the cell body or *soma*, and covers the entire axon except for the fine axon terminals that synapse on other nerve cells. Very small diameter fibers have no myelin sheath, but all larger fibers both inside and outside the CNS are covered with this insulating material. The sheath is interrupted every 2 mm or so by constrictions termed *nodes of Ranvier*, where myelin is either very thin or absent. A drawing of a longitudinal section through a myelinated axon is shown in Figure 6.20.

The process of conduction in a myelinated nerve fiber is termed *saltatory conduction* (from the Latin word "saltare" to "jump" or "skip"). It differs somewhat from that in a squid axon or small nonmyelinated mammalian fiber.

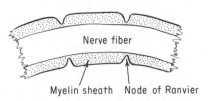

Figure 6.20. Longitudinal section of a myelinated nerve fiber.

Nerve fiber

Myelin sheath   Node of Ranvier

Conduction velocity, for example, is about 20 times faster in myelinated fibers than in nonmyelinated fibers of the same diameter. Many of the basic experiments on saltatory conduction were carried out by Ichiji Tasaki (see Tasaki, 1953) in Japan during the 1930s. This was a period when Japan was somewhat isolated from the Western world, and modern equipment was not available. His ingenious experiments were done with nothing more than "an old, rusty Helmholtz pendulum (timing device), combined with a pair of fine dissecting needles." Original research does not always require elaborate equipment and facilities.

In brief, the myelin sheath appears to act primarily as an insulator. If a nerve fiber is activated by electrical stimulation at a given node, the action potential with its associated currents resulting from the ion flows described above develops at that node. In nonmyelinated fibers breakdown of the nerve membrane barriers to ion flows move progressively along the axon (see Figure

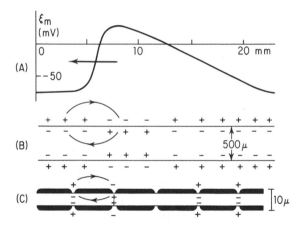

Figure 6.21. Propagation by local circuit stimulation. A, spatial variation of an action potential at a fixed time. Ordinate, transmembrane potential, ξ_m; abscissa, distance along fibers shown in **B** and **C**. Action potential is propagated at a speed of 20 meters per second to the left, as shown by the arrow crossing its upstroke. Note that the upstroke is much steeper than the downstroke.

B, unmyelinated nerve fiber. Plus and minus signs represent approximately the transmembrane voltage given accurately in **A**. Distance scale of A applies. Diameter of cell is grossly exaggerated with respect to length as shown. Arrows represent current flow in a local circuit or loop due to the differences in transmembrane potential caused by the different properties of the membrane: highly permeable to K^+ on left and right, even more highly permeable to Na^+ in central regions. Local circuit flow acts to reduce charge in inactive regions but has much less effect on charge in active regions because of high Na^+ permeability. Propagation is achieved by depolarizing action of local current flow.

C, same as **B** except myelinated. For clarity, distance between nodes is shown as 4 mm or twice actual distance. Because of low capacity of sheath, charge is shown only at nodes (amount of charge in whole internodal region is about one half that at the node). Local circuit flow is thus largely from node to node as shown by arrows. (Redrawn from Woodbury, 1965)

6.19). However in myelinated fibers the myelin sheath effectively insulates the fiber from these currents. Current flows in and out of the nerve fiber only at the nodes (Figure 6.21). Conduction along the nerve occurs when the ionic currents are large enough to cause a breakdown of the axon membrane barriers at the *next node of Ranvier*.

The current flow generated at the next node by an action potential at a given node is "electrotonic." As noted earlier, this means that it develops very rapidly everywhere along the nerve fiber. However, the strength of the current decreases exponentially as a function of distances away from the node where the action potential develops (Figure 6.21). The current density at the node next to the action potential node becomes sufficiently great that the membrane barrier breaks down and an action potential develops there. Consequently the time required for the action potential to "travel" from one node to the next is only the time required for the action potential to develop at the second node. It is as though the intervening myelinated region does not exist. Conduction jumps along the fiber from node to node, and is therefore very much more rapid in myelinated fibers than in nonmyelinated fibers. The effects of anesthetics verify this hypothesis. If anesthetic agents are applied on the myelin between nodes they are relatively ineffective in blocking transmission. However they are very effective when applied at the nodes of Ranvier (Tasaki, 1953).

RESPONSES OF WHOLE NERVES

Until now we have discussed analytic studies that have used single nerve fibers to determine the basic mechanisms of nerve conduction. Historically, the gross response of a whole peripheral nerve was recorded earlier, in the pioneering studies by Erlanger and Gasser (1937) and others. The way in which whole nerve activity is recorded illustrates nicely some general problems of recording electrical activity. A simple preparation is a frog peripheral nerve dissected out and laid across stimulating and recording wires in a moist chamber. The general arrangement for this type of experiment was illustrated and discussed in Chapter 3. Two ways of recording, and the types of responses obtained, are shown in Figure 6.22, A and B. In both cases the information recorded is simply the sum of all the action potential spikes of the individual fibers in the nerve. First, if we record activity from two adjacent recording electrodes on the nerve, a *diphasic* wave results, with activity initially negative at the first electrode relative to the second and then vice versa as the nerve impulses pass both electrodes (Figure 6.22A). Since the activities overlap, the net record obtained is the algebraic sum of the potentials developed at the two wires. We cannot accurately measure the absolute activity in the nerve. In Figure 6.22B, the nerve underlying the electrode furthest away from the stimulating wires has been killed by crushing. There is now a continuous current flow from the crushed-end electrode (b) to the electrode recording from intact nerve. This "killed-end" current is a steady dc current proportional to the resting membrane potential of the intact fibers. Since it is a steady dc current we can balance it out in our recording equipment (this is most commonly done by using a regular condenser-coupled ac amplifier). Activity conducted along the nerve now changes the potential at the intact nerve electrode relative to the killed end. The greater the activity, the greater the change in potential. Such a recording is *monophasic* (all in one direction away from the baseline level). The amplitude of this monophasic response, or more correctly the area under it, is directly related to the number of individual nerve fibers in the nerve which are active (Lorenté de No, 1947a, b).

If we record monophasically some distance from the stimulating wires and use a very fast recording speed on the oscilloscope to spread the nerve response out in time, the whole nerve response will have two or more humps in it. An example of such a nerve response is shown in Figure 6.23, taken from the classic monograph by Erlanger and Gasser (1937). The two humps are due to the fact

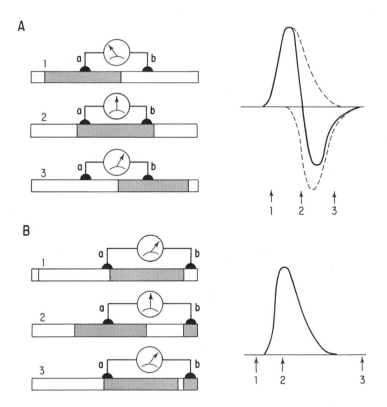

Figure 6.22. Recordings of the gross action potential of a whole nerve. **A**, diphasic recording. Both electrodes are on an intact nerve and the potential shifts first in one direction and then in the other as the impulses pass across the two electrodes. **B**, monophasic recording. One electrode is on the crushed end (b). The response is entirely of one polarity. (Redrawn from Patton, 1960)

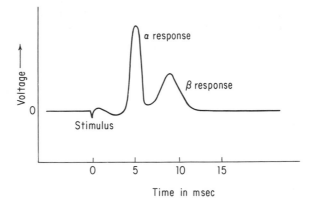

Figure 6.23. A monophasically recorded action potential from a peripheral nerve bundle. The two separate humps represent faster (α) and slower (β) conducting fiber groups. (Redrawn from Erlanger and Gasser, 1937)

that there are different groups of fiber sizes in peripheral nerve. Fiber diameters in a gross nerve do not have a single distribution of sizes but rather several different overlapping distributions of sizes. The composition of nerves in terms of fiber groups, and their anatomical and functional characteristics and connections will be described further in Chapter 12. It is sufficient here to remember that conduction velocity is directly related to fiber diameter. Hence small-fiber action potentials are conducted more slowly and arrive at the recording electrodes later in time than large-fiber action potentials, producing a later hump in the record.

SUGGESTED READINGS

Hodgkin, A. L. The ionic basis of nervous conduction. *Science*, 1964, **145**, 1148–1154.

Huxley, A. F. Excitation and conduction in nerve: quantitative analysis. *Science*, 1964, **145**, 1154–1159.

Ruch, T. C., & Patton, H. D. (Eds.) *Physiology and biophysics*. Philadelphia: Saunders, 1965. Chapters 1–3.

CHAPTER 7

SYNAPTIC TRANSMISSION: I. ELECTRICAL EVENTS

The subject of synaptic transmission has implications that extend far beyond the "simple" problem of how information passes from one neuron to the next. In our present state of knowledge it appears that the only manner in which neurons directly affect one another to a significant extent is by means of synaptic interactions. Thus all activity of the brain and all behavior of organisms is ultimately reducible to the interconnections and synaptic interactions among neurons.

Although the configurations of activity in populations of neurons that determine behavior can shift and alter in an almost infinite variety of complex patterns, a single nerve cell can do only two things: discharge or not discharge. Actually there are two quite different kinds of processes that occur in nerve cells. The action potential or *spike discharge*, discussed at length in Chapter 6, is probably the most familiar to you. This is the all-or-none nerve impulse that travels down the axon of the nerve cell and produces effects on other nerve cells at synapses. The size of a given spike discharge is constant, and once started it travels all the way down the axon to the synapses. The statement that nerves conduct in an all-or-none fashion refers to this spike discharge event. An analogy is often made with a *digital* computer: just as the spike discharge either occurs or doesn't, each element in the digital computer can be in only one of two possible states ("yes" or "no").

This decision made by a neuron to fire or not fire, however, depends upon an entirely different kind of activity, often termed *graded* activity. When the nerve cell body and dendrites are activated or stimulated by other nerve cells (at synapses on the cell), small shifts are induced in the electrical potential of the cell membrane. The amount of these shifts is proportional to the amount and kind of incoming activity. In fact the size of the graded potential varies in a continuous fashion. If the change in the graded potential is sufficiently large, the *spike discharge threshold* of the cell is reached and an all-or-none spike discharge travels down the axon. However if the graded potential does not reach spike discharge threshold, *no activity* is conducted down the axon. The occurrence of these graded potentials in the nerve cell body can be likened to a decision-making process. The neuron considers all incoming activity, and depending on the amount and kind of this activity, "decides" to fire or not fire. These graded potentials have often been compared to the operation of an *analogue* computer, which processes signals that vary continuously in amplitude.

Although somewhat hackneyed, the firing of a gun does provide a simple analogy to activation of a nerve cell. A small squeeze on the trigger produces nothing. If the squeeze is sufficiently hard to reach threshold for activating the firing pin, the cartridge discharges and fires a bullet. Two smaller squeezes given close enough together in time (so that the second squeeze occurs when the trigger is maximally pulled by the first squeeze) may also activate the firing pin (i.e. temporal summation). Alternatively, if the safety is on, the effect of the squeeze is nullified (i.e. inhibition). The velocity of the bullet has no relation to the strength of trigger squeeze; it is dependent only upon intrinsic characteristics of the cartridge and gun. In an analogous fashion, no axon discharge occurs in a neuron until the spike discharge threshold is reached. When the graded potentials induced in the cell cross this threshold a spike discharge is fired down the axon. The characteristics of the spike, such as its amplitude and velocity, have nothing whatever to do with the size of the graded potentials that trigger the spike; they are determined by intrinsic characteristics of the axon (primarily its size and the presence or absence of myelin).

In terms of influencing subsequent neurons, a neuron can only fire or not fire. If a nerve cell is discharging at a given rate, other activity impinging upon the cell can produce only two possible effects: it can either increase or decrease the output discharge rate. Consequently, all effects of neurons upon other neurons can be described in terms of two hypothetical processes, excitation and inhibition. Since neurons interact by means of synaptic interconnections, the processes of neural excitation and inhibition ought to be entirely explainable in terms of synaptic events. One of the great achievements of Twentieth-century neurophysiology has been the realization of this objective.

THE CONCEPT OF THE SYNAPSE

In the last century many neuroanatomists thought the nervous system was a single entity, a "reticulum," with continuous interconnections much like the muscle of the heart. The great neurohistologist Ramón y Cajal developed an overwhelming array of evidence opposing this idea and supporting the "neuron doctrine" (see Cajal, 1934, for a decisive review). This "doctrine" asserts that neurons are separate cells which interact through *functional* rather than structural connections. To give only one of the many lines of evidence, in the embryological development of the nervous system each separate nerve cell body develops processes (axons and dendrites) that grow out toward other neurons, rather than the entire system growing continuously. The functional connections that develop between neurons are now known to be close spatial juxtapositions between the neural elements involved (e.g. the small endings of an axon from one cell on the dendrites and cell body of another cell). These functional connections were termed "synapses" by the English neurophysiologist, Sherrington, who devoted his life to an analysis of reflex behavior in terms of excitatory and inhibitory synaptic actions of cells on other nerve cells. Eccles (1957, p. 2) has stated this approach succinctly:

> Essentially we can consider the behavior of the nervous system as being built up from the behavior patterns of each of its myriad nerve cells . . . this behavior pattern is defined at any instant by the two possible states of a cell, activation by an impulse or quiescence.

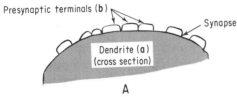

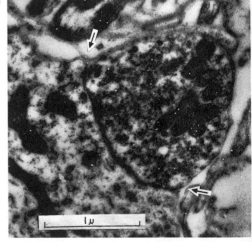

Figure 7.1. A, diagram of a cross section of a dendrite showing a number of presynaptic terminal knobs lying in close approximation to it. The spaces (not seen at this low magnification) between the knobs and the dendrite are the synapses. (Redrawn from Wycoff and Young, 1956) B, photomicrograph of a single synaptic space formed by a presynaptic terminal and a dendrite. The actual space is about 200 Å. (Taken from Palade and Palay as given in Eccles, 1957)

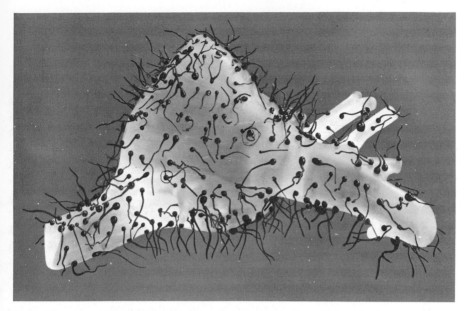

Figure 7.2. A reconstructed model of a spinal motor neuron showing the large number of small presynaptic knobs from other neurons terminating on it. (Taken from Haggar and Barr, 1950)

No one seriously questions the neuron doctrine today, at least for the mammalian nervous system (there are structurally continuous nerve nets and " synapses" in invertebrates). At the time Sherrington worked no one had seen a synapse or studied synaptic activity directly. Today there is extensive direct evidence concerning the structure and activity of synapses. Several synapses formed by presynaptic knobs on a dendrite are drawn in Figure 7.1A. The large structure (a) is a dendrite (an extension of the cell body) receiving activation from several " presynaptic knobs " (b's). At this low power magnification the contact appears direct. A high power magnification is shown in the electron photomicrograph of Figure 7.1B. The synaptic cleft, or space, is seen as a continuous separation between the presynaptic knob (a) and the postsynaptic membrane (b). The distance of separation is about 200 Å (2×10^{-5} mm). To appreciate the relative size of the presynaptic knobs (the terminals of the axon, which form the presynaptic structures) and the postsynaptic cell body, a model of a spinal motor neuron was constructed from serial sections of the nerve cells (Figure 7.2). In making such a model, the neural tissue containing the cell is cut in very thin slices and stained to show the axon terminals (see Chapter 3). A drawing or photograph is made of each section and the three dimensional model built up from the series of drawings. The small structures resembling pollywogs are the axon terminals ending in presynaptic knobs or " boutons," which lie in close apposition to the large cell body of the motor neuron. The synapse, then, is a physical separation or space (and the specialized boundary membranes involved) between the axon terminal of one neuron and the post-synaptic membrane of the dendrite or cell body or axon of another.

There are actually several types of synapses that have been described by electron microscopic studies of mammalian neurons (cf. De-Robertis, 1959; Palay, 1958; Whittaker and Gray, 1962). Type 1 synapses (*axodendritic*) are found only on dendrites. The dendritic fiber often sends out a small spine that actually forms the synapse with the axon terminal bouton of the presynaptic element (Figure 7.3A). In Type 2 (*axosomatic*) synapses the axon terminal bouton goes directly to the soma (cell body) or to the large dendritic stumps that merge into the soma (Figure 7.3B). There are no spines coming from the post-synaptic membrane for Type 2 synapses. The overall distribution of spines on a neuron are shown in Figure 7.3C. Type 1 synapses are further away from the cell body and axon hillock than are Type 2. Finally, a given axon terminal that forms two synapses always forms only Type 1 or only Type 2 synapses. Eccles (1964) initially suggested that Type 1 synapses mediate postsynaptic excitation and Type 2 synapses mediate postsynaptic inhibition. As will be described in this chapter, the all-or-none spike discharge of the cell is generated in the region of the axon hillock. Inhibition would then be close to the region of impulse initiation and excitatory influences would be considerably more remote. Inhibitory synapses on dendrites have since been described. Eccles has proposed the following more limited generalizations: (1) all spine synapses are Type 1 and excitatory; and (2) all synapses on cell bodies that are Type 2 are inhibitory. These more limited hypotheses still imply that inhibition tends to act near the region of the cell body where the spike discharge is initiated, and that excitation is more remote.

A third rather different type of synapses has also been described (Gray, 1962, 1963). This is the *axoaxonic* synapse, in which an axon terminal bouton synapses on a terminal bouton from another axon (Figure 7.3D). By such an arrangement, one axon terminal could directly influence the excitability of another axon terminal, which in turn controls the activity of another cell through the more familiar axodendritic or axosomatic synapse. These axoaxonic synapses have been found in afferent fiber terminals in several of the primary sensory systems, but have not been seen in cerebral cortex. Eccles (1964) summarized evidence suggesting that axoaxonic synapses mediate a special type of inhibition termed *presynaptic inhibition* (to be described later in this chapter). In summary, Eccles suggests that most Type 1 synapses mediate postsynaptic excitation, Type 2 synapses on cell bodies mediate postsynaptic inhibition, and axoaxonic synapses mediate presynaptic inhibition. Anatomically there are a variety of complex appearing synapses in the CNS whose organization and functions have yet to be determined. In the interests of simplicity, we might hope that Eccles' generalizations can be extended to all of these.

Recent developments in the study of synaptic transmission have been numerous and exciting. This is primarily due to the development of the micro-

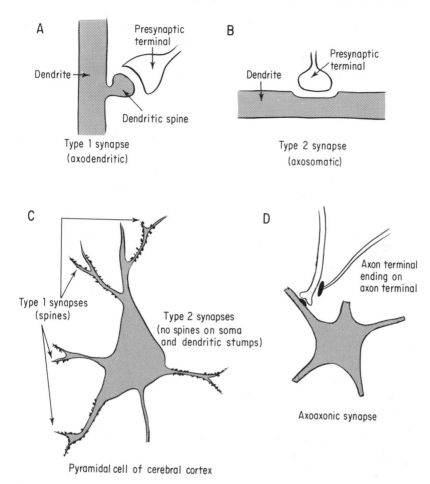

Figure 7.3. Various types of synapses. **A,** type 1 (axodendritic). The axon terminal ends on a spinous process that protrudes from the dendrite. **B,** type 2 (axosomatic). The axon terminal ends on the soma or large dendritic stumps near the soma. **C,** distribution of Type 1 and Type 2 synapses on a cortical pyramidal cell. Type 1 synapses indicated by small knobs and Type 2 by absence of knobs. **D,** an Axoaxonic synapse, where the axon terminal ends on another axon terminal. (Modified and redrawn from Hamlyn, 1962; Whittaker and Gray, 1962; Gray, 1963; Eccles, 1964)

electrode technique and the utilization of a simplified system, the *monosynaptic reflex* of the spinal cord. In order to investigate the mechanisms of synaptic activation it is necessary to measure the membrane potential of a neuron when it is being bombarded synaptically by other neurons. Since the largest mammalian neurons, the spinal motor neurons, have cell body diameters of about 70 microns (0.07 mm), a very small electrode is needed to penetrate the cell membrane, remain inside the cell, and still not damage the cell so much that it

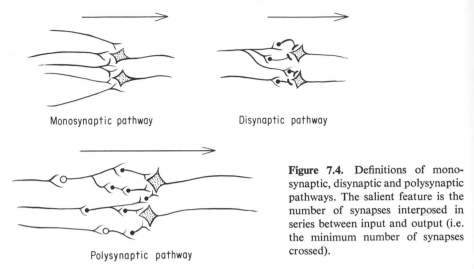

Monosynaptic pathway   Disynaptic pathway

Polysynaptic pathway

Figure 7.4. Definitions of monosynaptic, disynaptic and polysynaptic pathways. The salient feature is the number of synapses interposed in series between input and output (i.e. the minimum number of synapses crossed).

will not function normally. The microelectrode consists of a small wire or a saline-filled glass pipette having a tip diameter of less than 1 micron. The resistance of such an electrode is millions of ohms and very specialized electronic apparatus is necessary for its use (see Chapter 3).

Often our understanding of a general biological problem is greatly improved by the use of a model system. One example was the use of the Squid giant axon as a model for the study of nerve membrane potentials. Its size, simplicity, and durability permitted studies resulting in greatly increased knowledge of membrane and action potentials in a wide variety of nerve fibers that themselves could not be directly studied. In case of synaptic transmission the model systems have been reflex mechanisms of the spinal cord, particularly the monosynaptic excitatory reflex and the disynaptic inhibitory reflex of the spinal motor neuron. The term *monosynaptic* literally means "one synapse." A monosynaptic reflex has only one synaptic junction between the incoming sensory nerve fibers and the outgoing motor nerves. In any given monosynaptic pathway there are of course thousands or millions of actual synapses, arranged in parallel. However, an impulse in any one afferent fiber terminal crosses only one synapse to act on the motor neuron. This distinction is illustrated in Figure 7.4. There are thus only two groups of nerve fibers involved in a monosynaptic reflex, the incoming afferent fibers and the outgoing motor nerves. The term *disynaptic* means "two synapses" in series. An incoming impulse in an afferent fiber must first cross a synapse on to an interneuron, and the interneuron then acts on the outgoing motor neuron (Figure 7.4). Hence there must be a minimum of three classes of neurons in series. *Polysynaptic* simply means more than one synapse in series, and also may refer to disynaptic pathways. Typically, the interneurons in a disynaptic reflex (neurons between input and output fibers) exert an inhibitory influence on the motor neurons.

The methods and results of studies on spinal motor neurons have subsequently been applied to the analysis of many other neuron systems in the brain. Although many scientists have contributed greatly to our understanding of synaptic transmission, one individual, Sir John Eccles of Canberra, Australia is a dominant figure in the field. He was the pioneer in combining successfully the microelectrode recording technique and the use of the monosynaptic motor neuron reflex system for the study of synaptic transmission in the CNS. For his work he shared the Nobel prize in medicine in 1963 with Hodgkin and Huxley. Much of the material in this chapter summarizes the findings of his research.

EXCITATION

At this point it is necessary for us to assume certain anatomical and physical "facts" concerning reflex connections of the spinal cord to facilitate our discussion of synaptic mechanisms. The evidence for these connections and the behavioral functions of these reflexes will be discussed in greater detail in Chapter 12.

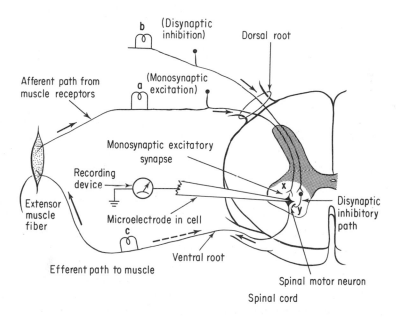

Figure 7.5. Schematic diagram of the experimental arrangement used to study monosynaptic excitation and disynaptic inhibition. Stimulation of different peripheral nerves (*a* and *b*) permits monosynaptic excitation (*x*) or disynaptic inhibition (*y*) to be induced in the motor neuron. Its activity is recorded by an intracellular microelectrode. The motor neuron can also be activated antidromically by stimulation of the ventral root (*c*).

A relatively weak electrical stimulus delivered to an *afferent* (incoming) nerve from a hind limb *extensor* muscle (muscle that causes the limb to extend when it contracts) causes excitation of the spinal motor neurons that go back to the same muscle, resulting in contraction of the muscle and consequent extension of the limb (Figure 7.5). At the same time, activity in the motor neurons going to the flexor muscles that produce contraction of the limb is inhibited, permitting the limb to extend. The excitatory pathway is monosynaptic and the inhibitory pathway is disynaptic. These facts are illustrated very schematically in Figure 7.5. By selecting the appropriate incoming nerves and spinal motor neurons we can study monosynaptic excitation and disynaptic inhibition effects on neurons separately.

Our discussion of excitation will deal with the monosynaptic excitatory pathway shown in Figure 7.5, and our initial discussion of inhibition will concern the disynaptic inhibitory pathway shown in the same figure. Figure 7.5 also indicates diagrammatically the type of experimental arrangements used to study excitation.

An afferent (incoming) nerve from a hind limb muscle is stimulated electrically at (a). Fibers of this nerve synapse directly on a motor neuron in the spinal cord at (x). The recording microelectrode has been inserted into the motor neuron and records the potential across the nerve cell membrane. In a typical experiment, no attempt is made to visualize or isolate a single cell directly. The microelectrode is simply pushed blindly into the spinal cord in the region of a given population of motor neuron cells. The criterion for determining that the microelectrode is inside a cell is a sudden shift of the base line from electrical neutrality to a value of about −70 mV (see Figure 7.6). This occurs when the electrode penetrates a cell membrane and then records that membrane potential. Remember that in most important respects the membrane potential phenomena of mammalian nerve cells are the same as for the squid giant nerve fiber. The

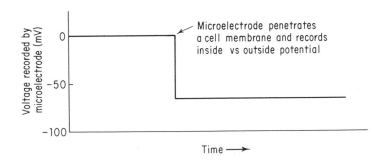

Figure 7.6. The dc electrical record as a microelectrode is pushed into a nerve cell. The voltage level is zero until the cell membrane is penetrated. Penetration of the membrane usually initiates a burst of spike discharges which are not shown. After penetration the electrode records the steady resting membrane potential of about −70 mV. Note: all intracellular recordings in this chapter are shown using the "positive up" convention.

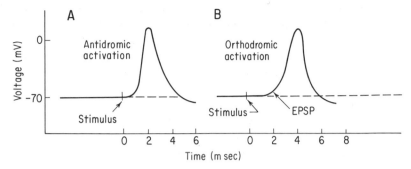

Figure 7.7.   Intracellularly recorded spike action potential of a nerve cell to antidromic and orthodromic (synaptic) activation. Note the slower rising phase (EPSP) with synaptic activation. (Redrawn from Coombs, Curtis, and Eccles, 1957)

response of Figure 7.6 is the electrical picture as the microelectrode is pushed into position in a cell. Actually when the microelectrode penetrates the cell it sometimes triggers a series of spike discharges, not shown in Figure 7.5, in addition to recording the −70 mV dc shift. We can now activate the cell in two ways, *orthodromically*, (normal direction of conduction) by stimulating the incoming fibers at (a) which synapse on the neuron, or *antidromically*, (opposite the normal direction of conduction) by stimulating the axon of the motor neuron itself at (c). This is accomplished by stimulating the ventral root, made up of the axons of many motor neurons as they leave the spinal cord. Such backward stimulation of the cell body allows us to see the "pure" action potential of the cell resulting from direct electrical stimulation. We can then compare this response with the normal orthodromic response resulting from synaptic activation.

An antidromic response of a single motor neuron is shown in Figure 7.7A based on data from Eccles. The microelectrode has been placed in the cell body and has measured a resting potential of −70 mV. After the stimulus, a spike or action potential develops. In most important features this spike potential is identical to the action potential for a squid axon. It overshoots the point of electrical neutrality by about 30 mV, recovers rapidly, and has a period of after-hyperpolarization. A number of ingenious experiments by Eccles and others (see Eccles, 1957) indicate that the ionic mechanisms for the resting membrane potential and the action potential are similar to those described for the squid axon. Thus the value of the resting membrane potential is due in large part to the differential distribution of potassium inside and outside. The spike represents the sudden influx of Na^+ along the electrochemical gradient and the after-potential (hyperpolarization) represents the later outflux of K^+. The total duration of this activity is about 1/100 of a second.

A diagram of the response of a motor neuron to orthodromic or normal synaptic activation is shown in Figure 7.7B. The spike potential has the same height as the antidromic response and the same after hyperpolarization. The ionic mechanisms here are the same. However there is one striking difference between the normal and antidromic response: the presence of a slower rising hump or inflection at the beginning of the spike potential in the normal, synaptically activated response. The stimulus in Figure 7.7B was above spike discharge threshold. The effect of giving a series of weak stimuli, increasing in intensity from A to I, is shown in Figure 7.8. Note that the size of the small potential shift that does develop is *dependent upon the amount of incoming activity* (i.e. stimulus strength to afferent nerve). This small *graded* response has been called by Eccles the excitatory postsynaptic potential (EPSP). This graded EPSP produces the small inflection at the beginning of the orthodromic spike in Figure 7.7. When the EPSP reaches a threshold value of about -60 mV—10 mV less than the resting membrane potential of -70 mV—the membrane barrier breaks down, Na^+ rushes in, and the spike potential develops and travels down the axon. The shift of potential during an EPSP is toward electrical neutrality, so the effect is called a partial *depolarization*. The most important feature of the EPSP is that it is *graded*. It is this graded response that provides the neuron with the capacity to integrate information continuously in time from the variety of sources impinging upon it and make the decision to fire or not to fire.

The size of the EPSP is a continuous function of the amount and kind of synaptic actions on the cell. Remember that a given nerve cell may have thousands of synaptic endings from other cells. In normal function the cell is constantly being bombarded through these synapses. The cell integrates all this incoming information continuously in time. The net result is a kind of over-all average of the information and is expressed by the cell in terms of the membrane

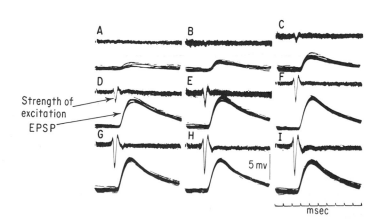

Figure 7.8.   Intracellularly recorded EPSP responses of a nerve cell membrane (lower tracing of each pair, A-I) to successively more intense excitation. The sharp spike on the upper line of each pair indicates the relative strength of excitation. Note that the EPSP increases with stronger stimulation in a graded manner. (From Coombs, Eccles, and Fatt, 1955a)

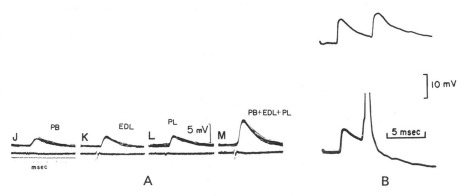

Figure 7.9. A, spatial summation. Intracellularly recorded EPSP of a spinal motor neuron to activation by several different nerves. Stimulation of any one produces a small EPSP; all three together give a large EPSP. B, temporal summation. As the two stimuli are given closer together in time the EPSPs add to yield a spike discharge. (From Eccles, 1957)

potential level. When the synaptic influences on the cell are such that this "average" membrane level shifts to spike threshold (about 10 mV less negative than the resting potential) an all-or-none spike is triggered and fires down the axon. The EPSP, then, reflects the graded "analogue computer" portion of the nerve response, which continuously adds activity in time until spike threshold is reached.

There are two different kinds of "summative" effects exhibited by nerve cells, *spatial* and *temporal* summation. Both of these phenomena are easily understood in terms of adding EPSPs. Spatial summation refers to the fact that stimulation of several different inputs at the same time may yield a large response, whereas stimulation of each input alone yields a small response. Suppose that there were three different input fibers forming synapses on a nerve cell. Suppose these represent terminals from three different afferent nerves (in a real cell there would be thousands of such synaptic terminals). EPSPs generated in the cell are recorded with an intracellular microelectrode. The size of the EPSP to stimulation of each input alone is small (Figure 7.9A). However, when all three inputs are stimulated at the same time, the EPSP is much larger and may even reach spike threshold where the cell fires an all-or-none spike potential down the axon. The cell adds together or summates the EPSPs induced at different spatial locations on the cell to produce a very large EPSP. It is important to remember that when a given synapse acts, it does not induce an EPSP just at that point on the cell body; the whole soma membrane shifts in potential. Hence when several EPSPs are initiated at different places on the soma, they will add together. Spatial summation is a necessary consequence of this fact.

Temporal summation refers to the fact that if a single input channel is activated two or more times in rapid succession, the response of the cell is considerably larger than to a single activation. Suppose that we stimulate only one input channel to a motor neuron. The response to a single stimulus is a small EPSP (Figure 7.9A). Next, we deliver two stimuli about 5 msec apart. Note that the second EPSP is added to the tail of the first and rises somewhat higher (first tracing in 7.9B). In the second tracing of Figure 7.9B the second stimulus is given about 2.5 msec after the first. The summed EPSP is now sufficiently great to give rise to an all-or-none spike discharge. Temporal summation, like spatial summation, is simply an illustration of the fact that EPSPs induced in a cell add together. Since the EPSP only lasts about 10 msec (in spinal motor neurons), temporal summation effects on a single cell will only occur if the stimuli are within this time interval.

An important distinction between the graded postsynaptic potential and the all-or-none spike potential concerns the nature of the cell membrane potential changes involved. The size of the EPSP is not determined by membrane characteristics but rather by the amount of synaptic activation (i.e. amount and kind of incoming information). The cell membrane potential simply shifts in a " passive" manner (much like the charge on a condensor) to the extent that it is activated. The size of the EPSP depends on the amount of synaptic bombardment of the cell. The spike potential, on the other hand is a triggered regenerative membrane response. Unlike the EPSP, the size of the spike (as well as its velocity) are determined by characteristics of the axon such as size and presence or absence of myelin. Characteristics of the spike are completely independent of the degree or kind of synaptic activation of the cell. Once initiated by an EPSP that crossed spike threshold, it always fires in exactly the same manner with exactly the same characteristics.

The distinction between the passive membrane response of the EPSP and the all-or-none spike is somewhat analogous to the distinction we made between passive and active membrane phenomena in discussing the squid axon membrane in Chapter 6. The experimental procedure used to investigate the nature of the ionic process underlying the EPSP involves an application of the *voltage clamp* method (also discussed in Chapter 6). An external source of current is applied across the cell membrane which holds or clamps the membrane at a given potential level. This level membrane potential can be varied by changing the strength of the clamping current. The results of such experiments demonstrated a linear (i.e. direct or straight line) relationship between amplitude of the EPSP and the membrane potential level (Coombs, Eccles, and Fatt, 1955a). In other words, the greater the " clamped " membrane potential level, the larger the EPSP, and vice versa.

It appears that whenever a cell is bombarded by an excitatory synaptic action, the result is a brief and limited short-circuiting of the membrane barrier that normally maintains the unequal distributions of ions. All small ions (e.g. Na^+, K^+ and $C.^-$) flow down their concentration gradients. Since the short-circuit is brief, partial and limited, these ion flows last only for a short time and die away as the barrier is reestablished. The graded character of the EPSP results from the fact that the degree of short circuiting of the cell membrane is a direct function of the degree of synaptic bombardment. Although the graded EPSP of the nerve cell is often referred to as the "decision-making" response of the cell (as we did earlier), there is no active decision process, simply a passive response to synaptic bombardment whose amplitude is predictable from physical-chemical laws of ion exchange.

There appears to be no selectivity in the type of ions that flow in producing the EPSP. The brief short-circuiting of the membrane barrier apparently opens the membrane to free passive diffusion of all small ions. Ionic flows will then be determined entirely by the electrochemical gradients resulting from differential concentrations and membrane potentials. Sodium, potassium, and chloride ions may all exchange—probably in that order of significance—since Na^+ ions have the greatest imbalance in the resting state and Cl^- ions the least.

INITIATION OF THE IMPULSE

The graded EPSP response is recorded from the cell body and dendrite and does not "conduct" down the axon as an all-or-none event. It has no influence on other cells. A number of experiments have attempted to determine the place on the neuron that first develops the all-or-none conducted spike potential. The results of these experiments suggest that the impulse is initiated at the axon hillock (see Figure 7.11). If the axon hillock is inactivated, the spike discharge threshold of the cell body and dendrites proper is about 25 mV—i.e. a shift from −70 mV to −45 mV would be required to activate the cell body directly. However the activation of the axon hillock region of the neuron requires only about 10 mV (Coombs, Curtis, and Eccles, 1957). Direct demonstration of this difference in threshold is rather complex, involving a double-barreled micro-electrode with one electrode just outside the cell membrane and one inside the cell (Terzuolo and Araki, 1961). Current is applied and the cell membrane potential shifted by this voltage clamp. Antidromic currents are induced by stimulating the axon, and the electrical responses of the cell measured. Locations of the responding portions of the cell (i.e. cell body *vs* initial segment) are determined by response latencies. Results of these experiments indicate that initial segment has a considerably lower threshold for spike initiation than does the soma-dendrite. Thus the action potential is believed to start in the axon hillock and travel down the axon. The spike discharge also then invades the cell body and dendrites backward from the axon hillock.

The differential thresholds of the axon hillock and cell body suggest that the intracellularly recorded spike discharge from a cell body might show both the low threshold axon spike and the somewhat later soma spike. If a fast time base is used to record the spike, this does appear to be the case. Figure 7.10A, taken from Coombs, Curtis, and Eccles (1957), illustrates the point nicely. The mono-synaptic spike discharge (upper trace labeled orthodromic activation) first shows the slowly rising EPSP that initiates a spike at about 10 mV positive to the

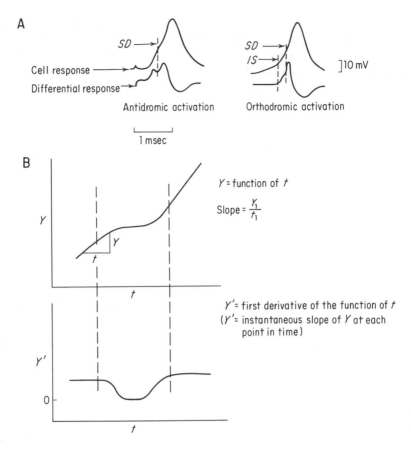

Figure 7.10. A, changes in the rising slope of the spike discharge. Upper traces show the actual potential changes and lower traces the differentiated potentials (rate change of potential). Antidromic activation yields only the "soma-dendrite" (*SD*) shift but orthodromic activation yields an earlier "initial-segment" (*IS*) shift as well. (Redrawn from Coombs, Curtis, and Eccles, 1957) **B,** graphical representation of the process of differentiation. The differential (*Y'*) is the graph of the slope or rate of change of the original function (*Y*).

resting membrane level. This is labeled *IS* for "initial segment" spike. The spike then rises rapidly to the all-or-none peak about of 100 mV. However there is a suggestion of an inflection at about 25 mV labeled *SD* for "soma-dendrite" spike. Actually the *SD* inflection in the spike response is not very convincing. It takes some imagination to see a real *SD* inflection in Figure 7.10A. The *SD* inflection is perhaps more clearly seen in the response to antidromic activation (left upper trace) when no EPSP is present.

Coombs, Curtis, and Eccles employed an ingenious and useful technique to demonstrate the presence of the *SD* inflection point on the spike response: *electronic differentiation.* Readers who have had calculus will immediately appreciate the fact that a plot of the first derivative of a function emphasizes changes in the slope of the original function, since it is a plot of the rate of change (i.e. change in slope) of the function. Electronic differentiation does just this; the original voltage signal is fed into the differentiating unit (which can be a very simple circuit involving only a resistor and a condenser) and the first derivative of the signal comes out. The nonmathematical reader is referred to Fig. 7.10B. The upper graph shows a signal (Y) which varied over time (t). The slope of the curve is the change that occurs in Y for each unit change in t. Where the curve is a straight line (first and last portions) the slope is constant. However the slope is continuously changing over the region where the curve is changing. It first decreases (less change in Y for a unit change in t) and then increases. The lower graph is simply a plot of the actual instantaneous value of the slope (y) calculated for each point on the upper curve. Since the slope does not change in the first and last portions of the upper curve, the lower curve is horizontal over these regions. Over the region where the upper curve changes, the lower curve shows marked changes corresponding to the changes in slope of the upper curve. Differentiation is simply a mathematical procedure for calculating the instantaneous value of the slope of the function at each point in time. If the function whose slope you wish to calculate is actually a voltage signal, the electronic differentiator performs the mathematical procedure for you.

The lower tracings in Fig. 7.10A are the electronically differentiated values of the spike potentials shown in the upper tracings. In other words they are plots of the slopes of the upper curves. There is only one change in the slope of the antidromic response corresponding to the *IS-SD* break: the initial segment first begins to fire since it has a lower threshold. The soma-dendrite fires later only, when its higher threshold value has been reached. In the orthodromic (i.e. monosynaptically induced) response, the onset of the *IS* spike and the onset of the *SD* spike are clearly seen in the differentiated record. In summary, the *IS* inflection represents initiation of the spike discharge at the axon hillock and the *SD* inflection is the subsequent activation of the soma-dendrite spike at a higher threshold. These points have been clearly demonstrated in recent studies by Terzuolo and Araki (1961) and Araki and Terzuolo (1962).

A controversy has developed over the question of whether or not the soma and dendrites of nerve cells are electrically excitable and can conduct all-or-none spike discharges (see Grundfest, 1961). As will be shown in the next chapter, synaptic transmission in mammals is normally chemical rather than electrical. This does not necessarily imply that the membrane is therefore inexcitable to electrical stimulation. However, as noted above, the soma-dendrite spike discharge threshold is several times higher than is the axon hillock threshold. Further, conduction velocity is very much slower in dendrites than in axons, usually less than 1 meter/sec. Using isolated nerve cells in tissue culture, Hild and Tasaki (1962) measured spikes in dendrites, which traveled at least 100 microns away from the soma at the slow rate of 0.1 meter/sec. It would appear that soma and dendrite membranes are electrically excitable and do conduct

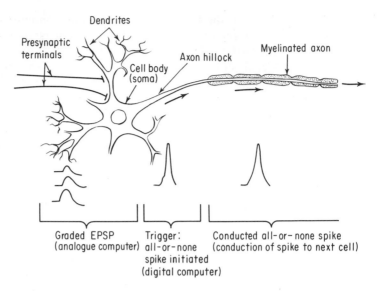

Figure 7.11. Summary diagram showing locations on the motor neuron of the events responsible for impulse initiation. Dendrites and cell body give graded EPSPs; the action potential is triggered in the initial segment (axon hillock) and travels down the axon. (Based on Eccles, 1957)

spike discharges, albeit less so and with slower conduction velocities than axons. Eccles (1964) has suggested that this lowered excitability may be due to the dense covering of synapses on the cell body and dendrites.

The final picture of synaptic excitation that emerges is illustrated in Figure 7.11. Synaptic activation causes graded responses in the cell body and dendrites. When the trigger threshold of about 10 mV less than resting potential is reached, an all-or-none spike discharge is initiated at the axon hillock, which travels down the axon and back along cell body and dendrites. If the axon is from a spinal motor neuron, it conducts the impulse to muscle fibers, resulting in muscle contraction. If the axon is from a type of cell that synapses on other cells in the CNS it conducts the impulse to these synapses. Thus the all-or-none spike travels down the axon to the presynaptic terminals and initiates graded postsynaptic responses in other neurons.

INHIBITION

The simplest possible way that an inhibitory system could act would be by increasing the negativity of the membrane potential beyond that of its resting level. As noted above, the resting membrane potential is normally about -70 mV, and a change of about 10 mV to the threshold level of -60 mV initiates spike discharge. If we could shift the membrane potential in the opposite direction to a value of -73 mV (for example), then an EPSP of 10 mV that had previously caused discharge of the cell would now only shift the membrane potential back to -63 mV—still 3 mV below the spike discharge threshold. This is essentially what takes place during inhibition; there is a brief *increase* in the negativity of the membrane potential. However, the reasons why this increased negativity inhibits the excitation of the cell are somewhat more complicated than is implied by the notion of a simple algebraic summation effect on the EPSP.

A diagram of the type of experiment used to study inhibition is shown in Figure 7.5. We are now stimulating the disynaptic inhibitory system (nerve at (b) in Figure 7.5), which has a synaptic inhibitory action on the motor neuron whose membrane potential we are recording. A series of motor neuron membrane potential responses to a graded series of nerve stimuli is shown in Figure 7.12, taken from Eccles (1957). As the stimulus increases from A through D, there is a brief increase or *hyperpolarization* of the membrane potential. In this experiment the increase reaches a maximum when the stimulus has increased to the level used in D, and does not increase further at the higher stimulus intensity (E). This brief hyperpolarization has been termed by Eccles the inhibitory postsynaptic potential (IPSP). The form of the IPSP is approximately similar to that of the EPSP, and although of somewhat shorter duration (about 8 msec), is essentially a mirror image. Just as with the EPSP the IPSP is a potential shift associated with a brief current flow. However, the current flow is of course in the opposite direction, resulting in hyperpolarization.

IPSPs have been recorded from nerve cells in a wide variety of structures in the CNS. Perhaps the most significant generalization concerning regional differences is that in higher regions of the brain the time course of the IPSP is *very much longer* than in cells of the spinal cord. The spinal motor neuron, and neurons forming the cells of origin of spinal afferent tracts, have IPSPs of about 8 msec duration. In the cerebral cortex, on the other hand, most IPSPs are 100 to 200 msec in duration (Phillips, 1956). Thalamic neurons also have IPSPs of 100 msec or more (Purpura and Cohen, 1962). Cells in the hippocampus may have IPSPs of over 200 msec duration (Kandel and Spencer, 1961). Thus a single inhibitory action on neurons can last more than 0.2 seconds in brain structures, a fact that would seem of some importance for theories of brain function.

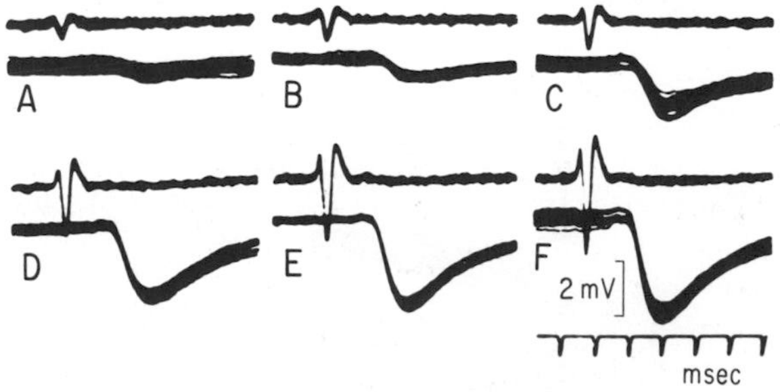

Figure 7.12. Increasing inhibitory "activation" of a motor neuron. The cell membrane potential shows a brief hyperpolarization (IPSP) which increases with increasing inhibitory activation. (Upper trace in each is the size of the afferent nerve volley eliciting the IPSP.) (Taken from Eccles, 1958)

The ionic mechanisms responsible for the IPSP are less well understood than for the EPSP. It appears that, as with the EPSP, the membrane becomes briefly permeable to certain ions. However unlike the EPSP, it does not seem to be permeable to all small ions. If it were, it would simply be a depolarizing EPSP rather than a hyperpolarizing IPSP (as noted above, the EPSP results from a brief increase in permeability to all small ions). Since the IPSP is a further *increase* in the negative potential of the membrane opposite in direction to the decreased negativity of the EPSP, the current (i.e. ion flow) must be in the opposite direction. Hence, the membrane must become *selectively permeable* to only certain ions. The most logical candidates are chloride and potassium. The equilibrium potentials of both these ions are more negative than the resting membrane potential. In fact the equilibrium potential of Cl⁻ is about 5 mV more negative than the resting membrane potential, which is just about the size of the maximum IPSP that can be induced. If the membrane did become permeable only to Cl⁻, for example, chloride ions would now flow down their concentration gradient and shift the membrane potential briefly to a more negative level, just as happens during the IPSP.

The experimental method used to attack this problem in the vertebrate spinal motor neuron involves electrophoretic injection of ions into the cell. Suppose, for example, that passive movement of chloride ions produces the IPSP. If we increase the internal concentration of chloride by introducing a KCl-filled pipette inside the cell and running a current through it, the differential concentration of Cl⁻ inside and outside the cell will change. Consequently, the electrochemical gradient will change; and the form of the IPSP should also change. This is illustrated in Figure 7.13, where an IPSP is first recorded; Cl⁻ is then electrophoretically injected into the cell, and the subsequent "IPSP" from identical stimulation of the same input is actually inverted, resembling an EPSP in form. Although the inverted IPSP now resembles an EPSP in form, it is still an IPSP. It still reflects inhibitory synaptic actions on the nerve cell. It is inverted in form simply because we have increased the concentration of chloride ions inside the cell to the point at which the equilibrium potential for chloride is somewhat more positive than the resting membrane potential. If the slight membrane barrier to Cl⁻ ions now breaks down as a result of postsynaptic inhibitory actions, the chloride ions will flow down their new concentration gradient in a direction opposite to the normal direction, thus producing a

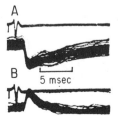

Figure 7.13. Injection of chloride ions in the nerve cell reverses the form of a hyperpolarizing IPSP and makes it appear like an EPSP. **A**, normal IPSP. **B**, after chloride injection. (Taken from Eccles, 1961)

positive going IPSP. Eccles (1964) has hypothesized that the membrane briefly becomes selectively permeable to both K^+ and Cl^- ions. The normal equilibrium potentials of these ions are such that brief passive movements would be expected to yield an hyperpolarizing potential change (IPSP).

The observed shifts in cell membrane potential that constitute the EPSP and the IPSP have permitted explanation of a wide variety of CNS phenomena in terms of synaptic mechanisms (see below). As would be expected, when an EPSP and an IPSP are simultaneously generated in a cell, a compromise voltage level results. Inhibitory activity suppress excitatory activity; strong excitatory activity can overcome inhibitory effects, etc.

The interplay of these two postsynaptic potentials thus produces the net excitability observed for a nerve cell. However, it is an oversimplification to state that the resulting excitability level is a simple algebraic sum of the EPSP and IPSP activity. The IPSP has a greater effect on an EPSP than would be so predicted. It must be kept in mind that during an EPSP or IPSP the membrane potential has shifted away from resting level and the discrepancies between the various "passive" potentials predicted from distributions of ions and the resting potential are now altered, resulting in differing discrepancies from "equilibrium" potentials (see Chapter 6). For example, the depolarization of the EPSP displaces the membrane potential further from the equilibrium potential for the IPSP. Hence an IPSP now yields a much larger absolute shift in membrane potential when it shifts the membrane potential toward its equilibrium potential (i.e. toward the chloride equilibrium potential). In addition the current flow during an hyperpolarizing IPSP is in the opposite direction to that during the EPSP. Although the details of these interactions are fairly complex, it is only necessary for us to realize that such effects occur, and are predictable from the postulated mechanisms for the EPSP and IPSP. The major point to keep in mind is that the EPSP and IPSP result from oppositely directed currents and shift the membrane potential in opposite directions. A net shift of the membrane potential up to about -60 mV must occur to reach firing threshold.

PRESYNAPTIC INHIBITION

There is another kind of inhibition of neuron activity present in the central nervous system having a longer time course than postsynaptic inhibition. Frank and Fuortes (1957) presented convincing evidence for its existence and termed it *presynaptic inhibition*. Subsequently, Eccles and his colleagues have amplified our understanding of it considerably (Eccles, 1963, 1964). The existence of this inhibitory effect is revealed by a very simple experiment. Suppose we stimulate an afferent nerve having monosynaptic input to a spinal motor neuron (*a* and *x* of Figure 7.5). We now deliver another stimulus to a different nerve (often called a conditioning stimulus) just prior to stimulation of the monosynaptic input. The monosynaptic EPSP elicited by the second stimulus is reduced in amplitude if the first (conditioning) stimulus occurs within about 1/4 second of the second stimulus. Figure 7.14 shows the percent reduction in the monosynaptic EPSP as a function of time after the conditioning stimulus. The depression of the monosynaptic EPSP is maximum at about 20 msec and lasts for more than 200 msec. This is a very long-lasting depressive or inhibitory effect when compared to the 8 msec IPSP.

The experiment just described merely demonstrates that the monosynaptic stimulus is less effective when preceded by a conditioning stimulus to certain other nerves. The various kinds of experimental arrangements used to study the depression effect, and some of the proposed explanations, are indicated in Figure 7.15. The experiment described above simply involves stimulating the conditioning nerve (b) and then stimulating the monosynaptic afferent nerve (a) and recording the postsynaptic potentials of the cell body with microelectrode M. There are at least two different classes of explanations that could account for the depression effect. Input (b) could exert long-lasting postsynaptic inhibitory effects on the cell through chains of interneurons. These are shown terminating either directly on the cell soma (y) or on a distant portion of a dendrite (z). Alternatively, the conditioning input could act directly on the monosynaptic excitatory synapses (x) to decrease their effectiveness.

Let us consider first the possible role of direct IPSP action on the soma (*Y* in Figure 7.15). If reverberating chains of neurons were involved, it would certainly be possible for IPSPs to be generated on the soma of the spinal motor neuron for several hundred msec. If this were the case, we would record IPSPs from the microelectrode (*M*) in the soma following the conditioning stimulus to (b). Frank and Fuortes (1957) demonstrated that in fact *no IPSPs* were generated in the soma. A variety of techniques such as ion injection and electrical stimulation of the cell via the microelectrode (see above) demonstrated conclusively that there was no change whatever in the excitability of the motor neuron membrane during the period of EPSP depression following the conditioning stimulus. Consequently the mechanism indicated by the circuit labeled *Y* in Figure 7.15 must be rejected.

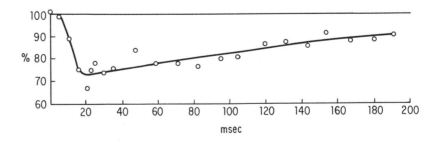

Figure 7.14. The time course of presynaptic inhibition. (Taken from J. C. Eccles, R. M. Eccles, and F. Magni, 1961)

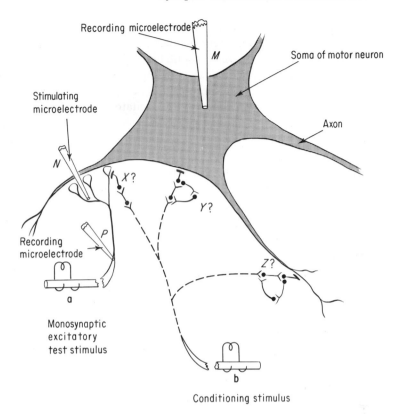

Figure 7.15. Various possible synaptic mechanisms that might produce "presynaptic inhibition." Mechanism X would act by altering the excitability of the afferent terminal of the monosynaptic afferent fiber; mechanism Y would act by inducing long-lasting postsynaptic inhibition of the motor neuron, and mechanism Z would act by inducing "remote inhibition" on the distal portions of dendrites.

Frank (1959) suggested an alternative mechanism illustrated by circuit Z in Figure 7.15 to account for the depression effect. Just as with Y, Z assumes a reverberating system of neurons that maintain a bombardment of inhibitory activity (IPSPs) on the motor neuron. However he postulated that they synapsed far out on the dendrites rather than on the soma. It is theoretically possible that IPSPs induced in dendrites remote from the cell body would produce inhibitory effects on the excitability of the cell, which simply could not be recorded by microelectrode (M) in the cell body. Frank (1959) proposed such an explanation and termed it *remote inhibition*.

While it remains to be demonstrated that remote inhibition does or does not occur in this situation, Eccles and colleagues have marshaled a convincing array of evidence favoring a quite different mechanism to account for the long-lasting depression effects of the conditioning stimulus on the monosynaptic EPSP.

Eccles' hypothesis is schematized by X in Figure 7.15. He assumed that the conditioning stimulus activated neurons that themselves synapsed on the synaptic terminal knobs of the monosynaptic fibers. These would be an instance of the axoaxonic synapse described at the beginning of the chapter. Eccles proposed that these synapses act on the presynaptic terminals of the incoming monosynaptic fibers to inhibit the induction of excitatory postsynaptic potentials in the motor neuron. In other words he suggested that it was a literal instance of presynaptic inhibition.

If Eccles hypothesis were correct, what kind of change in the membrane potentials of the monosynaptic afferent terminal knobs would be induced by the axoaxonic synapses of circuit X (Figure 7.15)? At this point we must assume without a proof a fact which has been demonstrated regarding the synaptic generation of EPSPs: the size of an EPSP is directly related to the size of the spike potential (i.e. the total shift in the membrane potential) that *arrives at the presynaptic terminal*. This is illustrated in Figure 7.16. If the membrane potential is at its normal resting level of about -70 mV, the spike potential will be a shift of about 110 mV (i.e. a brief shift from -70 mV to $+40$ mV, see Chapter 6). The EPSP induced after the spike reaches the terminal knob will be of a given

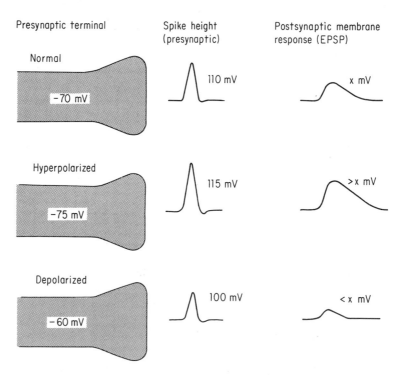

Figure 7.16. Hypothetical relationship of spike height in presynaptic terminal to size of EPSP induced in postsynaptic membrane.

level, as in Figure 7.16A. If a conditioning stimulus now acted on the presynaptic terminal in such a way as to induce an IPSP on the terminal, the terminal membrane would become hyperpolarized and might shift to −75 mV. The total shift during the action potential would now be 115 mV and a larger than normal EPSP would be induced in the membrane of the motor neuron (Figure 7.16B). This clearly cannot be the case in presynaptic inhibition since the EPSP is smaller, not larger, following the conditioning stimulus. On the other hand, if the conditioning circuit (X in Figure 7.15) induced a partial *depolarization* of the monosynaptic presynaptic terminals, say to a level of −60 mV, then the total shift in the action potential would be only 100 mV. This would induce a smaller than normal EPSP (Figure 7.16C). Since the latter effect is just what does occur in presynaptic inhibition, Eccles suggested that the conditioning stimulus acts through chains of interneurons to partially depolarize the membranes of the monosynaptic afferent terminal knobs.

Two different types of experiments have provided strong evidence favoring Eccles' hypothesis. The first and most direct line of evidence consisted simply in recording the membrane potentials of the afferent terminal fibers (microelectrode P in Figure 7.15) following the conditioning stimulus to (b). As postulated, the conditioning stimulus did cause a partial depolarization of the afferent terminal fibers (Eccles, Magni, and Willis, 1962). This partial depolarization has an identical time course to that of presynaptic inhibition (Figure 7.14).

The second line of evidence employs a technique developed by Wall (1958) for testing the excitability of afferent terminal fibers. A stimulating microelectrode (N in Figure 7.15) is inserted in the region of the afferent terminations. Stimulation through this microelectrode produces antidromic activation of the monosynaptic afferent nerve fibers. The size of the antidromic response can be measured by substituting a recording electrode for the stimulating electrode at point (a) of Figure 7.15. If the afferent terminals were partially depolarized following the conditioning volley to b, their excitability to direct electrical stimulation will be increased (thus if firing threshold in a fiber were −55 mV, an electrical stimulus at N would have to shift the membrane from the normal resting level of −70 mV to −55 mV to fire in the normal state, but if the conditioning circuit reduced the potential to −60 mV, the electrical stimulus at N would only have to shift the membrane from −60 mV to −55 mV, a total of 5 mV. Consequently, the electrical excitability of the fiber terminals should be increased following the conditioning stimulus. This is just what happens (Eccles, Magni, and Wallis, 1962). Again the time course of the increased antidromic response parallels exactly the time course of presynaptic inhibition.

A summary diagram of the mechanism for presynaptic inhibition is shown in Figure 7.17. Stimulation of the conditioning nerve activates a circuit of neurons that terminate in axoaxonic synapses on the afferent terminal knobs of incoming fibers having monosynaptic connections to the motor neuron. These act to partially *depolarize* the monosynaptic afferent terminal fibers for a period of more than 200 msec. If the monosynaptic fibers are stimulated during

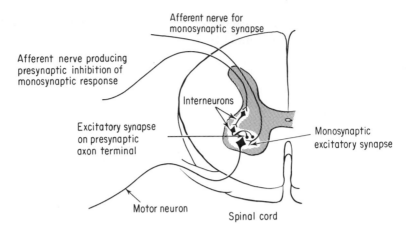

Figure 7.17. Mechanism postulated by Eccles to account for presynaptic inhibition. Interneurons terminate on the afferent terminals of monosynaptic excitatory afferent fibers, partially depolarizing them when activated. This yields a smaller than normal spike height in the afferent terminals, which yields a smaller than normal EPSP in the motor neuron. (See Eccles, 1964)

this time, the spike potentials reaching the terminal knobs will be smaller in magnitude, will release less transmitter substance and will induce smaller EPSPs in the motor neuron.

It is worth noting that the mechanism developed by Eccles and colleagues to account for presynaptic inhibition does not rule out Frank's "remote inhibition" as a possible type of inhibitory interaction among neurons. However, remote inhibition obviously cannot account for the demonstrated partial depolarization of afferent terminal fibers involved in presynaptic inhibition. Granit, Kellerth, and Williams (1964) have recently presented evidence suggesting the occurrence of a process resembling remote or dendritic inhibition in spinal cord motor neurons.

The very long time course of presynaptic inhibition merits reemphasis. An inhibitory effect lasting more than 2/10 of a second following a single stimulus obviously can play a significant role in neural control of behavior. The regions of the CNS where presynaptic inhibition has been found suggest a possible functional utility for this mechanism. It has been demonstrated in local spinal reflexes, on synaptic relays to ascending cutaneous and cerebellar tracts, at the gracile and cuneate nuclei, and in the somatic sensory region of the thalamus (Eccles, 1964). Descending tracts from the cerebral cortex and brain stem exert presynaptic inhibitory effects on incoming somatic afferent fibers (Eccles, 1964). In brief, presynaptic inhibition acts on incoming and ascending fibers that convey sensory information to the brain. The systems that exert presynaptic inhibition on these sensory fibers include both peripheral inputs and descending central tracts. Eccles suggests that presynaptic inhibition may function "as a negative feedback on the inflow of sensory information into the CNS" (1964,

p. 234). We will consider this further in our discussion of efferent regulation of incoming sensory information in Chapter 10.

Presynaptic excitation

Recent experiments suggest that another type of "presynaptic" synaptic process may occur (Lundberg and Vyklický, 1963; Mendell and Wall, 1965; Kandel and Tauc, 1964). In brief, it appears that under some conditions excitability changes in afferent fiber terminals may result in a larger than normal degree of synaptic excitation. The experimental demonstrations of this effect are rather complicated. Mendell and Wall, for example, utilized measurements of the *dorsal root potential* in the cat. If a dorsal root or afferent nerve is stimulated, a gross evoked response can be recorded from an adjacent dorsal root. This negative gross potential appears to reflect primarily the depolarization of the terminals of large afferent cutaneous nerves in the spinal cord (Barron and Matthews, 1938). Mendell and Wall showed that if small afferent nerve fibers (*C* fibers) were first stimulated tetanically (repeated high frequency stimulation), the dorsal root potential elicited by subsequent stimulation of the large afferent fibers has a positive component. They interpret this to mean that the large afferent fiber terminals are *hyperpolarized.*

Mendell and Wall also stimulated the afferent terminal fibers electrically through a microelectrode, and measured the amplitude of the antidromic volley. As predicted, the antidromic response was smaller when preceded by tetanic stimulation of *C* fibers. This would be expected if the terminals were in fact hyperpolarized by the conditioning stimulus to *C* fibers. Such a finding is the exact opposite of what occurs in presynaptic inhibition, where partial *depolarization* of the afferent terminals by the conditioning stimulus leads to an increased antidromic response.

The mechanisms involved in presynaptic excitation are not known. It may be that the small *C* fibers activate interneurons that synapse back on the large afferent fiber terminals and induce membrane hyperpolarization. This would lead to greater than normal spike height, which in turn might lead to greater release of transmitter substance at the excitatory synapses formed by the large afferent terminals on cells in the spinal cord, as suggested in Figure 6.16B. The process would then be analogous but opposite in effect to presynaptic inhibition. In any event the net effect of presynaptic excitation appears to be an increase in the amount of postsynaptic excitation evoked in cells in the spinal cord by the large afferent fiber terminals.

Synaptic interactions among neurons

Essentially all interactions among neurons in the mammalian nervous system occur at synapses. The four types of synaptic interaction described in this chapter, the excitatory postsynaptic potential (EPSP), the inhibitory postsynaptic potential (IPSP), presynaptic inhibition, and presynaptic excitation are the major kinds of synaptic processes that have been demonstrated for mammals. Other types of synaptic interactions are logical possibilities. Frank's remote inhibition may occur (Granit, Kellerth, and Williams, 1964), as could an analogous kind of remote excitation (i.e. excitatory influences acting on dendrites at such a distance from the some that no membrane potential change would be recorded from a microelectrode in the cell soma). However, at present these and other hypothetical synaptic processes remain only as possibilities.

The three best known types of synaptic interactions among neurons are diagrammed in Figure 7.18. The organization of the various synaptic endings is roughly characteristic for a variety of neurons including the spinal motor neuron. Excitatory endings are shown terminating on the dendrites (Type 1 synapse) and inhibitory endings terminating on the soma (Type 2 synapse). The The fiber terminals labeled a_1, a_2 and a_3 are endings which mediate the EPSP. When activated by spike discharges traveling down the axon terminals to the presynaptic knobs on dendrites, EPSPs are induced in the postsynaptic membrane of the cell (i.e. soma and dendrites). Spatial and temporal summation of excitation are mediated by these endings. For example, activation of a_1 alone or a_2 alone might not yield EPSPs large enough to initiate a spike, but activation of both together could yield sufficiently large EPSP to fire a spike down the axon (spatial summation). Alternatively, two stimuli to a_1 sufficiently close together in time could initiate a spike.

Terminals mediating the IPSP are labeled b_1, b_2 and b_3. In all cases the synaptic ending is on the cell soma. Activation of any of these channels induces the hyperpolarizing IPSP in the cell membrane. The two inhibitory channels labelled b_1 and b_2 represent inhibitory fibers from other neurons, b_2 showing a

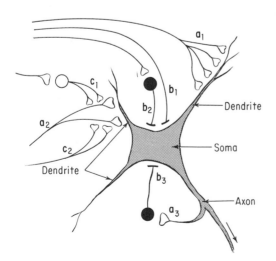

Figure 7.18. Summary of the three best known types of synaptic processes. Postsynaptic excitation shown at a_1, a_2 and a_3; postsynaptic inhibition at b_1, b_2 and b_3; presynaptic inhibition at c_1 and c_2. (See text)

small inhibitory interneuron, which itself is activated by an excitatory terminal. The activation of b_3 by an excitatory ending branching off from the motor cell axon is a very common type of organization. The branching fiber from the axon is called a *recurrent collateral* fiber. Such fibers typically synapse on inhibitory interneurons which act back on the soma of the cell and on neighboring cells.

Synaptic terminals mediating presynaptic inhibition are shown by c_1 and c_2. In both cases the terminal knobs synapse on the synaptic endings of excitatory channel a_2. The terminal knobs of c_1 and c_2 are themselves excitatory, and induce partial depolarization of the excitatory knobs of a_2. As described above, this results in a reduced EPSP in the postsynaptic from activation via a_2.

Although the organization of synaptic endings on the cell shown in Figure 7.18 is representative, there are actually thousands of synaptic endings on the cell. Figures 7.2 and 7.3C give some indication of the extensive number of synaptic terminals covering the cell soma and dendrites. In fact the soma and dendrites may have an essentially continuous covering of synaptic terminal knobs. In the normal state the cell is continuously being bombarded with excitatory and inhibitory synaptic influences, and many excitatory inputs are themselves being altered by presynaptic inhibitory (and excitatory) influences. The extent to which the cell is or is not firing all-or-none spike potentials down the axon is determined by the dynamic balance among these classes of synaptic events. This complexity of organization makes it very clear that the simple diagrams of the nervous system commonly shown in discussions of neural models and networks (i.e. each neuron synapsing on only one or two other neurons, and all synapses excitatory) must inevitably fail to predict the complexity of behavior of the real nervous system.

SUGGESTED READINGS

Eccles, J. C. *The physiology of nerve cells.* Baltimore: John Hopkins Press, 1957.
Eccles, J. C. *The physiology of synapses.* New York: Academic Press, 1964.
McLennan, H. *Synaptic transmission.* Philadelphia: Saunders, 1963.

CHAPTER 8

SYNAPTIC TRANSMISSION: II. CHEMICAL MEDIATION

In the last chapter we discussed at length the electrical phenomena associated with synaptic transmission. However we said nothing about how activity is actually transferred or transmitted from one neuron to another, or from neurons to effectors (muscle or gland cells). One of the most vigorous controversies in neurophysiology has concerned the nature of the mechanism whereby neural activity conducted to the presynaptic terminals of one neuron crosses the synaptic space to activate the postsynaptic membrane of another neuron to produce an EPSP or IPSP. The central point at issue in this controversy has been the nature of the mediating transmitter mechanism. The two major opposing theories have postulated either a chemical process or an electrical process (Figure 8.1). (The argument has sometimes facetiously been termed the "soup vs juice" controversy.) In the 1940s the evidence seemed to favor the electrical hypothesis. However, today the overwhelming mass of evidence favors the chemical theory, at least for the mammalian nervous system (electrical synapses have been found in certain invertebrates). It is of some interest to recall that Eccles shared the Nobel prize in 1963 primarily for his research efforts demonstrating the chemical basis of synaptic transmission. Yet in the 1940s he was one of the proponents of

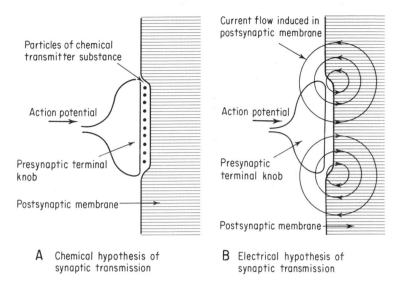

Particles of chemical
transmitter substance

Action potential
→

Presynaptic terminal
knob

Postsynaptic membrane

Current flow induced in
postsynaptic membrane

Action potential
→

Presynaptic
terminal knob

Postsynaptic membrane

A Chemical hypothesis of
synaptic transmission

B Electrical hypothesis of
synaptic transmission

Figure 8.1.   Schematic illustrating the chemical (**A**) and electrical (**B**) hypotheses of synaptic transmission. (See text)

the electrical hypothesis. In both instances his analyses were consistent with the bulk of available data.

The chemical theory of synaptic transmission assumes that when the axon spike potential reaches the presynaptic terminals, small amounts of some chemical transmitter substance are released across the synaptic space to activate the postsynaptic membrane, resulting in the graded postysnaptic potential. This idea is illustrated in Figure 8.1A. The electrical theory assumes a purely passive electrical process. When the axon spike potential reaches the presynaptic terminals, current flow in these structures induces current flow and hence graded postsynaptic potentials in the postsynaptic membrane, more or less as is the case in an ordinary electrical transformer. This theory is illustrated in Figure 8.1B. The evidence favoring the chemical theory (see Eccles, 1957, 1964) may be summarized as follows:

1. Both excitatory and inhibitory postsynaptic potentials can be recorded from the same motor neurons. Since the presynaptic action potential always has the same electrical characteristics only one kind of postsynaptic potential could be generated by electrical induction. It is thus difficult to conceive how an electrical process could give rise to an hyperpolarizing IPSP. On the other hand, it is easy to postulate two (or more) different chemical substances having opposite effects on the postsynaptic membrane.

2. There is no detectable potential change in the postsynaptic membrane

during the occurrence of the presynaptic action potential in the presynaptic terminals. The EPSP and IPSP begin only after the summit of the presynaptic spike potential has occurred. If electric induction were involved, the postsynaptic responses would have to develop with the presynaptic potentials in time (see Figure 8.1). However, if a chemical substance must be released and cross the synaptic space, the observed time courses of the pre- and postsynaptic potentials are consistent with each other.

3. In line with the above evidence, the irreducible synaptic delay time, the time between the occurrence of the presynaptic spike and the postsynaptic response, is about 0.3 msec. This is too long a time interval for electrical induction. On the other hand the calculated time required for diffusion of a chemical substance across the 200 Å synaptic space is about this long.

4. If the postsynaptic resting membrane potential is altered, either by imposing currents upon it with stimulating microelectrodes, or by injecting ions, the forms of the EPSP and IPSP alter markedly. The IPSP may even reverse in polarity. These effects cannot be explained by electrical induction, but are entirely explicable in terms of specialized changes in ionic permeability resulting from the actions of various transmitter chemicals.

5. It is possible to calculate the amplitude of the presynaptic spike at the presynaptic terminal and the amplitude of a postsynaptic response that it would generate on the basis of electrical induction. The observed postsynaptic response is many times larger than the calculated response. However, if the function of the presynaptic spike is to liberate a chemical transmitter substance, there need be no particular relationship between the amplitudes of the pre- and postsynaptic responses.

6. One argument that had been used against a chemical theory noted that the same axons can produce both excitatory and inhibitory effects on different spinal motor neurons. Since transmitter substances must be manufactured by the metabolic processes of the cell, a given cell and its axon terminals ought to have only one transmitter substance. (This is often referred to as Dale's principle after the neuropharmacologist H. H. Dale.) One way the chemical theory could handle this difficulty is to postulate that an interneuron exists in one channel. Suppose that a given incoming axon synapses directly on a motor neuron, exerting an excitatory effect, and also exerts an inhibitory effect on another motor neuron. If the axon terminal that produced inhibition actually ended in an excitatory synapse on a small interneuron, which in turn had an inhibitory synaptic action on the motor neuron, the effect would be consistent with Dale's principle. The axon would produce direct excitation of one motor neuron and would also produce excitation of the interneuron. The latter would in turn act to inhibit the other motor neuron. Thus the original axon would have a monosynaptic excitatory action and a disynaptic (two-synapse) inhibitory action. We discussed electrical aspects of these two reflex pathways in Chapter 7. Consistent with the chemical hypothesis is the fact that in every instance in which postsynaptic inhibition has been so studied, an inhibitory interneuron has been found to exist.

Specific transmitter substances

Since the evidence for chemical transmission is virtually conclusive, a vigorous search for specific transmitter substances is currently in progress. A number of requirements must be fulfilled in order to prove beyond question that a given chemical is in fact the excitatory or inhibitory transmitter substance at a particular type of synapse. These requirements can be more or less formalized as follows (see Paton, 1958, for a complete discussion):

1. Presynaptic terminals must contain the substance or an immediate precursor (a substance that becomes the transmitter).

2. Neural impulses in presynaptic terminals must cause liberation of the substance.

3. Injection of normal (i.e. very low) concentrations of the substance must cause activation of the postsynaptic cell membranes.

4. An enzyme that destroys or inactivates the substance must be found in the vicinity of the synapse.

5. If drugs are known that inactivate or block the action of the substance, they must block synaptic transmission at the synapse in question.

As of this writing, there is no type of synapse or possible transmitter substance in the CNS for which all of these criteria can be met. On the other hand, there are several instances in peripheral synapses or neuro-muscular junctions where specific transmitter substances have been identified. Acetylcholine (ACh) is the transmitter substance at the parasympathetic neuroeffector junctions (the junctions between the motor nerve cells and the smooth muscle or gland cells), the synapses of all autonomic ganglia and at the skeletal neuromuscular junctions. Noradrenalin appears to be the transmitter substance at the sympathetic neuroeffector junctions. We will consider these systems first, before examining possibilities in the CNS.

It may seem surprising that no transmitter substances have yet been found for synapses of the CNS. However the technical problems involved in satisfying the criteria listed above are enormous. It is simply not possible to isolate physically a given type of synapse from the CNS; many different varieties of synapses exist in conglomeration. In contrast, at the neuro-muscular junction or autonomic ganglion a particular type of synapse already exists in isolated "pure culture." It is relatively easy, for example, to perfuse solutions through the blood vessels of an autonomic ganglion and measure the chemical substances liberated. Since the ganglion presumably contains only one type of synapse, it may be removed for biochemical analyses. Synapses of the central nervous system are not amenable to such experimental methods.

TRANSMISSION IN PERIPHERAL AUTONOMIC SYNAPSES

Historically, the demonstration that synaptic transmission was chemical, and that the chemical was ACh, was made for the parasympathetic peripheral junctions long before comparable analyses of striate muscle junctions. Otto Loewi proved it to be chemical in 1921 and its identification as ACh followed from Dale's early studies (1914). We will examine some of these early experiments, both because of the importance of the findings and because they are classical examples of the kinds of experimental analyses necessary to provide conclusive evidence regarding chemical mediation of synaptic transmission.

It is perhaps well to recall here that the parasympathetic (cranio-sacral) division of the autonomic nervous system sends long efferent (preganglionic) fibers to ganglia lying close to the "target organs" (all the various peripheral organs such as the heart, stomach, viscera, sweat glands, pupillary muscles, etc. innervated by the autonomic nervous system). Short postganglionic fibers synapse on the heart, smooth muscle, or gland cells of the target organs (see Figure 8.3). The sympathetic system, on the other hand, has its ganglia close to the spinal cord and sends out long postganglionic fibers to synapse on target organs. The sympathetic portion was characterized as having "emergency" functions and the parasympathetic as having more regulatory or "homeostatic" actions. For example, activation of the sympathetic system speeds up the heartbeat and stops peristaltic contractions of stomach muscles. Note that the actual influences on muscle cells here are opposite; heart is facilitated and stomach inhibited. However, both actions are consistent with the energizing or emergency influence of the sympathetic system. Increased heart rate provides better blood supply to skeletal muscles, and inhibition of stomach muscle contractions temporarily stops digestive actions, thus tending to free the organism for action. The parasympathetic system, on the other hand, causes slowing of the heart beat and increased contractions of stomach muscles, actions that tend to conserve and sustain the organism. The preganglionic parasympathetic nerve, which incidentally acts to slow the heart, is the *vagus* nerve, a portion of the tenth cranial nerve.

The first suggestion that the autonomic nervous system exerted its actions by releasing chemical substances was perhaps that of Elliott (1904). He noted that he could obtain "sympathetic" responses from organs normally innervated by the *sympathetic* system—after having cut the sympathetic nerves—by injecting an extract of the adrenal gland. He proposed that the sympathetic nerve fibers locally released a comparable substance. In 1914 Dale studied the effects of chemicals obtained from various plants (muscarine, for example, from certain mushrooms), which mimicked the actions of the *parasympathetic* system. His investigations led him to conclude that the active agent was acetylcholine (ACh). He reported that acetylcholine itself produced "pronounced vagus-like inhibition of the heart, and various other effects of stimulating nerves of the cranial and sacral divisions of the autonomic system—secretion of saliva, contraction of the oesophagus, stomach and intestine, and of the urinary bladder." These studies constitute the first links in the chain of evidence leading to the conclusion that ACh is the parasympathetic mediator and that adrenal gland extract (adrenalin and/or noradrenalin) is the sympathetic mediator. They fulfill Requirement 3 on page 195. Requirement 5, that blocking agents work both on the neural systems and on the substances also was partially fulfilled in these early studies.

These experiments are suggestive, but they do not prove that ACh and adrenal extract are in fact the transmitters in the autonomic system. Their actions could be an accidental result of sensitivity of the target organs, indirect mediation by other neural or peripheral structures, etc. It remained to be demonstrated that the autonomic system in fact exerted its actions by synaptic release of these substances. This was done by Loewi in 1921. His experiment, like most crucial experiments in biology, was exceedingly simple. Recall again that stimulation of the parasympathetic vagus nerve causes slowing of the heart. He filled a frog heart with Ringer's fluid (physiological saline together with certain other chemicals necessary to preserve tissue function) and electrically stimulated the vagus nerve. This of course caused a slowing of the heart. He then put the Ringer's solution on a second frog heart and it immediately caused slowing of the second heart. Control studies showed that no such slowing of the second heart resulted if the vagus to the first was not stimulated. This proves beyond reasonable question that stimulation of the vagus releases a substance at the heart that causes slowing of the heart. Loewi termed the unknown substance "Vagusstoff." Loewi also demonstrated the converse result by stimulating sympathetic fibers. Ringer's solution taken from the heart after sympathetic activation caused an increased heart rate in a second heart.

Viewed from an historical perspective Loewi's experimental demonstrations of chemical autonomic mediation would seem to be conclusive. However it is in the nature of scientists to be skeptical, and a heated controversy ensued for several years following Loewi's experiments. By the early 1930s the evidence overwhelmingly favored Loewi's findings and interpretations. The methods and results of a more sophisticated version of Loewi's experiment, done by Bain in 1932, are shown in Figure 8.2. Here both the donor and recipient hearts are studied simultaneously, using a flow system to transmit the Vagusstoff. Subsequent experiments done in Loewi's laboratory in the late 1920s, based on the earlier findings of Dale (1914), demonstrated that the Vagusstoff released at the heart by the vagus nerve was acetylcholine. These experiments fulfill Requirements 1 and 2 listed above. Finally, Plattner (1926) demonstrated that the enzyme which inactivated ACh, acetyl cholinesterase (ACHE), was present in the heart (Requirement 4 page 195).

During this same period Cannon and associates were studying the nature of the substance released by the postganglionic sympathetic nerves. To cite only one example, Cannon and Uridil (1921) demonstrated that stimulation of the hepatic

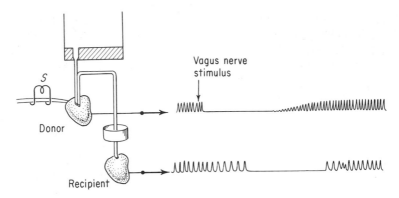

Figure 8.2. Experimental arrangement used by Loewi to demonstrate that electrical stimulation of the vagus nerve (*S*) released a chemical transmitter substance, "Vagusstoff" (acetylcholine). A flow system carried fluid from the donor heart to a nonstimulated recipient. The latter also slowed following stimulation. (Redrawn from Patton, 1960, as modified from Bain, 1932)

nerve (sympathetic nerve to the liver) caused the release of a substance from the liver that accelerated the heart and increased the blood pressure, just as does injection of adrenal gland extract. A number of subsequent experiments indicated that the postganglionic sympathetic transmitter substance (transmitter from postganglionic nerves to target organs) was either adrenalin (epinephrin) or a closely related compound (Cannon and Rosenblueth, 1937). More recent research has shown that norepinephrine (noradrenalin), differing chemically from epinephrine (adrenalin) only in that a methyl group, CH_3, is absent, is probably the transmitter rather than epinephrine (Von Euler, 1959).

Our discussion above has been limited to the substances mediating transmission from postganglionic fibers to target organs. It has been shown conclusively that the transmitter agent at all ganglionic synapses (junctions of preganglionic fibers with cells of the postganglionic fibers), both sympathetic and parasympathetic, is acetylcholine. Thus, ACh is the transmitter at the ganglionic and postganglionic neuroeffector synapses of the parasympathetic system, and at the ganglionic synapses of the sympathetic system, and norepinephrine is the transmitter at sympathetic postganglionic neuroeffector synapses (see Figure 8.3). There is at least one clearly demonstrated exception to this rule however: sympathetic postganglionic innervation of the sweat glands is mediated by ACh. Due in part to this exception, the distinction between sympathetic and parasympathetic portions of the autonomic system—which is made on purely anatomical grounds—is sometimes not used. Instead, the two general categories of action are distinguished on the basis of the reactivity of the peripheral organs to the chemical mediators, namely acetylcholine or noradrenalin. Those responding to acetylcholine are called *cholinergic* and those responding to noradrenalin (or adrenalin) are called *adrenergic*. For the most part, cholinergic = parasympathetic, and adrenergic = sympathetic.

We noted earlier that stimulation of the vagus nerve slows down the heart but increases stomach muscle activity. Both of these regulatory actions are mediated by the same transmitter agent, ACh. Here is an instance in which the same chemical transmitter produces opposite effects (excitation or inhibition) depending upon the receptor muscle. ACh is both an excitatory and an inhibitory transmitter substance in the parasympathetic system. Its opposite actions on the different muscles must be attributed to differences in the muscle cells, i.e. differences in the way the cells respond to ACh.

The medullary portion of the adrenal gland (adrenal medulla) is an interesting variant of the autonomic system. Embryologically it derives from the same tissues as do the sympathetic postganglionic nerve fibers. However instead of sending axons to target organs, the cells of the adrenal medulla secrete epinephrine and norepinephrine directly into the blood stream.

The neural organization and transmitter agents of the autonomic system appear to be a relatively neat and tidy package, as indicated in Figure 8.3. All preganglionic fibers secrete ACh, postganglionic parasympathetic secrete ACh, and postganglionic sympathetic fibers (except sweat glands) secrete norepinephrine. However, recent studies have complicated this picture somewhat. It appears that in the sympathetic ganglia, in addition to regular ACh transmission, there may be indirect activation of postganglionic cells via an *epinephrine*-releasing cell (R. M. Eccles and Libet, 1961). Furthermore there is evidence that both ACh receptor sites and AChE may be present on the *pre*ganglionic terminals

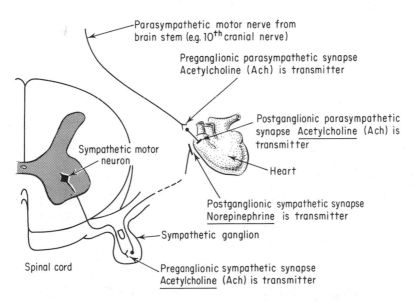

Figure 8.3. Summary of the organization and chemical transmitter substances involved in the peripheral autonomic system. The heart is shown as an example of a typical target organ.

as well as the postganglionic membranes (Koelle, 1961, 1962). These complications indicate that much remains to be worked out, even on the relatively "well understood" autonomic system. The interested reader can consult Eccles (1964) for further discussion.

Transmission at the Neuromuscular Junction

Development of our understanding of neuromuscular transmission also preceded analysis of synapses in the central nervous system. Microelectrode studies, particularly those by Katz and his colleagues, demonstrated the basic mechanisms involved. A wide range of experiments have satisfied all the necessary criteria listed above to show that transmission is chemical and that the transmitter substance is ACh (Del Castillo and Katz, 1954, 1957; Fatt, 1954; Fatt and Katz, 1951, 1952; Katz, 1962; Nachmansohn, 1955).

A schematic diagram of the neuromuscular junction is shown in Figure 8.4. The nerve axon terminal branches out to form an end plate on muscle fiber.

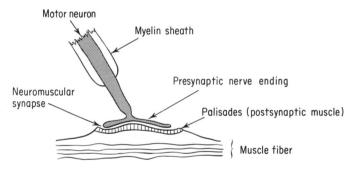

Figure 8.4. Schematic drawing of the neuromuscular junction. (Redrawn from Acheson, 1948)

The muscle fiber is structurally different directly under the nerve plate (palisades), the two being separated by a narrow synaptic space. Histochemical studies have shown that the postsynaptic membrane contains acetylcholine esterase (AChE), the enzyme that breaks down ACh. Bound ACh (see Chapter 5) is present in vesicles contained in the presynaptic nerve ending. An axon spike arriving at the presynaptic membrane releases a small amount of ACh. It is believed that a large number of sites each releases a packet or "quanta" of ACh containing from 1,000 to 10,000 ACh molecules. ACh combines with receptor molecules on the muscle membrane and is broken down by AChE. When ACh combines on the membrane, the ionic barriers normally present break down, ions flow down their electrochemical gradients and generate the end plate potential (EPP) (Figure 8.5). The EPP is analogous to an EPSP; when it reaches firing threshold an all-or-none impulse is propagated down the muscle fiber, resulting

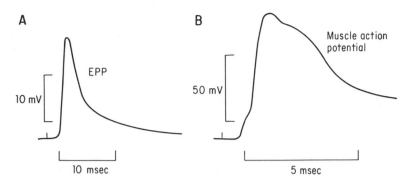

Figure 8.5. **A,** the muscle end plate potential (EPP) recorded intracellularly from a single muscle fiber (the fiber was treated with curare to prevent the development of the muscle action potential, which would mask the EPP response). **B,** intracellularly recorded muscle action potential (as in **A** but without curare). Note the difference in amplitude calibrations for **A** and **B**. The action potential (**B**) is six times larger than the EPP (**A**). (Redrawn from Fatt and Katz, 1951)

in contraction. Compounds that block ACh (e.g. curare) block neuromuscular transmission and compounds that inactivate AChE (e.g. prostigmine) cause prolonged activation of muscle fibers by permitting ACh to continue its activation. A complication for the tidy neuromuscular transmission schema has been introduced by observations suggesting there may be ACh receptor sites on the presynaptic *neural* elements of neuromuscular junctions (Werner, 1960a,b). It is not clear as yet just what role they may play in normal neuromuscular transmission.

Since ACh is released in quanta upon excitation, it is possible that spontaneous release of ACh quanta could occur in the absence of neural excitation. If this happens, very small EPPs ought to be recorded from the muscle fiber. Such is the case—these miniature spontaneous EPPs were first recorded by Fatt and Katz (1952). An example is shown in Figure 8.6. They are comparable in all characteristics to an impulse initiated EPP except that they are only about 1 percent of the EPP in amplitude.

In summary, the mechanisms of synaptic transmission across the neuromuscular junction are comparable to those for excitatory transmission in the

Figure 8.6. Spontaneous miniature end plate potentials recorded intracellularly from a muscle fiber. They occur in the absence of neural activation and are very much smaller in amplitude than is a neurally induced EPP. (Redrawn from Fatt and Katz, 1952)

CNS. Remember that historically these mechanisms were first worked out for the neuromuscular junction, and the chemical transmitter clearly shown to be ACh. Comparable identification of transmitter substances in CNS synapses remains to be made. We have emphasized studies of neural synapses in this book because of their greater relevance to general problems of brain function.

SYNAPTIC TRANSMISSION IN THE CNS

Eccles (1957, 1964) has presented considerable evidence that ACh is the transmitter substance for one excitatory synapse in the central nervous system. This synapse is formed by a recurrent collateral (branch of a fiber that curves back toward the original cell body) from the axon of the spinal motor neuron, which synapses on a small interneuron called the Renshaw cell. This cell in turn synapses on the same and neighboring motor cell bodies (see Figure 8.7). This two-neuron chain is another example of a disynaptic inhibitory system. When the motor neuron discharges a spike potential out along its axon, the recurrent collateral activates the Renshaw cell through an excitatory synapse at (a). The Renshaw cell in turn induces postsynaptic inhibitory effects back upon the motor neuron through the inhibitory synapse (b). The system may act in general as a brake or damping mechanism. If the motor neurons fire very rapidly, causing strong contractions of a muscle, the Renshaw cells are also activated and damp down the motor neuron activities, thus preventing overcontraction of the muscle. The Renshaw system can be activated for experimental purposes by antidromic stimulation of the motor neuron axon at (c).

We noted earlier that a given nerve cell ought to have the same transmitter substance at all its axon terminals. The main axon of the motor neuron connects to muscle fibers through the neuromuscular junction. The transmitter substance here is ACh. Since the recurrent collateral fiber that synapses on the Renshaw cell is a portion of the same axon, its transmitter substance ought to be ACh too. This alone does not of course constitute proof; additional evidence

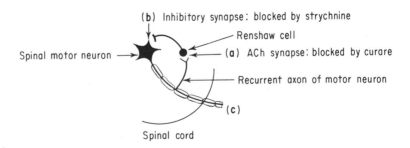

Figure 8.7. Schematic of the organization and transmitter actions for the Renshaw cell. (Redrawn from Eccles, 1957)

is available. Curare and related compounds block transmission at the neuro-muscular junction and other junctions where ACh is the transmitter agent. Curare also blocks activation of Renshaw cells.

Acetylcholine esterase (AChE), the enzyme that is found at the neuro-muscular junction and destroys acetylcholine, prevents continuing activation by a single release of ACh from the axon terminals. There are compounds termed anticholinesterases that inactivate AChE (e.g. D.F.P. and prostigmine). If an anticholinesterase is injected near a group of neuromuscular junctions, it will inactivate the AChE that is normally present. After activation of the motor neuron axons, ACh is released from the axon terminals at the neuromuscular junction. Normally this causes only a brief contraction of the muscle, ACh being rapidly broken down by AChE. However, if the AChE has been inactivated by injection of anti-AChE, ACh remains active at the synapse and continues to depolarize muscle fibers resulting in continuing contraction. A single antidromic stimulus to the axons of motor neurons (as at (c) in Figure 8.7) produces a brief burst of discharges in Renshaw cells lasting about 80 msec. After close injection of an anti-AChE, a single antidromic stimulus now results in repeated discharges of Renshaw cells lasting more than 1 second. The excitatory synapses on the Renshaw cell (a) thus are blocked by curare, and prolonged in their actions by anti-AChE in exactly the same way as is the neuromuscular junction. The presynaptic terminals of both, remember, come from the same motor neuron axons. Furthermore, close injection of ACh activates the Renshaw cells (Eccles, 1964).

Many compounds have been suggested as likely transmitter agents for the various excitatory and inhibitory synapses of the CNS. The experimental procedures for evaluating such compounds include extraction from neural tissue, and neural activation from close application by electrophoretic injection with concommitant electrical recording of cellular activity. Excitatory substances suggested include ACh, ATP, substance P, epinephrine, histamine and various amino acids (cf. discussions in Eccles, 1957, 1964). Substance related to amino acids, such as homeocysteic acid and N-methyl-D-aspartic acid, have recently held promise by virtue of their potent excitatory actions on neurons (Curtis and Watkins, 1961; Curtis, Phillis, and Watkins, 1961). Suggested inhibitory transmitter substances include factor *I*, gamma amino butyric acid (GABA), substance P, adrenalin, 5-hydroxytryptamine, etc. (see Curtis, 1963). However none of these has as yet been conclusively implicated.

MECHANISMS OF DRUG ACTION

The modern techniques and findings of studies on synaptic activity described above have resulted in a powerful new approach to the pharmacology of drug action.

A traditional method in the study of drug actions has been to look for

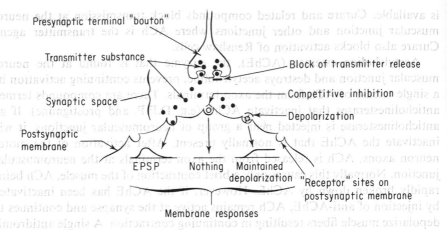

Presynaptic terminal "bouton"

Transmitter substance

Block of transmitter release

Competitive inhibition

Synaptic space

Depolarization

Postsynaptic
membrane

EPSP   Nothing   Maintained
depolarization   "Receptor" sites on
postsynaptic membrane

Membrane responses

Figure 8.8.   Various ways in which synaptic transmission may be blocked. Normal transmission is shown on the left. If the transmitter release is blocked, or the receptor site occupied by an inactive substance (competitive inhibition), there will be no postsynaptic membrane response. However if the receptor site is occupied by a depolarizing substance, the postsynaptic membrane will be permanently depolarized.

chemical similarities among compounds with similar functional effects. Often however, quite different substances seem to produce comparable behavioral effects. For example, strychnine and tetanus toxin both result in similar-appearing seizure patterns, but they do not appear to be chemically similar. It is now possible to explain a number of such effects on the basis of the synaptic actions of the substances. An example of such explanations was given above in our discussion of the effects of anti-AChE drugs such as DFP or prostigmine on the neuromuscular junction, the synapses of the recurrent collaterals of the motor axon on Renshaw cells, and the autonomic ganglia. The gross behavioral effects of such drugs, uncontrolled and long lasting contractions of the skeletal musculature, long lasting autonomic effects, etc. are all more or less predictable from the single synaptic action of these drugs: inactivation of AChE with resultant long lasting activation of postsynaptic structures by the undestroyed common transmitter substance, ACh.

In like manner, curare and a series of related compounds produce muscular paralysis and decreases in autonomic activity by blocking the normal transmitter effects of ACh at all "ACh" synapses. There are actually several ways in which blocking of the normal action of a transmitter agent can occur (see Figure 8.8). These include (1) competitive inhibition, in which the blocking agent substitutes for the transmitter substance on the postsynaptic membrane but does not activate the membrane, (2) long lasting depolarization of the postsynaptic membrane by the blocking agent so the transmitter substance cannot act, and (3) the prevention of the initial release of the transmitter substance from the presynaptic terminals. Curare and related drugs are believed to work by competitive inhibition. Botulinus toxin, on the other hand, which also blocks ACh synapses, is believed to do so by preventing release of the transmitter substance from the presynaptic terminals.

The synaptic action of another group of compounds, best exemplified by strychnine, is now thought to be understood. Strychnine has long been known as a central nervous system poison. In small doses it acts as a very potent stimulant or convulsant, causing uncontrolled muscular contractions and seizure activity. Before modern knowledge of synaptic physiology it was believed to act directly upon nerve cells as an excitant. Recent research has shown that it has quite a different mechanism of action: in fact, it is a synaptic blocking compound just as is curare. However it blocks inhibitory synapses of the type that normally induce postsynaptic inhibition (Eccles, 1957).

Examples of various types of synapses are shown in Figure 8.9, together with those transmitter substances and blocking agents known to act. Two examples of inhibitory synapses that act by inducing postsynaptic inhibition are shown. The disynaptic inhibitory pathway of muscle afferent nerves to antagonist muscle motor neurons is indicated by synapses a_1 and b_1. The a_1 synapse is excitatory—transmitter and blocking agents unknown. Activation at a_1 induces activity of the inhibitory interneuron, which in turn induces postsynaptic

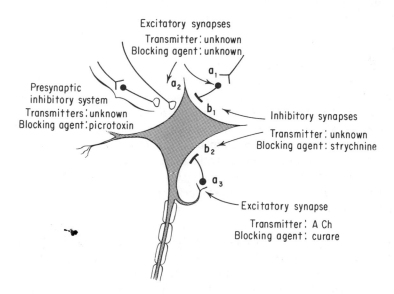

Figure 8.9. Synaptic transmitter and blocking actions in the spinal cord. Excitatory transmitters labeled a_1 and a_2, and their blocking agents, are unknown. The recurrent collateral excitatory synapse from the motor neuron on the Renshaw cell (a_3) utilizes ACh and is blocked by curare. Postsynaptic inhibitory transmitters (b_1 and b_2) are unknown, but they are blocked by strychnine. The presynaptic inhibitory system transmitters are unknown, but they are reduced by picrotoxin.

inhibition in the motor neuron at synapse b_1. It is here at inhibitory synapse b_1 that strychnine exerts its blocking action. In other words, strychnine exerts its excitatory influence on behavior by blocking or inhibiting inhibition. After strychninization the normally occurring IPSP of the motor neuron to activation of the pathway does not occur. The interneuron is still activated, but it can no longer exert its inhibitory influence.

Strychnine exerts a comparable effect on the disynaptic inhibitory pathway formed by recurrent collaterals of the motor neurons ending on Renshaw inhibitory interneurons that synapse back on the motor neurons (Figures 8.7 and 8.9). Again, it does not influence the excitatory synapse a_3 (Figure 8.9) formed by the recurrent collateral on the Renshaw cell. After stimulating the motor neuron either ortho- or antidromically the Renshaw cell is still activated in the presence of strychnine. However the inhibitory synapse that the Renshaw cell forms back on the motor neuron at b_2 (Figure 8.9) is blocked by strychnine. The Renshaw cell is still active but the IPSPs normally induced by it in the motor neuron no longer occur. This recurrent Renshaw inhibitory system, it should be noted, can equally well be blocked by curare acting at the excitatory synapse a_3 on the Renshaw cell (Figure 8.9). Both the transmitter (ACh) and the blocking compound (curare) are known for this synapse. Curare does not appear to block the excitatory synapse a_1 of the antagonist muscle pathway (Figure 8.9). Thus curare can serve to block one type of disynaptic inhibitory system (Renshaw) but not the other. Strychnine acts to block both types of inhibitory synapses on the motor neuron. Since strychnine does abolish most types of postsynaptic inhibition, such inhibitory control of the motor and other neurons is removed, resulting in "runaway" neural activity. This produces the strong and unco-ordinated muscular contractions characteristic of strychnine seizures.

Another poison, tetanus toxin, has blocking effects upon these inhibitory synapses comparable to those of strychnine. Strychnine is currently postulated to act analogously to curare, in that it combines with the inhibitory "receptors" of the postsynaptic membrane, thus blocking the transmitter substance, but without itself triggering the postsynaptic alterations in ion permeability leading to the IPSP. On the other hand, tetanus toxin may act analogously to botulinus toxin by preventing the release of inhibitory transmitter substance from the pre-synaptic terminals of the inhibitory interneuron (Eccles, 1964). The net be-havioral effects of both drugs are similar—removal of the inhibitory brakes from the motor neurons, with consequent increase in excitability.

There are still other convulsant drugs such as picrotoxin that have similar behavioral effects, but exert no measurable blocking action on postsynaptic inhibition. A very nice way to account for this would be to assume that picro-toxin suppresses presynaptic inhibition. This is apparently just what does happen (see Figure 8.9). Convulsant doses diminish both presynaptic inhibition and the presynaptic depolarization of afferent terminal fibers responsible for the inhibi-tion (Eccles, 1962). Since picrotoxin does not completely abolish presynaptic inhibition, it may also have other as yet unknown actions (Eccles, 1964).

Recent evidence suggests that the generalizations given above concerning the synaptic actions of strychnine may require some qualifications. An example of postsynaptic inhibition in the spinal cord that appears to be resistant to strychnine has been described (Llinas, 1964). Furthermore strychnine depression of postsynaptic inhibition in such brain structures as the cerebral cortex, thalamus, cerebellum and hippocampus has not yet been shown (see Eccles, 1964).

The various experimental procedures developed for study of the monosynaptic reflex have made it possible to analyze a variety of other drug effects on the CNS. For example, suppose a drug causes an overall depression of the monosynaptic reflex. This could be due to a decreased excitability of the postsynaptic spinal motor neuron membrane, or increased spike threshold of the cell, or increased amount of postsynaptic inhibition on the motor neuron, increased presynaptic inhibition, alterations in amount of activity in presynaptic terminals, changes in axon spike discharge, etc. These various possibilities can be experimentally differentiated, as demonstrated above for curare, strychnine and picrotoxin. Barbiturates (e.g. sodium pentobarbital, sodium pentothal, thiamylal sodium, etc.), the favorite anesthetics of the neurophysiologist, are believed to act primarily by reducing the amount of activity in afferent nerve terminals (Løyning et al., 1964). Large doses may also increase firing thresholds of the motor nerve cell membranes. Chloralose may act in part by prolonging and intensifying presynaptic inhibition (Eccles, 1964). Procaine (a form of local anesthetic similar to novocain) appears to increase the spike discharge threshold of the motor nerve membrane without altering resting or postsynaptic potentials (Curtis and Phillis, 1960; Aceves and Machne, 1963). Still other anesthetics such as ether, paraldehyde, urethane, and chloralhydrate appear to act primarily by reducing transmission through interneuron pathways (Schmidt, 1963).

There are literally thousands of drugs that affect brain activity in one way or another. Some of these act directly on cellular metabolism (e.g. cyanide) but the actions of many are undoubtedly more closely related to synaptic transmission. The analytic approach in terms of synaptic mechanisms may well provide many possibilities for explaining the potent effects of many diverse compounds upon the central nervous system, and hence upon behavior.

ELECTRICAL SYNAPTIC TRANSMISSION

The types of chemical synaptic transmission discussed above are characteristic of the mammalian nervous system. In contrast, there are both excitatory and inhibitory *electrical* synapses in certain invertebrates and fish. We will discuss examples of these only briefly; they are of interest because they do illustrate alternative modes of synaptic transmission. However such specialized systems may have no particular relevance to mammalian brain function.

Furshpan and Potter (1959) demonstrated in an elegant series of experiments that the abdominal ganglia of the crayfish have excitatory electrical synapses that conduct only in one direction. A drawing of the synapse and some of their experimental results are shown in Figure 8.10. The presynaptic response directly induces a postsynaptic response with *no time delay*. The current flow in the presynaptic terminal induces the response in the postsynaptic membrane in a manner analogous to an ordinary electrical transformer. However, antidromic activation of the postsynaptic fiber does not induce any appreciable potential in the presynaptic fiber. Apparently the membranes act as a rectifier, permitting current flow only in one direction. Anatomically the pre- and postsynaptic membranes are much closer together than in chemical synapses, and may even be fused in places to provide for direct electrical induction of current.

An example of electrical synaptic inhibition has been found in a rather specialized giant nerve cell in fish, the Mauthner cell (Furukawa and Furshpan, 1963). Two such cells are present in most fish. The cell body is composed essentially of two large dendrites and lies in the medulla. It sends a giant axon down the spinal cord, permitting very rapid conduction of information. Both inhibitory and excitatory postsynaptic potentials are generated in the cell by the usual chemical mechanisms. In addition however, it appears that direct electrical inhibition also occurs. Activation of fine nerve fibers synapsing on the axon hillock region of the Mauthner cell (the region of impulse initiation in nerve cells) induces electrically a very brief hyperpolarizing potential that can act to

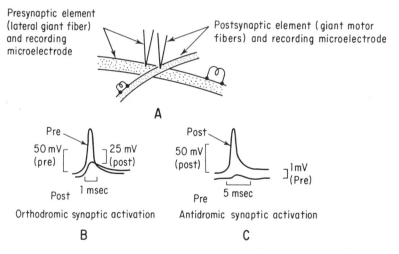

Figure 8.10. **A**, diagram of an electrical giant synapse in the squid. The two fibers are in contact at the region of the synapse. **B**, electrical synaptic activation. Note that the postsynaptic response (lower trace) begins at the same time the presynaptic spike arrives at the synapse. **C**, failure to transmit backward from the postsynaptic to the presynaptic element. Note the very much smaller induced (lower trace) response (about 100 times less, see different induced response amplitude calibrations). (Redrawn from Furshpan and Potter, 1959)

inhibit excitation of the cell. This hyperpolarization develops passively and simultaneously with the potential changes in the terminal nerve fibers. Subsequently, the usual chemically-induced IPSP develops. The electrical inhibition may serve to increase the speed with which inhibition develops in the cell since electrical effects are instantaneous, whereas chemically mediated postsynaptic inhibition requires about 1 msec to develop.

These intriguing demonstrations of electrical synaptic transmission actually serve to emphasize and reinforce the importance of the *chemical* nature of synaptic transmission in the mammalian nervous system. It is often said that neither the chemical nor the electrical theory of synaptic transmission is entirely correct —the actual sequence of events reducing ultimately to increased ion flows across the postsynaptic membrane. Since these ionic events are really an electrochemical process exhibiting both electrical and chemical aspects, synaptic transmission is said to be neither chemical nor electrical but rather a bit of both. Such a view is too great an oversimplification. It is quite true that ion flows are electrochemical events. However the most important feature of synaptic transmission concerns the mechanism whereby these ion flows are initiated in the postsynaptic membrane by activity in the presynaptic terminal fibers. In the mammalian CNS this mechanism is the release of chemical substances across the synaptic space.

Comparison of electrical and chemical synapses shows that they differ markedly from each other in terms of electrophysiological events, time relations, susceptibility to drugs, methods whereby they can be altered, etc. Our ultimate understanding of the ways in which the human brain functions in controlling and altering behavior will be directly related to the chemical rather than electrical nature of synaptic transmission. Let us take just one example to clarify the point. Since synapses are essentially the only places where nerve cells interact, the neural changes underlying learning must involve changes in synaptic function. In a conditioning experiment, for example, the "connections" between the conditioned stimulus and the conditioned response must be strengthened at some points in the CNS. This could occur by increased excitation, decreased inhibition, or combinations of both, at the regions of synaptic interaction. The kinds of structural and biochemical changes in nerve cells that will produce these alterations in synaptic actions would be quite different for electrical vs chemical synapses (compare, for example, Figures 8.9 and 8.10). Consequently, the fact that synaptic transmission is chemical rather than electrical makes a very real difference in our approach to the neural basis of learning.

SUGGESTED READINGS

Eccles, J. C. *The physiology of synapses.* New York: Academic Press, 1964.

McLennan, H. *Synaptic transmission.* Philadelphia: Saunders, 1963.

Ruch, T. C., & Patton, H. D. (Eds.) *Physiology and biophysics.* Philadelphia: Saunders, 1965 (Chapters 5–7).

CHAPTER 9

PATTERNS
OF
NEURAL
ACTIVITY

The basic goal of physiological psychology is an understanding of the fundamental neural processes underlying behavior. The phrase "neural processes" really means synaptic transmission; the nervous system is a complex series of interconnecting links that interact with one another at synapses. Hence all activity of the nervous system, and the resulting behavior of the organism, is fundamentally reducible to descriptions in terms of populations of synaptic events. Ultimately we might hope that behavior can be understood in terms of synaptic processes. Our discussion of synaptic transmission given in the previous chapters summarized the impressive progress to date in understanding the synaptic basis of the simplest reflex phenomena of the spinal cord such as monosynaptic excitation and disynaptic inhibition. Analysis of synaptic transmission has been based on one particular type of measure: the electrical potential across the membrane of the single nerve cell. Unfortunately it has not yet been possible to relate more complex behavioral events—particularly those of the intact organism—to the underlying synaptic processes. Studies of the integrative aspects of brain function and behavior to date have instead emphasized measurement of the electrical activity of populations of nerve cells. In this very brief chapter we will discuss some of the more common types of electrical activity recorded from the nervous system in such studies, and the extent to which these measures are understood in terms of the underlying synaptic processes. The remainder of the text will be concerned with current knowledge of the relations between neural processes and behavioral events.

The most commonly used measures of neural activity in studies of brain and behavior have been the EEG and gross evoked potentials. Other measures currently in use include single cell activity, slow potentials, massed unit discharges, and impedance changes. We discussed the basic techniques involved in obtaining most of these types of measures in Chapter 3. Remember that they are merely different ways of recording the underlying activity of the nervous system. The particular type of response measure used depends upon the techniques and measuring instruments employed, and the kinds of questions that are being asked of the nervous system.

EEG ACTIVITY

The electroencephalogram (EEG) is simply a tracing of the changes in voltage generated by the brain over time. In humans it is typically recorded from plate or needle electrodes on the surface of the scalp. Because of volume conduction effects (see Chapter 3), activity is recorded from large regions of cerebral cortex and even from subcortical structures. Analytic studies using animals can pinpoint active regions more accurately (not all regions of cortex are equally responsive) but the EEG is still a gross record from millions of cells. It might be expected that a gross measure obtained from millions of nerve cells would not show anything but " hash " or asynchronous activity. In the waking brain these cells are obviously involved in " processing " a huge variety of different types of activity or information. Any average record of their activity would likely show little more than a smear of " random " or at least unsynchronized responding. This does appear to be partially true, at least for the awake and alert organism. However under various other conditions rather striking regularities or waves develop. The fact that such waves are a prominent feature of the EEG is really rather more surprising than would be the absence of such regularities. It would seem that millions of cells are capable of being synchronized in their activity patterns.

Some of the various types of EEG waves are illustrated in the upper three lines of Figure 9.1. These are records of the ongoing voltage changes measured over time from the scalp of a human subject. The records on the left were obtained when the subject's eyes were open, and tend to show only random activity. However, when the subject's eyes are closed rather clear bursts of waves appear, particularly in the second and third lines. These waves, commonly called *alpha waves*, have a frequency of occurrence of 8 to 12 per second, and are fairly characteristic of the awake but resting mammalian brain.

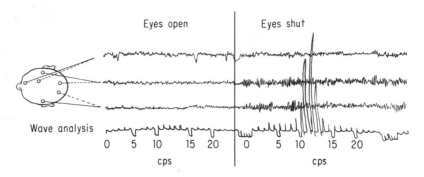

Figure 9.1. Examples of human EEG records (3 upper traces) and a frequency analysis (lower trace) of the EEG records. The wave analysis, which has a separate peak for each frequency component, indicates that the frequencies most commonly present with eyes shut are 8–12/second (large peaks on the wave analysis). (Redrawn from Walter, 1954)

It is difficult to see exactly what frequencies might be most prominent in the records of the upper three lines of Figure 9.1. Automatic computer devices called frequency analyzers are often used to provide this type of information. The bottom line of Figure 9.1 is the output of such a frequency analyzer. It measures the percent or relative occurrence of each frequency of wave in the upper records and displays them on a frequency histogram. The frequency components of the histogram are labeled at the bottom of the figure. The bottom line, then, is not a voltage-time tracing, but rather a frequency histogram, plotting percent occurrence of each frequency of wave. Note that there is very little activity at frequencies from 0 to 9 cps, a great deal of activity at frequencies ranging from 10 to 13 cps, and virtually none above 14 cps. The most common frequency in the record is at 12 cps. As you can see, the frequency analyzer provides a convenient method for exact measurement of the frequencies of EEG waves, a measure that simply could not be made on the original voltage-time tracings. Note that the frequency analysis on the left indicates no particular frequencies of waves are more prominent than others when the eyes are open. The wave activity is "random" in time.

Many suggestive correlations appear to exist between EEG activity and behavioral state. Berger (1929) who first described the human EEG, noted some of these. Typical EEG patterns recorded for differing degrees of alertness are shown in Figure 9.2. Fast low voltage activity of a more-or-less random character (beta waves) is commonly seen when an organism is alert and attending to stimuli (A). If the subject rests quietly with eyes open or closed, bursts of regular waves at a frequency of 8–13/sec appear (alpha waves or spindles, B). Not all persons, incidentally, show a good alpha rhythm. As the subject gets drowsy, the alpha activity may intensify, or disappear as in (C). As sleep develops, very slow large amplitude waves develop (delta waves, D). With very deep sleep or unconsciousness the EEG will be essentially flat (E). Finally, there is a stage of fairly deep sleep where the EEG record suddenly changes to the alert pattern shown in A, although the subject remains behaviorally asleep. This stage of sleep is called *paradoxical* sleep since the subject shows a waking EEG but is asleep. We will discuss paradoxical sleep in more detail in Chapter 14).

We have used rather loose terms to describe the behavioral state of the subject. Reliable independent measures of alertness must be used, e.g. the intensity of a sound necessary to elicit a verbal response may be employed to determine depth of sleep, etc. The behavioral state cannot be judged by EEG activity alone, as is shown by the apparent identity of the EEG recorded during the alert state and during paradoxical sleep. The absence of adequate measures of the behavioral state has been a serious limitation in many studies comparing EEG activity and behavior.

One of the characteristic patterns of EEG activity is the so-called alpha blocking response, first described and studied by Adrian and his colleagues

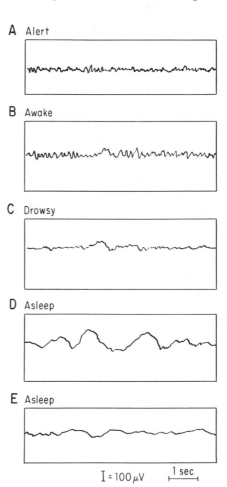

A Alert

B Awake

C Drowsy

D Asleep

E Asleep

$I = 100 \mu V$ 1 sec

Figure 9.2. Typical human EEG records during different states. Alpha waves (8–12/ sec) are most commonly seen in resting awake and drowsy states (**B** and **C**). In deep sleep a " paradoxical " sleeping EEG, which resembles the fast, low-voltage activity of the alert state (**A**), also develops. (Redrawn from Brazier, 1960)

(Adrian, 1944; Adrian and Matthews, 1934a; 1934b; Adrian and Yamagiwa, 1935). Alpha blocking is illustrated for both cat and man in Figure 9.3. It is comparable to the phenomenon of "EEG-arousal," both terms describing a sudden shift from the slower and regular high voltage waves of alpha activity to the low voltage fast or random activity characteristic of alertness. If a subject is sitting quietly and shows a clear alpha, a sudden stimulus of almost any sort "blocks" the alpha by eliciting the low voltage fast arousal pattern. There have been a vast array of studies concerned with the various conditions that influence alpha blocking. Of perhaps the greatest interest to the psychologist are those dealing with alerting or "attention," habituation, and conditioning (see the extensive reviews by Morrell, 1961, Lindsley, 1960).

Following the initial experiments by Moruzzi and Magoun (1949) and Lindsley et al. (1949), there have been numerous experiments suggesting that a common neural system is involved in both EEG arousal and behavior alerting. In addition to the general correlations between behavioral alerting and EEG arousal noted above it has been shown that sensory stimuli or electrical brain stimuli that yield EEG arousal appear also to elicit behavioral alerting or "attention." Furthermore, electrical stimulation of appropriate brain regions may improve behavioral performance (see the extensive discussion by Lindsley, 1960). We will examine these experiments in more detail in Chapter 14.

Sharpless and Jasper (1956) were the first to study habituation of EEG arousal systematically. Using normally sleeping cats with electrodes implanted over the cortex, they found that tones that initially produced EEG arousal gradually ceased to do so upon repeated presentation (habituation). Following habituation they withheld the tone for a long period of time; when the tone was presented they again obtained EEG arousal, thus showing spontaneous recovery of the habituated response. Their observations have been confirmed in many subsequent studies on animals and man. The Soviet psychologist, Sokolov, has carried out the most extensive investigations of habituation in man (see Sokolov, 1963). We will discuss these studies further in Chapter 17.

There is a very extensive literature on "conditioned" alpha blocking. The effect was first reported in 1935 by Durup and Fessard, who were studying alpha blocking to light using a camera to photograph the responses. They noticed that after a few trials the click of the camera shutter (which occurred at the same time as onset of light) by itself elicited the alpha blocking response. This has been considered a demonstration of conditioned response formation (Morrell, 1961), although as Knott and Henry (1941) pointed out such observations are more properly an example of sensitization rather than conditioning. One of the most careful early studies of "conditioned" blocking was by Jasper and Shagass (1941). The majority of the numerous subsequent studies on conditioned alpha blocking have not always used appropriate controls to demonstrate that they are dealing with conditioning rather than sensitization or some other phenomenon. Although it may prove to be erroneous to refer to the effects as conditioning or learning, it should be emphasized that "conditioned" EEG arousal

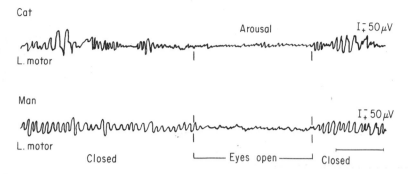

Figure 9.3. Examples of "alpha blocking" (EEG arousal) in both man and cat. (Redrawn from Rempel and Gibbs, 1936)

clearly involves changes in neural activity as a result of "training," and merits study in its own right. This area of research will be discussed more fully in Chapter 15.

The EEG has been most widely used in the diagnosis and study of abnormal neural conditions, particularly epilepsy. In *petit mal* epilepsy the patient shows a characteristic *spike* and *wave* pattern during seizures. An example is shown in Figure 9.4. Sometimes the spike and wave pattern is not clearly seen but can be elicited by a procedure called *photic driving*. A bright light is flashed at about the rate of normal alpha and tied up in a feedback circuit to the brain waves so that the frequency of flash becomes time-locked to the frequency of brain response. Even normal subjects report a variety of abnormal experiences under these conditions (see Walter, 1953). EEG activity has been reported to be correlated with a variety of other conditions, particularly drug effects. There have been suggestive studies attempting to relate EEG patterns to behavioral disorders such as schizophrenia but the evidence is as yet unconvincing (Glaser, 1963).

Although behavioral variables have not always been carefully controlled in studies of EEG activity, it is clear that the phenomenon is easily influenced by many conditions and has significant relations to behavior. Consequently, it is important to understand the neuronal basis of EEG activity. Two aspects of EEG phenomena have been subject to extensive investigation: alpha waves and the arousal response. Most studies have used cats; they show types of EEG activity comparable to those of man (see Figure 9.3). The alpha type response in the cat is usually called spindle waves, spindle bursts, or simply spindling. As in man, spindling is seen either when the animal is at rest, or when it is under barbiturate narcosis.

Moruzzi and Magoun (1949), in a now classic study, showed that rapid electrical stimulation of the midbrain reticular formation produced EEG arousal in an animal that was spindling. If the animal was simply drowsy or asleep, such stimulation produces behavioral arousal as well (French et al., 1952). Lesions of the midbrain reticular formation abolish the normal EEG arousal produced

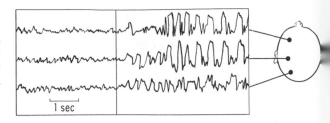

Figure 9.4. Onset of the "spike and dome" EEG waves characteristic of *petit mal* epilepsy in man. (Redrawn from Brazier, 1960)

by peripheral stimuli (Lindsley, Bowden, and Magoun, 1949) (see Chapter 14). In an analogous series of studies Jasper and his associates (see Jasper, 1960) showed that destruction of certain regions of the thalamus (diffuse thalamic system) abolish cortical spindling activity. It would thus appear that both EEG spindling (i.e. alpha) and EEG arousal are driven—or at least produced in some way—by influences from below the cortex. The diffuse thalamic system seems to predominate in spindling and the brain stem reticular formation in arousal. It is important to note, however, that repetitive activity in neural structures need not be driven from other sources. Neurally isolated slabs of cortex can exhibit repetitive activity (Burns, 1958).

What aspects of neuronal activity are responsible for the spindle waves and other EEG phenomena recorded from the cortex? Earlier it was thought that they represented averaged envelopes of nerve cell *spike* discharges, as is the case for a potential recorded from a peripheral nerve (see Chapters 3 and 6). Li and Jasper (1953) undertook an extensive study of the activity of single nerve cells in the cortex during spontaneous spindling and recruiting activity. Their results and those of subsequent investigations (see Jasper, 1960) led to some rather surprising conclusions. When fairly deep levels of anesthesia are used, *no spike discharges can be obtained from cortical cells, even though spindle wave activity is predominant.* Spindles thus can occur in the absence of cell discharges. This does not of course mean that spindles occur independently of nerve cell activity in the cortex. Cortical cells are still being activated from below, and exhibit the graded postsynaptic potentials in dendrites and cell bodies which normally regulate the all-or-none spike discharge firing patterns. Presumably, the anesthetic depresses activity to the point at which discharge threshold is not reached. Consequently, it appears that the electrical waves recorded in the EEG are in large part graded synaptic potentials (both excitatory and inhibitory). They are an index of the graded "analogue" operations of cortical cells which ultimately will determine actual discharge patterns. It is suggestive that inhibitory postsynaptic potentials last about 100 msec in cortical cells (Chapter 7), since this is the approximate time interval between successive alpha waves.

If both excitatory and inhibitory synaptic potentials are responsible for EEG activity, we might expect that in the waking or lightly anesthetized state, when cortical cells are firing, there will be no simple relation between patterns of cellular spike discharge and EEG wave patterns. This is just what Li and Jasper

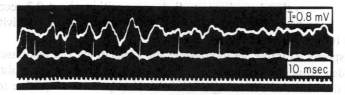

Figure 9.5. Illustration of the lack of correspondence between gross cortical surface EEG recorded (upper trace) and discharge patterns of a single cortical nerve cell (spikes in the lower trace). Bottom line is time calibration. Negative up. (From Li and Jasper, 1953)

found. An example of their data is shown in Figure 9.5. Some cells do fire in relation to waves, but others have quite different patterns which appear completely unrelated to EEG activity. Until a great deal more is known about which cells are active and what types of synaptic activity yield various portions of EEG patterns, it will not be possible to relate EEG waves to the behavior of nerve cells. Comparable problems are seen for EEG arousal patterns. Jasper, Ricci, and Doane (1958) found that single cell firing rate may increase, decrease or stay the same during arousal. Evarts (1963) reported *decreases* in spike activity of single neurons during EEG arousal associated with behavioral *awakening*.

The current state of knowledge in this area has been well summarized by Jasper, Ricci, and Doane (1958, p 278):

"Though the electrical activity of the brain is a sensitive indicator of cerebral events, . . . interpretation of such data is limited by the inadequacy of our knowledge of the basic physiological mechanisms and functional significance of brain waves. The manner in which electrical waves are generated on the cortical surface is still obscure and their true functional significance is even more uncertain. The blocking or arrest of slow rhythmic activity is usually considered a sign of "excitation," "arousal" or "activation" but evidence for this relationship is indirect and not entirely consistent."

GROSS EVOKED POTENTIALS

If a wire electrode is placed in an appropriate location in the brain, a sudden peripheral or central stimulus produces one or more shifts in the potential recorded by the electrode. Such evoked potentials can be recorded from many regions of the spinal cord and brain. In our present discussion we will emphasize potentials recorded from the cerebral cortex, simply because they are easy to obtain and have been widely studied. The form and characteristics of an evoked response are influenced by a wide variety of conditions, including the type of recording electrode (monopolar, bipolar, surface to depth, etc.), condition of the animal (type and degree of anesthesia) and recording apparatus. Most evoked responses that have been studied occur within about 0.2 seconds after a stimulus has been delivered, although much longer lasting activity can be recorded (O'Leary and Goldring, 1964).

As a specific example, let us consider the kinds of evoked responses that can be recorded from the cerebral cortex to a sudden auditory stimulus such as clapping the hands or delivering a brief electrical pulse to a speaker to produce a "click" sound. If we record monopolarly from the surface of the auditory area of the cortex in an animal anesthetized by a barbiturate such as sodium pentobarbital (Nembutal), the evoked response appears as in Figure 9.6. There is a latent period of about 9 msec after the click when no change in activity occurs, followed by a rapid positive wave, which is in turn followed by a longer lower amplitude negative wave. In this figure and most subsequent pictures of evoked responses, traces above the baseline are positive and below the baseline are negative. As we noted earlier, there is no agreement on one convention. Many authors use negative up and positive down. Each figure in this text indicates which convention is used. In a deeply anesthetized animal the initial positive wave may be the only response seen. If we search the surface of the cortex we will find that there is a relatively small region where the positive response is of largest amplitude, the amplitude falls off rapidly as we move away from that region, and other areas of the cortex do not exhibit any response. The evoked response is said to be _localized_. It is assumed that activity in the cortex underlying the electrode produces the evoked response. Although this is usually the case, volume conduction effects are such that it is possible to find even a fairly localized response that is not generated in the cortex at that locus (see Figure 9.7B).

As an illustration of the existence of superficially similar potentials of different origin, consider the following demonstration. If we use a relatively small needle electrode and push it down gradually through the cortex, the components of the evoked response alter form and polarity rather dramatically. An example is shown in Figure 9.7A. There have been a number of attempts to relate the changes in potential with depth to neuronal activity in the cortical layers (e.g. Amassian et al., 1955; Li et al., 1956a, b; Mountcastle et al., 1957; Perl and Whitlock, 1955; Spencer and Brookhart, 1961). Such analyses are complex and indirect, and will not be elaborated here. It is sufficient to note that if we look at the potential at the time after stimulation where it has a maximum positivity on the surface, the polarity shifts as we penetrate the cortex and becomes negative lower in the cortex. In effect there is a reversal of polarity in depth. If we

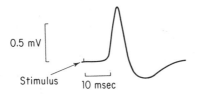

0.5 mV

Stimulus   10 msec

Figure 9.6. Example of a "typical" gross cortical evoked response recorded from the auditory cortex of the barbiturate anesthetized cat to a click stimulus (positive up).

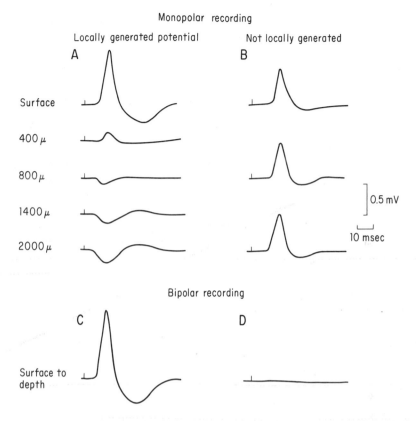

Figure 9.7.   Depth potential distributions of gross cortical evoked responses in the anesthetized cat (positive up). Micron (μM) numbers at left refer to depth below surface of cortex of recording electrode tip. **A**, click evoked response from auditory cortex of cat (as in Figure 9.6). Note that in the depths of the cortex the response is initially negative. This response is locally generated in the region of cortex penetrated by the electrode. **B**, click evoked response recorded from adjacent nonauditory cortex of cat. Note that there is no charge in the response in the depths of the cortex. This potential is not locally generated. **C**, bipolar surface-to-depth record of potential in **A**. The surface and depth monopolar responses add arithmetically to give larger response (amplifier records the *difference* between the responses). **D**, bipolar surface-to-depth record of potential in **B**. Since there is essentially no difference between the responses, the bipolar record indicates no response. (Modified from Thompson, Johnson, and Hoopes, 1963)

assume that there is a current "sink" in the depths of the cortex, say in about layer 5, corresponding to the large negativity, and a surface current "source," then current flow would generate potentials such that the depth pattern shown in Figure 9.7A would result. It has been hypothesized that incoming activity to sensory cortex, which enters in layer 4, activates the pyramidal cells of layer 5 via interneurons. The pyramidal cells send long apical dendrites to the surface of the cortex and axons down below the cortex, and could serve to generate the sources and sinks responsible for the observed depth distribution of potential (see Chang, 1959).

A surface response to click stimulation which does not appear to be generated locally in the cortex can be recorded from a neighboring region of cortex (Figure 9.7B). Note that there is no change in the appearance of this response as the electrode is pushed down through the cortex. Such a response is probably generated from some subcortical structure or nearby cortical region. If we placed one electrode below the cortex and another on the surface, and recorded between them bipolarly, the click response from auditory cortex would have a larger amplitude than the monopolar surface response (Figure 9.7C). This is due to the fact that the amplifier records the difference between the two points, thus measuring the difference between the surface positivity and the depth negativity. However, for the response of Figure 9.7D the bipolar record across the cortex shows no response at all. There is no difference between the surface and depth potentials and hence a flat response line results. The two methods of depth distribution and bipolar recording across the cortex serve as control procedures which demonstrate whether a given surface response is generated locally in the cortex or from some more distant region.

So far we have examined the primary auditory evoked response in an anesthetized animal. The form of the response differs in some respects in the unanesthetized preparation. As shown in Figure 9.8 the initial positive response is comparable in form (although much lower in amplitude), but there is a larger negativity, followed by a second positivity, and still another negativity. These later components of the response are often not seen in the anesthetized animal and are quite variable in the waking brain. Because of this variability, investigators have used computers to obtain average responses. Such methods will demonstrate a very small signal "buried" in background activity. An example of the power of these procedures is illustrated in Figure 9.9. The signal is completely unrecognizable in single responses, but emerges clearly in the computed average response.

The computer averaging method is particularly useful when responding brain-evoked responses from the surface of the scalp in man (as was done in Figure 9.9). Many types of ongoing and irrelevant electrical activity are present, which mask the real response. The computer measures the amplitude of the trace at each point in time, stores these measurements, repeats the entire procedure on the next trace, and so on. It then computes the average amplitude of each point of the trace and displays the "averaged" trace. In Figure 9.9 the first trace shows only random activity, but by the time 32 traces are averaged

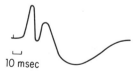

Figure 9.8.   Gross cortical evoked response to click stimulation recorded from the auditory cortex of the waking unanesthetized cat. Note later response components not seen in the anesthetized state (positive up). (Compare with Figure 9.6.) (Redrawn and modified from Galambos, 1960a)

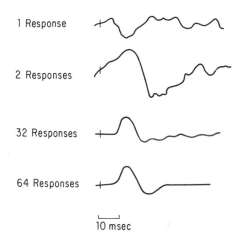

Figure 9.9. Use of an average response computor to average out spontaneous background "noise." The trace is a gross EEG record from the scalp overlying the somatic sensory area of man and the stimulus is a brief shock to the finger. A single response (top trace) does not show any indication of an evoked response, but by the time 32 successive responses are averaged together, a clear evoked response can be seen emerging from the "noise" (positive up). (Redrawn from Brazier, 1962)

together the "real" response is clearly present. The effectiveness of the method depends upon the fact that the real response is evoked by the stimulus and always has the same time relation to the stimulus (i.e. it is always positive 15 msec after the stimulus). Background activity is *not tied to the* stimulus but occurs randomly in time in relation to the stimulus. It is sometimes positive (as after 2 responses), and sometimes negative (as in the first response). Consequently the *average* of the background activity taken over a number of traces is zero.

Another type of evoked response can be recorded from association areas of the cortex (first reported by Amassian, 1954). These areas do not exhibit any evoked activity in the barbiturized animal but show clear responses to all modalities of stimuli when chloralose anesthetic is used or when the animal is in an unanesthetized state. Examples of such a response to auditory, visual, and tactile stimuli from a point in the posterior association cortex of cat are shown in Figure 9.10, both for the chloralosed state and for the unanesthetized state. In general, both primary and association evoked responses are of lower amplitude and have greater variability in the waking brain than with various types of anesthetics.

Still another type of cortical-evoked response can be recorded in the barbiturized animal, the so-called "secondary discharge," first described by Forbes and Morison (1939). This is a predominantly positive response with a very long latency of 100 msec or more to tactile stimulation. Late responses of this sort can also be recorded from the cortex of the waking animal to other modalities of stimulation. Figure 9.11 shows the response described by Forbes and Morison, and a computer averaged response to light flash (Brazier, 1960), both exhibiting the same very long latency.

If the cortex is directly stimulated electrically, and a surface recording electrode placed close by, a short latency negative direct cortical response (DCR) can be recorded. The DCR was first described by Adrian (1936), and has been

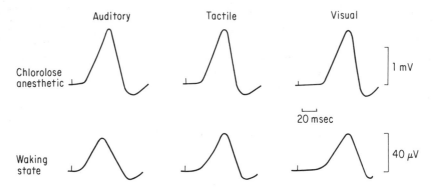

Figure 9.10. Comparison of gross evoked "association" responses from a posterior association area of cat (suprasylvian gyrus) to three modalities of stimulation using chloralose anesthetic (upper traces) or the normal waking state (lower traces). Note the different amplitude calibrations. In the waking state the response is about 1/20 the amplitude of that obtained using chloralose (positive up). (Based on Thompson, Johnson, and Hoopes, 1963; Thompson and Shaw, 1965)

studied extensively by Chang (1951) and others. An example of a DCR is shown in Figure 9.12. The DCR can be altered by a variety of conditions, including anesthetic depth, drugs, etc. and appears to represent summated postsynaptic potentials (Stohr, Goldring, and O'Leary, 1963). The significance of the DCR, other than as an example of responsiveness of neural tissue to electrical stimulation, appears as yet to be somewhat unclear.

There have been many studies attempting to relate amplitudes of various types of evoked responses to behavioral variables, particularly habituation and conditioning (see the review by Morrell, 1961b). We will examine these experiments in Chapter 17.

What are the neuronal mechanisms underlying gross evoked responses? If proper controls are used it is clear that cortical-evoked potentials reflect activity in the region of cortex underlying the recording electrode. However, the kinds of neural processes responsible are not easily characterized. Evoked cortical

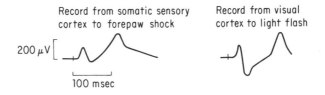

Figure 9.11. Comparison of primary and "secondary" gross cortical evoked responses to somatic sensory and visual stimulation in the barbiturate anesthetized cat (positive up). (Redrawn from Forbes and Morison, 1939; Brazier, 1960)

potentials are comparable to EEG activity in that they may be recorded even when there is a total absence of all-or-none spike discharges in neurons. Thus they appear in part at least to reflect graded synaptic potentials in dendrites and cell bodies of neurons rather than actual discharges. Just as with EEG activity, they represent the graded analogue operations of nerve cells. Unlike the waves of EEG activity, however, many single cell discharges bear a clear and fixed temporal relation to the stimulus and to the gross evoked response. In addition, the initial rising portion of the gross primary sensory cortical-evoked response often includes the presynaptic spike discharges of the afferent fibers carrying information to the cortex (Chang, 1959). These are most easily seen in evoked responses of the visual cortex, particularly if the stimulus is an electric shock to the optic nerve. The afferent fibers have several different groups of sizes and thus conduct at slightly different velocities.

A recent study by Fox and O'Brian (1965) suggests that at least under some circumstances a very close relationship may exist between the gross evoked response of the visual cortex and the latency histogram of discharges of a single cell in the visual cortex. Thus the maximum frequency of cell discharges occurs during the *initial positivity* of the evoked response, few discharges during the

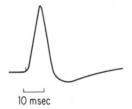

Figure 9.12. A direct cortical response (DCR). Stimulating electrodes and a recording electrode are placed together on the surface of the cortex (negative up). (Redrawn from Chang, 1951)

10 msec

after negativity, and so on. However, it must be remembered that the polarity and form of gross potentials depend upon many factors such as the geometry of the generating structures. Furthermore, it is not possible to specify whether the various components of a given gross surface response reflect excitatory or inhibitory synaptic processes, or complex combinations of these. Hence general conclusions relating gross responses and single cell discharges would seem premature.

The neural mechanisms responsible for some components of at least one type of evoked potential, the *cord dorsum* response recorded grossly from the dorsal surface of the spinal cord to afferent nerve stimulation, appear to be more fully understood. An example of the cord dorsum is given in Figure 9.13. The slow P wave component appears to reflect presynaptic inhibitory activity induced in the presynaptic afferent terminal fibers. The N_1 and N_2 components are believed to represent postsynaptic activity of identified groups of interneurons (see Eccles, 1964).

Attempts to unravel the relations between components of gross evoked responses and underlying synaptic mechanisms have been extensive. It is from

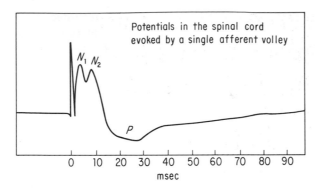

Figure 9.13. The cord dorsum response recorded from the surface of the spinal cord to afferent stimulation. N_1 and N_2 reflect activity of interneuron groups and the later P wave is associated with presynaptic inhibition. The initial spike reflects the afferent volley arriving in the cord (negative up). (Redrawn from Gasser, 1937)

this pioneering work by such men as Bishop, Adrian, Eccles and others that our current views of evoked potentials as summated, graded synaptic potentials have developed. However the problem of what types of synaptic activity from which types of neurons are responsible for the components of most gross responses remains a "mystery wrapped in an enigma."

SINGLE CELL DISCHARGES

One disadvantage of evoked response procedures is the necessity for a stimulus sufficiently abrupt to drive synchronously an evoked response through the nervous system. In nature most stimuli are continuous and ongoing in time rather than sudden. Recording the spike discharges of single cells extracellularly provides exact information about the response patterns of a given cell to any kind of stimulus, sudden or ongoing. As will be seen in later chapters, a great deal of significant new information highly relevant to the psychologist's interest in behavior has resulted from this approach.

The actual response recorded is simply the spike all-or-none discharge of a given cell (see Figure 9.14). In principle this is much easier to understand than the complex gross evoked response. However, procedural details are more difficult, and the demonstration that one is dealing with a single cell in a healthy (i.e. normally firing) condition is not always easy (see Mountcastle et al., 1957). The most common criterion that activity is being recorded from a single cell is spike height. Although the spike occurs with varying frequency in Figure 9.14, its height is always the same. It is usually fairly safe to assume that this reflects activity from only one cell. When recording extracellularly, the amplitude of a spike is determined by the distance of the cell from the electrode, the size of the spike generating membrane (i.e. cell body), and other factors. Different cells will usually generate different sized spikes for a given electrode placement. Consequently, a constant spike height usually reflects activity of the same cell. Perhaps the best criterion that the cell is not damaged is the length of time it can be held by the electrode. A good cell can often be held for up to two hours or longer.

Figure 9.14. Example of extracellularly recorded spike discharges of a single nerve cell (in somatic sensory cortex of the cat). Note that the spike height remains virtually constant but frequency of discharge varies markedly. The much increased discharge frequency beginning halfway across the top trace and extending to near the end of the third trace is the response of the cell to sensory stimulation. (From Mountcastle, 1957)

The greatest interpretive limitation of the single cell method is that you are recording from only one cell out of a population of many thousands or millions of active cells. The type of cell often cannot be identified, and it is almost certain that even relatively large samples of single cell activity (say 200 cells) will be extremely biased samples from the total active population. A combination of single unit and gross evoked response data generally will provide the greatest amount of information.

Dc RESPONSES

The study of slow potentials (SP shifts) in the brain is a very new area of research, although interestingly enough the first experiment where brain electrical activity was recorded (by Caton in 1875) reported dc current flows. Dc recording is technically a good deal more difficult than the more commonly used capacity-coupled input recording of EEG and evoked responses. Today, excellent dc amplifiers are commercially available but good nonpolarizing recording electrodes are not and must be prepared (see Chapter 3).

An example of an SP shift is shown in Figure 9.15. The stimulus situation is exactly comparable to that of Figure 9.12 in which a direct cortical response to electrical stimulation was recorded, the only difference being that we are now recording dc on a very slow time base. After the initial response, which appears as a sharp spike on this time base, there is a very long lasting negative shift in the potential level. The baseline level is reached here after about a half minute. Most kinds of evoked responses have associated dc shifts, particularly if trains of stimuli are given, among them cerebral and cerebellar responses to peripheral stimulation and to direct stimulation, and also cerebral cortical recruiting responses. Single responses evoked by peripheral stimulation often do not exhibit any SP shifts.

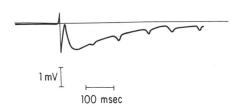

1 mV

⊢————⊣
100 msec

Figure 9.15. Example of the slow cortical potentials recorded with a dc amplifier. This is a response recorded from the cortex to direct electrical stimulation (i.e. a DCR), much like the response shown in Figure 9.12 except that a dc amplifier is used. Note slower time base here; the initial sharp upward spike here is the entire response shown in Figure 9.12. (Redrawn from Goldring, Stohr, and O'Leary, 1963)

In addition to such long lasting SP shifts, steady dc voltages can be recorded from various points in the brain. In rabbits, the potential of the surface of the cortex is from 0.5 to 5.5 mV positive to the potential level in the ventricle (Goldring and O'Leary, 1951). Such steady voltage differences are believed related to the orientation of cellular elements in the cortex (O'Leary and Golding, 1964). Dc shifts are observed in a wide variety of abnormal conditions including anoxia, heating or cooling of brain, injury, spreading depression, and hypoglycemia (O'Leary and Goldring, 1964). However their occurrence in various normal states are perhaps of greater interest insofar as brain-behavior relations are concerned.

The general significance of dc potentials is in part related to the possibility that field effects may influence neuronal function. The behavior of cortical neurons whose dendrites extend from layer 5 to the surface might be altered by the changing dc field existing across the cortex. Thus degree and duration of depolarizing and hyperpolarizing currents in the cells could be influenced by dc field effects. Such considerations have led to studies of applied dc polarization. If a relatively strong surface positive polarization is applied across the cortex, the amplitude of EEG waves increases, the initial positive component of the evoked response disappears, the negative component increases in size, and the number of single cell discharges increases. Just the opposite effects are produced by surface negative polarization (Asahina and Yamanaka, 1960; Bindman et al., 1962; Bishop and O'Leary, 1950; Goldring and O'Leary, 1951; Landau et al., 1962). An example of the effects of surface positive and surface negative dc polarization applied across the cortex on evoked responses is shown in Figure 9.16.

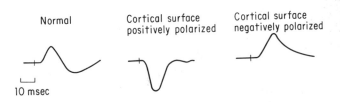

Normal

Cortical surface positively polarized

Cortical surface negatively polarized

⌐⌐
10 msec

Figure 9.16. Effects of dc fields applied across the cortex on a visual evoked response (positive up). (Redrawn from Bishop and O'Leary, 1950)

The gestalt psychologist Wolfgang Köhler was one of the first to suggest that dc fields might play a significant role in cortical function. He conducted several experiments on cat and man attempting to relate recorded dc field shifts to visual and auditory perception (Köhler and Held, 1949; Köhler and O'Connell, 1957; Köhler and Wegener, 1955; Köhler, et al., 1955). However, experiments by Lashley et al. (1951) and Sperry et al. (1955) showed that implanting metal needles, foils, and dielectrics in the cortex, which should alter dc field effects, did not alter visual discriminations in the least. Recent studies have noted altered degrees of SP shifts following pairing of neutral and SP inducing stimuli (Morrell, 1961b; Rusinov, 1953). We will examine these experiments further in Chapter 17.

Although the effects of applied dc fields on cortical activity noted above are unequivocal, the intensity of effective applied fields is considerably greater than those normally present in the cortex. Consequently, it remains to be determined whether such dc fields as do normally exist play a significant role in CNS function in addition to being a reflection of certain ongoing processes in the brain.

Suggested readings

Brazier, M. A. B. *The electrical activity of the nervous system.* (2nd ed.) New York: Macmillan, 1960.

Bureš, J., Petráň, M., & Zachar, J. *Electrophysiological methods in biological research.* (2nd ed.) New York: Academic Press, 1962.

IO

SENSORY PROCESSES

S ome of the more spectacular advances in physiological psychology to date have been in the area which traditionally occupies common ground between psychology and physiology: sensory psychophysiology. This was of course the earliest branch of psychology to develop; Weber enunciated his famous law relating stimulus and sensation as early as 1834. The ease of specifying the physical characteristics of stimuli has undoubtedly been a major factor in the rapid growth of this field. Learning, motivation, and other inferred processes have no such obvious physical starting points. A great deal of knowledge has been obtained in the study of sensory processes simply by presenting physical stimuli and recording the behavioral response of the organism. A classic example is the relation between the spectral sensitivity of the eye and the absorption spectrum of visual "purple." If the absolute light intensity threshold of human observers is determined for all visible wavelengths, a wavelength-threshold curve can be drawn which is essentially identical to the absorption spectrum of the visual purple substance in the rods of the human eye. The establishment of such identical functional relations between physical and physiological process on the one hand, and human behavior on the other, is of course a basic goal of physiological psychology.

With the advent of gross measures of electrical activity in the receptors and brain, a great deal of new information was obtained, including such basic findings as the spatial projections of receptor fields to the central nervous system. In addition, relations have been established between behavioral responses of the organism and electrical responses of the brain. An example of this is Bartley's demonstration of brightness enhancement: if a light is repeatedly flashed at the alpha frequency of the human EEG (about 8–12/sec), human observers judge it as being brighter than the same light flashed slower or faster (Bartley, 1938). Neural events related to cortical alpha activity thus influence the "perceived" brightness of a flashing light. The development of microelectrode techniques has resulted in still another revolution in the field of sensory psychophysiology. The behavior of single neurons can now be precisely defined and related to stimulus characteristics and to the behavior of the organism. Outstanding examples are Hubel and Wiesel's studies of the categories of natural visual stimuli that will activate nerve cells of the visual system and Mountcastle's analysis of the characteristics of cell responses to somatic sensory stimuli (e.g. touch, joint movement, etc.).

The vast literature that has developed in this field can only be sampled in the present volume. Comprehensive reviews on many aspects of sensory physiology by outstanding authorities are available in Volume I of the *Handbook of Physiology* (Field, 1959) as well as in more specialized sources. Equally comprehensive reviews of the psychophysical aspects of sensory function are also available (Stevens, 1951). We will attempt here to indicate the organization of sensory systems, and will touch on some areas of current interest.

THE CODING OF STIMULI

The fundamental problem in sensory function concerns the manner in which stimuli are coded in the nervous system. Physical stimuli come in a variety of forms, light, sound, heat, pressure, soluble molecules, etc., which can change continuously, often in terms of several physical characteristics. A light can alter in intensity, in wavelength, in physical extent, in duration, and so on. Since man can "perceive" (i.e. respond differentially) to literally millions of different physical stimuli, it is obvious that stimulus characteristics must somehow be coded by the sensory receptors and sensory nerves. In what manner is a physical stimulus identified and responded to as heat, red, a 1000-cycle tone, a pretty girl, etc.?

In 1826, Johannes Müller published his formal theory of "specific nerve energies" in an attempt to solve the problem of how nerve fibers code sensory stimuli. From the time of the Greeks most people had assumed that a given stimulus somehow impressed its characteristic directly on the "mind" or brain. Müller noted the now obvious fact that gross sensory quality depends on *which* nerve is stimulated, not on how it is stimulated. Visual receptors of the retina, and the optic nerve, can be stimulated by light to the eye, by pressure on the eye ball, by electric shock, by mechanical irritation, and so on. In all cases the subject reports <u>*visual*</u> sensations. It is not the stimulus that determines gross sensory quality, but rather the receptors and nerves activated by stimuli. Müller left open the alternative possibilities of different nerves carrying different kinds of impulses or different nerves going to different places (see Boring, 1942).

It is self-evident that the gross differences in stimulus quality between the various sensory modalities are determined by where the sensory nerves go. Any kind of activation of the optic nerve produces visual sensations because the nerve goes to the visual system of the brain. In like manner, activation of the auditory nerve produces auditory sensations because that nerve goes to the auditory pathways, and so on. The mechanisms underlying the differences in sensory quality within a given sense modality, such as different colors, different frequencies of tone, touch *vs* pressure, and so on, are less obvious (we will often refer to these differences in quality within a modality as submodalities). As we will see, it appears that both patterns of spike discharges in nerve cells and differential physical locations or projections of nerve cells in the nervous system may be involved in the coding of submodalities. Recent microelectrode studies have indicated that a surprising degree of differential representation of stimulus quality exists. In many cases the various characteristics of stimuli activate different cells in the brain. It is important to remember, incidentally, that different stimulus qualities may be coded differently at various levels of the CNS. There are possibilities for very complex interactions among nerve cells at every synaptic junction in the central nervous system.

The most direct and obvious type of coding process concerns the transformations of physical stimuli into nerve impulses by the various sensory receptors, a process referred to as *transduction*. Most receptors share a number of common features, schematized in Figure 10.1 (modified from Davis, 1961). External

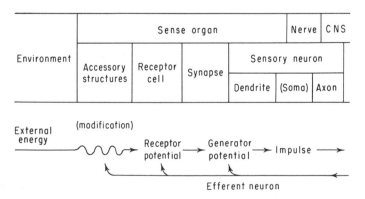

Figure 10.1. Generalized scheme of sensory receptor action (not all features shown here are present in all sense organs). (Modified from Davis, 1961)

energy in the form of light, sound, pressure, heat, soluble molecules, etc., im-
pinges on receptors, which in turn initiate spike discharges in sensory nerve cells.
Some receptors have *accessory structures*, such as the Pacinian corpuscle of the
pressure receptor or the tectorial membrane of the ear, which serve to focus,
alter, amplify or localize the particular stimulus. The stimulus or accessory
structure then activates the *receptor cell.* Examples of receptor cells are the rods
and cones in the retina of the eye or the hair cells in the cochlea of the ear. Not
all receptor systems have receptor cells; the Pacinian corpuscle, for example, is
an accessory structure surrounding the sensory neuron with no intervening
receptor cell (see Figure 10.3).

Activation of receptor cells produces graded electrical activity, which Davis
terms the *receptor potential.* This activity in turn results in activation of the
dendrite of the sensory neuron by transmission across the synapse between the
receptor cell and the sensory neuron. Activation of the sensory neuron dendrite
produces a graded response in the dendrite, just as in the dendrites and cell
body of any neuron, as described in Chapter 7. The graded dendrite response,
if sufficiently large to cross firing threshold, initiates an all-or-none spike discharge in the initial segment of the sensory neuron, which is conducted along
the sensory nerve fiber into the CNS. Finally, efferent neural pathways terminating on receptor systems permit the CNS to influence or "gate" activity of
accessory structures, receptors, and sensory neurons.

Davis terms the graded response of the sensory neuron dendrite the *generator
potential.* There is considerable disagreement concerning the definition of receptor and generator potentials (see Pringle, 1962). We have adopted the definitions
given by Davis (1961), which seem consistent and related to the structures
involved. Receptor potentials are generated by receptor cells, and generator
potentials are responsible for generation of spike discharges in sensory nerve
fibers. Disagreement has arisen because some receptors, notably mechanical
receptors of skin like the Pacinian corpuscle, have no receptor cells. The stimulus
acting on the accessory structure (Pacinian corpuscle) directly induces a graded
potential in the dendrite of the sensory nerve cell. We would term this a generator
potential; there is no receptor potential because there is no receptor cell. However, some authorities would call it a receptor potential. (As you can see, it is
really a semantic problem; everyone is agreed on the processes that occur.) A
major point to keep in mind is that in receptor systems such as the ear or eye,
there are receptor cells yielding receptor potentials and sensory neuron dendrites
yielding generator potentials. In all cases, the generator potential actually
initiates spike discharges in the sensory nerve fibers.

A given receptor system is much more sensitive to certain types of stimuli
than to others. Sherrington termed such stimuli *adequate stimuli.* The adequate
stimulus for the eye is light energy within a certain wavelength range. Pressure
on the eye ball will also induce visual sensations, but the amount of energy
required is very much greater. Stimuli of this type, to which the receptor is
relatively insensitive, are often called "inadequate" stimuli. (Inadequate stimuli

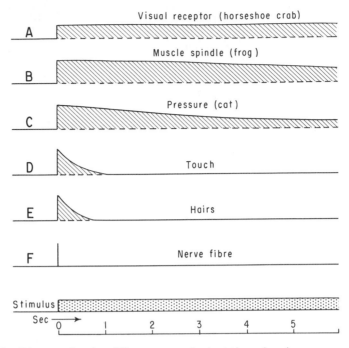

Figure 10.2. Diagram showing different rates of adaptation of various sense organs to a continued stimulus. (Modified from Adrian, 1928)

are frequently used in experiments; an electric shock to peripheral nerves is one of the neurophysiologist's favorite methods of stimulation.) The greater sensitivity of receptors to a particular type of stimulation is determined both by the accessory cells and by the receptor cells.

Adaptation is characteristic of most receptors. If a constant stimulus is presented to the receptor, the output, measured in terms of frequency of spike discharges in the sensory nerve fibers, decreases from a high initial level to some lower level or to zero. Examples of the degree of adaptation of several types of receptors are shown in Figure 10.2. It is common to describe receptors as being either slow-adapting (A, B, and C in Figure 10.2) or fast-adapting (D, E, and F in Figure 10.2).

THE SOMATIC SENSORY SYSTEM

Receptor Processes

A wide variety of different forms of sensory receptors have been found in skin. You might expect that after 100 years of study there would be some agreement on the functional properties of these variously formed structures, but such is not the case. The classical view was that the four basic modalities of cutaneous sensation were subserved by four specific types of receptors: pain—by fine nerve endings, cold—by Krause endbulbs, warmth—by Ruffini corpuscles, and touch —by Pacinian and Meissner's corpuscles. However, recent work by Weddell and co-workers has shown that all of these sensations can result from appropriate stimulation of the cornea, which apparently has only free nerve endings (Lele and Weddell, 1956). Nevertheless, there is solid evidence showing that many skin receptors are "tuned" to respond to only one modality. Direct measurements on Pacinian corpuscles, (pressure receptors) show them to be exquisitely sensitive to mechanical displacement—a movement of 0.5 μ in 100 msec being sufficient to cause excitation (Gray and Malcolm, 1950). By recording spike discharges from single afferent fibers, the range of stimuli delivered to the appropriate skin area effective in eliciting activity can easily be determined. Pacinian corpuscles, very sensitive to pressure, are insensitive to thermal stimuli. Other skin receptors are primarily sensitive to heat or cold, still others will respond to both thermal and mechanical stimuli, and finally, some will respond to all types of stimuli. Touch stimuli tend to activate the largest diameter cutaneous afferent fibers, as well as smaller fibers. The small diameter C fiber group tend to respond to all varieties of stimulation. In terms of adaptation rate, pressure receptors are of two types, fast adapting and slow adapting (see Figure 10.2). Most receptors activated by bending hairs, for example, give a fast burst of activity and then show adaptation. The majority of kinesthetic receptors, on the other hand, appear to be slow adapting (Rose and Mountcastle, 1959).

The consensus of anatomical opinion regarding skin receptors can perhaps be summarized by a somewhat oversimplified but rather tidy subdivision into two categories related to pathways in the CNS. Henry Head initially proposed a functional separation of somatic sensibility into *epicritic* (specific light touch and pressure) and *protopathic* (more primitive and diffuse sensations of touch, pain, and temperature). Specifically identified receptors exist for pressure: Meissner's corpuscles in outer layers of skin, comparable structures surrounding hair roots, and deeper lying Pacinian corpuscles. In addition the muscle spindle organs and Golgi tendon organs convey information from muscles. All of these give rise to larger myelinated fibers that segregate into the medial branch of the dorsal root as they enter the cord. In the spinal cord they give rise to reflex connections (Chapter 12) and to ascending pathways destined for cerebral cortex (lemniscal system) and cerebellum. This is the epicritic system concerned primarily with light touch, pressure and position sense. All other skin afferents come from nonspecific fine nerve plexes in the skin, which in earlier years were incorrectly identified as various specific receptors. These smaller fibers, mostly nonmyelinated, enter the cord through the lateral branch of the dorsal root, and have reflex connections and relays to ascending paths. In particular they relay to the spinothalamic tract, a multisynaptic pathway conveying pain, temperature, and diffuse touch to the reticular formation, thalamus and cortex.

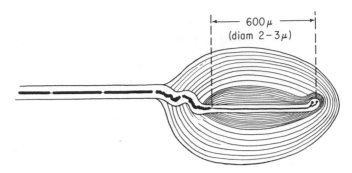

Figure 10.3 Diagram of a Pacinian corpuscle. The nerve fiber is continuous, but loses its myelin sheath (indicated by the dashed lines) as it enters the central core. (Redrawn from Quilliam and Sato, 1955)

The process whereby a mechanical or tactile stimulus is transformed into an electrical event activating an afferent nerve fiber is not well understood (for that matter the conversion, i.e. transduction, processes are not yet thoroughly understood for any receptor system). The Pacinian corpuscle has been the most extensively studied cutaneous receptor system. A longitudinal cross section through a Pacinian corpuscle (taken from the abdomen of a cat) is shown in Figure 10.3. A single myelinated nerve fiber enters the corpuscle. The corpuscle itself is composed of a great many concentric layers of connective tissue, which in cross section resemble the layers of an onion. The axon loses its myelin sheath where it enters the central core of the corpuscle. Pressure or mechanical deformation of the corpuscle results in spike discharged in the nerve fiber. It appears that the terminal portion of the sensory nerve within the corpuscle responds electrically in a graded fashion, analogous to the EPSP of a nerve cell body and dendrites (see Figure 10.4). There is a direct relation between degree of mechanical displacement and amplitude of the graded electrical response of the system (Gray and Sato, 1953). Several displacements superimposed on the receptor will produce summed effects. Thus the *generator potential* is an analogue or graded response whose amplitude is determined by stimulus strength (Figure 10.4). All-or-none spike impulse initiation is believed to occur where the myelin sheath

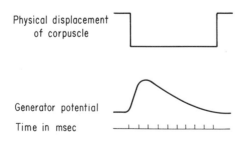

Figure 10.4. Generator potential of a Pacinian corpuscle in response to a physical displacement. Note that although the degree of displacement is constant, the corpuscle response declines to zero. (Redrawn from Gray and Sato, 1953)

begins (Gray, 1959). Adaptation of the discharges to a constant mechanical stimulus, incidentally, appears to be in large part the result of mechanical factors in the Pacinian corpuscle. A constant displacement of the surface of the corpuscle causes only a transitory displacement of the central core surrounding the nerve fiber and hence only a transitory generator potential (Figure 10.4; Gray, 1959). The corpuscle itself changes shape so that a constant mechanical pressure results in decreasing amount of pressure on the nerve fiber.

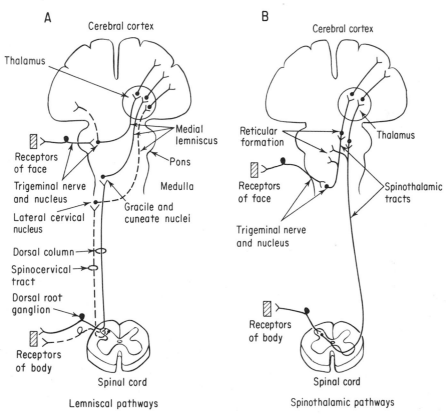

Figure 10.5.   Schematic diagrams of the lemniscal and spinothalamic pathways of the somatic sensory system.

Central Pathway

As noted above, there are two distinct pathways in the spinal cord and brain stem carrying cutaneous information to the cerebral cortex. We will label one of these the *lemniscal* system and the other the *spinothalamic* system (after Rose and Mountcastle, 1959). The lemniscal pathway, particularly the long-known *dorsal column* system, is best understood. As indicated in the diagram of Figure 10.5 (solid lines in A), afferent fibers from tactile and kinesthetic receptors enter the spinal cord, turn upward in the dorsal columns and ascend to make their first synapse on cells in the *gracile* (lower trunk and legs) and *cuneate* (upper trunk and arms) nuclei in the lower medulla. This is the first central synapse of the lemniscal system. Fibers from these nuclei then *cross* and ascend in a tract called the *medial lemniscus* to synapse in the thalamic relay nucleus, the ventrobasal complex (also called the ventral posterior medial and lateral nuclei VPM, VPL). Fibers from these thalamic nuclei project to somatic sensory areas I and II of the cerebral cortex. In addition there is a trigeminal portion from the face which enters in the 5th cranial nerve to synapse in the 5th nerve nucleus, and from there *crosses* to the other side and enters the medial lemniscus. It appears that there may also be an ipsilateral pathway from the 5th nerve nucleus joining the medial lemniscus on the same side, although the evidence is not entirely clear (Rose and Mountcastle, 1959). The major pathway is contralateral, left body surface to right brain center, because the ascending system crosses in the brain stem.

A second spinal pathway that contributes to the medial lemniscus, sometimes termed the spinocervical tract or Morin's pathway (see Figure 10.5, dotted lines in A), has been delineated more recently (see Morin, 1955; Lundberg and Oscarsson, 1961; Norrsell and Voorhoeve, 1962; Andersson, 1962). Input from a wide variety of somatic receptors relays in the dorsal horn (i.e. synapses on cells in the dorsal portion of the spinal gray matter) on the same side from which it enters the cord. The axons from the second order neurons ascend in the dorsal portion of the lateral column (spinocervical tract) on the same side of the cord and relay in the lateral cervical nucleus in the upper cord. From here the third order neurons cross and join the medial lemniscus to relay in the ventrobasal complex of the thalamus and project to cortical somatic sensory areas I and II. Both the dorsal columns and the spinocervical tracts are rapid conducting systems conveying a wide variety of somatic sensory information toward the cortex.

Afferent fibers carrying pain and temperature information, and some tactile information as well, synapse on large cells in the dorsal horn of the spinal cord. Many of the secondary fibers cross and ascend the spinal cord, probably in several different pathways (see Lundberg, 1964a), relay through interneurons in the brain stem reticular formation, and reach the thalamus (Figure 10.5B) There is an analogous component of the spinothalamic system in the trigeminal nerve carrying pain and temperature from the face. Many of the fibers appear to end in the ventrobasal complex of the thalamus, thus relaying to somatic sensory areas I and II of the cortex. It appears that there may be an ipsilateral component of the spinothalamic tract as well. There is a good deal of indirect evidence (see Rose and Mountcastle, 1959) suggesting that many fibers of the spinothalamic tract end in a somewhat different region of the thalamus. This is an area lying between the ventrobasal complex and the medial geniculate body (the auditory relay in the thalamus), which has been termed the posterior nuclear group (Rose and Woolsey, 1958). This thalamic region is known to have connections to somatic sensory area II of the cortex (see Chapter 11).

Brief mention should be made of the spinocerebellar systems. There are two major pathways, the *dorsal* and *ventral spinocerebellar tracts*, that convey all varieties of somatic sensory information destined for the cerebellum. We will consider these systems further in our discussion of the cerebellum (Chapter 13). Finally, there are still other ascending spinal tracts, less well characterized, which we will not consider here. The reader is urged to consult Lundberg (1964a) for a comprehensive review of ascending spinal pathways.

A number of studies have demonstrated that the ascending reticular formation of the brain stem receives somatic sensory input (French et al., 1962; Starzl et al., 1951). These studies hypothesized that collateral afferent fibers from the medial lemniscus system turn and enter the reticular formation. However considerable evidence indicates that the collateral fibers carrying somatic sensory information to the reticular formation come predominantly from the spinothalamic system (Rose and Mountcastle, 1959).

Functional Properties of the Lemniscal System

The somatic sensory system appears to make use of both spatial representation and spike discharge frequency in solving the problem of coding sensory information. We will examine the "epicritic" lemniscal system first; a good deal more is known about its anatomical relations and physical characteristics than is the case for the "protopathic" spinothalamic system. There is a clear spatial segregation of different regions of the body surface at all levels of the lemniscal system from skin to cerebral cortex. As we will see in the next chapter, there is a complete regional layout of the skin surface on the cerebral cortex. The ventrobasal complex of the thalamus also contains an areal representation of the body surface, but the relations between skin area and thalamic region are more difficult to see here. The skin is a two dimensional structure; and it is mapped out on the cerebral cortex in essentially a two dimensional fashion (the cortex can be viewed as a sheet or layer of cells covering the brain). However, the thalamus is a three dimensional structure; and the mapping of two dimensional skin to three dimensional thalamus is difficult to picture.

Each small region of skin surface projects to a small region or "cube" of cells in the thalamus. We can get an idea of the organization of the projection system by looking at a map of a cross section through the thalamus. Figure 10.6 (from Mountcastle and Henneman, 1952) shows a *somatotopic* map of the representation of skin regions on a cross section of the monkey thalamus. Each little picture shows the region of skin surface that when stimulated by light tapping produces gross evoked responses at that location in the thalmus. There is a rather precise and discrete region-to-region representation of skin surface areas in the ventrobasal complex. The nervous system appears to code the location of stimuli on the body surface in terms of regional locations in the thalamus and cortex.

Microelectrode studies, particularly those of Mountcastle and his colleagues (Poggio and Mountcastle, 1963; Mountcastle, Poggio, and Werner, 1963) have demonstrated that a subtle refinement of the principle of spatial representation

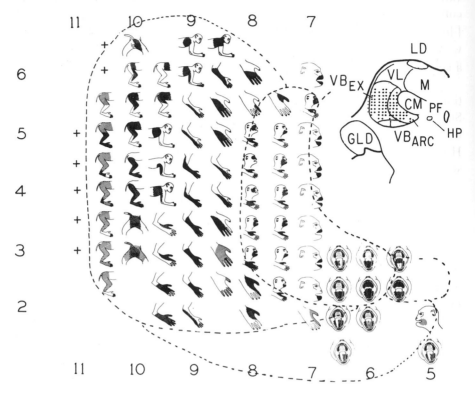

Figure 10.6. Representation of cutaneous tactile sensibility in one frontal plane of thalamus of monkey as determined by the evoked-potential technique. Insert drawing prepared from photographic reconstruction of the frontal section; dots indicate positive points and each figurine drawing is arranged accordingly. Tactile stimulation of areas marked on figurines evoked responses at points indicated. Gradation of intensity of the evoked potentials, from most to least, is indicated by solid shading (black) and crosshatching. With exception of ipsilateral mouth regions (most ventromedial figurine) all responses were obtained only from stimulation of contralateral side of body and head. Crosses indicate points at which faint responses, probably in fibers of passage, were recorded on stimulation of ipsilateral side. Vbex, Ventrobasal complex, external portion; Vbare, ventrobasal complex, arcuate portion; CM, nucleus centrum medianum; VL, ventrolateral complex; HP, habenulopeduncular tract; GLD, lateral geniculate body. (From Mountcastle and Henneman, 1952)

can serve to code the various submodalities of somatic sensation in the thalamus. Within a given block of tissue in the ventrobasal complex representing a particular region in the body surface, small blocks or cubes of cells are responsive to different submodalities. There are three basic submodalities, light touch to the skin, deep pressure to the fascia below the skin, and joint movement. Within the block of thalamic tissue representing a finger of one hand, some small blocks of tissue contain cells activated only by light touch, other blocks have cells responsive to only deep pressure, and still other blocks have cells responding only to joint movement.

Cells of the ventrobasal complex in the thalamus are very specific. Any given cell is responsive only to one of the three modes of stimulation, regardless of the condition of the animal. In the monkey, roughly 42 percent of the ventrobasal cells respond to skin stimulation, 32 percent to deep pressure, and 26 percent to movements of the joints. Thus the type of submodality of the somatic sensory stimulus is specifically and rigidly coded in the thalamus in terms of spatial representation. The region or extent of skin area stimulated that will activate a given cell in the ventrobasal complex is relatively small. In the monkey, the average area of skin ranges from 0.2 cm^2 on the fingers and toes to 20 cm^2 on the back. The areal extent of the receptor region (i.e. skin) that will activate a given neuron is called the *receptive field* of that cell (see Figure 10.9).

In our discussion of the topographical attributes of the subcortical portions of the lemniscal system we have emphasized the thalamic relay station; the greatest amount of data have been obtained from the third order neurons of this structure. Comparison of the representations and receptive fields for the first order afferent fibers and the second order neurons projecting from the gracile and cuneate nuclei to the thalamus indicates that both convergence and divergence take place. In general, the size of the receptive fields for nerve cells increases as the system is ascended. Cells in the thalamus are activated by wider skin region than are first order afferent fibers. Nonetheless there is, if anything, increased discriminatory capacity in higher order cells. We will examine this seeming paradox further when we consider the somatic sensory cortex (Chapter 11). It is sufficient here to note that complex excitatory and inhibitory interactions among neurons can increase the discriminatory ability of thalamic and cortical cells.

Mountcastle, Poggio, and Werner (1963) have demonstrated that cells of the ventrobasal complex responsive to joint movement *code* the degree of movement precisely in terms of spike discharge frequency. Figure 10.7 is a graph showing the activity of a ventrobasal neuron driven by extension of the contralateral knee of a monkey. The graph relates the steady-state frequency of spike discharges (impulses per second) of the cell to the number of degrees of angular movement of the knee joint. Each dot is an average of many determinations. All the dots appear to fall rather close to the smooth curve drawn through them. Note that the spontaneous discharge rate in the absence of stimulation is about 24/sec. Threshold for this cell is a joint position of about 70 degrees; when the angle is increased beyond this, the discharge frequency of the cell increases above the spontaneous activity level.

At first glance the curve of Figure 10.7 does not appear to have any particular form. On closer examination it proves to resemble a type of mathematical relationship called a *power function*. The general form of the power function in this situation is:

$$F = K\theta^n$$

in which F is the frequency of spike discharge of the neuron, θ is the angle of

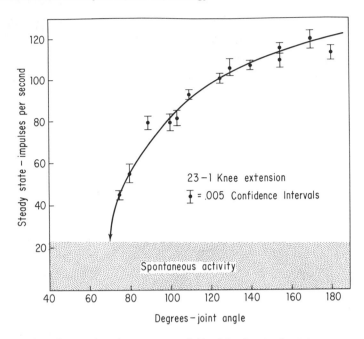

Figure 10.7. Plot of nerve impulses per second (dots) in the steady state versus angle for a ventrobasal thalamic neuron driven by extension of the contralateral knee (lines and bars include 99.5 per cent of the data around each point). The rate of spontaneous activity is the means of many different records of it, obtained over a 3-hour period of study. The curve is one arbitrarily drawn by eye; its intercept with the spontaneous activity level is defined as the threshold. or the edge of the excitatory angle, for the cell. (From Mountcastle, Poggio, and Werner, 1963)

the joint in degrees, and K and n are simply numerical constants. In fitting the curve to the power function equation, it is best to express the actual spike discharge frequency (F) relative to the spontaneous rate (C) as $F - C$. By the same token, the actual joint angle (θ) is expressed relative to the threshold angle (θ_t) as $\theta - \theta_t$. The equation now becomes:

$$F - C = K (\theta - \theta_t)^n$$

or:

$$F = K (\theta - \theta_t)^n + C$$

When this equation is solved for the actual data of Figure 10.7, it becomes:

$$F = 13.9 (\theta - \theta_t)^{429} + 24$$

In dealing with mathematical relationships of this kind, it is often helpful to transform them into linear (i.e. straight-line) functions. Linear relationships are perhaps the easiest to deal with and visualize. A simple linear equation has the form:

$$Y = nX + k$$

The equation given above for the data of Figure 10.7 can be transformed into a linear equation by taking the logarithm of both sides:

$$\log (F - C) = n \log (\theta - \theta_t) + \log K$$

This log equation expresses a linear relationship between the log of cell discharge frequency and the log of joint angle.[1]

The linear relationship between $\log (F - C)$ and $\log (\theta - \theta_t)$ is illustrated in Figure 10.8. The fit of the data to the straight line function is virtually perfect. For the nonmathematical reader, who by this time may have begun to despair, the essential point of all the algebra is simply this: the extent to which the data points fall on a straight line function in the plot of Figure 10.8 relating log frequency to log angle indicates the extent to which the original data of Figure 10.7 relating frequency to angle are fit (described mathematically) by a power function. The "goodness-of-fit" of the log—log data to a straight line can be measured quantitatively by calculating a Pearson product-moment correlation coefficient (r). As you may recall from statistics, a perfect linear relationship between two variables yields an $r = 1.0$ and no relationship yields an $r = 0$. The correlation coefficient calculated by Mountcastle and his associates for the data of Figure 10.8 is $r = 0.98$! Hence, the relationship between log frequency and log angle is virtually a perfect linear function. This in turn means that the relationship between the original measures of frequency of spike discharge and extension angle of the joint is perfectly described by the power function.

There is a particular significance in the fact that the relationship between

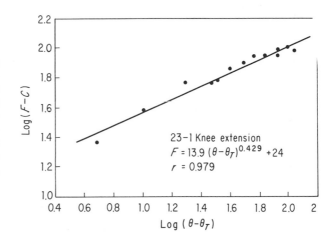

Figure 10.8. A replot of the data of Figure 10.7 after logarithmic transformation. The straight line is the best fit to these values. r = the Pearson product moment correlation coefficient. Note the nearly perfect fit. (From Mountcastle, Poggio, and Werner, 1963)

23–1 Knee extension
$F = 13.9 \ (\theta - \theta_T)^{0.429} + 24$
$r = 0.979$

[1] Thus if we make the following identities for the terms in the general linear equation: $Y = \log (F - C)$, $X = \log (\theta - \theta_t)$ and $k = \log K$, the resulting equation has the general linear form of $Y = nX + k$.

A

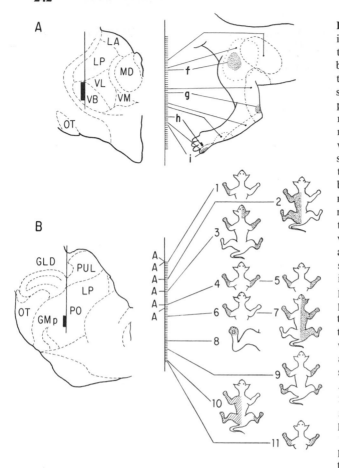

B

Figure 10.9. A, data obtained in a microelectrode penetration that passed through the ventrobasal nuclear complex of the thalamus of a cat. The reconstruction of the penetration is presented at the left; in the region marked by a thick line neurons were observed that were activated by somatic sensory stimuli delivered to the contralateral side of the body. In the drawing to the right the expanded scale (50-micron intervals) represents the responsive region of the ventrobasal complex. The areas indicated by lines and shading on the figurine drawing of the cat indicate the positions and extents of the peripheral receptive fields of the neurons observed; at positions (f), (g), and (i) neurons were isolated which were activated by light mechanical stimuli delivered to the skin. At position (h) a neuron was isolated which was activated by gentle rotation of the metacarpophalangeal joint of the third toe of the contralateral forepaw. The other fields represented are those of the several neurons active together at the levels indicated. The entire sequence of receptive fields is typical of the rather precise topographical pattern of representation of the contralateral body surface in the ventrobasal nuclear complex. Abbreviations: LA, lateral anterior nucleus; LP, lateral posterior nucleus; MD, mediodorsal nucleus; VB, ventrobasal nuclear complex; VL, ventrolateral nucleus; VM, ventromedial nucleus; OT, optic tract. (Redrawn from Poggio and Mountcastle, 1960) **B**, data obtained in a microelectrode penetration that passed through the posterior nuclear group of the thalamus of a cat. The penetration is reconstructed in the drawing at the left. In the region marked by the heavy line, active and drivable neurons were observed that displayed the "posterior group properties" described in the text. The responsive region is indicated by the expanded scale (20-micron intervals) shown at the right. "A" indicates levels at which neurons were isolated that were activated only by sound. Figurine drawings 1 through 9 show the peripheral receptive fields of cells that were activated by light mechanical stimuli delivered to the body surface; the cells whose receptive fields are shown by drawings 10 and 11 could be activated only by stimuli that were destructive of tissue. It is important to note that in contrast to the data shown in Figure 10.9A the sequence of receptive fields here composes no topographical pattern. In many other penetrations of the posterior group the auditory, nociceptive, and mechanoreceptive cells, as well as those responsive to all three forms of stimulation, were indiscriminately mixed in the dorsoventral direction. GLD, lateral geniculate body; Pul, pulvinar nucleus;

stimulus and neural response follows a power function, over and above the fact that a clear and precise relationship exists. As we will see at the end of the chapter, a great many psychophysical functions relating stimulus magnitudes to the judged magnitudes of sensations reported by humans follow this same type of power function.

We have discussed the lemniscal system as though it were a unitary functional system. However, you will recall that two quite distinct spinal pathways, the dorsal columns and the spinocervical tracts, contribute somatic sensory information to the lemniscal system (see Figure 10.5). Results of careful lesion-behavior studies by Norrsell (1962, 1967) suggest that there may be some functional differentiation in these pathways. Dogs were trained to respond (forelimb lever press for food reward) to a weak air-puff tactile stimulus delivered to the hind limb. Sections of the spinocervical tract produced a marked transitory impairment of the conditioned response, but sections of the dorsal column had no effect. However, joint sections of both pathways produced severe and sometimes permanent loss of the response. On the other hand responses conditioned to strong electric shocks of the hind limb skin (which would activate many ascending spinal pathways, including the spinothalamic system discussed immediately below) were unaffected by any of these lesions.

Functional Properties of the Spinothalamic System

As described above, afferent fibers conveying pain, temperature, and diffuse touch synapse either directly or via interneurons on the cells of the dorsal horn of the spinal cord. These cells give rise to contralateral (and probably ipsilateral) ascending pathways, which synapse in many regions of the brain stem and midbrain, particularly in the reticular formation. At least a portion of the system eventually terminates in the thalamus, partly in the ventrobasal complex and partly in the posterior nuclear group.

Hunt and Kuno (1959) studied the receptive fields for the dorsal horn cells of the spinal cord. They found that the receptive fields were extremely large, often including much of the body surface on both sides. This contrasts markedly with the very small and discrete receptive fields for the dorsal column fibers of the lemniscal system. In addition, they found that many dorsal horn cells discharged only to painful stimuli (defined as stimuli that definitely injure tissue).

Poggio and Mountcastle (1960) undertook an extensive investigation of the response properties of the cells in the posterior nuclear group of the thalamus in the cat. Cells in this region can be activated by ipsilateral skin stimulation, in contrast to the purely contralateral projection of the lemniscal system. From this fact, it can be inferred that the posterior group serves as a relay for at least a portion of the spinothalamic system. Figure 10.9 compares examples of

PO, posterior nucleus; GM$_P$, medial geniculate body. (Redrawn from Poggio and Mountcastle, 1960)

response properties of cells in the ventrobasal complex and the posterior nuclear group. Cells in the posterior thalamic group could hardly differ more from those of the ventrobasal complex. First, there appears to be no somatotopic representation of the body surface in the posterior region. Second, there is no spatial representation of submodalities. Third, the receptive fields are extremely large, sometimes in including virtually the entire body surface. Finally, some cells respond to both mechanical and painful stimuli. There are some cells that respond only to painful stimulation and not to mechanical stimulation; however, they are scattered throughout the posterior nuclear region rather than being organized into only one portion. It would appear that this region of the thalamus must play a basic role in the elaboration of painful sensation, but the nature of this role is obscure.

THE VISUAL SYSTEM

Most organisms including even single celled animals can respond to light energy. However, the vertebrate visual system is designed to do much more than simply signal the presence or absence of light. A detailed image of the external world is projected on the *retina* (the layers of receptors and nerve cells at the back of the eye). This structure transforms and codes the image into nerve impulses which carry a representation of the external visual world to the brain. The precision of detail vision is surprising: the image of the full moon on the retina has a radius of about 0.1 mm. Considerable detail can be seen within this image. Lines that are much narrower than the single receptor cells of the retina can easily be seen. In addition to detail vision, the vertebrate visual system is particularly sensitive to movement of objects in the visual world. The faster a predator normally moves, and the faster its prey moves, the more acute must the movement vision of each be to insure survival. In the following discussion of the visual receptors and pathways, try not to lose sight of the basic coding problems involved in delivering a representation of the external visual world, and particularly movements in that world, to the brain.

It used to be thought that the retina acted more or less like a photographic camera. Detail vision would thus depend on the size of the receptor cells, i.e. the "grain" of the image would be the receptor cells themselves. There are two major factors which modify this view. First, there are 100 times as many rods (one type of visual receptor cell) as optic nerve fibers in man. The "grain" of the retina is really the grain of the optic nerve fibers. A single fiber that can be activated by any of 100 rods cannot tell the brain which rod was involved. Second, as Rushton (1962) has emphasized, the retina is really more like a television camera than a photographic camera:

> Its purpose is not to fix a picture upon the retina, but rather to transmit in a code of nerve impulses the more dramatic features of the ever changing retinal scene. Our rods and cones are 100 million reporters seeking "copy." That which continues unchanging is not "news" and nothing will induce them to report it.

Experiments by Riggs, Ratliff, Cornsweet, and Cornsweet (1953) demonstrated that if an image is stabilized on the retina it *fades away*. Normally the eye is continuously making small and very rapid movements, so that all retinal images are continuously shifting back and forth on the retina. Riggs and his associates devised an optical system in which the visual object was reflected to a viewing screen from a small mirror attached to the side of a contact lens on the cornea of the eye. The image moved with the eye ball and thus was always projected on the same retinal elements. Under these conditions, most objects tend to fade out in a few seconds. This rather striking adaptation does not normally occur because the image is shifted to different receptor cells by eye movements.

Receptor Processes

There are two basic types of photoreceptor cells in the retina of the eye: *rods* and *cones* (see Figure 10.12). The rods are sensitive to very dim illumination *(scotopic* vision), whereas the cones require greater intensities of light and are more involved in acuity and color aspects of visual function (*photopic* vision). Although not always structurally distinct in invertebrates, rods and cones are easily differentiable in mammals (Granit, 1959). This differentiation of structure and function in rods and cones, often subsumed under the *duplicity theory*, is of fundamental importance. The center of the visual field, i.e. the region we see most clearly when we look at an object, projects upon the *fovea*, which is composed entirely of cones. The foveal cones have an almost one to one relation to outgoing nerve fibers. The rods have their greatest density about 20° of *visual angle* (the angle in degrees between the direct line of sight projecting to the fovea and the projection of any other position in the visual field) away from the fovea (thus you can see a dim star best if you look about 20° away from it). There are about 125 million rods and six million cones in the human retina, but only about one million optic nerve fibers. Hence many receptors will activate each nerve fiber, particularly in the peripheral regions of the retina where rods predominate.

There are at least two visual pigments (chemicals responsive to light) in receptor cells of the mammalian retina, *rhodopsin* in the rods and *iodopsin* in cones. Let us consider first the reactions of rhodopsin. When light falls on a rod, the rhodopsin immediately breaks down into *retinene* and *opsin*. Retinene has a relatively simple chemical structure closely related to Vitamin A (thus the necessity of Vitamin A for adequate night vision), and opsin is a complex protein (Wald, 1959). There are two different biochemical pathways whereby rhodopsin can be resynthesized, either from retinene and opsin, or from Vitamin A back to retinene and then combination with opsin (see Figure 10.10). The important point is that when rhodopsin is broken down by light, the retinene and Vitamin A produced are in isomeric forms (see Chapter 2), which do not recombine. They must be altered enzymatically to other isomeric forms for resynthesis of rhodopsin. A diagrammatic scheme of the process is shown in Figure 10.10.

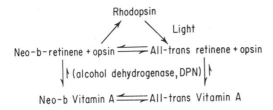

Figure 10.10. Summary schematic of the major steps in the breakdown and formation of rhodopsin. (From Hubbard and Ward, 1959)

The visual pigment of the cones, iodopsin, breaks down upon exposure to light into two substances: retinene, in the same form as that from rhodopsin, and a different protein termed *photopsin*. In other words the visual pigments of the rods and cones are both made up of retinene and a protein, with only the protein differing, and the chemical reactions of both are comparable.

We have spoken of two visual pigments, rhodopsin and iodopsin. Actually, there appear to be a great many different pigments in vertebrates, depending upon the species and upon whether the receptor is a rod or a cone. However, in all cases the pigment is composed of retinene and a type of protein opsin. It is the opsin that differs. As Wald puts it, "one retinene and many opsins." In fact it appears that most organisms with eyes, including squid and lobster, as well as vertebrates, have the same retinene, namely neo-b-retinene, in combination with some type of opsin (Wald, 1961). However, every species has a different opsin. In human rods there is one rhodopsin, composed of neo-b-retinene and a particular opsin, and in human cones there are three iodopsins, the latter being made up of neo-b-retinene and three different opsins (Wald, 1961).

Ingenious experiments by Stiles, Rushton, and Wall, (see *Visual Problems of Color*, 1961) have provided some very strong indirect evidence concerning the *absorption spectra* (wavelengths of light that are absorbed) of the three types of iodopsin found in the human cones. In brief, the method is as follows (see Rushton, 1957). A very narrow beam of light is shone in the eye. The light passes through the foveal portion of the retina (only cones), is reflected from the back of the eye, passes back again through the retina and out of the eye. The amount of light reflected out of the eye can be measured and the amount absorbed calculated from the measurements and careful consideration of other factors. The amount of light absorbed depends upon the degree of bleaching of the cone pigments in the retina. Hence the degree of cone bleaching resulting from pre-exposure to various wavelengths of light can be measured. Although the techniques are exceedingly difficult, and many possible sources of error exist, results seem fairly consistent. There appear to be three types of cone pigments, with absorption maxima at about 440 (blue), 540 (green), and 590 (red) mμ. These findings constitute a very real triumph for the three receptor theory of color vision first propounded by Thomas Young in 1802.

A number of aspects of visual sensation, particularly relating to brightness and color phenomena, can be deduced very accurately from the biochemical properties of rhodopsin and the iodopsins. Foremost among these is the virtually perfect correspondence between spectral sensitivities for rod and cone vision and absorption spectra of the rod and cone pigments (Figure 10.11). Another striking correspondence concerns the time courses of rod and cone *dark adaptation*. If the eye is exposed to a bright light, it requires up to 30 minutes for the rods to reestablish maximum sensitivity (i.e. to dark adapt). The spontaneous rate of synthesis of rhodopsin in solution follows virtually the same curve as does the rate of rod dark adaptation. Cone dark adaptation is much more rapid, requiring about 6 minutes. Again, the rate of synthesis of iodopsin in solution is about the same (Wald, 1961).

The response of the rods to visual stimulation is about as sensitive as it can be. Hecht, Shlaer, and Pirenne (1942) demonstrated in a rather striking experiment that a rod can be stimulated by a *single quantum* of light energy. A quantum, remember, is the irreducibly small unit or packet of light energy. They found that six quanta striking on the retina, each interacting with a different rod, can produce a visual sensation in man. (The interested reader is urged to consult their paper for an instructive demonstration of the scientific method at its best). As we noted earlier, a quantum of light entering a rod causes rhodopsin to be broken down into retinene and opsin. The opsin appears to play a particular, but as yet unknown, role in the generation of receptor activity (Wald, 1959). Unfortunately, the transduction process whereby the breakdown of rhodopsin and iodopsin (or the action of the opsins) results in production of a *receptor potential* and activation of the bipolar cells whose dendrites connect to the rods and cones remains obscure.

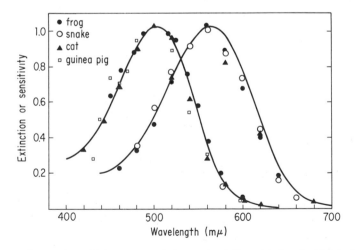

Figure 10.11. Spectral sensitivity curves of rhodopsin (left) and iodopsin (right), determined chemically. Points are Granit's (1947) determinations of spectral sensitivity measures from various animals using microelectrode recording from retinal cells in dark and light adaptation. (From Wald, Brown, and Smith 1955)

The basic organization of receptors and nerve cells in the retina is indicated in Figure 10.12. Rods and cones are in close apposition to the dendrites of the bipolar nerve cells. These in turn synapse on *ganglion* cells whose axons form the optic nerve. In addition, the receptors are interconnected by horizontal nerve cells, and the bipolar and ganglion cells are interconnected by several varieties of amacrine or association type neurons. The retina is actually a very complex neural system and is perhaps best thought of as a " little brain " lying between the photoreceptors and the optic nerve. Embryologically, the retina grows out from the brain rather than being formed peripherally. Although there is only one cell (the bipolar cell) in the main line between the receptors and the ganglion cells, the various interconnecting association cells add a great deal of complexity to the system.

If a gross electrode is placed on the cornea and another (indifferent electrode) is placed either behind the eye ball or elsewhere on the body, a complex electrical potential called the *electroretinogram* (ERG) can be recorded when a light is shined in the eye. A typical ERG is shown in Figure 10.13. There are usually

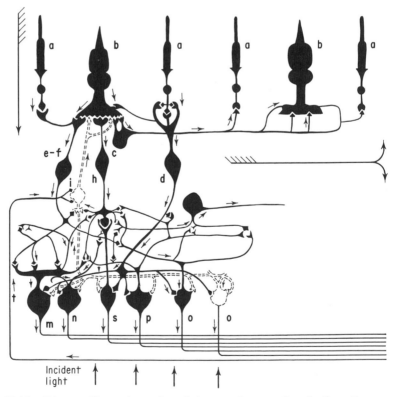

Figure 10.12.   Diagram illustrating a few of the neural connections in the retina: a, rods; b, cones; c, d, e, f, h, bipolar cells; m, n, o, p, s, ganglion cells. Note the efferent cell (light dots) conducting neural activity back to the receptor cells. (Redrawn from Polyak, 1941)

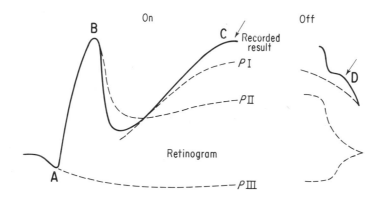

Figure 10.13. The electroretinogram (ERG) and its analysis. The four prominent features are: **A**, the first negative deflection, the a-wave; **B**, the rapidly following positive b-wave; **C**, the slower c-wave; **D**, the "off-effect," or d-wave. Granit's analysis into the three components, *P*I, *P*II, and *P*III, is shown by the dotted lines. (Redrawn from Bartley, 1941)

three waves or inflections (a, b and c in Figure 10.13) when a light is turned on, and a fourth (d) when the light is turned off. Earlier it was hoped that certain of these waves might reflect the receptor or generator potentials of the rods and cones. Unfortunately this hope has not been realized. Although receptor potentials may be partly responsible for some portion of the ERG, the inflections do not appear to represent receptor processes exclusive of neural activity in the retina.

On the basis of many different lines of evidence Granit has suggested that three underlying processes, labeled *P*I, *P*II, and *P*III in Figure 10.13, add together to produce the over-all ERG. *P*I is a slowly developing positive potential. Recent evidence from microelectrode studies indicates that it may not reflect either receptor or nerve cell activity, but rather metabolic activity in the pigmented epithelial cells of the retina (Brown and Wiesel, 1958). No components or processes of the ERG appear to reflect activity of the ganglion cells. Antidromic activation of them by tetanic stimulation of the optic nerve has no effect on the ERG (Granit and Helme, 1939). Furthermore, a normal ERG is obtained after total degeneration of the ganglion cells following optic nerve section (Noell, 1953). At the moment, some authorities feel that the initial portion of *P*III, giving rise to the (A) inflection, may represent receptor activity (Brown and Wiesel, 1959), and the *P*II component responsible for the (B) inflection may represent excitation of bipolar cells by receptors or excitation of ganglion cells by bipolars, or both (Granit, 1962).

The Visual Pathways

The major afferent pathways of the visual system are relatively simple (Figure 10.14). In lower vertebrates such as the frog the entire optic nerve from

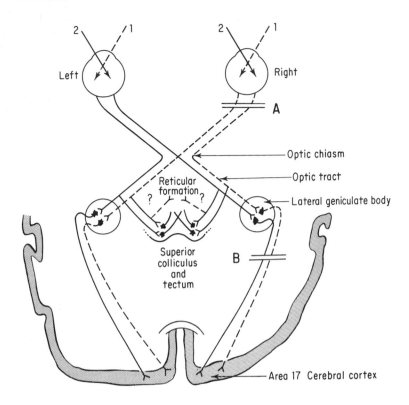

Figure 10.14. Schematic diagram of the visual system. Section at **A** eliminates input from right eye, but section at **B** eliminates input from the right half of each eye. (Modified from Gardner, 1952)

the right retina goes to the left side of the brain, and vice versa. In higher verte-brates, where some degree of binocular vision exists, a portion of each optic nerve goes to each side of the brain. In man, (Figure 10.14) optic nerve fibers from the left half of the retina (representing the right half of each visual field) project to the left *lateral geniculate* body of the thalamus and fibers from the right half of each retina project to the right lateral geniculate body. The resorting of fibers takes place at the *optic chiasm*, the point at which the two optic nerves come together. Although the retina grows out from the brain embryologically, and the optic nerve fibers are at the very least second-order fibers (receptors–bipolar cells–ganglion cells) convention dictates that the fibers from retinas to chiasm are called optic nerves and those from chiasm to CNS are called optic tracts. The optic tracts synapse in the lateral geniculate body, the thalamic relay nucleus with projections to the visual region of the cerebral cortex. Each lateral geniculate body is typically composed of several layers or regions, three in cat and six in primates. In cat the top and bottom layers receive optic tract fibers from the contralateral eye and the middle layer from the ipsilateral eye. In the six-layered primate geniculate body (layers termed 1 to 6 from ventral to dorsal) layers 1, 4, and 6 receive projections from the contralateral eye and layers 2, 3, and 5 from the ipsilateral eye.

Although the projections from optic tract to lateral geniculate body to cerebral cortex constitute the main visual pathways in higher vertebrates, there are several other pathways. Some optic fibers project to the *superior colliculus* in the midbrain. In lower vertebrates like frog, which have no cerebral cortex or lateral geniculate body, the superior colliculus is the major receiving area for visual projections. There are four separate layers of cells in the frog superior colliculus that appear to be differentiated functionally as well as histologically (see below). A portion of the optic tract fibers also connect to the *pretectal area* (a region in front of the superior colliculus) in the midbrain. This pathway appears to mediate the pupillary reflex response to light (i.e. contraction of pupils in bright light, Magous and Ranson, 1935). Electrophysiological evidence indicates the existence of projections from the visual system into the midbrain reticular formation (French, Verzeano, and Magoun, 1953). Anatomical data suggests that this might be due to a pathway from the superior colliculus to the reticular formation (Brodal, 1957). Finally, there appears to be a projection of optic tract fibers to the hypothalamus, at least in birds, where it is believed to be involved in the control of reproductive and migratory behavior (Benoit, 1962).

Functional Properties of the Visual System

A great deal of information processing takes place in the retina. Discharges of optic nerve fibers do not necessarily bear a direct relationship to the simple activation of rods and cones by light. An observation that emphasizes this point is the fact that optic nerve fibers exhibit spontaneous discharging in the absence of light stimulation of the retina (Granit, 1955). In fact the total amount of activity in optic nerve fibers may be greatest when the eye is in total darkness!

One of the first studies of optic nerve activity (using the optic nerve of the eel) was by Adrian and Matthews (1928). They used a technique of massed unit discharge measurement (recording the spike discharges of many hundreds of fibers simultaneously with a large wire arranged to give a "smear" representing gross amount of activity in the nerve; see Chapter 3). When a light was shone briefly in the eye, there was an initial rapid frequency of discharge that declined to a slower steady state, followed by another brief increase in activity when the light was turned off.

Adrian (1928) had earlier defined the concept of receptive field for tactile nerve fibers as the amount of skin area activating a given nerve fiber (see above). Adrian and Matthews were able to establish the approximate size of the receptive fields for fibers of the eel optic nerve. In the visual system, the receptive field of a given nerve cell is simply the area of retina that will cause firing of the cell when stimulated by a small test patch of light. Because they recorded gross activity from the optic nerve they had to use indirect methods. In essence, they found that if an area no larger than about 1 mm was stimulated, the area, and the duration, and the intensity of the test light were interchangeable in terms of amount of nerve activity produced. These effects paralleled well-established psychophysical relations for visual sensation in humans under certain conditions. The interchangeability of duration and intensity (Bunsen-Roscoe law), for example, holds for all photochemical substances and for human visual sensations if a very small test light is presented for a brief period of time. Since the relationship is characteristic of *photochemical* substances, it is determined in the retina solely by the light sensitive pigments of the rods and cones. If complex neural interactions were involved, such a relationship would likely not hold. Indeed, for long duration stimuli it does not hold.

Hartline (1938, 1940) studied receptive fields of optic nerve fibers in the frog directly by recording the activity of single fibers using a microelectrode. An example of his findings is given in Figure 10.15A. The three concentric circles represent the size of the receptive field in the retina as a function of intensity of

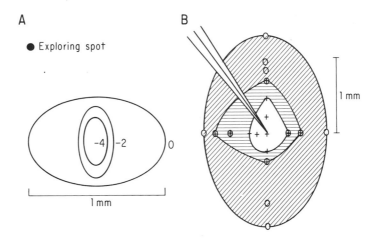

Figure 10.15.   **A,** chart of the receptive field of a single optic nerve fiber of the frog. Each circular line encloses a retinal region within which the exploring spotlight (relative size shown by black dot)—of an intensity, the log of which is given on the line—produces a response from the fiber. On each line the indicated intensity is the threshold; the set of curves constitutes a contour map of the distribution of the retinal sensitivity to light with reference to this particular fiber. (Hartline, 1930)   **B,** cat retina. Distribution of discharge patterns within receptive field of ganglion cell (located at tip of electrode). Exploring spot was 0.2 mm in diameter, about 100 times threshold at center of field. Background illumination approximately 25 mc. In central region (crosses) "on" discharges were found, whereas in diagonally hatched part only "off" discharges occurred (circles). In intermediary zone (horizontally hatched) discharges were "on/off." Note that change in conditions of illumination (background, etc.) altered discharge pattern distribution. (Figure taken from Granit, 1962, modified from Kuffler, 1953)

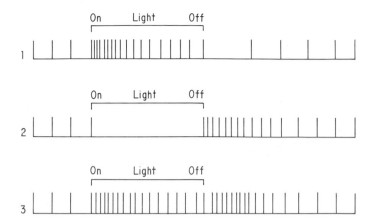

Figure 10.16.   Diagram illustrating response properties of three fibers in the optic nerve firing spontaneously and in response to illumination. 1, *on* fiber; 2, *off* fiber; 3, *on-off* fiber. (From Granit, 1955)

test stimulus, the brightest light giving the largest field. All receptive fields were not excitatory. Sometimes activation anywhere within the field reduced or inhibited spontaneous activity of the fiber. He also observed that slight movements of the test light or of shadows across the receptive field produced marked bursts of activity. Additional studies by Barlow (1953) indicated that excitatory receptor fields have an inhibitory surround region larger than the purely excitatory field. A ring of light around but outside the field for a given ganglion cell could prevent excitation of the cell by a test light shined on the field.

In Hartline's studies noted above, three types of optic fiber discharge patterns were observed (see Figure 10.16): *on* fibers, which give an initial burst and then fired at a slower steady rate while the light was on; *off* fibers, which gave a burst only when the light was turned off; and *on-off* fibers, which gave brief bursts only when the light was turned on and off. Receptive fields of cat ganglion cells were investigated by Kuffler (1953). Examples of his findings are shown in Figure 10.15B. In some cells illumination of the center of the field induced "on" discharges, the periphery induced "off" discharges, and an intermediate zone induced "on-off" discharges. Other cells were just the reverse, with "off" discharges in the center, and "on" discharges in the periphery. These relatively complicated effects resulting from simple illumination of the retina undoubtedly involve complex excitatory and inhibitory interactions among neurons in the retina.

Hartline (see Hartline and Ratliff, 1957, 1958; Hartline, 1963) has developed an elegant theoretical analysis of the action of lateral inhibitory effects, using as a simplified model system the eye of the horseshoe crab *Limulus*. The compound eye of this animal has several hundred separate receptors (ommatidia) each with a separate nerve. Initially it had been hoped that each nerve was a separate private line whose activity reflected purely receptor processes. However, it turned out that the nerves are interconnected by inhibitory fibers just after they leave the receptors. These lateral interactions are entirely inhibitory. Hartline was able to express the interacting influences of different receptors on one another precisely in terms of mathematical equations. These equations accurately describe the behavior of the entire system.

The degree of information processing or coding that can occur in the retina is strikingly illustrated by the experiments of Lettvin et al., 1959 and Maturana et al., 1960 on the frog retina. The experimental arrangement they used is illustrated in Figure 10.17. Activity of single optic nerve fibers was recorded by microelectrodes. A variety of stimuli were used, including lines, edges, dots of various sizes, checkered patterns, etc. These were moved about the frog's visual field by the simple magnet device shown in Figure 10.17. They found that all optic nerve fibers could be grouped into one of five categories, defined in terms of stimulus characteristics:

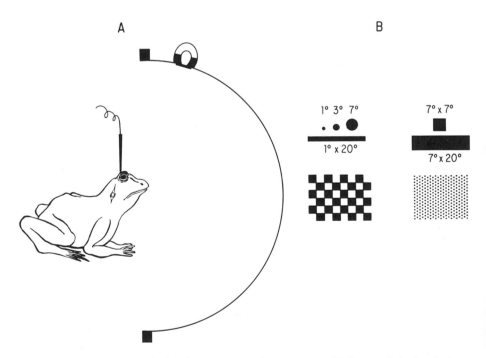

Figure 10.17. A, schematic drawing of the relations between the frog and the hemisphere that constitutes the experimental visual field. **B,** scale drawings of some of the objects used as stimuli. The degrees indicate their diameter when placed inside a hemisphere of the same radius as that represented in **A.** The actual hemisphere used was larger, 14 inches in diameter. (From Maturana et al., 1960)

1. *Sustained edge detectors.* The effective stimulus is an edge of an object lighter or darker than the background moved into the receptive field of the cell and kept there. These cells appear to fire as long as the edge is there. General changes in illumination do not activate the cells.

2. *Convex edge detectors.* These cells respond most when a small dark object with sharp (i.e. contrasting) edges is moved into the receptive field and moved about within the field. They do not respond to general changes in illumination. The authors refer to these cells as " bug perceivers."

3. *Changing contrast detectors.* These units respond best to sharp dark or light edges moving in particular directions across the visual field.

4. *Dimming detectors.* These cells respond to a darkening of their receptive fields, and correspond to Hartline's *off* fibers. They may respond for a period of many seconds after illumination is dimmed, but respond maximally when the dimming occurs.

5. *Dark detectors.* These cells fire continuously with a discharge frequency *inversely proportional* to light intensity.

Perhaps the most impressive aspect of these beautiful experimental findings is the fact that the categories of effective stimuli resemble those usually characterized as "complex perceptual processes." Selective response to bug-like objects moving in a bug-like fashion does not require "awareness," or even learning. The transformations are done at the level of the retina. It is not necessary to invoke any mysterious perceptual processes to account for the frog's "perception" of a bug.

The functional categories of frog optic nerve cells exhibit a remarkable degree of differential spatial representation in the CNS. In frog, the optic nerve fibers project to the superior colliculus, which can be subdivided histologically into four separate layers. *A given layer receives all the fibers of one of the categories listed above.* The first layer receives all fibers from category 1, the second layer all fibers of category 2, and so on. The fifth category, dark detectors, projects to the third layer as well. Thus the functional differentiation of fiber types in terms of stimulus characteristics is coded spatially in the superior colliculus.

Lettvin et al. summarize their findings as follows:

The output from the retina of the frog is a set of four distributed operations on the visual image. These operations are independent of the level of general illumination and express the image in terms of : (1) local sharp edges and contrast; (2) the curvature of edge of a dark object; (3) the movement of edges; and (4) the local dimmings produced by movement or rapid general darkening. Each group of fibers serving one operation maps the retina continuously in a single sheet of endings in the frog's brain. There are four such sheets in the brain, corresponding to the four operations, and their maps are in registration. When all axonal connections between eye and brain are broken and the fibers grow back, they reconstitute the original retinal maps and also arrange themselves in depth in the original order with no mistakes. If there is any randomness in the connections of this system, it must be at a very fine level indeed.

The degree of information processing that occurs in the retina in higher vertebrates does not seem comparable to the remarkable actions of the frog retina. In fact Hubel and Wiesel (1961) found that the receptive fields described by Kuffler, and the response patterns ("on," "off," and "on-off") seem to be maintained even at the level of the lateral geniculate body in the cat. There was some degree of transformation from optic tracts fibers to lateral geniculate cells in that the amount of suppression of central "on" excitatory fields by peripheral illumination was greater. Furthermore, single optic tract spikes could produce repetitive discharges in the geniculate cells. Nonetheless, the complexity of stimulus coding at the level of the optic tract and the lateral geniculate body of the cat was very much less than in the retina of the frog. As we will see in the next chapter, very complex information coding processes occur in the *cortical* visual cells of the cat. It seems that higher vertebrates do their stimulus processing a good deal further from the receptors.

Color Vision

So far we have considered only the spatial and temporal aspects of visual stimuli. Differential response to wavelength or "color" is a very fundamental aspect of vision. Unfortunately the relationships between stimulus wavelength and neural responses seem extremely complex, and are not well understood. There has been a good deal of work at the level of retinal ganglion cells, particularly by Granit and his associates (see Granit, 1955; 1959; 1962). In frog, pigeon, and the mammals so far studied (rat, guinea pig, cat) ganglion cells can be grouped into two types, which Granit has called *dominators* and *modulators*. Dominators respond to a wide range of wavelengths, and generally yield frequency *vs* threshold curves very similar to the rhodopsin curve (see Figure 10.11). Modulator curves are much narrower, each cell responding only to a restricted band of wavelengths. In the cat, for example, certain ganglion cells will respond to "red" wavelengths, others to blue, still others to yellow, and a fourth group to green. It is tempting to ascribe the response curve of dominators to the actions of the rod, and the various types of modulator curves to the actions of various types of cones. However, the real situation is probably not this simple. It must be remembered that a good deal of neural processing has gone on between the rods and cones and the ganglion cells. Furthermore, there can be convergence of a great many rods or cones on ganglion cells, and even interactions of both rods and cones on given ganglion cells. Nonetheless, it is clear from Granit's work that at least in terms of discharges sent up the optic nerve, different fibers do respond differentially to different wavelengths of light.

DeValois and colleagues (DeValois et al., 1958a; 1958b; DeValois and Kitoi, 1959; DeValois, 1960; DeValois and Jones, 1961; DeValois, 1965) have investigated the response patterns of cells in the lateral geniculate body of the primate to colored light. Remember that the lateral geniculate body in each thalamus of the primate has six layers. DeValois found that activity of cells in the different layers differed in terms of discharge characteristics. Most of the cells in layers

5 and 6 give "on" responses to light with little or no inhibition to light of any waveléngth. Most cells in layers 3 and 4, on the other hand, either increase or decrease rate of firing when the eye is stimulated with light, depending on the wavelength. Cells in the ventral layers, 1 and 2, are inhibited by light of all wavelengths and fire "off" responses.

The ventral layer inhibitory cells have broad spectral sensitivity curves with peaks of sensitivity in the region of 510 microns in the dark adapted state. In other words these cells appear to resemble in response characteristics the behavior of rods. Most of the cells in dorsal layers (which, remember, come from the two separate retinas) have quite narrow sensitivities; each responds to only a single narrow range of wavelengths. DeValois and associates found that the color selective cells in these layers fall into five spectral sensitivity categories with peak sensitivities of the various elements being found at 440, 510, 550, 580, and 620 microns. Behavior of these cells resembles the behavior of the modulator ganglion cells described by Granit. The cells of the intermediate layers of the lateral geniculate body (again coming from the two separate eyes) respond to various wavelengths and in what DeValois calls an "opponent" manner, with excitation to one spectral region and inhibition to another spectral region. These cells appear to be of several types; e.g. red "on"-green "off" cells, blue "on"-yellow "off" cells etc. (see Figure 10.18). DeValois' data indicate that different cells appear to code different wavelengths of light, and that interaction patterns of the cells in the middle layers can provide for rather complex coding of stimulus wavelength properties. It is of interest that the spectral sensitivities of the "highly tuned" cells, i.e. cells responding to a narrow wavelength range of light, agree very closely with the pigment curves obtained by Rushton for the human eye in the studies mentioned earlier. These cells may reflect rather precisely the photochemical characteristics of the cones.

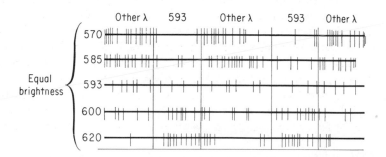

Figure 10.18. Example of responses of an "opponent" cell from the lateral geniculate body of the monkey. The cell is of the type that normally increases firing rate to green and decreases firing rate to red. In this experiment responses of the cell to shifts from various other wavelengths ("other λ") to a standard (593) and back were studied. Note that when the cell is firing (to "green"—570) it decreases firing to 593, but when its firing rate was low (to "red"—620 left bottom) its firing rate increases to 593. (From DeValois, 1965)

Evidence of a quite different sort from microelectrode recordings of retinal potentials suggests a possible relationship between glial cell activity in the retina and the behavior of neurons in the visual system relevant to color vision. Svaetichin (1953, 1956) described a slow graded *"S-potential"* recorded by a microelectrode in the vicinity of the rods and cones in the fish retina. There appear to be two types of S-potential, the *L* (luminosity) response, an intracellularly recorded hyperpolarization that lasts as long as the stimulus, is proportional to stimulus intensity and responds to a broad range of wavelengths, and the *C* (chromatic) response, which exhibits hyperpolarization to some wavelengths and depolarization to others (see Figure 10.19; from MacNichol and Svaetichin, 1958). The *L* response appears to be generated from giant horizontal glial cells in the most distal portion of the retina (i.e. furthest from the nerve cells) and the *C* response is believed to be recorded from the Müller fibers, glial elements surrounding the bipolar neurons in the retina (Svaetichin, et al., 1961).

If it can be assumed that the hyperpolarizing portion of the *C* response is related to inhibition or decreased tendency of neuron firing and the depolarizing portion to an increased neuron firing tendency, then it might be expected that certain optic nerve fibers and neurons higher in the visual system would fire *on* responses to wavelengths at one end of the spectrum and *off* responses to wavelengths at the other end of the spectrum. This is in fact the way DeValois'

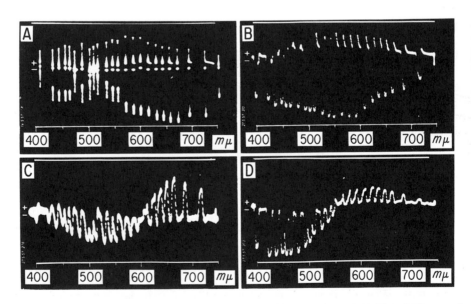

Figure 10.19. Examples of "luminosity" (**A** and **B**) and "chromaticity" (**C** and **D**) type *S* potentials recorded from fish retina. Each record is the *S* potential response to a number of test lights of various wavelengths. The **C** response has opposite polarities for red and green light and the **D** response has opposite polarities for blue and yellow light. (From MacNichol and Svaetichin, 1958)

"opponent" cells behave (see above). It is a rather considerable inference to assume that shifts in the membrane potentials of retinal glia cells control the firing levels of retinal ganglion cells. Svaetichin et al. (1961) and MacNichol (1964) suggest that the S-potentials are signs of metabolic changes in glial cells induced by activity of adjacent neurons. The altered metabolism of the glial cells might then, in turn, alter the activity of the neurons. The correctness of this hypothesis will only be decided by future research.

The opposing responses of the C type S-potential to different wavelengths of light and the similar type of opposing *on* and *off* discharges of DeValois' "opponent" cells as a function of wavelength are very reminiscent of the theory of color vision first proposed by Hering. He suggested that there were three complex chemical receptor substances, one for black—white (today this would be the rhodopsin in rods), another for red—green, and a third for yellow—blue. Each complex substance would respond to one or the other of the pair of colors, depending upon a variety of conditions such as previous exposure to light and metabolic factors. In this context it is of considerable interest that DeValois' "opponent" cells in the lateral geniculate body are of two types, one responding differentially to red—green and the other to blue—yellow. MacNichol (1964) suggests that perhaps the retinal color receptors are of the three types postulated by Young's theory (i.e. Rushton's evidence, see page 246) and the behavior of the optic nerve fibers, possibly as a result of retinal glial cell actions, are consistent with Hering's theory.

THE AUDITORY SYSTEM

In contrast to the million or so fibers in the optic nerve of man, each auditory nerve has only about 28,000 fibers. Nevertheless, the total number of single tones discriminable on the basis of frequency and intensity is about 340,000. Curiously enough this is approximately the same as the total number of single visual stimuli discernible on the basis of frequency (wavelength) and intensity of light (Stevens and Davis, 1938). The nature of the mechanisms underlying this efficiency in the auditory system has puzzled investigators for many years. Historically there have been two major theories of auditory pitch discrimination: (1) the *place* theory (Helmholtz), which assumes that each tone frequency activates a different portion of the auditory receptor, and (2) the *frequency* theory, which proposes that the frequency of the tone is reflected in the frequency of auditory nerve fiber discharges (Rutherford). Recent developments in the field, stemming particularly from the work of von Békésy, Davis, Tasaki, and Stevens have shown that the more correct view lies somewhere in between these extremes. Hallowell Davis (1959; 1961) has elaborated a comprehensive theory which appears to be satisfactory in the light of current knowledge. Much of our present discussion is based on his views.

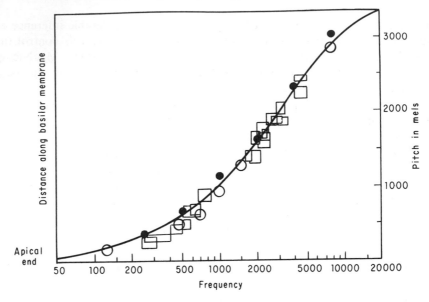

Figure 10.20. Comparison of the pitch-function with data locating the positions on the basilar membrane which are stimulated by tones of various frequencies. The linear extent of the basilar membrane is represented by the ordinate (left) and along the same axis is laid the pitch-scale (right). The curve represents the pitch-function; the hollow rectangles and circles and the filled circles show the locations in the cochleas of guinea pigs of stimulation by various frequencies. (Stevens and Volkmann, 1940)

The distinction between the terms "pitch" and "frequency" is often a source of confusion to the student. Frequency refers to a physical characteristic of the *stimulus*: the actual frequency of vibration of the sound waves in the air, commonly expressed in cycles per second (cps). Pitch refers to the "subjective sensation" or behavioral response correlated with the frequency of a sound. The relationship between pitch and frequency is graphed in Figure 10.20. It tends to be logarithmic rather than linear or one-to-one. Note that while the pitch scale (in mels) on the left ordinate is linear, the frequency scale on the abscissa is logarithmic. Because the curve relating the two functions is approximately linear throughout most of its extent, pitch and frequency are related logarithmically.

The mel scale is simply an equal interval scale. A tone assigned a scale value of 1000 mels is one which has been judged by observers to be twice as high in pitch as a tone of 500 mels; a tone of 500 mels is twice as high as a tone of 250 mels; and so on. The relationship between mels and frequency is neither a simple nor a direct one-to-one correspondence. While a tone of 1000 cps sounds roughly twice as high as a tone of 500 cps, a tone of 10,000 cps sounds twice as high as a tone of 2000 cps, not 5000 cps. Another way of looking at the mel scale is in terms of just noticeable differences (jnds) between frequencies.

A frequency jnd is the number of cps a tone must be increased in frequency above the standard tone to be just noticed as higher. At 1000 cps the size of the jnd is about 3 cps; a tone of 1003 cps sounds just noticeably higher under ideal listening conditions than a tone of 1000 cps. A single mel unit would equal roughly 3 cps at 1000 cps. However when the standard tone is 10,000 cps the jnd is about 20 cps. A single mel unit would equal 20 cps here. The mel scale is identical with the cumulative jnd curve, as indicated in Figure 10.20.

A similar dichotomy exists between the physical and "subjective" scales in the case of sound intensity. The relationship between the judged *loudness* (subjective measure) of a tone and the amount of physical *energy* in the tone is approximately logarithmic. This relationship was described a number of years ago by the development of the decibel (dB) scale for measuring sound intensity. The decibel scale is based on the logarithm of the sound energy level (actually 10 times the logarithm of the ratio of a given sound energy to the lowest threshold of sound energy). Consequently, the judged *loudness* of sounds corresponds in an approximately linear fashion with the decibel scale of sound intensity. The relationships between pitch and frequency and between loudness and intensity are examples of *psychophysical functions*: relations between psychological or behavioral judgments of stimuli and physical characteristics of stimuli. We will discuss some of the more general aspects of psychophysical relationships at the end of the chapter.

Receptor Processes

The anatomy of the auditory receptor system is unfortunately (for the student) rather complicated (see Figure 10.21). Excellent discussions are available in

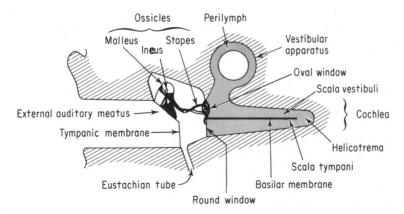

Figure 10.21. Schematic drawing of the human ear. The coiled cochlea has been straightened out to give a clear view of the basic anatomical relationships. (From von Békésy and Rosenblith, 1951)

Stevens and Davis (1938), von Békésy, and Rosenblith (1951), and von Békésy (1956). In brief, the external ear canal ends in the *tympanic membrane* (ear drum). This connects through three small bones (*ossicles*) of the middle ear to a membrane covering the end of the *cochlea*. This structure is a coiled tube shaped much like a snail shell. The tube is filled with fluid and contains within it a smaller tube, the *cochlear duct*, which in turn contains the sense organ proper. A cross section through the tube of the cochlea is shown in Figure 10.22. Sound vibrations transmitted through the ossicles cause movement of fluid, which in turn produces vibrations of the *basilar membrane*. This rather stiff membrane bends relative to the *tectorial membrane*, thus bending and activating the *hair-cell* receptors lying between. These receptors are innervated by fibers of the auditory nerve, whose cell bodies lie in the spiral ganglion embedded in the skull. Axons of these fibers enter the CNS and synapse in the *dorsal* and *ventral cochlear nuclei* in the medulla.

Identification of the particular aspects of receptor and neural processes that determine various aspects of sensory experience or behavior is one of the fundamental goals in the analysis of sensory processes. The absolute loudness threshold is a good case in point. In humans, the total range of audible frequencies is from 15 to 20,000 cps. However the ear is most sensitive to tones between 1000

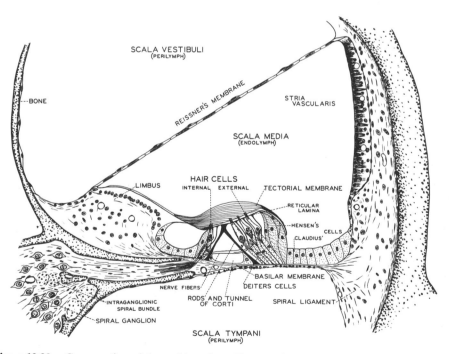

Figure 10.22.   Cross section of the cochlear duct. The actual receptors are the hair cells lying in the spiral organ (of Corti) on the basilar membrane. (From Davis et al., 1953)

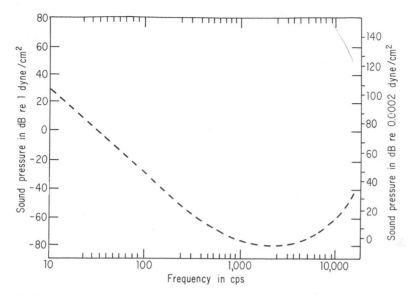

Figure 10.23. The absolute auditory threshold curve for man. This is actually an average based on results from a variety of different types of measures. (Based on Licklider, 1951)

cps and 4000 cps. As frequency is increased or decreased away from this region of maximum sensitivity, increasingly greater sound energy is required to make the tone audible. The curve relating absolute threshold and frequency is shown in Figure 10.23. Several lines of evidence (Davis, 1959) indicate that the physical characteristics of the external and middle ear structures determine the form of the frequency-threshold curve.

The acoustical and mechanical properties of the ear canal, ear drum, and the middle ear bones determine the efficiency with which sounds of various frequencies are converted to mechanical vibrations and transmitted to the cochlea. In humans, these structures have greatest efficiency in the 1000 to 4000 cps range, and drop off in efficiency as the frequency becomes higher or lower. Because the absolute threshold curve is determined by the physical properties of these accessory auditory structures, it might be expected that size of an animal (i.e. the size of its external and middle ear structures) would influence its threshold curve. In general this seems to be true. Among mammals, elephants have the lowest frequency curve and small animals like the rat or mouse have very much higher frequency sensitivity curves. Man, incidentally, has a relatively "middle" frequency range. Cats can hear sounds ranging from about 30 cps to 70,000 cps. There are some important exceptions to this general rule. Both bats and porpoises can hear sounds of up to about 100,000 cps. However these animals are exceptional in that they make use of a very specialized echo location system. They emit very high frequency pulses of sound and determine the position of objects in space by the characteristics of the reflected sound pulses.

The ear is about as sensitive as it can be to sound energy, at least in the frequency region of best threshold (around 2000 cps in humans). The degree of sensitivity of the human ear is quite remarkable; a movement of the ear drum of a less than 1/10 the diameter of a hydrogen atom can result in an auditory sensation! If the ear were more sensitive than this the random Brownian movements of air molecules would produce a constant roaring sound, which would tend to mask auditory stimuli. Thus, paradoxically, if the ear were more sensitive it would be less sensitive. As a matter of fact persons with very good hearing are able to detect Brownian movement under ideal listening conditions.

The movements of the basilar membrane in the cochlea to auditory stimuli were analyzed in a series of elegant experiments by von Békésy (cf. 1951), who was awarded the Nobel prize in 1962 for his work. In essence, he showed that if a tone of given frequency is presented, a traveling wave of fluid is set up in the cochlea. The traveling wave causes a maximum displacement in a given region of the basilar membrane. The location of this maximum displacement on the membrane is related to the frequency of the tone (see Figure 10.24). Some rather complex mechanical effects occur, due to the differential stiffness of the membrane. The net result is that high-frequency tones selectively distort regions of the basilar membrane close to the base of the cochlea, intermediate tones distort a portion of the membrane from apex to an intermediate region, and low frequency tones tend to distort the entire membrane. These response characteristics all can be predicted from analogous physical models of the cochlea (e.g. a fluid-filled tube containing a semielastic membrane; see Zwislocki, 1953). The cochlea acts simply as a complex mechanical analyzer of the auditory stimulus. The region of greatest distortion of the basilar membrane produces the greatest amount of bending of hair cells and consequently the greatest differential activation of the auditory nerve fibers.

At this point it might be well to recall the two major theories concerning pitch coding, namely place *vs* frequency. The findings of von Békésy actually seem to offer some support for each. There is a tendency for a given frequency of tone to produce greatest distortion at a given region of the basilar membrane. The original place theory proposed by Helmholtz assumed that the basilar

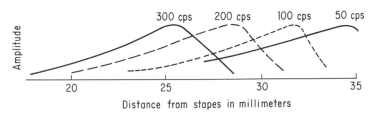

Figure 10.24.   Amplitude of movement of the basilar membrane as a function of distance from the stapes (see Figure 10.21) for four different frequencies of tone. (Redrawn from von Békésy, 1947)

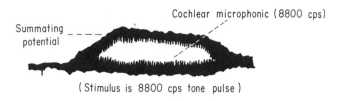

Cochlear microphonic (8800 cps)

Summating
potential

(Stimulus is 8800 cps tone pulse)

Figure 10.25. The cochlear microphonic (rapid fluctuations) and the summating potential (over-all envelope of the cochlear microphonic) in response to a brief 8800 cps tone pulse. The cochlear microphonic responds at the same frequency as the stimulus. (Redrawn from Davis, 1959)

membrane was a very large series of highly tuned elements much like tuning forks, or the strings on a harp. Von Békésy's data, particularly for high frequencies, support this view if modified to the extent that small differences in degree of distortion of the membrane can serve as "tuned elements." In general the higher the frequency, the closer the distortion is to the base of the cochlea. The large open circles of Figure 10.20 and the right ordinate refer to the relative location of the place of maximum distortion along the basilar membrane as a function of frequency (for both guinea pig and man). The relative locations correspond almost exactly to the relationship between pitch and frequency!

On the other hand, von Békésy observed that low frequency tones tend to activate the entire basilar membrane equivalently, and intermediate tones activate a substantial portion of the membrane. The differential distortion of the membrane does not seem great enough to provide for our very sensitive ability to discriminate pitch, and there is no differential distortion to code low frequency tones. Human psychophysical studies provide some interesting corollary data on this point. If a steady "white noise" (all frequencies equally represented in the stimulus) is presented it has a "sssssh" sound somewhat resembling an air jet. There is no particular frequency or pitch associated with the sound. Since all frequencies are present in the stimulus, the basilar membrane exhibits no differential distortion. If the noise is now presented as a series of brief pulses of white noise, the sound takes on a pitch related to the frequency with which the pulses are delivered (Miller and Taylor, 1948). This relationship holds only for low frequencies. Thus, for low frequencies a pitch can be heard even though there is no differential distortion of the basilar membrane. It would appear that at least for low frequencies some type of frequency coding occurs in the cochlea other than the analysis into place of distortion along the basilar membrane.

If a gross recording electrode is placed on the cochlea near the auditory nerve, several types of signals can be recorded. The most noticeable of these is the *cochlear microphonic*, discovered by Wever and Bray (1930). This is an electrical response that follows the frequency and intensity characteristics of the auditory stimulus *exactly* (see Figure 10.25). If a Beethoven symphony is played into the ear of an anesthetized cat and the electrically recorded cochlear micro-phonic is amplified and connected to a speaker you will hear the symphony with essentially no distortion. The cochlear microphonic is literally a microphone; sound waves are converted to electrical pulses in exactly the same manner as in a microphone.

The discovery of the cochlear microphonic seemed to provide very strong evidence favoring the frequency theory of pitch coding. It was initially believed that the electrical pulses of the cochlear microphonic were spike discharges of the auditory nerve. This would mean that the frequency of discharges in the auditory nerve exactly follow the input frequency of any sound. However, it soon became apparent that the cochlear microphonic did not represent nerve activity. In the cat, for example, it can follow sound frequencies up to 70,000 cps, which is a great deal faster than any nerve fiber can respond (2000 cps is about the highest frequency recordable from a nerve fiber). Furthermore, it can be recorded after death, is not affected by anesthetics, and does not fatigue. It appears that the cochlear microphonic is produced by the hair cells in the cochlea and may represent a receptor or generator potential. The hair cells are bent with a frequency that follows the input sound frequency. The cochlear microphonic seems to result from a transducer action of the hair cells quite analogous to the conversion of mechanical vibrations into electrical pulses by the crystal in a phonograph cartridge. It has been suggested that the same kind of *piezo-electric* effect may be involved in both (Stevens and Davis, 1939). Although the cochlear microphonic has been considered by many as merely an accidental electro-mechanical by-produce resulting from bending of the hair cells, Davis, Tasaki, and many other authorities favor the view that the terminals of the auditory nerve fibers are directly activated by the flows of current associated with the cochlear microphonic, i.e. it is a generator potential.

A much slower potential shift, the *summating potential*, can also be recorded (Figure 10.25). This appears as the envelope (over-all outline) of the activity of the cochlear microphonic. As seen in Figure 10.25, the cochlear microphonic has the same frequency as the stimulus (here 8800 cps) and the summating potential is simply the total baseline shift associated with it. There are two components of the potential, a negativity and a positivity, which apparently are generated by different mechanisms in the cochlea. The negative summating potential is attributed to the internal hair cells and the positive component (and the cohlear microphonic) to the external hair cells in the cochlea (Davis et al., 1958). It has been suggested that the negative summating potential may act as a generator potential, together with the cochlear microphonic, to activate the auditory nerve fibers (Davis, 1961).

The grossly recorded auditory nerve response contains a number of com-ponents which have been labeled N_1, N_2, and N_3 respectively (see Figure 10.26). These responses represent the sums of individual nerve fiber spikes responding in the usual all-or-none fashion to auditory stimuli, and can be differentiated experimentally from the cochlear microphonic. The first component, N_1, is

Figure 10.26. The grossly recorded auditory nerve response to a loud click (negative down). N_1 is the initial response, and N_2 and N_3 are later responses usually seen only with intense stimuli. (Redrawn from Davis, 1959)

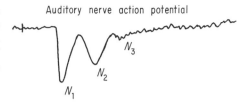

Auditory nerve action potential

always present if a brief synchronous stimulus such as a click is given. N_2 and N_3 appear with increasingly intense stimuli, and are believed to represent repetitive firing in some of the nerve fibers. The time intervals between the three components are about 1 msec, corresponding to the refractory period of the nerve fibers.

The grossly recorded auditory nerve potential does exhibit some frequency following. For tones of up to more than 3000 cps the gross evoked response of the nerve follows the frequency of the tone. Thus a tone of 500 cps produces 500 evoked responses/sec in the nerve, a tone of 2000 cps produces 2000 evoked responses/sec, and so on. These observations provide a neural basis for direct coding of the frequencies of low frequency tones in terms of nerve discharge frequency (Wever, 1949). An interesting problem occurs when we consider these findings together with the fact that the refractory period of an individual auditory nerve fiber is about 1 msec. No single fiber in the auditory nerve can discharge much more than 1000/sec, and yet the gross nerve response can follow up to nearly 4000/sec. This has been explained in terms of a "volley" principle (Wever, 1949). It is assumed that different sets of fibers alternate firing so that each individual fiber fires no more than 1000/sec. Different sets of fibers alternate in such a manner that the gross nerve potential follows up to 4000 cps. The relationship between the amplitude of the gross auditory nerve evoked response (which is directly related to the number of fibers discharging) and tone frequency provide rather neat confirmation of the volley theory. As indicated in Figure 10.27, the nerve response amplitude decreases in step functions as the frequency of the tone is increased (Stevens and Davis, 1938). The first drop occurs at about 800 cps, presumably the point at which all individual fibers stop following the stimulus frequency and two subsets begin to alternate. The amplitude of the gross response decreases to half its initial value at 800 cps. Subsequent abrupt drops in nerve response amplitude occur at successively higher frequencies.

In summary, it appears that both place of excitation on the basilar membrane and frequency of nerve responses are important in coding tone frequency. For high frequencies, place is most important but for lower frequencies (below 4000 cps) synchronous discharges in nerve fibers also play a role. Intensity may be coded both by total number of fibers activated and by activation of high threshold fibers (i.e. nerve fibers that require considerable bending of the hair cells to be stimulated). The nerve fibers are stimulated by the bending of the hair

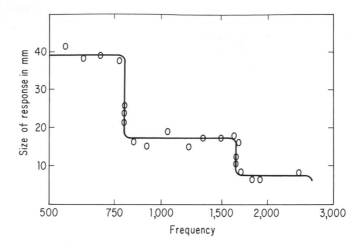

Figure 10.27. The initial size of the action-potential in the auditory nerve of a cat as a function of frequency. The sudden drops in the curve are due to the fact that above a critical frequency (800 cycles in this experiment) the individual fibers cannot follow the frequency of the stimulus, but must alternately respond to every other vibration. At twice this critical frequency each fiber responds only to every third vibration. (Stevens and Davis, 1938)

cells, possibly as a direct result of the generator potentials, the cochlear micro-phonic and the negative summating potential, produced by the hair cells.

The Auditory Pathways

The ascending auditory pathways are indicated in Figure 10.28. The incoming auditory nerve fibers synapse in the *dorsal* and *ventral cochlear nuclei*. From here they are relayed via the *superior olive* or directly to form the tract of the *lateral lemniscus* on both sides. Auditory input is thus bilateral, each ear connecting to both sides of the brain. Fibers branch off from the lateral lemniscus to the cerebellum and apparently to the ascending reticular formation. The main tracts may synapse in the lemniscus, or in the *inferior colliculus* in the roof of the midbrain. From here the major pathway projects to the medial geniculate body of the thalamus. An efferent pathway concerned in reflex activities projects from the inferior colliculus to the superior colliculus. Cells of the medial geniculate body project to the auditory area of the cerebral cortex. Cells in the auditory cortex are thus at least 5th order, there being four synapses interposed between the auditory nerve fibers and the cortical cells.

There are several general principles of organization exhibited by the auditory system. First and foremost, tone frequency has a clear spatial representation at all levels from the basilar membrane to the cerebral cortex (Woolsey and Walzl, 1942; Tunturi, 1944; Rose et al., 1963; cf. also the general review and discussion by Ades, 1959). As in other sensory modalities the receptor elements are represented in a spatial manner at each relay in the auditory system. In fact there appear to be several such representations of the cochlea at some levels. The possible significance of these spatial representations will be explored further in our discussion of the cerebral cortex (Chapter 11).

Microelectrode studies of single nerve cells have added a great deal of new information concerning coding processes in the auditory system. First, units can be found at all levels above the auditory nerve that (1) fire to the onset of a tone,

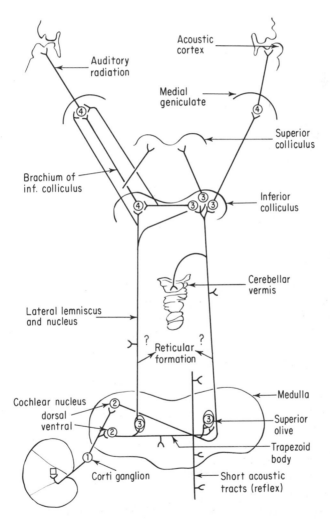

Figure 10.28. Schematic diagram of the auditory pathway. Numbers indicate the order of the neuron, starting with the sensory neuron as number 1. (From Davis, 1951)

or (2) decrease their firing when a tone is on, or (3) discharge continuously to a maintained tone. In addition many more complex patterns of response can be found (Rose et al., 1963; Hind et al., 1963). Fibers of the auditory nerve exhibit spontaneous firing in the absence of stimulation, which may not be influenced by tone stimuli (Tasaki and Davis, 1955). However, at the first synaptic relay the cochlear nucleus, spontaneous activity can be markedly reduced by presentation of sounds (Galambos and Davis, 1943).

Most nerve cells in the auditory system from the auditory nerve to the cerebral cortex have a limited range of " best frequencies." Examples of tuning curves for cells of the auditory nerve, trapezoid body, inferior colliculus, and medial geniculate body are shown in Figure 10.29, from Katsuki (1961). When the activity of a single cell has been isolated by a microelectrode, the tuning curve is obtained by presenting a wide range of tones of various frequencies and intensities. Typically, the threshold intensity that just causes the cell to fire is determined at each of a number of different frequencies. The tuning curve is thus a frequency-threshold curve, plotted in an analogous fashion to the human frequency

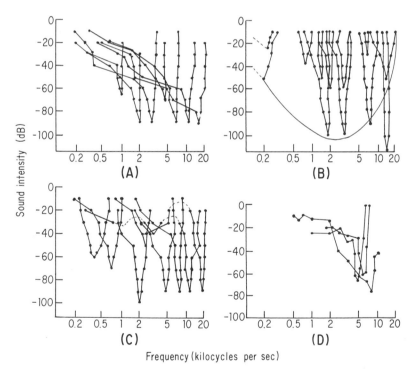

Figure 10.29.   Response "areas" (i.e. relative intensity of stimulus that will fire cell as a function of frequency) for single nerve cells of the (**A**) cochlear nerve, (**B**) inferior colliculus. (**C**) trapezoid body, and (**D**) medial geniculate body. (From Katsuki, 1961)

threshold curve of Figure 10.23. The "best frequency" range is the frequencies at which the cell is fired by the lowest intensity stimuli.

Most fibers of the auditory nerve have tuning curves that exhibit a fairly sharp high frequency cut out, but respond to a wide range of low frequencies. As a matter of fact, they resemble the physical distortions of the basilar membrane determined by von Békésy (see Figure 10.24). The tuning curves of cells at progressively higher levels of the auditory system tend to be progressively sharper, as seen in Figure 10.29. As the system is ascended the range of frequency to which a cell will respond becomes increasingly narrow, particularly for cells having high best-frequencies.

One of the difficulties noted above for a place theory of pitch was that the distortion pattern of the basilar membrane was much too broad to account for differential frequency sensitivity. However the data of Figure 10.29 suggests that neural processes serve to sharpen the discriminability of cells in the auditory system. The effect probably results from inhibitory synaptic interactions among cells at all levels of the system.

While the cell tuning curves shown in Figure 10.29 are fairly typical, a number of variations and modifications occur. In an extensive study of cells in the inferior colliculus (Rose et al., 1963, Hind et al., 1963) many different types of cell firing patterns were observed. Examples of the firing patterns of six different cells in in the inferior colliculus are shown in Figure 10.30. The method of data presentation in this figure deserves some comment. In the response pattern for cell B, for example, the column of upright dashes at the extreme left indicates the onset of the tone stimulus (the tone lasts half as long as the data is collected in A, B and C; and as long as data is collected in D, E and F). Each dash represents the onset of a separate stimulus, and the row of dots following the dash represents spike discharges of the cell. Each spike response of the cell is indicated by a dot, and the distance along the dot row is the time the response occurs after the simulus, as indicated by the calibration at the lower right. The 20 rows simply represent 20 separate presentations of the stimulus to obtain an indication of the reliability of spike discharge patterns. Thus in the sixth row of cell B, a smear of 3 dots occurs about 10 msec after the stimulus, followed by a later dot at about 23 msec. This means that the cell fired a rapid burst of 3 spikes 10 msec after the stimulus and another spike 23 msec after the stimulus. The initial burst of spikes at 10 msec occurs after every stimulus (i.e., in all rows) and is thus a reliable characteristic of the cell. The occasional later spikes are irregular and may be random discharges not related to the stimulus.

The six cells of Figure 10.30 all exhibit firing patterns that differ somewhat, ranging from cell A, which fires only a very brief initial burst of spikes 10 msec after the stimulus, to cell F, which has no initial burst but instead exhibits considerable firing all the time the stimulus is on. Note that the discharges are not synchronous on repeated stimulus presentations in F, but rather somewhat irregular in time. Cells B, C, D and E are intermediate types showing increasing

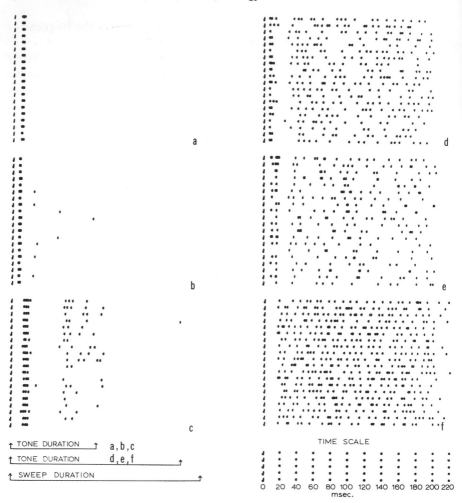

Figure 10.30. Firing patterns of six neurons in the inferior colliculus, which illustrate the more common varieties of discharge sequences. Each sample consists of 20 repetitions of the same tone; all stimuli delivered to the contralateral ear (see text). A: stimulus: 14.0 kc, 50 dB. B: stimulus: 19.0 kc, 40 dB. C: stimulus: 6.1 kc, 70 dB. D: stimulus: 2.6 kc, 60 dB. E: stimulus: 1.34 kc, 80 dB. F: stimulus: 3.8 kc, 80 dB. (From Rose et al., 1963)

amounts of later asynchronous activity following an initial burst of activity at about 10 msec.

The intensity coding of auditory cells also has some interesting features. As the tuning curves of Figure 10.29 indicate, the range of frequencies that will excite a given cell is narrowest for very weak stimuli. This range broadens as stimulus intensity is increased. A somewhat different effect is often seen when the intensity of the best frequency for a given cell is increased. As the stimulus intensity grows above threshold the cell may reach a maximum of discharges, and then decrease in its activity as the intensity continues to increase. An example of such a cell from the inferior colliculus is shown in Figure 10.31. At 10 dB above threshold the firing pattern is irregular, with a long onset latency. At 20 and 30 dB the cell is maximally activated, but above 30 dB the degree of activity decreases markedly. At 80 dB the cell gives only one spike discharge to each stimulus. Note also that the onset latency of the first spike decreases from 10 to 30 dB, but remains stable at higher intensities. Many cells stop firing when high intensity stimuli are presented. It would appear that many cells have " best intensities " as well as best frequencies. Such observations suggest that stimulus intensity may be coded in a rather complex fashion in terms of number of spike discharges at higher levels of the auditory system. Synaptic inhibitory mechanisms are probably responsible for the decreased frequency of firing in many cells at higher stimulus intensities. The spike discharge pattern in a given

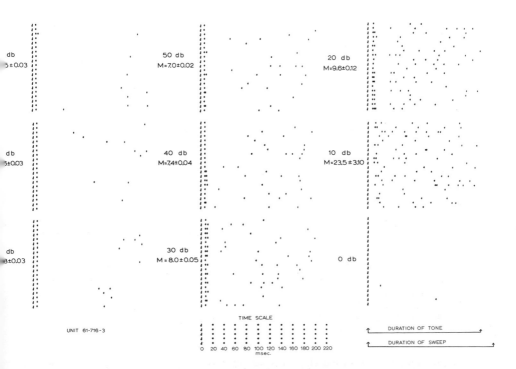

Figure 10.31.   Firing patterns of a cell in the inferior colliculus to tones of 4.3 kc (best frequency) at different intensities. An early onset burst is separable as a distinct event at all but near-threshold intensities. Silent period lengthens as more intense stimuli are used. Essentially an onset firing pattern for intense tones. Stimulation of the contralateral ear; tone duration, 200 msec; repetition rate, 1/sec. Upper numbers: intensity of the tone in dB sound pressure level (SPL); lower numbers: mean latent period to the first spike (M) in msec. (From Rose et al., 1963)

cell in the CNS is determined at any moment by the balance of excitatory and inhibitory synaptic action on it and on all prior cells that influence its behavior. It could be, for example, that cells exhibiting inhibitory actions on the cell of Figure 10.31 or on prior cells that normally activate these cells are themselves stimulated only at higher stimulus intensities. Thus activation of these cells would shift the balance from excitation to inhibition, producing decreased responsiveness of the cell in question to higher stimulus intensities.

In our discussion of the auditory system so far we have ignored the fact that the stimulus can be delivered to either ear. While it is true that the auditory system is bilateral, in that each ear connects to both sides of the brain (see Figure 10.28), there are a great many differences in neural activity (and in the sensations of sounds) depending on how the two ears are stimulated. Thus localization of sounds in space depends upon two sorts of cues: a difference in the intensity of the sound at the two ears (particularly for high frequencies), and a difference in the " phase angle " or time of arrival at the two ears (especially for low frequency sounds). It might be expected that stimuli presented to the two ears will influence auditory cells differently than stimuli to one ear alone. Rosenzweig (1954) demonstrated that the amplitude of gross evoked responses to click stimulation recorded from the auditory areas on both hemispheres of the cerebral cortex differed. In brief, if an evoked response is measured from the right auditory cortex, its amplitude is greater if the click is delivered to the left ear prior to the right ear and less if the right ear is stimulated first (it is greatest if both the stimuli are simultaneous) and vice versa. A difference of less than 0.5 msec in the time of stimulation of the two ears can produce a significant differential evoked response amplitude.

Cells in a portion of the superior olive (see Figure 10.28) appear to be specialized for differentiation of time of arrival of stimuli at the two ears. Stotler (1953) has described the rather remarkable anatomical characteristic of these cells. They typically have two large dendrites, one pointing medially and one laterally. Most afferent terminals on the medial dendrite come from the contralateral side and most terminals ending on the lateral dendrite come from the ipsilateral side of the auditory system. Galambos, Swartzkopff, and Rupert (1959) recorded (extracellular microelectrodes) the responses of four cells believed to be of this type in the cat. Figure 10.32 illustrates the behavior of one of these cells, typical of the group. The graph is a plot of the probability of response (an index of the number of times the stimulus elicits a cell spike) against the time interval between clicks delivered to the two ears. If the click to the right ear preceded the click to the left ear by from 0.5 to 1.0 msec the response was completely suppressed.

At the level of the inferior colliculus a number of complex interactions for binaural (2 ears) stimulation have been described (Hind et al., 1963). If stimulation of one ear causes a unit to fire, stimulation of the other ear alone may cause discharge or no discharge. If the former occurs, the unit usually responds more to contralateral than ipsilateral stimulation. If the latter occurs, stimulation of

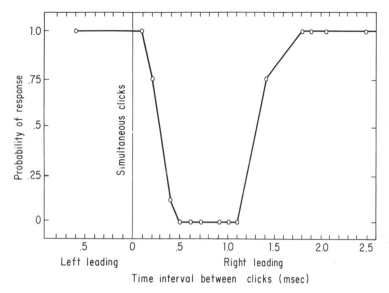

Figure 10.32. Effect of interaural time difference upon probability of unit response for a neuron in the superior olive. When click to right ear leads left ear by 0.5–1.1 msec the unit never responded. (Redrawn from Galambos, Swartzkopff, and Rupert, 1959)

both ears often produces a decrease in responsiveness over the excitation produced by stimulation to one ear alone. Hind and colleagues described a cell that would respond infrequently and erratically to stimulation of the ipsilateral ear but fired much more to stimulation of the contralateral ear. Stimulation of both ears caused an increase in the frequency of cell discharge over either alone. The best frequency for the cell was about 850 cps. If the tone were presented to the two ears 180° out of phase, so the maximal amplitude of the sound wave at one ear preceded the other by about 0.6 msec, the cell responded much more than if the cell was activated by an inphase binaural tone. These observations are but a few examples of the many types of stimulus coding processes that are seen in the auditory system. Rose, et al. (1963) have emphasized that each cell in the inferior colliculus has its own somewhat unique pattern of discharges to auditory stimulation. We will probably not fully understand the neural codes until many various types of cell response patterns have been studied at each synaptic level of the system.

THE CHEMICAL SENSES

Taste

It is commonly known that most qualitative aspects of taste are really due to stimulation of the olfactory system. Onion and apple cannot be distinguished

Figure 10.33. Normal taste bud on fungiform papilla of rat. Diameter of taste bud is about 60μ. (From Beidler, 1965)

if the nose is kept closed. Taste proper is classically described as having four qualities: sour, sweet, bitter, and salty. A good deal has been learned in recent years about the nature of neural responses to taste stimuli, particularly through the work of Beidler, Pfaffmann, and Zotterman, and their many associates and students (see Pfaffmann, 1959a; Zotterman, 1963). However the mechanisms whereby chemicals activate receptor cells, and these in turn initiate activity in afferent neurons are not well understood.

Taste receptors are found on the top and sides of the tongue and associated throat structures. A taste bud is drawn in Figure 10.33. The sensory nerve fibers enter at the bottom, and each fiber terminates on one or two receptor cells. Chemicals diffusing into the pore from the surface of the tongue activate the receptor cells. It has been suggested (Kimura and Beidler, 1956) that the receptor potential in taste receptors is also the generator potential—i.e. the potentials developed by the receptor cells in response to chemicals directly activate the sensory nerve fibers. It is commonly assumed that receptor cells are permanent; once they are formed embryologically they remain throughout life. Beidler et al. (1960) have demonstrated that just the opposite is the case for taste receptors.

The average life of a taste bud appears to be a matter of *days*; they are constantly undergoing degeneration and replacement.

There is some differential localization of taste buds on the tongue in terms of quality: sweet at the tongue tip, sour at the sides, bitter at the back, and salty elsewhere. Individual taste buds (papillae) may be sensitive to one, two, three or all four qualities. The relations between taste qualities and chemical characteristics of substances can be fairly well characterized for sour and salty tastes, but are somewhat obscure for sweet and bitter tastes. Sour appears closely related to the concentration of hydrogen ion and relatively independent of the remaining portion of the molecule. A wide variety of different acids of the same strength taste about the same.

All substances with salty tastes are salts, or more specifically, water soluble salts composed of positive and negative ions. Unlike the correlation between the H^+ ion and sour, both the positive and the negative ions may contribute to the salty taste. Sweet tastes are usually associated with organic compounds, the most common being sugars, glycols and alcohols. However many other categories of organic compounds also taste sweet, and as yet no common chemical structures or characteristics have been established. Bitter substances may be either organic or inorganic. No satisfactory correlations with chemical structures or compounds have yet been developed. It is of interest that a good many substances (e.g. saccharin) taste sweet on the tip of the tongue and bitter on the back of the tongue, where bitter sensitivity is greater.

Gross recording of activity in the taste nerves has proved difficult. Since adequate stimulation of taste receptors involves diffusion of chemicals over the tongue, no synchronous evoked responses occur in the nerve; the nerve fibers fire in a very asynchronous manner. Beidler developed a method of recording integrated "hash" for taste nerves, which gives an over-all picture of activity in the nerve. The nerve is placed on gross wire electrodes or a large *microelectrode* is inserted in the nerve and the multiple unit hash picked up is fed through an electronic integrating circuit to yield a measure of average activity. Examples of integrated records from the rat chorda tympani nerve resulting from application of various chemical solutions to the tongue are shown in Figure 10.34. The

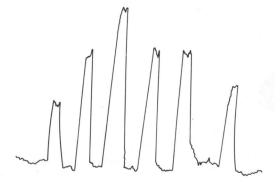

Figure 10.34. Integrated response of the rat chorda tympani nerve to hydrochloric, citric, formic, oxalic, acetic and hydrochloric acids (reading from left to right) at pH 2.5. Duration of response, 10 to 20 sec. (Redrawn from Beidler, 1957)

height of each reflects the total amount of single fiber hash activity in the nerve.

Microelectrode recording of the activity of single taste nerve fibers has provided a great deal of new information. Unfortunately, it has complicated rather than simplified our understanding of the system. In view of the fact that four discriminable qualities of taste can be described it might be expected that different nerve fibers are separately activated by the four types of stimuli, but such is not the case. Examples of response profiles for six fibers of the rat taste nerve are shown in Figure 10.35 (taken from Pfaffmann, 1955). Each bar within a unit profile represents response (in spike discharges/sec) to a different chemical substance. The shaded response in E is the relative amount of activity picked up in the gross nerve by the integrative technique. Only two of the six fibers are in any sense selective, fiber A responding to salt and fiber B to sweet. Only fibers

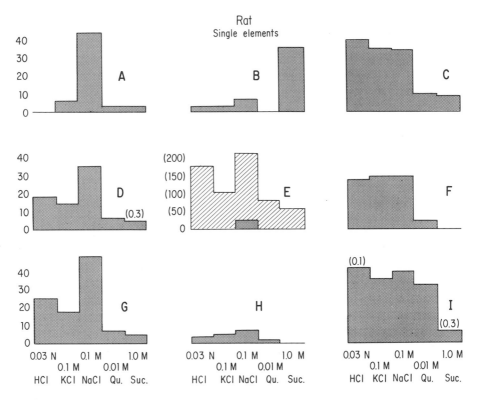

Figure 10.35. Bar graphs summarizing frequency of response during the first second to five standard taste solutions in nine different single fiber preparations in the rat. Sucrose of 0.3 *M* (molar) was used as test solution in elements **D** and **I**, 0.01 *M* HCl in element **I**. In all other cases concentrations are as shown on abscissa. Cross-hatched bar graph superimposed in figure for element **E** shows relative magnitude of integrator response for test solutions. Figures in parentheses give magnitudes in arbitrary units. Note that only elements **D** and **G** resemble the response of the total nerve. (From Pfaffmann, 1955)

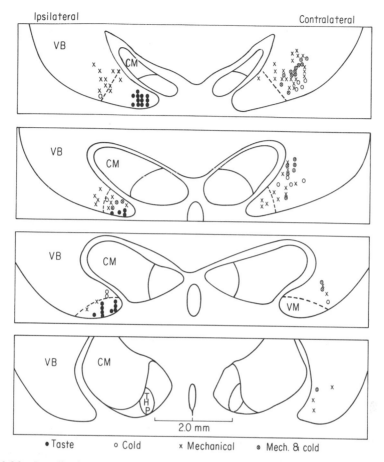

Figure 10.36. Localization of electrophysiologically isolated single neurons in the squirrel monkey thalamus responsive to stimulation of the tongue. VB, ventrobasal complex; CM centrum medianum; VM ventromedial portion of VB. (Redrawn from Benjamin, 1963)

D and G resemble the over-all activity of the entire nerve. Coding of taste quality would seem to be rather complex.

Afferent fibers from taste buds enter the CNS through the 7th, 9th and 10th cranial nerves, and relay in the solitary nucleus of the brain stem. From here they may or may not cross to the opposite side, and then ascend together with the fibers of the somatic sensory lemniscal system of the thalamus. From the lemniscus to the cerebral cortex, fibers subserving taste input travel in close conjunction with somatic sensory fibers of the lemniscal system. At the thalamus they appear to project to the most medial portion of the ventrobasal complex, sometimes termed the ventromedial complex.

The location of the thalamic neurons responding exclusively to taste stimulation in the squirrel monkey are indicated in Figure 10.36. The taste cells lie in

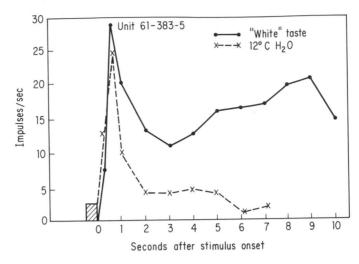

Figure 10.37. Frequency plot of the responses of a single thalamic neuron in the rat to solutions flowed on the tongue. (Benjamin, 1933)

the most medial portion of the ventrobasal complex (i.e. medial to the neurons responding to tactile stimuli), and are ipsilateral. Some thalamic taste cells respond to more than just taste stimuli, particularly in the rat. Figure 10.37 illustrates responses of a thalamic neuron to "white taste" (as the author describes it, an atrocious mixture of quinine, sodium chloride, hydrochloric acid, and sucrose) and to cold. Nonetheless, most thalamic "taste" cells are responsive to taste stimuli and not to tactile stimuli. This is of some importance in view of the fact that all natural taste substances also provide tactile stimulation of the tongue. Spatial localization of neuron activation thus appears to be a fundamental principle for functional differentiation of taste and touch stimuli.

In the rat, there is a very restricted cortical region bordering the somatic sensory tongue area, which receives projection from the thalamic taste area and subserves behavioral taste discriminations (Benjamin and Pfaffmann, 1955). For the monkey, the thalamocortical relations for taste are not well understood. In fact one investigator has suggested that the primate cortical taste area may not be in cortex at all, but rather in the claustrum, which lies just below the insular cortex (Benjamin, 1963). Regions of the insular cortex also appear to play a role in the taste behavior of primates (Bagshaw and Pribram, 1953; Blum, Chow, and and Pribram, 1950).

Olfaction

Elucidation of the chemical basis of odor has been extremely difficult. Most theories of olfaction have attempted to relate the molecular characteristics of odorants to the basic qualities of odors. Unfortunately, there is as yet little agreement concerning the relevant chemical characteristics of substances and even less agreement on the nature or even the number of basic types of odors.

Olfactory theories can be subdivided into *structural* theories specifying that some structural or chemical features of the odorant molecules must come into direct physical contact with the receptors in the olfactory epithelium of the nose, and *radiation* theories postulating that absorption and radiation of heat or light energy by the odorant molecules stimulates the receptor cells. Two basic variants of the latter type of theory are the *infrared* theory—which assumes that odor quality depends on the odor molecules absorbing heat energy of various wavelengths, depending on molecular structure (Beck and Miles, 1947)—and the *Raman* shift theory—which assumes that the amount of shift in wavelengths of reflected ultraviolet light determines the type of odor sensation. Recent evidence makes it appear unlikely that radiation theories are valid. Ottoson (1956), for example, has shown that if a thin membrane which transmits light and heat is placed over the olfactory receptor cells they cannot be activated by odor molecules.

There are several different types of structural theories, ranging from specifications of the presence or absence of certain active chemical groups on the odor molecule to the "stereochemical" theory (Amoore, 1962a and b; Moncrieff, 1949), which asserts that the over-all size and shape of the odor molecule is the determining factor in odor quality. Perhaps the greatest difficulty plaguing structural

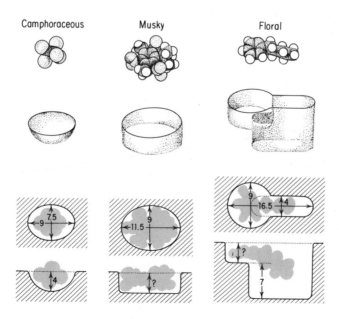

Figure 10.38. Examples of shapes of several types of basic odorant molecules and hypothetical shapes of receptor sites on the hair cells. (From Amoore, 1964)

theories is the lack of agreement on the number and nature of odor qualities. Most observers agree with at least some of the six classical categories established by Henning (1924): fragrant, ethereal, resinous, spicy, putrid, and burnt. An extensive factor-analytic study of human judgments of odor quality (Wright and Michels, 1963) yielded only five factors, plus a trigeminal component. This latter effect, incidentally, which results from activation of tactile and pain receptors innervated by the fifth cranial nerve, is often a confounding factor in olfactory studies in which it has not been separately identified. Amoore (1962a) has identified seven factors, based in part on descriptions of chemical odors by chemists and in part on the structural characteristics of the molecules.

Perhaps the most interesting of recent approaches is the stereochemical theory. This was first suggested by Moncrieff (1949) and elaborated by Amoore (1962a, b). It assumes that olfactory receptors have differently shaped receptor holes into which differently shaped molecules fit (see Figure 10.38). Actually, of the seven basic odors categorized by Amoore, five are said to depend on the shape of the molecule and receptor site and two on electrical characteristics of certain odorous molecules. Although it would be premature to assess this relatively new theory now, some evidence seems consistent with it. For example, the odor qualities of several new compounds were correctly predicted on the basis of their molecular shapes (Johnston and Sandoval, 1960).

The olfactory receptor cells are somewhat unique in that the receptor cell is also the primary sensory nerve cell. As diagrammed in Figure 10.39, the dendrites of the nerve cell protrude small hairlike endings into the nasal mucosa. These hair-dendrites are the receptors proper; contact of these hair-dendrites by odorous molecules is the adequate stimulus for smell. Activation of the hair cells by odors produces a relatively slow and long lasting generator potential (Otto-son, 1963, see Figure 10.40). In terms of our definitions of receptor and generator potentials given earlier this is both; it is produced by the receptor cells, but since the receptor cell is the dendritic part of the neuron it also generates a spike discharge in the neuron.

Gesteland et al. (1963) were able to record spike discharges from the axons of olfactory receptor-nerve cells in the frog. They found that certain classes of odors tended to activate maximally different cells, but each unit tended to behave in a somewhat individual manner. It is of interest that several of the major types of odors activating different neurons agreed with the classification by Amoore (see discussion by Amoore, 1964).

Axons of the several million olfactory receptor-neurons project into the olfactory bulb (see Figure 10.41) where they collect into *glomeruli* (conglomerations of nerve fibers). In the rabbit, for example, each glomerulus receives input from about 26,000 receptor-neurons. The major afferent pathway from the olfactory bulb, the lateral olfactory tract, is made up of axons of mitral cells (see Figure 10.41). These have their cell bodies in the bulb with the dendrites projecting into the glomeruli. In contrast to most neurons, it appears that all synapses on mitral cells are on dendrites (axodendritic) and none on cell bodies.

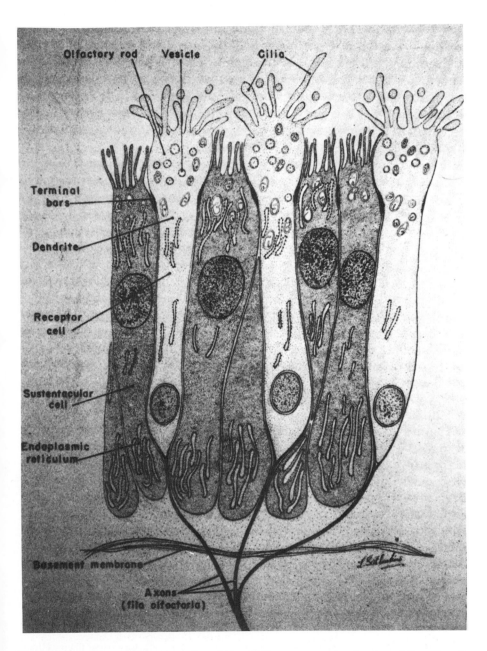

Figure 10.39. Schematic representation of the olfactory mucosa showing the relationships of the various cell types (From De Lorenzo, 1963)

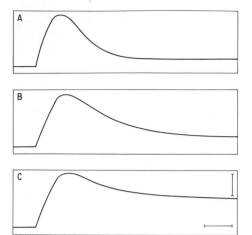

Figure 10.40. Generator potentials of olfactory receptor in response to A, amyl acetate; B, butanol; C, oil of cloves. Vertical line, 1 mV, time bar 1 sec. (Redrawn from Ottoson, 1956)

There are about 24 mitral cells for each glomerulus in the rabbit (Allison, 1953). The other type of afferent neuron from the bulb is the tufted cell (see Figure 10.41). This has its dendrites in the glomeruli, and its axon crosses in the anterior commissure to terminate in the olfactory bulb on the opposite side of the brain.

The grossly recorded electrical activity of the olfactory bulb is of two types (see Figure 10.42). *Spontaneous* waves which occur in the absence of olfactory stimulation are of relatively high frequency and somewhat irregular. They are

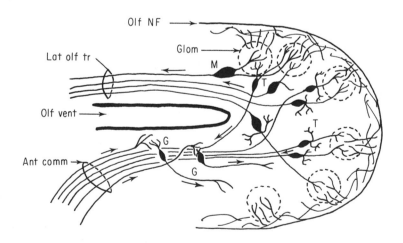

Figure 10.41. Wiring diagram of the olfactory bulb. Olf NF, olfactory nerve fibers; Glom, glomerulus; M, mitral cell; T, tufted cells; G. grandle cells; Lat olf tr, lateral olfactory tract; Olf vent, olfactory ventrical; Ant comm, anterior commissure. (Redrawn from Adey, 1959)

suppressed by anesthesia but will occur after destruction of the olfactory epithelium (Adrian, 1950). Upon presentation of odorants, lower frequency, rather regular waves are *induced*, which may range in frequency from 10 to 60 per sec. Unit cellular discharges occur in synchrony with these waves (Adrian, 1950). In an animal exhibiting spontaneous waves an odorant will block spontaneous activity and elicit induced waves (Adey, 1959). There is evidence both from gross and microelectrode studies indicating that different regions of the bulb may be differentially sensitive to different "qualities" or at least different categories of odors (Adrian, 1953; 1954; Mozell and Pfaffmann, 1954). In a recent microelectrode study (Phillips and Michels, 1964), discharges of mitral cells in various locations of the opossum's olfactory bulb were compared for odors representing the extremes of the five factors analyzed in the human factor analytic study of odor quality (Wright and Michels, 1963). Odors with large positive factor loadings had a facilitative effect on mitral cell activity in the anterior bulb and odors with large negative loadings had facilitative effects on mitral cell discharges in the posterior bulb.

Figure 10.42.   Spontaneous waves (left half of tracing) and the slower induced waves, resulting from presentation of amyl acetate, recorded grossly from the olfactory bulb of the anesthetized rabbit. (Redrawn from Adrian, 1950)

0.1 sec

Earlier it was thought that a great deal of the limbic system was involved in olfactory function, including the hippocampus, amygdala, and hypothalamus. More recent evidence has shown that the direct central connections of the olfactory system are much more restricted. The only regions of the brain which can properly be called olfactory are some structures clustered about the termination of the lateral olfactory tract on the base of the brain. These include the olfactory tubercle, the prepyriform cortex, a portion of the amygdaloid nuclei and the nucleus of the stria terminalis (Clark and Meyer, 1947; Meyer and Allison, 1949, Fox et al., 1944; Kaada, 1951). Although there may well be higher order connections to various portions of the limbic system (MacLean et al., 1952; Fox et al., 1944), it is probably erroneous to consider these regions as primarily olfactory.

One aspect of olfactory bulb activity that is of considerable interest is the rapid adaptation to repeated olfactory stimuli. The reader will undoubtedly have noticed that initially strong odors seem to decrease in intensity rapidly. This rapid adaptation is also seen for the gross rhythmic electrical response of the olfactory bulb (Adrian, 1950). Interestingly enough, the adaptation effect cannot be ascribed entirely to adaptation of the receptor cells. Ottoson (1959) has shown that the receptor-generator potential of the receptor cells decreases only partially after the initial stimulus application, and maintains a steady level as long as the odor is present. Moulten (1963) has recently demonstrated that adaptation of electrical activity in the bulb is virtually abolished if certain *efferent* paths from the olfactory areas of the brain to the olfactory bulb are sectioned. Consequently, much of the adaptation effect appears to be the result of a central regulatory action by the brain on the bulb, rather than an intrinsic characteristic of the receptors or of the olfactory bulb itself.

COMMON FEATURES OF SENSORY SYSTEMS

Several rather important and general principles have emerged in the course of our discussion of sensory systems. The similarities in receptor actions noted at the beginning of the chapter are a case in point. Regardless of whether or not the specialized receptor cells are present, all receptor systems generate slow graded potentials whose amplitudes are a function of the stimulus strength. These graded potentials ultimately act as generator potentials initiating spike discharges in the primary sensory nerve fibers. A less fortunate common feature of all sensory systems is our lack of understanding of the transduction mechanisms whereby the generator potentials are produced by stimuli.

Stimulus Coding

Because nerve spike potentials do not differ intrinsically from one another (except in velocity) there are only two possible ways in which incoming stimulus information can be coded by nerve fibers: differing places of termination in the central nervous system, or temporal pattern (frequency) of spike discharges. Both types of coding seem to be utilized in all sensory systems. In each system the receptor elements have a clear spatial representation at all levels of the CNS. In virtually all sense modalities the physical or spatial layout of the *receptor* surface is projected throughout the ascending sensory portion of the nervous system in a topographically intact manner. In the somatic sensory system it is the body surface, in the visual system it is the retina, and in the auditory system it is the hair cells along the basilar membrane. (These do not of course represent the *same* aspect of sensation in all modalities—local sign for the somatic system and position in visual space for the visual system are perhaps comparable, but tone pitch is not. However, each may well represent the most *important* aspect of the stimulus in terms of its biological significance.) As will be described in Chapter 11, all three major sensory systems display at least *four* separate projections of the receptor surface on the cerebral cortex in mammals. There must surely be some significance in this surprising reduplication.

A more subtle kind of spatial coding of stimulus quality is found at the cellular level in all sensory systems. Different cells respond to different types or submodalities of stimulation. In the somatic system light touch, deep pressure, and joint movement are so differentiated. In the visual system wavelength or "color" is coded in this manner. In the auditory system both pitch and loudness are to some extent so represented. Taste and odor qualities also have some degree of cellular differentiation. In most instances this type of *quality* coding by the nerve cells appears to reflect some aspects of the initial differential coding of stimuli by receptor cells. However, the relations are not "isomorphic": there is not a separate group of cells for each taste quality or each color. Instead, different cells respond differently to different combinations of stimulus qualities.

A still more subtle higher order type of spatial coding is exhibited by cells that are at least one synapse removed from the sensory afferent fibers. The more abstract or "perceptual" aspects of stimulus characteristics may be represented by different groups of cells. The optic nerve fibers and cellular layers in the superior colliculus of the frog are the clearest example of this. A separate subpopulation of fibers is activated by each of several rather abstract categories of stimuli (convex edges, buglike objects, etc.). Each subpopulation projects to a different layer of the superior colliculus. In summary, there are at least three levels of organization for spatial coding of stimulus characteristics: topographical projection of the receptor surfaces, differential cellular representation of stimulus quality within each modality, and cellular differentiation of the "perceptual" categories of stimuli.

The spike discharge frequency of sensory cells seems to be related to the intensity or degree of stimulation. In general, a stronger stimulus elicits greater generator and/or receptor potential and an increased frequency of firing in the afferent fibers. However the relationships are not always direct or monotonic, particularly for higher order cells. Many cells of the inferior colliculus, for example, *decrease* their spike discharge rate, and may even change their pattern of discharge, as tone intensities increase. Perhaps the clearest example where degree of stimulus is coded by spike discharge frequency is in the cells of the ventrobasal complex activated by joint movement. An almost perfect log-log relationship holds between the degree to which the joint has been extended and the steady-state discharge frequency of the nerve cells.

Spontaneous Activity

A somewhat unexpected characteristic of most sensory systems is the fact that the sensory nerve fibers exhibit considerable spontaneous activity in the absence of stimulation. The optic nerve maintains a high rate of spontaneous discharges even when the eye is in total darkness. In fact the spontaneous discharge rate may be greater than the rate induced by light stimulation. In like manner, many auditory nerve fibers and cells of the cochlear nucleus exhibit spontaneous discharges, as do fibers from a variety of mechanoreceptors. It is likely that spontaneous activity, and its modulation by stimuli, plays an important role in higher order stimulus coding. If the nerve fibers of a receptor system are firing at a given baseline level, changes in sensory stimulation in either direction away from this level can be coded by increases or decreases in firing rate. As Granit (1955) has emphasized, frequency modulation of baseline spontaneous activity is an extremely significant coding mechanism. Visual stimulation markedly alters spontaneous discharges of the optic nerve. Although sound stimulation seems to have little effect on the spontaneous activity of auditory nerve fibers, it does alter spontaneous activity of cells in the cochlear nucleus, which is more analogous to the optic nerve, there being two synapses between receptor and responding cell in each case. Vestibular organs, joint receptors, the olfactory bulb, and other receptor systems appear to utilize spontaneous activity for coding. Granit (1955) has suggested that spontaneous activity, in addition to serving possible coding functions, may play a more general role in activating or energizing such central structures as the reticular formation.

Adaptation

Adaptation, defined as a decrease in the output of receptors in response to a constant stimulus, is a common occurrence in most sensory systems. It is useful to distinguish between *adaptation* and *habitation*, the latter defined as decrease responsiveness of nerve cells or of an organism to a constant stimulus not attributable to receptor adaptation. A good deal of confusion has resulted from the sometimes interchangeable use of these concepts. In this text adaptation is used in reference to receptor processes and habituation refers to response decrements resulting from central processes. These are the definitions developed by Harris (1943) in his classical discussion of habituation.

Although most receptor systems exhibit adaptation, the mechanisms differ considerably. In the Pacinian corpuscle, for example, the rapid adaptation seen in afferent nerve discharges results from the changing shape of the accessory corpuscle in response to a constant physical distortion. In the rods and cones of the retina, adaptation results from the establishment of a biochemical "steady state" in the receptor itself, determined by the intensity of illumination. The fact that stabilized images fade away suggests that the extent of adaptation of the rods and cones to a constant illumination may be considerable. Olfactory "adaptation" is a particularly interesting case. The receptor potentials do exhibit some adaptation to a constant olfactory stimulus. However, the much greater "adaptation" shown both by the electrical activity of the olfactory bulb and by olfactory sensation appears to be under the control of central neural processes. It is perhaps more properly an instance of habituation.

The characteristic response of a receptor when a steady stimulus is turned on is an initial maximum of activity followed by a decrease to some lower level of steady-state activity or to zero (see Figure 10.2). The consequence of this adaptation is that the number of nerve cells in the CNS activated during the steady stimulus may be smaller than the number activated by the stimulus onset.

Another way of stating it is that more cells are used to code stimulus onset than are used to code steady-state stimulus. Most neurons of the inferior colliculus, for example, fire a compact burst of spikes to tone onset, and relatively few fire at a steady rate as long as a tone is on. It is important to emphasize that such differences are not solely due to receptor adaptation. In the auditory system, the ratio of number of cells firing " on " bursts to those firing steadily increases markedly from auditory nerve to auditory cortex. This is unquestionably due to complex excitatory and inhibitory synaptic interactions among nerve cells at all levels of the system.

Central Control of Sensory Input

It has been demonstrated relatively recently that the CNS can exert *efferent* or *centrifugal* control over incoming sensory information in virtually all sensory modalities. In the auditory, visual, somatic sensory, and olfactory systems efferent fibers that project down to the receptors or to early central synaptic relays can exert direct control over sensory input. The first such centrifugal control system to be discovered was the gamma motor neuron system, where central influences on the gamma motor neurons produce alterations in the sensory output of the stretch receptors in muscles. We will consider this system separately in the context of reflex activity in Chapter 12.

Some years ago Rasmussen (1946) demonstrated anatomically that an efferent fiber system (the olivocochlear bundle or tract of Rasmussen) arises in the vicinity of the superior olive in the brain stem and terminates on the contralateral cochlea. These efferent fibers appear to come in contact with either the inner hair cells or the afferent auditory nerve fibers as they leave the hair cells. Galambos (1956) demonstrated that electrical stimulation of this tract produces a marked suppression of auditory nerve responses (recorded at the round window of the cochlea) evoked by click stimulation (see Figure 10.43). The possibility that changes in tension of the middle ear muscle mediated the effect was ruled out: the suppression was still obtained after section of the middle ear muscles. Section of the olivocochlear bundle below the level of electrical stimulation abolished the suppression effect, indicating the essential role of the bundle. Desmedt and Mechelse (1958) and Desmedt (1960) have demonstrated another inhibitory system which seems to act at the level of the cochlear nucleus. This system appears to take origin from the insular region of the cerebral cortex (see Chapter 11), and courses down to the cochlear nucleus in close anatomical approximation to the classical ascending auditory pathway. Electrical stimulation of this system causes a reduction in evoked responses of the cochlear nucleus to click stimulation. However, the evoked auditory nerve responses recorded at the round window do not change, demonstrating that the effect is not due to suppression at the level of the receptors or auditory nerve fibers.

Hagbarth and Kerr (1954) carried out an extensive investigation of centrifugal influences on responses of the somatic sensory system. They stimulated

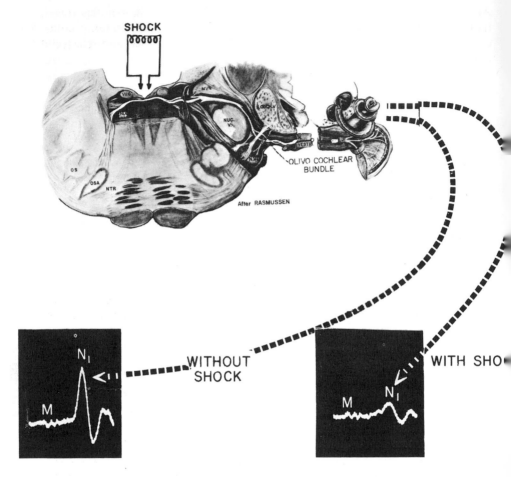

Figure 10.43. Anatomic plan of the olivo cochlear pathway and illustration of its function. The cross section of the medulla shows cells of origin (OSA) and anatomic course of fibers to the cochlear spiral. Shocks applied where it decussates markedly reduce the amplitude of the auditory nerve discharge evoked by a click (N_1) without influencing the hair cell response (M). (Galambos, 1960b)

dorsal roots and measured both the primary afferent fiber response in the dorsal columns (lemniscal system) and the relayed response in the lateral columns (spinothalamic tract). Electrical stimulation in a number of regions of the CNS including the reticular formation, sensory motor areas of the cerebral cortex, and cerebellar cortex, resulted in a marked depression of the synaptically relayed response in the lateral columns. The dorsal column primary response did not change, suggesting that possible systemic factors such as blood pressure drop were not responsible for the decrease of the synaptically relayed response. Subsequently, Hernández-Peón and Hagbarth (1955) and Hernández-Peón et al. (1956) showed comparable suppression effects for the lemniscal relay nuclei (gracile and cuneate) and the relayed response of the 5th nerve to electrical stimulation of the reticular formation or sensory-motor cortex.

Granit (1955) and Granit and Kaada (1952) demonstrated that electrical stimulation in the general region of the midbrain reticular formation could produce either increases or decreases in the frequency of firing of individual ganglion cells of the retina. Some years ago Ramon y Cajal (1909) described very fine efferent fibers passing out along the optic nerve. Dodt (1956) found a spike response in the retina to electrical stimulation of the optic nerve which did not appear to be an antidromic response (its latency was too long) and probably represented activity conducted in the fine efferent fibers. It is possible that the effects described by Granit were conveyed to the retina by the small fiber system. Spinelli, Pribram and Weingarten (1965) have described responses in the optic nerve evolved by tactile and auditory stimuli. They suggest these may represent efferent activity in the pathway.

Finally, Kerr, and Hagbarth (1955) showed that stimulation of a variety of central olfactory structures, including the prepyriform cortex, amygdaloid nucleus and olfactory tubercule produced diminution in the activity of the olfactory bulb. We note earlier that Moulton (1963) eliminated the rapid habituation of olfactory bulb activity in response to odors by section of the olfactory projection system at the base of the brain. Ramon y Cajal (1909) had described efferent fibers originating in these areas and passing out to the bulb. This fiber system may well mediate the suppression effect. While efferent suppression of incoming activity in the taste pathway has not yet been studied, it is likely that a similar effect will be found.

You may recall from our discussion of presynaptic inhibition in Chapter 7 that Eccles (1961) suggested this may be the synaptic mechanism involved in efferent suppression of incoming sensory activity. Andersen, Eccles, and Sears (1962; 1964) and Carpenter, Lundberg, and Norrsell (1962; 1963) independently demonstrated that such is indeed the case for the inhibitory influences of the sensorimotor cortex on relayed activity in the somatic sensory system. They measured several indices of presynaptic inhibition (i.e. primary afferent depolarization) in the spinal cord, including the P wave of the cord dorsum potential, the dorsal root potential, and the excitatory changes in dorsal root fibers. Brief tetanic electric stimulation of the appropriate region of somatic sensory area I or II produced clear evidence of presynaptic inhibition acting on the afferent terminals of the incoming sensory afferent fibers in the spinal cord (see Figure 10.44). A cord dorsum response containing a large P wave could be evoked, a clear dorsal root potential was elicited, and the excitability of dorsal root fibers increased markedly. There was a clear topographical correspondence; stimulation of the hind paw area of the somatic sensory cortex elicited the greatest amount of presynaptic inhibition in the afferent fibers coming from the hind leg, and so on.

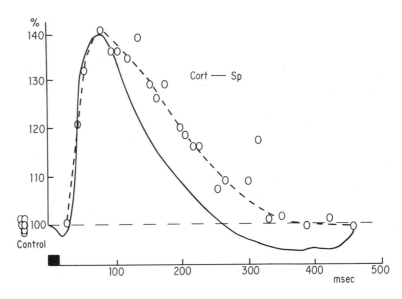

Figure 10.44. Time course of presynaptic inhibition induced in afferent fibers (from hind leg) in the spinal cord by repetitive electrical stimulation of the homologous (and contralateral) region of the sensory-motor cortex. Dashed lines and open circles show the excitability of the afferent nerve fibers, and the solid line is the dorsal root potential. Both are measures of degree of presynaptic inhibition. Cortical shocks indicated by solid bar on time line. (Redrawn from Andersen, Eccles, and Sears, 1964)

It appears very likely that the suppressive effects in the somatic sensory system described by Hagbarth and Kerr (1954) may be mediated by descending systems projecting down from a variety of brain structures to the spinal cord which exert presynaptic inhibitory influences on the incoming terminals of the somatic sensory afferent fibers (see Lundberg, 1964b). Although suppression effects described for the other sensory modalities have not yet been analyzed in a comparable manner, it is quite possible that presynaptic inhibition may be the chief synaptic mechanism involved in all cases.

The potential significance of the efferent sensory control systems is considerable. The amount and kind of incoming sensory information can be controlled and "gated" at the level of the sensory afferent fiber terminals and the first synaptic relays in sensory systems. Sensory information can be prevented from reaching higher levels of the CNS. There is as yet no unanimity of opinion concerning the possible roles of efferent control systems in brain function and behavior. Hernández-Peón (1955) has suggested that they mediate the reduction in the amplitude of gross evoked activity in sensory systems reported to occur during "habituation" and "attention." The extent to which the efferent sensory control systems are involved in such phenomena is unclear. We will consider this issue in more detail in Chapter 15.

Psychophysical Aspects of Sensory Processes

The earliest branch of psychology to develop was sensory psychophysics, the study of the quantitative relationships between the physical characteristics of stimuli and their "subjective" characteristics as judged by human observers. Discriminable stimuli appear to differ in two quite distinct ways: quality and quantity. For example, difference between a taste and a sound is one of quality; each, however, can vary in intensity. Stevens (1957; 1961) has used the term *metathetic* to refer to stimulus dimensions based on quality and *prothetic* for the intensity dimension. In the visual system, color and location in visual space are metathetic, brightness is prothetic. In the auditory system pitch is methathetic and loudness is prothetic. In the somatic sensory system location on the skin surface (local sign) is metathetic and intensity of stimulation is prothetic.

Although psychophysics has been more concerned with the quantification of prothetic scales, some rather striking relationships have been found for at least one metathetic scale: tone pitch. As was indicated in Figure 10.18, one and the same curve relates tone frequency to the mel (pitch) scale, the cumulative jnd (just noticeable difference) scale, and the position of maximum distortion along the basilar membrane. All these functional relationships are identical.

THE STUDY OF PROTHETIC CONTINUA. The relations between stimulus intensity and judged intensity began with Weber's early observation that the amount by which a given stimulus must be increased to be just noticeably more intense than the initial stimulus was directly proportional to the initial strength of the stimulus. If we let Φ be the initial stimulus intensity, Weber's law can be expressed as:

$$\frac{\Delta\Phi}{\Phi} = \text{a constant}$$

in which $\Delta\Phi$ is the just noticeable change in Φ. The approximate truth of this observation seems quite apparent. An intense stimulus must be increased by a greater amount to sound just noticeably more intense than is necessary for a weak stimulus. Fechner generalized this by making the further assumption that all jnds are "equal." There has been a good deal of argument over whether or not all jnds are in fact subjectively equal. In a sense, all that is meant by the assumption is that a just noticeable change in a stimulus is always just noticeable, regardless of the initial intensity of the stimulus. If the size of the just noticeable difference is symbolized as $\Delta\Psi$, Weber's law now becomes

$$\Delta\Psi = k\frac{\Delta\Phi}{\Phi}$$

in which k is a constant. By the use of simple calculus this can be stated in the familiar form:

$$\Psi = k \log \Phi$$

As most readers probably know, this relationship is at best only approximately true; it doesn't hold for extreme values.

Stevens (1957, 1961) has demonstrated that a somewhat different type of relationship between stimulus intensity and judged intensity appears to be more general. This is the power-law relationship. If instead of assuming that the amount of change in the psychological variable is constant ($\Delta\Psi$ a constant), it is assumed that the amount of judged change is proportional to the judged absolute stimulus value, the following relationship obtains:

$$\frac{\Delta\Psi}{\Psi} = k\frac{\Delta\Phi}{\Phi}$$

By integration this can be reformulated as a simple power law:

$$\Psi = k\Phi^n$$

in which the exponent n is simply a number.

In contrasting these alternative formulations it is important to specify the manner in which the judged stimulus intensity is measured. As Stevens has emphasized (1961) the type of psychophysical relationship obtained depends upon the method of measurement. Two alternative methods that have been commonly used are measurement of jnds and magnitude estimation. In using jnds, the size of the jnd in physical stimulus terms is measured and the scale is simply the number of jnds. In magnitude estimation the observer estimates the "absolute subjective strength" of a stimulus relative to a standard. Figure 10.45

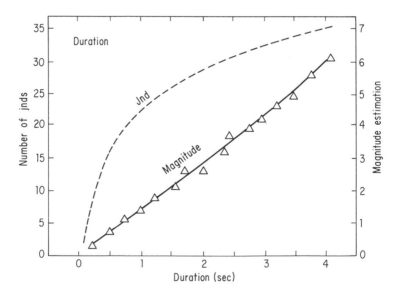

Figure 10.45. Two kinds of psychological measures of apparent duration. Triangles: mean magnitude estimations by 12 observers who judged the apparent durations of white noises. Dashed curve: discriminability scale obtained by counting off jnds. (From Stevens, 1961)

illustrates the relationships between actual and judged *duration* of a stimulus. Using the jnd method the number of stimulus duration jnds is logarithmically related to the duration of the stimulus. However the judged duration of the stimulus obtained by the method of magnitude estimation appears to be linearly related to the stimulus duration. Actually it is an example of the power-function relationship, $\Psi = k\Phi^n$, in which the exponent n equals 1, so $\Psi = k\Phi$, a simple linear equation.

Because physical stimulus intensity is usually greater than zero at absolute sensory threshold, the general power relationship is more correctly expressed as: $\Psi = k(\Phi - \Phi_0)^n$ where Φ_0 is the stimulus intensity at absolute threshold. Stevens has shown that this relationship holds for all stimuli where it has been measured. The value of the constant k depends in large part on the actual physical measurement scale used (gm, lb, etc.), and the exponent n is dependent upon the particular type of stimulus. Table 10.1 (from Stevens, 1961) lists the values of the

TABLE 10.1.   REPRESENTATIVE EXPONENTS OF THE POWER
FUNCTIONS RELATING PSYCHOLOGICAL MAGNITUDE
TO STIMULUS MAGNITUDE ON PROTHETIC CONTINUA

Continuum	Exponent	Stimulus conditions
Loudness	0.6	Binaural
Loudness	0.54	Monaural
Brightness	0.33	5° target, dark-adapted eye
Brightness	0.5	Point source, dark-adapted eye
Lightness	1.2	Reflectance of grey papers
Smell	0.55	Coffee odor
Smell	0.6	Heptane
Taste	0.8	Saccharine
Taste	1.3	Sucrose
Taste	1.3	Salt
Temperature	1.0	Cold, on arm
Temperature	1.6	Warmth, on arm
Vibration	0.95	60 cps, on finger
Vibration	0.6	250 cps, on finger
Duration	1.1	White-noise stimulus
Repetition rate	1.0	Light, sound, touch, and shocks
Finger span	1.3	Thickness of wood blocks
Pressure on palm	1.1	Static force on skin
Heaviness	1.45	Lifted weights
Force of handgrip	1.7	Precision hand dynamometer
Autophonic level	1.1	Sound pressure of vocalization
Electric shock	3.5	60 cps, through fingers

exponent for a wide variety of stimuli. The influence of the value of the exponent on the form of the curve is illustrated in Figure 10.46, in which both the physical stimulus intensity and the judged intensity are plotted on the linear scales. The

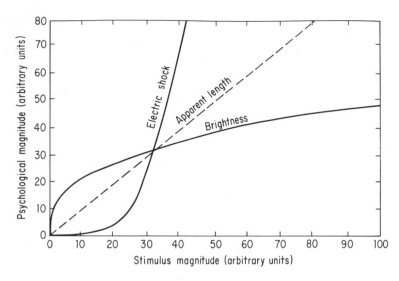

Figure 10.46. In linear coordinates the subjective magnitude functions are concave upward or downward depending on whether the power-function exponent is greater or less than 1 (See Table 10.1 for exponents.) (From Stevens, 1961)

exponent for electric shock is considerably greater than 1 (actually about 3.5), so the curve rises increasingly more rapidly. Brightness of a visual stimulus, on the other hand, has an exponent of less than 1 (about 0.33), so the curve increases rapidly at first and then tails off. Apparent length has an exponent of about 1 and is thus linear. As Stevens notes, when the value of n is less than 1 the transformation is a compression, in that a very wide range of stimulus intensities are compressed into a small range of subjective values. If the exponent is greater than 1 just the opposite effect occurs; the small range of physical stimulus values is expanded into a wider range of judged values.

One advantage of the power law relationship is that if the curve is plotted with both scales in logarithmic form the curve becomes a straight line. The curves of Figure 10.46 are all linear when replotted in Figure 10.47 in log-log form. In other words, the extent to which a log-log plot of stimulus intensity vs estimated intensity is a straight line is the extent to which the two variables are related by a power function. Earlier in the chapter we presented the striking findings by Mountcastle, Poggio, and Werner (1963) indicating that the relationship between frequency of firing of "joint" neurons in the thalamus and extent of joint movement was a perfect power function (see Figures 10.7 and 10.8). This, then, is an instance where the frequency of firing of a thalamic neuron is related to the extent of joint movement by the same power relationship that holds between subjective judgment of degree of joint movement and the actual physical extent of joint movement. In other words the relationship between the physical stimulus and the subjective experience of that stimulus is the same as the relationship between the stimulus and the discharge frequencies of thalamic and cortical neurons.

Although it is perhaps too great an oversimplification, it might be suggested that while prothetic stimulus dimensions are coded in terms of frequency of nerve cell discharges, metathetic continua are coded in terms of differential spatial representation—i.e. intensity is coded in terms of discharge frequency, and quality is related to the place where afferent fibers terminate. Certainly the gross differences in quality between different sensory modalities are so coded by place. Furthermore, dimensions like location on body surface, position in visual space, and tone frequency appear to be coded in this manner.

The power relationship between physical stimulus intensity and judged intensity holds over a wide range of stimuli. Although it has been suggested that the transformations from physical intensity to "judged" intensity are likely to occur at the receptors (Stevens, 1961), there is limited evidence available to settle this point at present. Actually, the frequency of afferent fiber discharge in the muscle spindle organ (stretch receptor) appears to be related to muscle stretch according to logarithmic rather than a power function (Matthews, 1933). The demonstration by Mountcastle et al. (1963) that thalamic "joint" neurons are related to joint movement by the power function suggests that whether or not the entire transformation occurs at the receptor level, it has occurred by the thalamocortical level. If this turns out to be the case for other stimulus modalities, it would imply that frequency of cell discharge at the thalamocortical level may determine the "subjective" judgment of stimulus intensity.

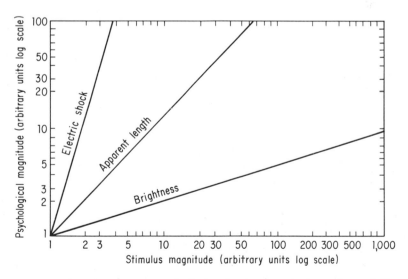

Figure 10.47.   Scales of apparent magnitude for the three prothetic continua of Fig. 10.46 plotted in log-log coordinates. The slope of the line corresponds to the exponent of the power function governing the growth of the psychological magnitude. (From Stevens, 1961)

In summary, it is perhaps worth re-emphasizing again some of the general features by sensory systems. The basic transduction mechanisms whereby physical stimuli are transformed into the graded receptor and/or generator potentials that produce spike discharges in sensory nerve fibers remain unknown. A variety of coding methods are utilized by sensory systems: nerve fiber spike discharge frequency, modulation of spontaneous discharge rate, and place of termination of afferent fiber terminals. Transformations of coding can occur at all synaptic levels of the nervous system. The work on visual coding in the frog *vs* the cat (see Chapter 11) suggests that more complex coding may occur further from the periphery in higher vertebrates (frog optic nerve fibers code at a level of abstraction comparable to neurons of the cerebral cortex in the cat). Perhaps the most important lesson to be learned from the nature of stimulus coding in the CNS is that even the most complex or abstract subjective perceptual aspects of sensory experience are coded by individual nerve cells. It is unnecessary to invoke any mysterious processes in addition to nerve cell activity to "explain" perception. Finally, the existence of efferent control systems from the CNS to receptors and early relay nuclei suggests that the brain may exert rather direct control over incoming sensory information.

Suggested readings

Field, J. (Ed.) *Handbook of physiology. Section I: neurophysiology.* (Vol I). Washington, D.C.: American Physiological Society, 1959.

Rosenblith, W. A. (Ed.) *Sensory communication.* New York: Wiley, 1961.

Stevens, S. S. (Ed.) *Handbook of experimental psychology.* New York: Wiley, 1951.

Sensory receptors. Cold Spring Harbor Symposia on Quantitative Biology. (Vol. XX). New York: Cold Spring Harbor Laboratory of Quantitative Biology, 1965.

II

SENSORY AND MOTOR FUNCTIONS OF THE CEREBRAL CORTEX

Psychologists have long been particularly fascinated by the structure and functions of the cerebral cortex. A number of considerations justify viewing this structure as primarily subserving the elaboration of the more complex and modifiable aspects of behavior. The cerebral cortex represents the most recent evolutionary development of the vertebrate nervous system. (Our discussion here will be limited to the neocortex, the six layered cerebral cortex that has become elaborated in mammals. Older and more primitive types of cortex having fewer than six layers are also found in mammals, and are relatively extensive in some lower forms. The terms "cerebral cortex" or "cortex" are used in this text to mean cerebral *neocortex*.) Fish and amphibians have no cerebral cortex, and reptiles and birds only a rudimentary indication of cortex (see Chapter 4). Within the mammalian series the more primitive mammals such as the rat have a relatively small, smooth cortex. As the phylogenetic scale is ascended, the amount of cortex relative to the total amount of brain tissue increases in a regular manner. Within primates, this same relationship is seen. More primitive monkeys such as the marmoset and squirrel monkey have relatively small, fissureless cortical surfaces compared to higher forms. More advanced primates such as rhesus monkey, chimpanzee, and man have enormous and disproportionate increases in amount of cerebral cortex. In general terms there is a correlation between the extent of cortical development for a species, its phylogenetic position, and the degree of complexity and modifiability characteristic of its behavior.

The specific sensory projection systems discussed in the last chapter can be said to "end" at the cerebral cortex. The apparent implications of such a statement may be misleading. Primary sensory systems can easily be traced from receptors to cortex by anatomical, electrophysiological and neurobehavioral techniques. However, they cannot be traced as such beyond the modality-specific cortical projection fields. The sensory areas of the cerebral cortex appear to be the last or "highest" regions in the brain where interrelations can be found between stimulus parameters and neural response patterns. Certain motor systems, on the other hand, can be traced from the cortex to muscles. Since higher organisms respond differentially to literally millions of different physical stimuli, it is obvious that some types of "coding" processes persist from sensory input through complex central processes to influence motor output. However, the nature and organization of the processes intervening between sensory projection systems and motor outflow remain obscure. In this chapter we will consider the anatomical structure of the cerebral cortex, and the organization and functions of the sensory and motor areas. The more "integrative" aspects of the cortical functions will be examined later (Chapter 15).

The cortex is a multiple layer of nerve cells about 2 mm thick which overlays the cerebrum. In higher forms having fairly extensive areal development of cortex, many fissures have developed. A fissure (or sulcus) is simply an infolding of cortex, such as would occur if you pressed the skin of an orange inward with the edge of a ruler. The cortex is present on both banks (sides) of a fissure and is of normal thickness except at the bottom, where it is usually thinner. The development of fissures has permitted an enormous increase in the amount of cortex in higher primates without undue enlargement of the rigid skull casing. Comparison of the fissure patterns for squirrel monkey, rhesus monkey, and man in Figure 11.1 illustrates this point. It has been estimated that more than three quarters of the total amount of cerebral cortex in the human brain lies within fissures. There are two fissures which serve as major cerebral landmarks: the central fissure (fissure of Rolando), which allows us to differentiate the cerebrum into anterior and posterior halves, and the temporal or Sylvian fissure, which serves to demarcate the temporal lobe.

Some rather complex terminology has developed to designate various regions of the brain in relation to fissures. For our purposes it is only necessary to remember the few major subdivisions that are shown in Figure 11.2. The anterior portion of the cortex lies in front of the central fissure. It is customarily divided into precentral and frontal regions, the frontal lobe extending from the front of the brain back to the precentral cortex. The temporal lobe lies below and behind the temporal (Sylvian) fissure. The remaining postcentral cortex is usually

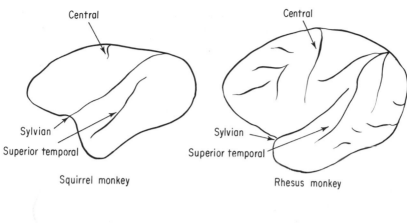

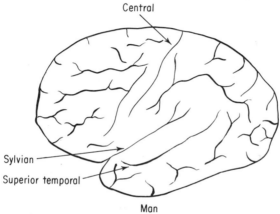

Figure 11.1.   Relative development of fissures in three primate brains. Three fissures, the central, the sylvian, and the superior temporal, are present in all primate brains. The brains are not drawn to scale; the brain of the Squirrel monkey is actually much smaller than that of the Rhesus; and the Rhesus is much smaller than the human brain. (The brains are all facing left.)

divided into the occipital lobe, which is the posterior portion, and the parietal lobe, which extends from the occipital lobe to the central fissure. To help remember these subdivisions, it is useful to keep in mind the following somewhat oversimplified set of relationships between cortical structure and function: occipital lobe = vision, parietal lobe = skin and muscle senses, part of temporal lobe and temporal fissure = hearing, precentral cortex = motor or movement control. All remaining parietal, preoccipital, temporal, and frontal areas, which seem to be neither sensory or motor in function, have been called "silent" or "association" areas. It is possible to subdivide the cortex into a variety of distinct areas or regions, but our view of this regional organization depends in

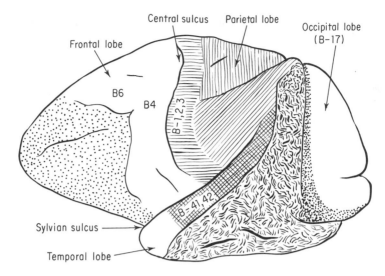

Figure 11.2.   Major subdivisions of the primate cortex. The central sulcus (i.e. fissure) separates the frontal and parietal lobes, and the sylvian sulcus defines the temporal lobe. Shadings indicate the histological subdivisions by von Bonin and Bailey. The numbers refer to Brodmann's designations for the various primary sensory and motor regions. Regions not identified by numbers are silent or "association" areas. (Based on von Bonin and Bailey, 1951)

part on the methods employed. Three major approaches may be distinguished: anatomical, electrophysiological, and neurobehavioral. Fortunately, the general findings are in rough agreement, although significant and troublesome contradictions do exist in the more detailed comparisons between results of the different approaches. For convenience, we will first consider the anatomical organization of the entire cerebral cortex, and then discuss the electrophysiological organization and behavioral functions of the various sensory and motor regions individually.

Aɴᴀᴛᴏᴍɪᴄᴀʟ ᴀɴᴀʟʏsɪs ᴏꜰ ᴄᴏʀᴛɪᴄᴀʟ ᴏʀɢᴀɴɪᴢᴀᴛɪᴏɴ

Cytoarchitectonics

If a cross section is cut through the cerebral cortex from surface to depth (at a right angle to the surface) and viewed under a microscope, a number of characteristics can be distinguished. It is usually possible to see six general layers or regions of cell bodies from surface to depth that seem to differ from one another in appearance. Even before the days of careful microscopic analysis, it was noticed that sections taken from different places on the cortex looked different from one another. Some of these differences are so obvious that they can be seen with the naked eye. For example, a section from the posterior pole (occipital lobe) shows a clear white line running along in the cortex about half way from surface to depth. This line is not seen in sections taken from other

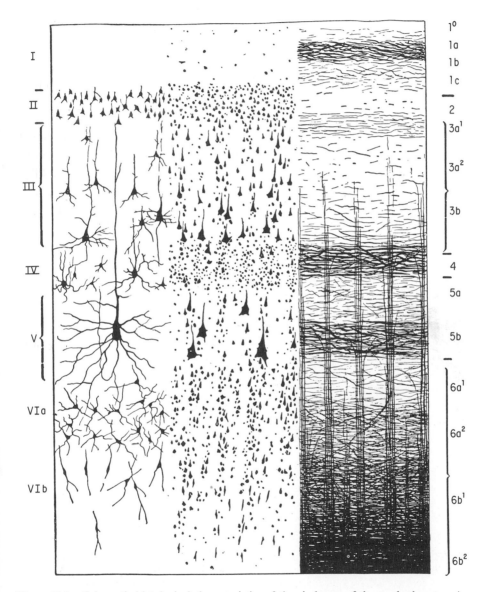

Figure 11.3. Schematic histological characteristics of the six layers of the cerebral cortex. A few examples of typical nerve cells are shown on the left, the distribution of cell bodies in the middle, and the distribution of fiber processes on the right. (From Ranson and Clark, 1959, after Brodmann)

regions of the cortex. Microscopic analysis of the appearance of cross sections of cortex obtained from different regions of the cortex constitutes the study of *cytoarchitectonics* (literally, the " science of the architecture of cells "). A possible analogy would be a topographical map of the earth's surface. Areas having different characteristics (i.e. mountains, hills, plains, etc.) are differently coded. In the same way, cytoarchitectonics attempts to subdivide the cortex into regions, each having a similar cross-sectional appearance within its boundaries but differing from other regions. The boundaries of the various cytoarchitectonic maps of the cortex that have been published, incidentally, show considerably more variability than would topographical maps of the earth for the past few thousand years.

A variety of different staining methods must be used to obtain a complete picture of the detailed organization of the cortex. Nissl stains for cell bodies, Weigert methods for cell fibers, methods that stain all cortical structures, and methods that stain only a few cells in their entirety are all complementary procedures. The six layers from surface to depth into which the cortex can be

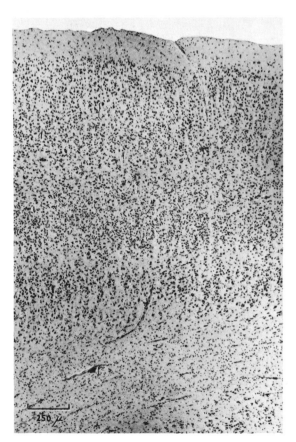

Figure 11.4. Cross section through cortex of human occipital lobe stained by the Nissl method (for cell bodies). Can you distinguish the six layers diagrammed in Fig. 11.3? (From Sholl, 1956)

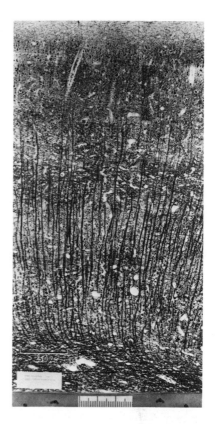

Figure 11.5. Section from same region as in Figure 11.4, stained by a reduced silver method to show both cell bodies and fiber processes. (From Sholl, 1956)

subdivided are of necessity somewhat arbitrary and qualitative. In the latter part of the nineteenth century many authorities subdivided the cortex into eight or more separate layers. It is common today to describe the cortex in terms of six layers, after Lorente de Nó's analysis (1938), which in turn is the outgrowth of previous work by Brodmann, Cajal, and many others. It must be remembered that neurons in almost any layer of the cortex may have fibers extending to or beyond all layers. However, the division is made primarily in terms of cell body appearance and distribution.

Figure 11.3 illustrates a general schema of the cortical laminations, showing a few typical cell bodies and their processes on the left, the distribution of cell bodies in the middle, and the fiber distributions on the right. Actual photomicrographs of a section stained for cell bodies (Nissl method) and also for other processes (reduced silver method) taken from human visual cortex are shown in Figures 11.4 and 11.5 (Sholl, 1956). To appreciate the difficulty in identifying and dividing laminations, see if you can subdivide the section of cortex (Figures 11.4 and 11.5) into six layers according to the diagram in Figure 11.3.

In brief, the layers from surface inward may be named and described as follows.

1. *Molecular layer* (plexiform layer). Many fibers but only a few cells, mostly horizontal cells of Cajal and granule cells.
2. *External granular layer* (layer of small pyramids). Mostly small pyramidal cells and Golgi Type II cells.
3. *Medium pyramid layer*. Medium sized and larger pyramidal cells.
4. *Internal granular layer*. Mostly Golgi Type II granule cells with fewer smaller pyramids.
5. *Large pyramid layer*. Medium or large pyramids.
6. *Spindle cell layer* (fusiform layer). Mostly spindle cells.

The names of the cells most commonly found in the various layers are simply descriptive of their appearance (see Figure 11.3). In terms of interconnections, the various types of cells can be divided into four basic groups (Lorente de Nó, 1938):

1. Small cells with horizontal dendrites and axons are called horizontal cells of Cajal in layer 1 and spindle cells in layer 6 (axons of the latter bend and penetrate into white matter).
2. Granule cells (stellate cells) are cells with short branching axons and many branched dendritic trees. They include the granule cells of layer 1 and the Golgi Type II cells of layers 2 and 4.
3. Pyramidal cells are pyramid shaped cells which send axons down into white matter below the cortex and long apical dendrites toward the cortical surface. In addition they have many short dendrites nearer the cell body. Pyramids are found primarily in layers 2, 3, and 5.
4. Cells sending axons toward the surface of the cortex. Although not named as such above, these cells are found in essentially all layers of the cortex.

An even simpler schema has more recently been suggested, which includes all cortical cells as either pyramidal or stellate (granular) (Sholl, 1956). These can then be subdivided in terms of where the axons go. Photomicrographs of individual stellate and pyramidal cells are shown in Figure 11.6.

Although the details of organization vary considerably from place to place in the cortex, the basic points listed above appear to hold. Two simple generalizations may be made, which should help to keep this organization in mind, and suggest possible functions associated with different types of cells. First, afferent fibers projecting into the cortex from the modality specific sensory systems (auditory, visual and somatic) appear to terminate on granule cells in layer 4. In "primary sensory areas" of the cortex this layer is consequently much enlarged. Second, pyramidal cells of layer 5 are much enlarged in the region of the motor cortex (here they are called giant pyramidal cells or Betz cells) and send their axons all the way to the spinal cord, where they influence the motor nerve cells that control muscle activity.

In terms of the simple catagorization of cortical cells as either pyramidal or stellate there is a basic distinction in the organization of afferent connections

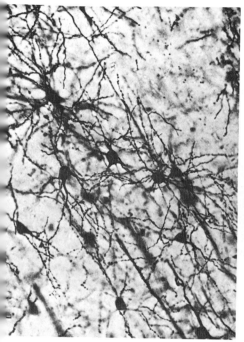

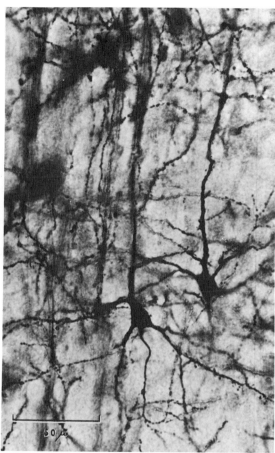

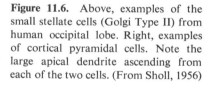

Figure 11.6. Above, examples of the small stellate cells (Golgi Type II) from human occipital lobe. Right, examples of cortical pyramidal cells. Note the large apical dendrite ascending from each of the two cells. (From Sholl, 1956)

(Sholl, 1956). Pyramidal cells can be influenced by two types of afferents, those ending on the cell body and nearby dendrites and those terminating on the apical dendrites some distance away from the cell body. It is of interest to recall Eccles' hypothesis (1964) that at least for pyramidal cells, terminations on the cell body and adjacent dendrites may be inhibitory in function and terminations some distance from the cell body on the apical dendrites are more likely to be excitatory in function. Stellate cells, on the other hand, are under the influence of only one comparatively local set of afferent fibers, which terminate close to the cell body.

Regional subdivisions of the cortex are based on the relative changes in the appearance of the six cortical layers in different areas of the cerebral cortex. Since no two pieces of cortex are exactly the same in histological characteristics, it is possible to make a good many subdivisions. Campbell described 20 areas, Elliott Smith increased this to 50, and in 1919 the Vogts described over 200 separate cortical fields. Brodmann's map, which is still used most widely today, has about 50 areas. For a time it was hoped that such detailed architectonic studies would permit analysis into elementary functional units of the cortex. However, more recent work makes it seem unlikely that this goal will ever be achieved.

One of the greatest difficulties in cytoarchitectonics is the fact that the histological (i.e. cross-sectional) appearance of the cortex usually changes gradually from one region to another. There are exceptions; the primary visual area of the occipital lobe has a sharp boundary. However, for the most part changes are gradual. To carry our earlier analogy with topographical maps further, consider a region that changes from level plains to high mountains. The transition may be color-coded as a sharp boundary, just as is an indicated boundary on a cytoarchitectonic map of the cortex. However, if we look at geographical features at the boundary line there may be similar foothills on both sides. In contrast, there is a marked difference in the geological appearance of the central mountainous region and the center of the plains region. By the same token, cortical cross sections taken from the central portions of two different regions might appear quite different from one another. However, the transition from one region to the other may be so gradual and continuous that no clear boundary exists. One worker might draw an arbitrary dividing line between the two regions, another might indicate a transition zone, and still another might separate the boundary zone into a third region—different from the other two. The latter boundaries could in turn be further differentiated, and so on.

An excellent illustration of the problem of boundary regions in cytoarchitectonics has been provided by Bok (1959). He notes (pp. 54–57) that many of the finer subdivisions between areas are demarcated by boundaries that coincide with bends or sulci in the cortex, and shows that the apparent histological changes are exactly what one would expect to see if an histologically uniform cortex were so bent and folded. In other words, the apparent boundaries may not be due to changes in histological organization of the cortex but rather to changes in the physical curvature of a uniform cortex.

In 1946 Lashley and Clark published a careful and quantitative analysis of cytoarchitectonic methods. In the course of other research they had need of cortical maps of two types of monkeys, Spider and Rhesus. Each worker therefore proceeded to prepare such maps independently of the other. When they compared their completed maps they found that there was disappointing lack of agreement. The extensive investigation that followed was an outgrowth of this initial disagreement. The conclusions of their study have raised some questions concerning the functional significance of highly detailed cytoarchitectonics, particularly for association areas of the cortex. They found enormous individual variability, and highly significant differences in the histological characteristics of many regions of cortex among animals of the same species (most earlier maps had been based on a single specimen). They were unable, for example, to find any uniform subdivisions within the prefrontal cortex. Perhaps partly as a result of this study, there has been a tendency away from the use of highly·detailed cytoarchitectonics in the analysis of the organization and functions of association areas of the cortex.

However, there are many regions that can reliably be differentiated using histological criteria. The schematic illustration for a generalized primate brain shown in Figure 11.2 is based on a cytoarchitectonic study by von Bonin and Bailey (1947) (Brodmann's numbers are also given for these regions). The striate cortex of the occipital lobe (Brodmann's area 17) is the cortical projection of the visual system; the auditory cortex is found in the ventral bank of the temporal fissure (Brodmann's areas 41 and 42); the post central gyrus contains the cortical projections of the somatic system (Brodmann's areas 1, 2, 3). These regions are all characterized by an expansion of layer 4 and are called sensory koniocortex by von Bonin and Bailey. Cortex of the precentral gyrus contains the giant pyramidal or Betz cells in layer 5 and is called motor cortex (Brodmann's areas 4 and 6). The remaining areas of the cortex have neither a predominant layer 4 nor particularly enlarged pyramidal cells in layer 5, and present a somewhat uniform appearance.

RETROGRADE THALAMIC DEGENERATION.   An alternative method of defining cortical fields is in terms of their relations with the various thalamic nuclei. We noted in the last chapter that many thalamic nuclei project (i.e. send fibers) directly to the cerebral cortex. If the cortex is removed, the terminations of these fibers are destroyed. This induces characteristic changes (chromatolysis) and degeneration of the cell bodies in the thalamus. Anatomical analysis of the pattern of thalamic degeneration following cortical damage is an example of the use of *retrograde degeneration* techniques. A precisely limited region of cortex is removed and a period of weeks allowed for degeneration to occur before the animal is sacrificed. Nissl stains are used to demonstrate degenerated cell bodies in thalamic nuclei. For example, after removal of the visual cortex, the lateral geniculate body degenerates entirely. In like manner, after ablation of prefrontal cortex, the dorso-medial nucleus of the thalamus completely degenerates.

Figure 11.7 illustrates the fields of the cerebral cortex receiving reasonably discrete projections from thalamic nuclei (based on Walker, 1938). Note particularly that the occipital lobe receives projections from the lateral geniculate body (LGB), the visual relay of the thalamus; the ventral bank of the temporal fissure receives projections from the medial geniculate body (MGB), the thalamic auditory relay nucleus; the postcentral gyrus receives projections from the ventrobasal complex, consisting of ventralis posterior lateralis (VPL) and ventralis posterior medialis (VPM), the thalamic relay nuclei for the ascending lemniscal system mediating somatic sensory stimulation. The precentral motor cortex receives projections from ventralis lateralis (VL)—the nucleus of the thalamus—which in turn receives input from the cerebellum (see Chapter 14). These cortical areas can be characterized as the receiving areas for thalamic nuclei relaying sensory (LGB; MGB; VPL; VPM) and cerebellar (VL) information.

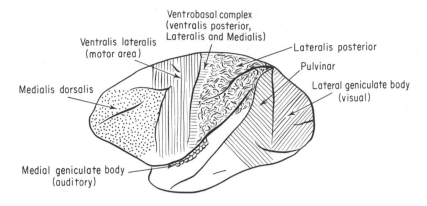

Ventrobasal complex
(ventralis posterior,
Lateralis and Medialis)

Ventralis lateralis
(motor area)

Lateralis posterior

Pulvinar

Medialis dorsalis

Lateral geniculate body
(visual)

Medial geniculate body
(auditory)

Figure 11.7. Cortical regions defined in terms of retrograde thalamic degeneration. Terms refer to the nucleus of the thalamus that exhibits degeneration when the cortical area is removed. Blank areas of cortex appear to have no essential projections from the thalamus. (Based on Walker, 1960)

The nuclei cited above receive projections from various sensory or motor systems. Rose and Woolsey (1949) have termed such nuclei *extrinsic*. There are other discrete cortical projections from thalamic nuclei, as seen in Figure 11.7. For example, the prefrontal region of the cerebral cortex receives projections from the dorso-medial nucleus (MD) of the thalamus, and certain regions of the posterior association cortex receive projections from the pulvinar nucleus (P) and the nucleus lateralis posterior (LP) of the thalamus. These thalamic nuclei however do not receive any major projections from outside the thalamus, most of their connections apparently coming from other structures within the thalamus. Rose and Woolsey have termed such nuclei *intrinsic* nuclei. Still other regions of the cortex (areas not labeled in Figure 11.7) appear to have few or no direct projection fibers from thalamic nuclei. Pribram has suggested (1958) that cortical areas be termed extrinsic or intrinsic following Rose and Woolsey's subdivision for the thalamus. Extrinsic areas would then correspond to primary sensory and motor cortical areas, and intrinsic areas to much of the remaining "association" cortex.

The method of retrograde degeneration is fairly straight-forward when dealing with the direct and concentrated projections of either extrinsic or intrinsic thalamic nuclei. If a given region of cortex is removed, a discrete region of the thalamus completely degenerates. However this classification is complicated by the fact that there appear to be a number of nuclear regions in the thalamus that do not show total degeneration as a result of any localized or restricted cortical lesion. Nevertheless these regions of the thalamus do degenerate after total decortication. Rose and Woolsey (1958) have introduced a most important concept regarding characterization of thalamic degeneration following cortical lesion. They distinguish between *essential* projections and *sustaining* projections from thalamus to cortex. An example taken from their work (see Figure 11.8) is as follows: Ablation of auditory areas I and II in the cat causes almost complete degeneration of the medial geniculate body (except for a small region of the posterior geniculate body). However, there is no appreciable degeneration in a neighboring nuclear region, which they have termed the posterior nuclear group. Ablation of somatic sensory area II of the cerebral cortex of the cat in like manner causes little degeneration in the posterior nuclear group. However joint ablation of the auditory fields and somatic sensory area II produces essentially total degeneration of the posterior nuclear group. Rose and Woolsey therefore postulate that either cells in the posterior nuclear region of the thalamus send branching axons to the two cortical fields, or that the thalamic cells of sustaining regions send axon branches to essential regions. They feel that electrophysiological evidence favors the second possibility.

Although there may be discrepancies in detail between the methods of cytoarchitectonic analysis and retrograde degeneration, it is encouraging to note that major cortical fields are equivalently identified by both techniques. Thus the visual, auditory and somatic sensory areas, motor area, and certain association areas appear almost identically defined on the basis of both types of evidence. As will be seen below, the results of electrophysiological and lesion-behavior studies are also reasonably consistent with these basic and relatively gross subdivisions of cortical areas.

ORGANIZATION AND FUNCTIONS OF SENSORY AND MOTOR AREAS OF THE CEREBRAL CORTEX

The general locations of auditory, visual, and somatic sensory and motor regions of the cortex have been known since the nineteenth century from lesion and anatomical studies. Understanding of the more detailed organization had to await the development of electrophysiological techniques involving stimulation and recording. Adrian (1940) and Marshall, Woolsey, and Bard (1941) first described the "somatotopic" organization of the somatic cortex of the cat. It was found that abrupt stimulation of a given skin region by a sudden tap or electric shock resulted in evoked responses in a restricted region of the somatic cortex in the anesthetized animal. There was an orderly arrangement of projection such that a representation of the entire skin surface could be plotted on the cortex. Subsequent research has shown this to be a general finding for auditory, visual, and somatic areas of the cortex in all mammals. We might term the general phenomenon *receptotopic* organization. Sensory receptors have a spatial representation along the cortex, skin location for somatic cortex, retinal location (and hence position of objects in space) for the visual cortex, and basilar membrane (and hence frequency) for the auditory cortex. In like manner the musculature appears to be represented in the somatic motor cortex in an orderly topographical arrangement.

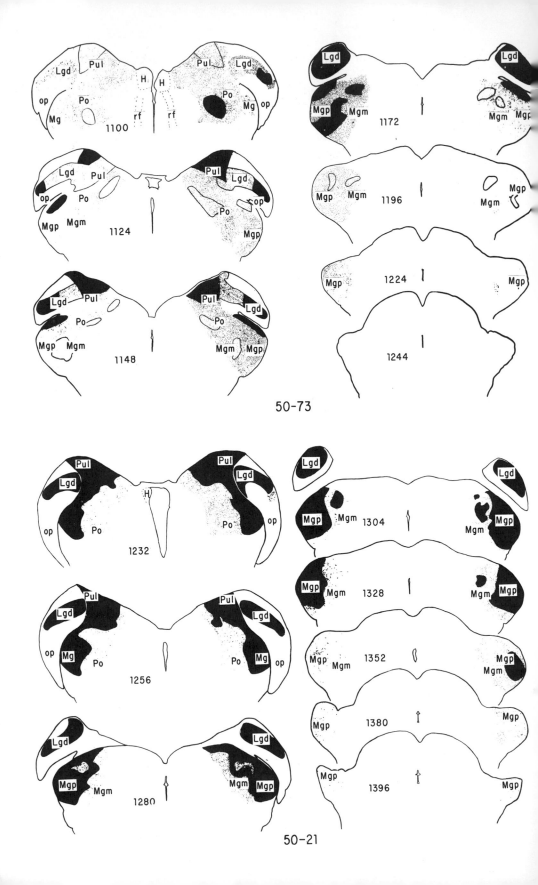

50-73

50-21

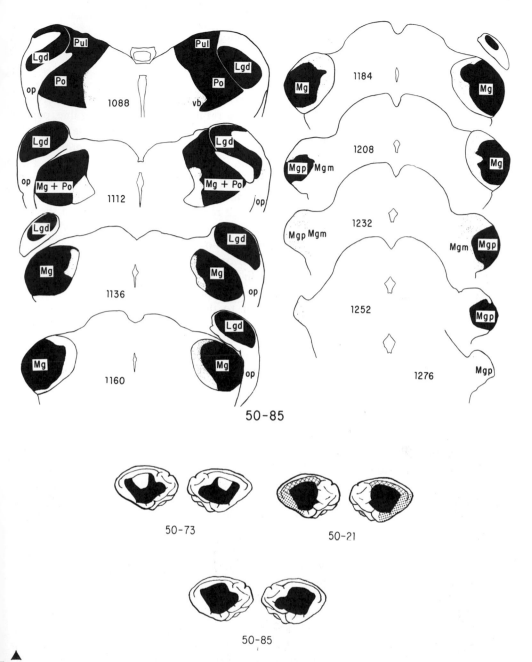

Figure 11.8. Illustration of sustaining thalamocortical projections. Animal 50–85 has both the auditory areas and somatic sensory area II removed (area of lesion in solid black), and exhibits total degeneration (solid black) of the posterior nuclear area in the thalamus. In animal 50–73 a portion of the auditory cortex was spared and a large portion of the posterior nuclear area did not degenerate (dots in thalamic region labeled Po). Somatic sensory area II was spared in animal 50–21, and again a large portion of the posterior nuclear area did not degenerate. Thus both cortical areas must be removed before the posterior nucleus will exhibit extensive degeneration. (From Rose and Woolsey, 1958)

Somatic Sensory Cortex: Electrophysiological Analysis

About the turn of the century Sherrington proposed a separation between motor and sensory cortex. Taking the central fissure as the dividing line, cortex just anterior to it (Brodmann's areas 4 and 6) was believed to be primarily concerned with the control of movement and was termed the *motor cortex*. The sensory cortex just posterior to the central fissure (Brodmann's areas 1, 2, and 3), which receives the primary projections of the system conveying information from the skin receptors (lemniscal system), was termed the *sensory* or *somatic sensory* cortex. Research in more recent years has emphasized the fact that the distinction between somatic sensory and motor areas is very much a relative matter. Each area seems to share most functions of the other.

The degree of overlap of functional organization of the sensory and motor areas, which will be detailed below in this and the next sections, led Woolsey (1958) to propose a most appropriate terminology. He labels the entire region somatic cortex. The portion posterior to the central fissure is called somatic sensory-motor, and that portion anterior to the central fissure is called somatic motor-sensory. We have separated our discussion of the two regions, and will often refer simply to the primary motor area (*M*I) or the primary somatic sensory area (*S*I), purely as a matter of convenience. Keep in mind, however, that these are relative terms for two different regions that form a closely interrelated system, the somatic cortex.

The extent of somatic sensory area I (*S*I) corresponds to the postcentral gyrus (Brodmann's areas 1, 2, and 3) in primates. Cortex in this region is sensory koniocortex, with enlargement of layer 4, and contains representation of the skin, muscle and joint receptors. The typical kind of experiment that defines these regions combines very discrete adequate stimulation of the skin surface (tap or hair bending) with mapping of the gross cortical evoked response pattern to each locus of stimulation in the barbiturate anesthetized animal (see Marshall, Woolsey, and Bard, 1941). The system, incidentally, is extremely sensitive; rapid bending of a single hair will produce a measurable evoked response on the cortex. The mapping is accomplished by first removing the scalp, skull and dura, and placing a recording electrode wire on the cortex. The body skin surface is then stimulated until the region which produces clear evoked responses for the given electrode position delimited. The electrode is then moved to another position on the cortex, and the whole procedure repeated. The entire sensory cortex is mapped in this manner in small steps.

When the mapping procedure has been completed, a figurine chart is constructed from the data (see Figure 11.9). A very large drawing of the cortical field is made, and the region of the animal's skin that produced maximum evoked responses for a given cortical point is drawn at that point. The figurine chart of Figure 11.9 is an example of such a map for the postcentral gyrus of the Rhesus monkey. On the basis of results such as these, a "homunculus" (little man) can be reconstructed to show the relative degree of representation of each body

Figure 11.9. Figurine maps of somatic sensory area I (postcentral gyrus) in the Rhesus monkey. Solid portion of each figurine indicates region of body surface stimulated that produces maximum evoked responses at that point on the cerebral cortex. Shaded portions give smaller responses upon stimulation and blank portions of figurines are skin regions that do not produce cortical responses at a given cortical focus. Solid line on left represents contol fissure and dotted line to its left represents bank of fissure. Solid lines at top represent medial wall of hemisphere "folded out." Note that the head has two separate areas of projection separated by the hand area. (From Woolsey, 1958)

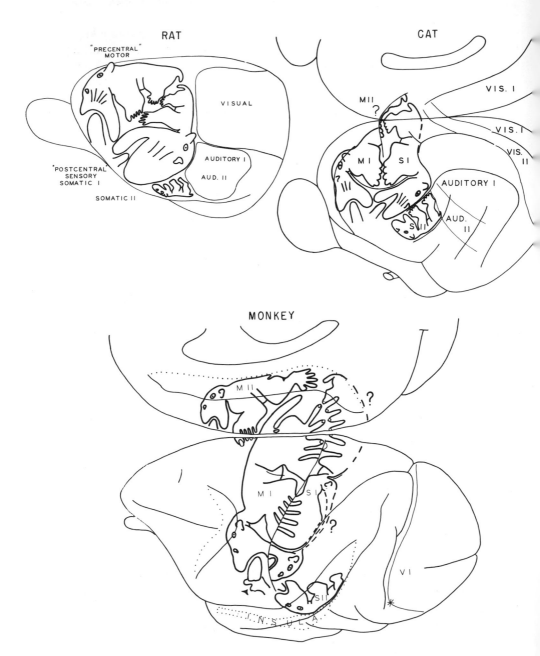

Figure 11.10. Somatic sensory and motor area "homuculi" for rat, cat, and monkey. *S*I, somatic sensory area I; *S*II, somatic sensory area II; *M*I, primary motor area; *M*II, supplementary motor area. Note that the cortical homuculi of the rat are relatively representational, but the monkey homuculi are much distorted by the large hand and foot areas. (From Woolsey, 1958)

region. Such a homunculus is given in Figure 11.10 for rat, cat, and monkey. (Woolsey, 1958; see also Woolsey, 1964). In all three animals, the orientation of the homunculus is similar, with the foot and trunk more dorsal, and the hand and face more lateral. Under these experimental conditions (i.e. barbiturate anesthesia and adequate skin stimulation), representation in *SI* is *contralateral*; skin on the left side of the animal projects to the right hemisphere of the cortex and vice versa. This contralaterality results from the fact that the lemniscal system crosses from the input side to the opposite side in the brain stem (see Chapter 10). There is one exception to the principle of contralateral projection to somatic cortex. Input from the lower portion of each side of the face and the inside of the mouth projects to the somatic cortex on both hemispheres, i.e. projection is bilateral

Although the general representation in *SI* is comparable for all mammals, there are considerable differences in detail. The homunculi drawn in Figure 11.10 are of course not to be taken literally. They do indicate the relative amount of cortex devoted to each region of skin surface, and the topographical relations. Boundaries are simply drawn in to identify regions of skin surface. For the rat, the amount of cortex devoted to different regions is somewhat proportional to the actual skin surface area, although the face region does exhibit relative enlargement. However, in the monkey the pattern is extremely distorted and almost unrecognizable because of the disproportionate enlargement of the cortical hand and foot areas.

A very fundamental generalization may be made concerning projections of body surface to cortex; *the amount of cortex devoted to a given region of body surface is directly proportional to the use and sensitivity of that region.* In the case of the monkey, the amount of cortex devoted to the hand and foot areas is so great that they have "pushed" other skin representation regions aside. Thus the hand areas has enlarged so much that it has split the head area into two spatially separate fields, with the ear and back of the head above the hand area and the face below the hand area along the postcentral gyrus.

These same relations have been determined for man by Penfield and Rasmussen (1950). In the course of necessary neurosurgical procedures, Penfield electrically stimulated different regions of the human cortex and determined response characteristics from verbal report of the patient (these procedures can be done with a minimum of discomfort in the human using local anesthetics). The sensations reported by most patients, incidentally, were a numbness, tingling, or feeling of "electricity" localized to the appropriate skin regions. All body sensations were localized to the contralateral body surface. The representation of body surface on the cortex of *SI* along the postcentral gyrus is shown in schematic cross section in Figure 11.11. Here the exaggerated size of the fingers is even more pronounced and the face is also much enlarged. It would appear that so far as the cortex is concerned, man is mostly fingers, lips and tongue. A comparison of the Figures 11.10 and 11.11 shows that the relative development for cortical projection of skin can be traced from that of the rat, in which there

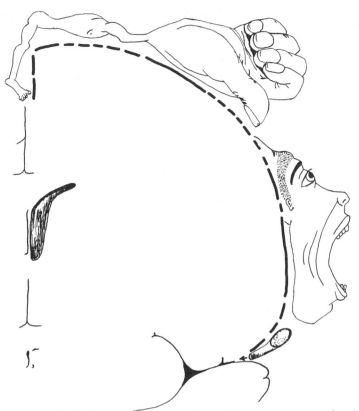

Figure 11.11.   Homunculus for human SI (postcentral gyrus) shown on a cross section through the hemisphere. As far as the cortex is concerned, man is mostly fingers, lips, and tongue. (From Penfield and Rasmussen, 1950)

is little distortion of the homunculus, to that of man, in which differential enlargement of important skin regions has produced considerable distortion of the cortical homunculus.

The generality of this principle has been illustrated within a single phylum, carnivores, in the striking results obtained by Welker and his associates (Welker and Campos, 1963; Welker and Seidenstein, 1959; Welker et al., 1964). In carnivores such as the dog only a relatively small amount of cortical tissue along one portion of the gyrus is devoted to representation of the forepaw. In the racoon, another carnivore, the gyrus has expanded enormously and several new fissures have developed that demarcate the separate fingers of the forepaw. The differential development of the cortical forepaw region in the two species is paralleled by differences in the behavior of the animals. In contrast with the dog, the racoon explores his environment primarily by touch, and much of this tactile exploration is carried out by the forepaws. Even within carnivores, then, there is a close and direct relationship between amount of use and sensitivity of a portion of the body and the relative development of its cortical representation.

In 1940 Adrian published a description of a "second" sensory area in the cat, spatially distinct from SI, which appeared to be predominantly a representation of the paw. Subsequent studies (see Woolsey, 1958) have shown this region to have complete representation of body surface, just as in somatic sensory area I. It has therefore been termed somatic sensory area II (SII). The total area of cortex devoted to SII is smaller than for SI, and representation is not as discrete (see Figure 11.10). Furthermore, projection is bilateral; both sides of the body project to each SII area. There are slightly differential projections to SII for the two sides of the body but overlap is considerable. The orientation and organization of SII is shown in relation to SI in Figure 11.10. It has a similar relative organization in all mammals studied from rat to man. Response in SII is not dependent on the presence of SI. After chronic ablation of SI, the projection of body receptors to SII remains the same. In other words, information does not come to SII only by relaying through SI. Projection to SII occurs independently of SI.

There is also a somatic sensory projection to the "motor" cortex lying anterior to the central fissure. Under deep barbiturate anesthesia this motor region cannot be activated by light touch or tap stimuli to the skin; however, evoked responses can be obtained from motor area cortex if electrical shocks are delivered to the dorsal roots (Woolsey, 1953). Malis, Pribram, and Kruger (1953) have shown that precentral responses can also be evoked by electrical stimulation of cutaneous nerves.

There are several possible indirect routes whereby somatic sensory information could be relayed to the motor cortex. The cerebellum sends fibers to nucleus Ventralis Lateralis in the thalamus, which projects to motor cortex. Malis, Pribram, and Kruger eliminated this possibility by showing that evoked responses still occurred in motor cortex to cutaneous nerve stimulation following removal of the cerebellum. Alternatively, activity could be relayed from somatic sensory area I of the cortex to motor cortex. These two areas are anatomically interconnected by a well-developed bundle of "U" fibers, which go from sensory to motor cortex, passing underneath the central fissure. This possibility was eliminated by ablation of SI; evoked responses still occurred in motor cortex. Consequently projection of information from body receptors to motor cortex is independent of cerebellum and somatic sensory cortex. However, it is much less pronounced than is projection to somatic sensory cortex.

Penfield and Jasper (1954) have obtained complementary data from studies on the human brain. They reported that 25 percent of the points that elicit somatic sensations lie in front of the central sulcus. The nature of the sensation appears to be the same regardless of whether the stimulus is applied in front or behind the sulcus. However there apparently is a desire to move the extremity when precentral stimulation is delivered, but not following postcentral stimulation. The somatotopic organization of the sensory projection to the motor cortex appears to be more or less a mirror image of that projecting to the somatic sensory area I lying behind the sulcus. It corresponds, as we will see later, to the homunculus found on the motor cortex for representation of muscles and movement.

Our discussion of sensory projections to somatic cortex has so far been in terms of skin or cutaneous nerve stimulation. For many years it was believed that the sensory information from muscle spindle organs concerning degree of muscle stretch did not reach the cerebral cortex. This type of sensory input is conveyed from the muscle receptors to the CNS by the group I fibers, the largest diameter (and thus fastest conducting) afferent nerve fibers, and has well known and important reflex connections and projections to the cerebellum (see Table 12.1, Chapter 12). In 1958 Amassian and Berlin reported in a brief communication that group I afferent nerves from the forelimb did project to the somatic cortex of cat. This observation was confirmed and extended in a careful study by Oscarsson and Rosén (1963). They found that selective electrical stimulation of the group I afferent nerves (being the largest diameter fibers they have the lowest electrical stimulation threshold) from the forelimb (but *not* hindlimb) of the cat produced a limited and discrete field of very short latency evoked responses in the somatic center. The region activated extended for several millimeters posterior to the cruciate sulcus with maximum activation just anterior to the postcruciate dimple, in the dorsal portion of the somatic sensory area I forepaw field as defined by Woolsey (see Figure 11.10). Oscarsson and Rosén suggested that this area might be a region of motor cortex in the cat. Interestingly, they found no group I projection to somatic sensory area II of the cortex.

Subsequently, Landgren and Wolsk (1966) demonstrated still another cortical projection field from forelimb group I muscle afferents in the cat. This is a small (1 square millimeter) region that lies in the lower bank of the anterior suprasylvian sulcus between areas SI and SII (it would lie in the fissure just above the SII forepaw field indicated in Woolsey's figurine map for the cat in Figure 11.10). Whether this area represents a " group I portion " of SII or is part of still another somatic sensory cortical field is not known.

With the development of microelectrode techniques, a good deal of new information has become available concerning the detailed organization of the somatic cortex. Perhaps the most striking new findings have come from the work of Mountcastle and his associates (Mountcastle, 1957; 1961; Mountcastle and Powell, 1959a, b; Mountcastle, Davies, and Berman, 1957; Mountcastle, Poggio, and Werner, 1963). Either barbiturate anesthetized animals or unanesthetized animals with all pain input to the head eliminated by nerve section are used. The animal's head is placed in a rigid holder. After the cortex is exposed, a sealed chamber is fastened to the skull, and an indium-filled glass micropipette introduced. The microelectrode is inserted into the cortex perpendicular to the surface, and extracellular discharges of isolated single nerve cells are measured in response to various types of stimulation of skin and joint. The over-all organization of the somatic sensory cortex revealed by single cell activity is quite comparable to the organization described above in terms of gross evoked responses. Cells in a given body region of *SI* tend to respond to stimulation of that body region. The extent of skin area that will activate a single cell, incidentally, is called the *receptive field* of that cell.

Mountcastle and his colleagues have obtained some rather fundamental and important findings. The observations of perhaps the greatest interest concern the cortical representation of the various modalities of somatic sensory stimulation. Within a particular region of body representation, say a finger area, a given cell usually can only be activated by one type of stimulus. Thus one cell might respond to light touch, another to pressure, and another to joint movement. Furthermore, cells responding to a given type of stimulus tend to lie in a column from surface to depth of cortex. Columns representing the different modalities lie close together within the cortical region representing each small area of body surface. An example of this spatially distinct representation of the various somatic sensory modalities, termed *columnar organization*, is shown in Table 11.1.

TABLE 11.1.   TYPES OF STIMULI THAT ACTIVATE CORTICAL CELLS IN *SI* CORTEX OF THE CAT FOR 119 RIGHT ANGLE PENETRATIONS OF THE CORTEX.*

Stimulus	Number of cells	Percent
Deep	31	26.0
Skin-hair	30	25.5
Skin-pressure	9	7.0
Skin-mixed	30 (Hair-pressure-11) (Hair-11) (Pressure-3) (Skin-5)†	25.5
Skin-deep mixed	19	16.0
TOTALS	119	100

    * Eighty-four percent of the penetrations yielded cells that were only skin receptors or only deep receptors. These data illustrate the columnar organization in the *SI* cortex in terms of types of stimulation (from Mountcastle, 1957).
    † No further identification obtained.

Columnar representation of modalities represents a further elaboration of the principle of receptotopic organization of the cerebral cortex. It is a striking example of the extent to which spatial localization of input can provide a basis for Müller's law of specific nerve "energies" (see discussion in Chapter 10). Different modalities of stimulation activate separate and discrete columns of cells within the cortex, which in turn can serve as the basis for the various somatic "sensations" (i.e. differential responses to stimulation).

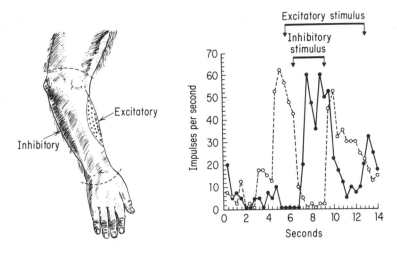

Figure 11.12. Afferent inhibition. A neuron of *SI* cortex of the monkey was activated by stimulation of the dotted excitatory area on the forearm, but inhibited by stimulation of the inhibitory surround area. Behavior of this neuron shown as open circles and dotted line in graph. Another neuron (solid dots and line in graph) was excited by stimulation of the inhibitory region of the forearm but inhibited by stimulation of the excitatory region. (From Mountcastle and Powell, 1959)

The area of skin that will activate the average cortical cell in *SI* is considerably larger than the area of skin that will activate a single cutaneous afferent fiber. In cat, for example, the receptive fields for cortical neurons may be 100 times larger than the receptive fields measured for dorsal root fibers (Mountcastle, 1961). This would seem to imply that the system is throwing away a great deal of information in the course of projection from skin to cortex. Projection is diverging rather than converging. To take a specific example, a given cortical cell might have a receptive field of 10 square millimeters of skin on the forearm of a monkey. Light touch anywhere within this skin area causes discharging of the cell. However, the monkey can easily discriminate between touches delivered to different regions of the receptive field. How is this possible?

Mountcastle and his associates have demonstrated a very important type of *afferent inhibition* that can serve to sharpen the discriminability of cortical cells to skin stimulation. Figure 11.12 is an example of one of their experiments. A cortical cell, whose activity is indicated by the dashed line in the graph, has an excitatory receptive field on the monkey's forearm (dots). When this region is touched (excitatory stimulus at about 5 sec. on the graph), the discharge frequency of the cell increases markedly. However, there is a much larger *inhibitory* field surrounding the excitatory field on the forearm. When this surrounding region is stimulated (inhibitory stimulus) activity of the cell drops immediately to zero and remains there until the inhibitory stimulus is removed. Following this removal of inhibition, discharge frequency of the cell returns to its initial high level. Activity of a nearby cell is inhibited by the excitatory stimulus (solid line in graph) and markedly excited by the inhibitory stimulus. These two cells are very close together in the cortex; activity from both was recorded by the same microelectrode placement. This type of *surround inhibition* spatially limits the region of cortical cells activated by a peripheral stimulus, and serves to sharpen the differential activation of cortical cells by skin stimuli. Thus a stimulus to a given location on the skin is excitatory for a limited region of cortical cells, but inhibits activity of nearby cells. Conversely, a stimulus to a closely adjacent region of skin will tend to inhibit some of the cells excited by the first stimulus and excite cells inhibited by the first stimulus. This in turn will sharpen the degree of differential responding of the population of cortical cells influenced by the two stimuli. Consequently a finer behavioral discrimination is possible.

The columnar organization in the cortex for different modalities of somatic stimulation described above may be said to be a static system. It is easily seen in anesthetized animals, and seems to reflect a basic structural feature of the somatic sensory system. Surround inhibition is to some extent suppressed by deep anesthesia. However, frequency and pattern of nerve discharges in the thalamo-cortical somatic sensory system are markedly dependent on anesthetic state. The striking observations of Mountcastle, Poggio, and Werner (1963) on the manner in which thalamic cells code extent of joint movement—in terms of the same power function that holds for psychophysical judgments of extent of joint movement (see discussion of Chapter 10)—holds only for the unanesthetized preparation. It is likely that a good many of the "dynamic" characteristics of neural activity can be observed only in the unanesthetized animal.

Recent microelectrode data suggest that there may be a regional functional differentiation of submodality representation on SI that corresponds very closely with the cytoarchitechtonically defined subdivisions (i.e. Brodmann's areas 1, 2, and 3). It appears that at least in some primates, very light touch of the skin surface will activate cells only in Brodmann's area 3, whereas deep pressure preferentially (although not exclusively) activates cells in areas 1 and 2 (W. I. Welker, personal communication).

The types of stimuli that will activate cells in somatic sensory area II of the cortex differ in some rather important features from those that activate cells in area SI. You may recall from our discussion of thalamic relay neurons of the somatic sensory system (Chapter 10) that cells in the ventrobasal nuclei tend to be "discrete," having small and modality specific receptive fields, whereas cells in the posterior nucleus tend to be "diffuse," having very large receptive fields, responding to painful as well as tactile stimulation, and often to auditory stimulation in addition (see Figure 10.9). Most cells studied in area SI (cat) tend to be of the discrete type, although there are a few of the diffuse type (Mountcastle and Powell, 1959). However both types of cells are common in SII (Carreras and Levitt, 1959; Carreras and Andersson, 1962; Andersson, 1962). Further, gross evoked response analyses suggest interaction of responses to auditory and somatic stimulation in area SII (Berman, 1961a, b). Finally, it is of considerable interest that gentle movement of joints, a very effective and often specific stimulus for many cells in area SI, has been reported not to activate *any* cells in area SII (Carreras and Andersson, 1962; Andersson, 1962). Such marked differences in the types of stimuli that will activate cells in the two areas suggest certain functional distinctions. Unfortunately neurobehavioral studies comparing the behavioral roles of SI and SII in terms of these functional differences remain to be done (see pp. 328–332).

Motor Areas of the Cerebral Cortex

The location of the " primary " motor cortex (MI) has been known for nearly 100 years. Fritsch and Hitzig (1870) showed that stimulation of the anterior portion of the cerebral cortex in the dog elicited muscle movements of the opposite side of the body. This cortical region contains giant Betz cells and is primarily concerned with control of movement. Sherrington's early experiments suggested that the pattern of muscular representation going laterally from the midline was leg, body, arm, neck, face. However, the results of numerous subsequent comparative studies by Woolsey and his colleagues (see Woolsey et al., 1950a,b; Woolsey, 1952; Woolsey, 1958) have considerably altered our understanding of motor cortex organization. Studies on man by Penfield and colleagues (Penfield and Rasmussen, 1950) are in general agreement with the animal studies.

The analytic method used by Woolsey and colleagues is quite simple. After the animal is deeply anesthetized (barbiturates), he is hung freely suspended by clips in the back muscles to permit free movement of the extremities. The motor cortex is exposed and an electrical (60 cycle) stimulus lasting one second or so is delivered to a discrete point on the surface of the cortex. If muscular movements are elicited, the stimulus intensity is reduced to a value just above threshold and the movement response observed and recorded. A summary of the findings of such experiments is indicated in Figure 11.10, for rat, cat, and monkey. The diagrams indicate the region of the body that moves following cortical stimulation. The proportional cortical representation of body areas in motor cortex in these animals is somewhat comparable to that seen for somatic sensory cortex; but the homunculi are less distorted, particularly in monkey. As may be seen, the hand area does not separate body and face, but rather lies in the appropriate relative location. These diagrams also illustrate clearly that the primary motor cortex is in many respects a mirror image of the primary somatic sensory cortex. The primary motor cortex controls muscles on the contralateral side of the body (i.e. right motor cortex to left side of body). The one exception to this rule is in the motor face area, which has bilateral control of the lower face and jaw muscles. This corresponds to the bilateral representation of the lower face in somatic sensory area I.

The type of movement elicited by electrical stimulation of the primary motor cortex in the deeply anesthetized animal is of considerable importance for an understanding of central control of movement. If a somewhat suprathreshold stimulus is used (the stimulus, remember, being a relatively long duration 60-cycle current), an organized movement such as flexion of the arm, rotation of the wrist, or flexion of the finger occurs. Such results led to the dicta that "movements, not muscles" are represented in the motor cortex (Walshe, 1943). Chang, Ruch, and Ward (1947) completed a very careful study on the cortical control of eight individual muscles acting on the ankle joint of the Rhesus monkey. They found that with just threshold stimuli a single muscle would sometimes contract without activity in any other muscle. Each separate muscle had a slightly different cortical locus, which would yield contraction of that muscle alone. In general, extensor muscles were more responsive than flexors. Thus it appears that *muscles, as well as movements,* may be represented in the motor cortex. However, the fact that stronger stimuli do yield "movements" rather than disorganized and conflicting contractions in the separate muscles involved is surely significant as well.

Some authorities have emphasized that the same response may not be elicited when a given portion of motor cortex is repeatedly stimulated, implying that there may be some plasticity in the cortical control of movement. Actually, the particular kind of movement evoked by cortical stimulation depends on many factors, one of which is the resting position of the limb (Ward, 1950). Interestingly, Ward found that whatever the initial position of the limb, stimulation of a given cortical point moved the limb to the same final position. This control does not appear to be organized in the cortex itself, since the same results were obtained by stimulation of underlying white matter after removal of the motor cortex. Proprioceptive reflex pathways, both spinal and supraspinal, appear to be responsible for the effects.

The discreteness of cortical localization of movement in the motor cortex appears to depend in large part on the nature of the electrical stimulus. The studies described above reporting very localized control of movement have generally used a 60 cps current of one second or longer duration. A quite different picture emerges if weak, short duration single shocks are applied to the motor cortex. Landgren, Phillips, and Porter (1962 a, b) recorded intracellular responses of spinal motor neurons as an index of the effects of motor cortex stimulation in the baboon. Their methods (weak single anodal pulses of about 0.2 msec to the cortex) produced monosynaptic activation of spinal motor neurons via the pyramidal tract (see Chapter 13). They found that minimal stimulation of regions of the motor cortex as large as 20 square millimeters produced monosynaptic EPSPs in forearm and hand spinal motor neurons. As would be expected from this observation, different spinal motor neurons were activated by markedly overlapping regions of motor cortex. Thus the basic connections between motor cortex and spinal motor neurons are such that large areas of motor cortex project in an overlapping fashion to various spinal motor neurons. The discretely localized movements elicited by long 60 cps stimuli are no doubt the result of complex synaptic interactions at various levels from cortex to spinal cord.

THE SUPPLEMENTARY MOTOR AREA. In addition to the primary motor area there is a second complete representation of the body musculature on the cortex, the supplementary motor area (MII). Penfield and Welch (1951) described its existence in man, and Woolsey et al. (1950a,b) worked out its detailed organization in the monkey. Most of the region lies on the medial wall of the cortex, dorsal and somewhat anterior to the primary motor area (see Figure 11.10). The supplementary hand area extends over the lateral surface into the area some have termed "premotor" (see below). Much of the area lies buried in the cingulate sulcus, which lies just above the cingulate gyrus on the medial wall of the hemisphere. The supplementary motor area does not necessarily function via the primary motor cortex, but has its own independent output. Stimulation of MII elicits the same pattern of movements after chronic ablation of all primary motor cortex with total degeneration of the efferent systems from the primary area.

THE PREMOTOR AREA. Earlier investigators viewed the primary motor area as identical with Brodmann's histologically defined area 4. Area 6, which lies just anterior to 4, was termed the "premotor" area. Electrical stimulation of the premotor field generally produces movements involving the body and limbs that appear to be more complex than those produced by stimulation of the primary motor area, (Fulton, 1949a). Hence the region was believed by some to mediate a higher order of cortical organization. However, the studies by Woolsey et al. (1950a,b) provides a much simpler explanation of the characteristics of area 6. In their complete and detailed mapping of motor cortex, they found that much of the "premotor" area is included within that portion of the primary motor field that will elicit movements of the body musculature, plus the arm and face regions of the supplementary area. In an animal freely suspended from its back, contraction of the body musculature (e.g. back, abdomen, pelvic girdle) could result in complex appearing motions, such as twisting to one side, with concomitant arm movement, etc. Furthermore, if the "premotor area" is excluded from the primary motor cortex, the animal has no primary motor representation of the back musculature. In other words, much of the premotor cortex is really a part of the primary motor cortex. The remainder of it is included in a part of the supplementary motor field, plus a portion of the autonomic motor region (see below). It is important to recognize that there is no disagreement over the experimental findings here, only over their interpretation. Woolsey and his associates present a view that is perhaps more consistent with the total picture of the motor organization in the cerebral cortex.

MOTOR RESPONSES FROM SOMATIC SENSORY AREAS. As we noted earlier, electrical stimulation of the primary somatic sensory area of the cortex will also elicit movements (Kennard and McCulloch, 1943). The pattern of movement evoked by such stimulation corresponds very closely with the organization of the sensory projection to somatic sensory area I (Woolsey, 1958). Stimulation of the somatic sensory region representing the hand elicits movement of the hand, and so on. The same pattern of movement can be elicited in somatic sensory cortex after earlier total ablation of all primary and supplementary motor cortex with complete degeneration of the motor pathways from these areas, and complete elimination of the U fiber interconnections between sensory and motor areas (Woolsey et al., 1953). Consequently we must conclude that a separate efferent projection system controlling movement arises in the primary somatic sensory cortex. Studies on the squirrel monkey (Benjamin and Welker, 1957; Welker et al., 1957) yielded a comparable picture for somatic sensory area II; motor responses evoked by electrical stimulation of SII coincide with the somatotopic organization of the region.

The important feature that distinguishes motor responses elicited by stimulation of somatic sensory areas from those produced by stimulation of the motor areas of the cortex is the response threshold. A considerably stronger electrical stimulus is necessary to elicit movements from somatic sensory areas (Woolsey, 1958).

SUPPRESSOR STRIPS AND SPREADING DEPRESSION.   Some years ago it was noted that electrical stimulation of certain regions of the rostral portion of the motor cortex appeared to inhibit the movements initiated by stimulation of the more central regions of the motor field (Dusser de Barenne and McCulloch, 1941). These areas were termed "suppressor strips," and were believed to act via the basal ganglia and reticular formation to inhibit the effects normally produced by stimluation of the motor cortex. The results of a series of carefully controlled experiments by Marshall (Marshall, 1950; Marshall and Essig, 1951; Marshall, 1959) suggest that these suppressor strips are more likely to be examples of *spreading depression*. This phenomenon, first described by Leão (1947), consists of a slowly expanding depression of spontaneous electrical activity that spreads over the cortex in a period of minutes and lasts for several minutes. Decreased excitability, a large dc shift, and vasodilation accompany the development of such cortical depression. The phenomenon can be initiated by almost any kind of trauma to the cortex, including strong electrical stimulation. Furthermore, it can be induced in most all regions of cortex. It would appear that the spreading depression developed following stimulation of "suppressor strips" results in a decreased excitability of the primary motor cortex to direct stimulation. Spreading depression can also be induced by electrical stimulation of the motor cortex if comparably intense stimuli are used.

ADDITIONAL EFFECTS OF CORTICAL STIMULATION.   Stimulation of a region anterior to the primary motor areas which corresponds roughly to Brodmann's area 8 (just anterior to B6 in Figure 11.2), elicits eye movements. For this reason, frontal eye fields, as they are called, have often been characterized as a separate and specialized motor region. Actually there appear to be several subregions that produce various types of eye responses, some of which are representations of the eye and eyelid muscles in the face region of the *primary* motor area (Smith 1949). The extent to which the remaining portions function as a separate cortical mechanism for both skeletal and autonomic muscular control of the eye is as yet somewhat unclear (see Bard, 1956, p. 1194).

The motor areas described above have all been related to control of the skeletal musculature. In addition stimulation of several regions of the cortex will elicit various responses from the peripheral autonomic system. The regions of particular interest in this connection lie on the medial wall of the hemisphere (anterior cingulate gyrus), and also include the basal temporal cortex underlying the temporal and frontal lobes in both monkey and cat. A variety of autonomic activities, including cardiovascular changes, pupillary responses, salivation, sweat gland activity, etc., can be elicited by stimulation of these regions. In addition, behavioral concomitants of such responses have been noted including respiratory changes, "alerting" and facilitation and inhibition of skeletal muscular activity (Kaada, 1951). These cortical regions are often included as a portion of the *limbic system*, and will be considered further in Chapter 15.

What are "Motor" areas? In the normal waking animal, electrical stimulation to almost any area of the cortex through chronically implanted electrodes may elicit movements (Lilly, 1958). It would be too great an oversimplification to call a given region of the brain "motor" simply because movements occur when it is electrically stimulated in the waking animal. Shock to the skin elicits a variety of avoidance movements, but the skin is not termed a motor area. More specifically, if the auditory cortex is electrically stimulated, an animal will show a variety of movements. In fact, he tends to "orient," and generally act *as if* he had heard a sound. Indeed, when the auditory area of the human cortex is stimulated during neurosurgical procedures the patient generally reports having heard a buzzing sound (Penfield and Rasmussen, 1950). In short, stimulation of various sensory and other regions of the brain often tends to elicit both reflex and learned responses. This is merely an example of the obvious fact that organisms respond to stimulation. To call all such areas motor would be to say that all stimulation that produces behavior is motor, which would seem to be a *reductio ad absurdum*. It is perhaps more meaningful to limit "motor" to those regions on the output side of the CNS having relatively direct connections with the spinal and cranial motor neurons. Electrical stimulation of areas having such connection will tend to elicite movements even in the deeply anesthetized animal.

Somatic Sensory and Motor Areas: Neurobehavioral Analysis

There are relatively few studies concerned with the behavioral functions of somatic sensory cortex. Tactile discriminations have perhaps received the greatest amount of attention. Early experiments by Ruch and his associates (Ruch, 1935; Ruch, Fulton, and German, 1938) on monkeys and chimpanzees indicated that ablation of the postcentral gyrus (*SI*) produces only a very transitory impairment in the ability to discriminate roughness, and a somewhat more serious decrease in the ability to discriminate weights. Much greater deficits in these discriminations occurred if additional large lesions of the parietal "association" cortex were made. Somatic sensory area II (SII) was not removed in these experiments. A more recent experiment by Orbach and Chow (1959) compared lesions of SI and SII in monkeys on a variety of somesthetic discriminations and reported that SI lesions produced greater deficits than did removal of SII.

A classical experiment by Allen (1947) indicated that SII played a significant role in tactile discrimination. Dogs were trained to lift a foreleg (food reward) in response to brushing of the skin of the back *with* the grain of the fur once per second (positive stimulus), and not to lift the foreleg if the back was brushed *against* the grain once per second or with the grain three times per second (negative stimuli). After joint bilateral ablation of SI and SII the dogs could never relearn the differential response. They characteristically lifted the leg to all types of stimulus, and could never learn to inhibit response to the negative stimulus. Bilateral ablation of SI alone produced only a brief loss of the discrimination with a fairly rapid relearning of correct differentiation to both sets of stimuli. Interestingly enough, when SII alone was removed bilaterally the animals had considerable difficulty relearning the discriminations, particularly the one involving a differentiation between fast and slow stimuli. It should be noted that in all cases the lesions in Allen's study removed rather more than SI and SII.

Zubek compared the effects of removing SI and SII on roughness discrimination in rats (1951) and cats (1952). Rats were blinded (to avoid visual cues) and trained to discriminate rough versus smooth cylinders. Although bilateral ablation of SI and SII severely impaired the discrimination, it was eventually relearned. Bilateral removal of SI alone produced only transitory loss of the discrimination. Bilateral ablation of SII alone caused even less impairment. Control animals showed that lesions placed outside SI and SII had no effect on the discrimination.

In Zubek's (1952) study of somatic sensory ablation in cats, the animals were trained to run down one or the other alley of a straight runway maze having interchangeable rough (sandpaper) or smooth floor boards. Several grades of roughness were used. Four different bilateral lesions were employed; occipital cortex (control lesion), SI, SII, and SI plus SII. The occipital lesion had no effect, SI ablation or SII ablation produced some deficit, and removal of SI plus SII resulted in permanent loss of the discrimination. Although the generality of these findings is somewhat limited by the fact that there was only one cat in each lesion condition, the permanent abolition of roughness discrimination by joint bilateral ablation of SI and SII has been confirmed by subsequent research (Benjamin and Thompson, 1959). The latter study also investigated the effects of such lesions on newborn kittens. Bilateral ablation of SI and SII plus varying amounts of motor cortex in the newborn animal yielded no impairment whatever in rough versus smooth discrimination when the animals were trained six months later. The adult lesion animals were also given a six months' recovery period, but were unable to learn the rough versus smooth discrimination. Absolute thresholds for the rough versus smooth discrimination, obtained by varying the courseness of the sandpaper floor boards, were identical in infant operants, unoperated infant controls, and in unoperated adult controls. The only clear deficits shown by the animals operated in infancy consisted of markedly increased differential thresholds between degrees of roughness. The Weber fraction (just noticeable change in sandpaper particle size divided by the comparison standard particle size) were about 0.95 over all standards for the infant operants and about 0.70 for unoperated control animals.

Results of the lesion studies described above may seem somewhat inconsistent. Actually, these experiments illustrate the effects of several variables which are generally of considerable importance in cortical lesion studies. The most obvious of these is size of lesion, or extent to which all appropriate sensory projection fields are removed. Removal of SI alone, or SII alone, yields only temporary impairment of tactile discrimination. Two other variables of importance are phylogenetic position of the animal and age at lesion. Bilateral ablation of SI and SII in rats produces a severe but reversible loss of roughness discrimination. However, the loss is irreversible in dog and cat. Lesions made in infant animals yield much less impairment than comparable lesions in adults.

Studies comparing the effects of SI versus SII ablations are disappointing in view of the functional differences in types of stimuli that will activate cells in the two areas. As noted above in our discussion of the organization of somatic sensory cortex, strong or painful stimuli activate many more cells in SII than in SI, and gentle joint movements activate cells in SI but not in SII. An obvious experiment, for example, would be to compare SI and SII lesions in a task where joint movement was the CS. Such experiments remain to be done.

Perhaps the most crucial variable, and the one that is most often overlooked in assessing the results of behavioral tests of cortical lesion, is the nature and complexity or difficulty of the behavioral tasks involved. Allen's study is an excellent case in point. If the dogs had only been required to respond to the simple occurrence of a tactile stimulus, it would have been concluded that bilateral ablation of SI and SII had little effect. However, if they had only been trained in the more complex differential response to two different kinds of tactile stimuli, the lesion might have been considered to abolish all ability to make tactile discriminations. Of considerable importance in Allen's experiment was the fact that the dogs had great difficulty withholding or inhibiting response to the negative stimulus following lesion. Results of Zubek's and Benjamin and Thompson's experiments on cats are consistent with Allen's findings. Adult cats cannot learn to respond differentially to rough versus smooth floors, following bilateral abalation of SI and SII. This type of deficit was still present in the infant operants of the Benjamin and Thompson experiment. In spite of the remarkable recovery of function for roughness discrimination shown by these animals, a clear deficit was still seen in a more subtle form of differential responding, in which different degrees of roughness were the positive and negative stimuli. In contrast to the permanent losses in *roughness* discrimination following total bilateral removal of areas SI and SII, Norrsell (1966) has shown that *light* tactile discriminations (response to weak air puff to hindleg skin in dog) are lost but relearned following bilateral ablation of the electrophysiologically defined hindlimb areas of SI and SII.

To summarize, interpretations of neurobehavioral studies must be tempered by consideration of the numerous variables such as size of lesion, age and phylogeny of animals, nature of behavioral tasks, amount of pre- and post-operative training, etc., and by the realization that these variables may well interact in a complex manner in any given experiment. There is no reason to suppose that regions of the cerebral cortex function in terms of simple categories like "touch" that are imposed upon the cortex by the investigator. Neuro-behavioral studies planned in terms of the response characteristics of cells in the various cortical somatic sensory areas are urgently needed.

In our discussion above of the neural organization of somatic sensory cortex, we noted that the group I afferent nerve fibers from muscle spindle organs that carry information regarding the degree of muscle stretch project to two separate areas of the cortex in the cat. Results of an ingenious study by Swett, Bourassa, and Inoue (1964) indicate that animals appear unable to make use of this in-formation in learned discriminations. They implanted chronic stimulating electrodes in forelimb and hindlimb muscle and cutaneous nerves in cats, and trained the animals to press a lever for food reward in response to nerve stimula-tion. At the end of the experiment the animals were anesthetized and neurograms recorded more proximally from the stimulated nerves to identify the nerve fiber groups responding to the electrical stimulus (see Table 12.1). The results were clear-cut and striking. Stimulation of cutaneous nerves produced consistent behavioral responses even when the electrical stimuli were too weak to yield any visible nerve evoked potentials. On the other hand, stimulation of the afferent nerves from muscles of strengths sufficient to activate all group I fibers and many group II fibers (virtually all sensory input from the muscle spindles and Golgi tendon organs) produced no behavioral responses whatever! It was necessary to use a current nearly four times stronger than group I threshold to elicit be-havioral responses from muscle nerves.

In view of the known projections of somatic sensory information to the pre-central motor areas of the cortex, it is disappointing that so few studies of tactile discrimination have involved ablation of both sensory and motor areas. Kruger and Porter (1958) compared the effects of lesions including both somatic (SI and SII) and motor areas with those removing only somatic sensory areas on tactile form discrimination in monkeys. Although there was relearning of the dis-crimination following SI and SII removal, the large lesions prevented relearning. This experiment is somewhat ambiguous, however, because the large lesions invaded posterior parietal cortex. The experiments by Ruch and associates noted above reported permanent losses in form discrimination following large parietal lesions where motor cortex was intact.

The differential effects of motor and sensory lesions upon cortical "reflex" responses ("hopping" and "placing") were investigated by Bard and Woolsey (Bard, 1938; Woolsey, personal communication). In the hopping reaction, the hopping response of the leg, elicited by requiring the animal to support himself on the leg and then shifting the position of the body, is based on kinesthetic cues. It is abolished by lesions of the primary motor area but not of the somatic sensory area. The placing response, a placing of the paw on a surface after the paw has touched the edge of the surface, involves tactile input and is selectively abolished after lesions of the paw representation in *SI*. Recent studies have complicated interpretation of these results. Tactile placing responses can be elicited in cats with prior ablation of all somatic sensory neocortex if certain stimulants such as the drug amphetamine are given (Meyer, Horel, and Meyer, 1963).

The severity of impairment resulting from lesions of the motor cortex is a function of the phylogenetic level of the organism. The rat seems virtually unaffected, the cat exhibits temporary deficits with marked recovery, and the primate has long lasting and severe motor dysfunctions. In general, some degree of permanent extensor rigidity (extension of the limbs) develops in most mammals, but only appears when the animal is suspended at rest, i.e. suspended with the legs hanging freely. The paralysis following removal of motor cortex of the monkey was once believed to be virtually complete, but a careful study of such preparations by Travis and Woolsey (1956) indicates that this need not be the case. If the lesion is made in several stages with intensive "physical therapy" interspersed, monkeys will recover a surprising degree of motor control of gross movements. Lesions of motor cortex do not seem to impair *learned* behavior other than in terms of the increased clumsiness of performance (Lashley, 1924). We will discuss the effects of removing sensory-motor areas of the cortex on motor behavior in more detail in Chapter 13.

Auditory cortex: electrophysiological analysis

The general location of the auditory cortex on the temporal lobe (and buried in the Sylvian fissure in man) has been known for many years. However, electrophysiological analysis of cortical auditory areas is relatively recent. The organization of auditory projection fields seems to be rather complex; at least six different regions have been described for the cat. We will postpone discussion of these complexities for the moment and consider first the detailed organization of the major auditory field, primary auditory cortex (*AI*). As indicated in Figure 11.13, *AI* lies in the temporal region, occupying most of the middle ectosylvian gyrus in cat. If we were to map gross cortical evoked potentials in response to abrupt auditory stimuli (click or hand clap) in an animal deeply anesthetized with barbiturates, large evoked responses would be seen primarily in area *AI*. Correspondingly, massive retrograde degeneration of the thalamic auditory

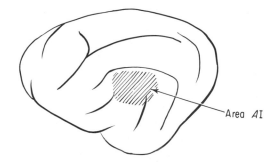

Figure 11.13. Approximate location of the primary auditory cortex (AI) in the cat. Brain is facing left. The fissure just above AI is the suprasylvian sulcus; the two fissures that extend below the area are anteriorly, the anterior ectosylvian sulcus, and posteriorly, the posterior ectosylvian sulcus.

Area AI

relay nucleus, the medial geniculate body, occurs only when cortical lesions are made in area AI.

In 1942 Woolsey and Walzl demonstrated the existence of receptotopic organization in the primary auditory area of the cortex of cat. In an analogous fashion to the representation of the skin surface on the somatic cortex, the receptor surface of the auditory sensory apparatus (basilar membrane) is "laid out" along the auditory cortex. As you will recall, the different portions of the basilar membrane distort differentially when the ear is stimulated by tones of different frequencies (Chapter 10). This results in differential activation of portions of the auditory nerve fibers. Woolsey and Walzl dissected away the bony covering of the cochlea and electrically stimulated different portions of the auditory nerve fibers along the baslar membrane. A highly schematic diagram of their experiment is given in Figure 11.14. Their results indicated that different portions of the basilar membrane are represented in different regions of the auditory cortex. Remember that frequency representation (i.e. physical distortion) of the basilar membrane runs from high frequencies at the base of the membrane to low frequencies at the apex. As indicated in Figure 11.14, the base of the basilar membrane (high frequency) projects to the anterior portion of AI and the apex (low frequency) to the posterior portion. Indeed, the representation of the basilar membrane is "laid out" along the auditory cortex.

A more direct demonstration of the spatial representation of tone frequency along the auditory cortex was made by Tunturi (1944) using the barbiturate-anesthetized dog. He stimulated the ear with brief tones of various frequencies and intensities and mapped the evoked response fields on AI, using topical application of strychnine. The use of strychnine was a crucial factor in these experiments. Without it, a brief tone will evoke potentials over a wide region of the auditory cortex. Amplitudes of the responses may be somewhat larger in one portion of the field, but the differences are often hard to see. For reasons not fully understood, if strychnine is placed on a portion of the cortex and allowed to diffuse into the cortical tissue, evoked response amplitudes will be considerably enhanced (so-called "strychnine spikes") when that region of cortex is maximally activated by neural input. Although the synaptic actions of strychnine here may well be analogous to the postsynaptic inhibitory blocking effect it

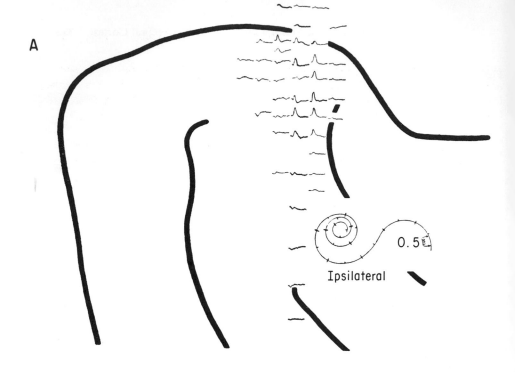

A

0.5 ms

Ipsilateral

Base stimulus

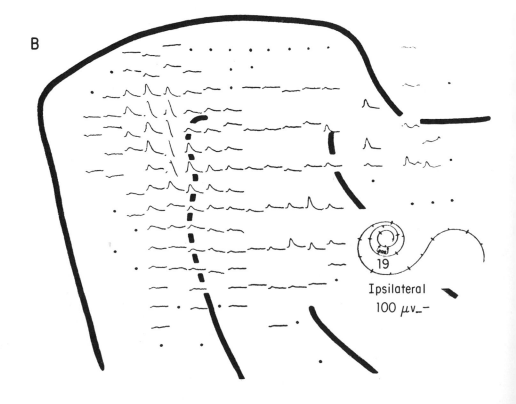

B

19

Ipsilateral

100 μv

Apex stimulus

exerts in the spinal cord, such actions have yet to be demonstrated in the cortex. Whatever the mechanisms, the net result seems to be that the differential responsiveness of the activated portions of the cortex is very much sharpened or enhanced. Tunturi was able to map frequency representation along the auditory cortex in one millimeter steps.

A diagram summarizing results of several of Tunturi's experiments on auditory area I of the dog is shown in Figure 11.15. The parallel lines running from top to bottom are "equal frequency" lines. To take a specific example, suppose we place a small patch of strychnine (shaded square) over a portion of the cortex on the line labeled 1000 cps, and record evoked responses from this small region to tones of various frequencies. Large strychnine spikes will only be obtained from this region for tones close to 1000 cps (actually from about 950 cps to 1050 cps). If we strychninize another region, say in the 5000-cps line, only tones of around 5000 cps will yield strychnine spikes from this area, and so on. The auditory cortex appears to be very selectively tuned to frequency. It is as though the basilar membrane has been unrolled and laid down along the auditory cortex. It should be emphasized that the results indicated in Figure 11.15 are schematic and based on average data. Best frequency representation in individual animals exhibits considerable variability. Comparable data have been obtained for the cat by Hind (1953) using methods similar to those of Tunturi.

The frequency layout on the cortex indicated in Figure 11.15 is subdivided into several regions by dashed lines running at right angles to the equal frequency lines. These regions, labeled by ranges of tones intensity in dB, illustrate the very interesting finding reported by Tunturi (1952) that tonal loudness seems to be represented at right angles to frequency along the auditory cortex. A weak tone (0–14 dB) of 1000 cps, for example, will evoke strychnine responses only from the most dorsal portion of _A_I. As loudness is increased, the band of evoked responses extends progressively more ventral along the 1000 cps line. However, this differential intensity representation holds true only for the _contralateral_ ear. Stimuli of different loudnesses delivered to the left ear will evoke differential responsive regions only on the right auditory area; there is no differential responsiveness on the left cortex to stimuli of differing loudness presented to the left ear, and vice versa for stimuli to the right ear. To summarize, frequency is laid out along the auditory cortex bilaterally, high frequencies anteriorly and low frequencies posteriorly, and loudness appears to be represented at right angles to frequency, but only for the contralateral ear.

The studies described above utilized animals deeply anesthetized with barbiturates when demonstrating tonotopic organization. More recently Tunturi

◀ ───

Figure 11.14.   Cochleotopic organization of the auditory cortex of the cat (brain facing right). Electrical stimulation of the base of the cochlea (A) (A–0.5 mm from base), produces evoked responses at the anterior region of _A_I. Electrical stimulation of the apex of the cochlea (**B**) (B–19 mm from base), yields responses predominately at the posterior portion of _A_I (note also the anterior response field lying more ventral to apex stimulation; this is a portion of auditory area II). Base of cochlea responds to high frequencies, apex to low frequencies. (From Woolsey and Walzl, 1942)

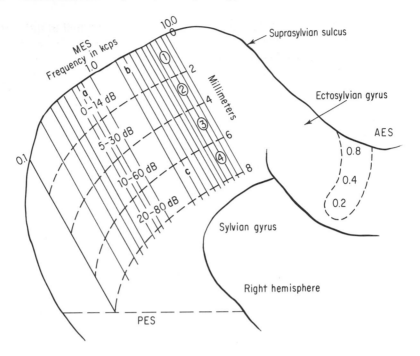

Figure 11.15. Tonotopic organization of the auditory cortex of the dog (brain facing right). MES, middle ectosylvian area; PES, posterior ectosylvian area; AES, anterior ectosylvian area. Solid lines on MES are best-frequency lines: a given frequency evoked maximum responses on a single line. Frequency expressed as the number of kilocycles per second. For example, the line labeled 1.0 is the region of the cortex showing maximum evoked responses to a 1000 cps tone. The layout of frequency appears to be a logarithmic function of distance above the cortex. Intensity of tones appears to be represented at right angles to frequency, at least for the contralateral ear (see text). (From Tunturi, 1952)

(1960) was able to show the same tonotopic representation on the auditory cortex of the unanesthetized dog. Hind et al. (1961), have reported comparable tonotopic organization in the auditory cortex of the unanesthetized cat with somewhat different procedures, employing chronically implanted electrodes. Spatial representation of frequency along the cortex is thus a "static" characteristic of the system that is not much influenced by anesthesia.

Recent investigation using microelectrode recording of single nerve cells have added important new observations on the organization of the auditory cortex. Hind et al. (1961a) recorded extracellular discharges of cells in the primary auditory cortex (*A*I) of cat in response to tones of various frequencies and intensities. Typically a cell had a "best frequency" in which the threshold was much lower than at other frequencies (i.e. frequencies at which nerve cell discharges could be obtained with much weaker tones than for other frequencies). Examples of frequency threshold curves for several cells are shown in Figure

11.16. These response curves were determined by varying the intensity of tones at each of a number of frequencies to determine the threshold intensity for each frequency. Note that the cell with the lowest "best frequency" (left cell in Figure 11.16) has a relatively broad threshold contour but that cells with higher best frequencies have narrower tuning curves (compare these with the considerably broader tuning curves for cells of the auditory nerve, Figure 10.29, Chapter 10). Several other rather interesting phenomena were noted. For example, in many cells, if the "best frequency" used to stimulate the cell became increasingly louder, the cell would cease firing. Thus there is no simple increasing relation between tone intensity and discharge of the cell. Another finding of interest was that some cells (about 13 percent of those studied) have more than one "best frequency" (cf. Figure 11.16). These were often octave multiples, i.e. if one best frequency were 1000 cps the other would be 2000, if one were 5000 the other would be 10,000, and so on. This suggests a possible basis for the common observation that tones separated by octaves sound "more alike" than tones closer together or further apart in frequency. The tonotopic organization of AI revealed in this microelectrode study was essentially comparable to that described in earlier studies, although the relation between best frequency and distance along the cortex tended to be more linear than logarithmic. This would suggest that perhaps relatively more cortex is devoted to high frequencies than is indicated by the diagram of Figure 11.15.

ADDITIONAL AUDITORY FIELDS.   In our discussion of the somatic sensory cortex, we saw that there were several body surface projection fields on the cortex in addition to the primary SI area, namely SII and sensory projections to the motor fields. This principle of multiple sensory projection fields holds for the auditory and visual regions of the cerebral cortex as well. Indeed, the auditory cortex at the moment appears to consist of six separate receptotopic projection fields, at least in the cat, in which it has been most extensively studied. In fact under certain conditions, such as in the unanesthetized animal or the chloralose anesthetized animal, it is possible to obtain cortical evoked responses to auditory

Figure 11.16. Tuning curves for three cells in primary auditory cortex of the cat. Each curve shows the minimum energy (sound pressure level, SPL) that will activate the cell plotted as a function of frequency. The cell on the left has only one "best frequency" but the cell on the right has two "best frequencies," separated by about one octave. (Redrawn from Hind et al., 1961a)

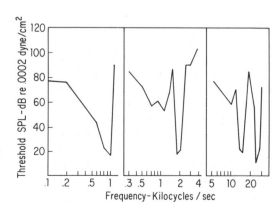

stimuli in still other areas, suggesting that more than 70 percent of the entire cortex may be "auditory." Problems of definition become crucial in deciding which areas are indeed "auditory." Several criteria can be used to distinguish auditory areas from other regions that yield "auditory" responses, including presence of receptotopic representation of the basilar membrane (i.e. frequency), absence of response to nonauditory stimuli, and presence of projection fibers from the auditory region of the thalamus. Perhaps the least ambiguous definition, which we will adopt here, is in terms of receptotopic representation. All auditory fields having differential representation of frequency are found in the temporal lobe; in cat they are all contained within the region delimited by the suprasylvian sulcus (see Figures 11.13 and 11.17). Auditory response fields in association areas outside this temporal region do not appear to exhibit any receptotopic organization, i.e. are equivalently responsive to different stimulus frequencies (Thompson and Sindberg, 1960), and are best excluded (see Chapter 15 for a further discussion).

In the original experiment by Woolsey and Walzl, in which the receptotopic organization of area AI was demonstrated, a second auditory field (AII) was also described. This region lies just ventral to auditory area I (see Figure 11.17) and has a receptotopic organization that runs in the opposite direction to that in AI. The apex of the basilar membrane (low frequency) lies anterior in AII and the base (high frequency) lies posterior. Auditory areas I and II have also been defined in the temporal fissure of the monkey by Kennedy, Kiang, and Sutton (1956).

Subsequent studies (Downman and Woolsey, 1954; Sindberg and Thompson, 1962) indicated that there is still a third major auditory area, which lies posterior and ventral to AI and AII. This region is for the most part on the posterior ectosylvian gyrus in cat and is termed "auditory area Ep." The layout of the basilar membrane runs dorsal to ventral in this region, with the base (high frequency) dorsal and the apex (low frequency) ventral (see Figure 11.17). Area Ep is independent of AI and AII in that evoked responses to auditory stimulation

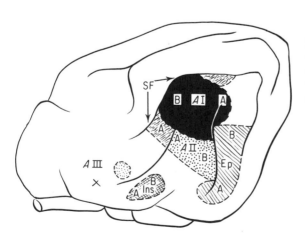

Figure 11.17. Auditory areas of the cerebral cortex of the cat (brain facing left). AI and AII are the originally defined auditory cortex. Area Ep is the posterior ectosylvian field, Ins is the insular region, AIII is the auditory field in SII, and SF is the suprasylvian fringe area. These areas all appear to have "tonotopic" organization. (From Woolsey, 1961). (Letters "A" and "B" refer to projections from apex and base of cochlear).

are still present in Ep following ablation of *A*I and *A*II. In addition, there are clear anatomical interconnections between area *A*I and area Ep. Electrical stimulation of area *A*I yields evoked responses in dorsal Ep and vice versa.

Some years ago Tunturi (1945) reported finding a small auditory evoked response field in somatic sensory area II, overlapping the ear region of *S*II in the dog. Bremer (1953) subsequently demonstrated the existence of this area in the cat. There is a potential problem in demonstrating an auditory field overlapping a somatic representation of the head and ear. A standard method of stimulus presentation is simply to place a loud speaker close to the ear and deliver sounds through it. A loud speaker click can also be a tactile stimulus. The pressure wave of the loud click can under some conditions produce a clear touch sensation on the skin and thus yield evoked responses in somatic sensory regions of the cortex. A free field click stimulus to the ear could provide either an auditory-evoked response, a tactile-evoked response, or both, in the ear region of *S*II. The methods and control procedures used by Tunturi and Bremer, such as delivering a click through a closed cylinder and tube directly to the ear drum, excluded the possibility the response is somatic sensory in nature.

An auditory response field lying ventral and anterior to *A*II in a region of the cortex that is called insular cortex, was first seen in 1953 by Woolsey and Pfaffmann (unpublished observations, see Figure 11.17). Subsequent experiments in Woolsey's laboratory (Loeffler, 1958; Sindberg and Thompson, 1962) indicated that this region has a receptotopic organization, with the base of the basilar membrane more dorsal and the apex more ventral. A series of studies by Desmedt and colleagues (see Desmedt, 1960) independently described auditory evoked responses in this insular field and also reported the occurrence of short latency visual-evoked responses there. More recently, short latency responses to somatic sensory stimulation have been obtained from the insular region as well (Thompson, Johnson, and Hoopes, 1963). Thus although the region appears to have receptotopic organization of the basilar membrane, it may perhaps be more properly considered as a "polysensory" cortical field rather than a purely auditory response field. However, at the moment custom dictates that it be referred to as the auditory insular area. The work of Desmedt and associates suggests that this cortical region may play a special role in the descending efferent auditory system that acts at the level of the cochlear nucleus to control auditory input. Electrical stimulation of the insular cortex causes a reduction in the amplitude of click-evoked responses recorded from the cochlear nucleus (see discussion in Chapter 10).

Finally, Woolsey and associates (see Woolsey, 1961) have reported the existence of a sixth auditory field having receptotopic organization, the "supra-sylvian fringe" area (*SF* in Figure 11.17). This region lies on the lower bank of the suprasylvian sulcus and overlaps on the surface of the cortex. The base of the basilar membrane is represented on the dorsal portion just above *A*I, and the apex lies on the surface of the anterior ectosylvian gyrus just below area *A*I.

The multiplicity and complexity of the auditory-evoked response fields poses very difficult problems of interpretation. Although there are suggestions from lesion-behavior experiments (discussed below) indicating that all areas may be important in auditory discrimination, and that a gross functional differentiation might be made between the more dorsal and the more ventral regions, there is as yet no evidence indicating what particular functions, if any, are subserved by the electrophysiologically defined areas.

Auditory cortex: neurobehavioral analysis

In general terms, bilateral ablation of auditory cortex produces deficits in a variety of auditory discrimination tasks. However, the specific nature of the losses has been extremely difficult to pin down. Early studies (Pennington, 1941; Raab and Ades, 1946) demonstrated that when various responses are conditioned to sounds, ablation of auditory cortex produces loss of the conditioned responses, but they can be relearned. Allen (1945) made the important observation that if dogs were conditioned to respond (lift foreleg) to one sound but not to another, this differential response could not be relearned after large bilateral lesions in the auditory cortex. As was the case in Allen's somatic sensory lesion study (see above), the animals made the response to both sounds following lesion and could not be trained to inhibit response to the negative stimulus.

Auditory discriminations based on intensity cues are impaired by bilateral ablation of the auditory cortex. However, both absolute auditory thresholds and differential intensity discriminations can be relearned to normal levels following

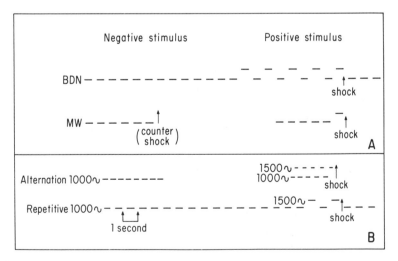

Figure 11.18.   **A,** methods of stimulus presentation and training used in studies of effects of auditory cortical lesions on frequency discrimination. (BDN refers to Butler, Diamond, and Neff, 1957; and MW refer to Meyer and Woolsey, 1952. Procedures shown in **B** were used by Thompson, 1960)

such lesions (Kryter and Ades, 1943; Raab and Ades, 1946; Rosenzweig, 1946). This fact complicates lesion studies of auditory frequency discrimination. Since the perceived loudness of tones varies as a function of frequency (see Chapter 10), two tones having the same physical intensity but differing in frequency may well differ in loudness too. In the lesion studies of frequency discrimination described below, loudness of tones was typically varied in a random fashion so that it could not serve as a cue in place of the frequency change.

Meyer and Woolsey (1952) undertook an extensive investigation of the possible roles of the several electrophysiologically defined cortical auditory fields of the cat in frequency discrimination. They trained the animals in a Brogden-Culler wheel (1936) using instrumental shock-avoidance conditioning. The wheel is much like a "squirrel cage" with the shock grids forming the enclosing floor. The cats were required to run in the wheel to avoid shock following the positive stimulus, which consisted of a series of 1-second tone pips of one frequency followed by one tone of different frequency (see Figure 11.18). The negative stimulus consisted of a series of tones all of the same frequency. Animals with essentially all the auditory areas of Figure 11.17 removed were completely unable to relearn the frequency discrimination. This result is quite consistent with Allen's findings. Interestingly enough, if any substantial portion of the auditory field, such as the ventral Ep and insular areas, or the area overlapping SII, or area AI, was left intact the frequency discrimination *could* be relearned. It didn't seem to matter which area was left, as long as some auditory cortex was preserved intact. Tone intensity discrimination training was used as a control procedure. Even those animals that could not relearn frequency discriminations following lesion were able to relearn intensity discrimination. An anatomical analysis of the thalamic degeneration in these animals, by Rose and Woolsey (1958), indicated that those lesions resulting in inability to relearn the discrimination produced essentially total degeneration of the medial geniculate body plus degeneration in the posterior nuclear group. Animals that could relearn had significant sparing of cells in the medial geniculate body and posterior nuclear group i.e. a considerable number of cells in these thalamic regions did not degenerate.

In 1957, Butler, Diamond, and Neff reinvestigated the effects of removing auditory cortex on frequency discrimination in the cat. They used shock avoidance conditioning in a hurdle box. The animal was required to jump from one compartment of the box to the other when the positive stimulus was presented, to avoid shock. The method of stimulus presentation used is illustrated in Figure 11.18. It differs somewhat from previous methods in that there is no discrete negative stimulus. The base tone (e.g. 800 cps) is presented all the time, *on* one second, *off* one second, throughout. The positive stimulus is introduced as an alternating tone of different frequency (e.g. 1000 cps) followed by shock for response failure. This can be characterized as an "ongoing background stimulus" method. Following bilateral ablation of auditory cortex, all animals quickly relearned the frequency discrimination. These results stand in direct contradiction to the earlier experiments by Allen and by Meyer and Woolsey. In general, the lesions by Butler et al. were smaller than those of Meyer and Woolsey, sparing significant portions of the ventral aspects of area Ep, and the insular area. Nonetheless the minimal effective lesion (i.e. lesion producing total inability to relearn the discrimination) by Meyer and Woolsey is essentially identical to the maximal lesion by Butler et al.

An analysis of the possible reasons for the contradictory findings of Meyer and Woolsey, and Butler, Diamond, and Neff was undertaken by Thompson (1960). There are three possible sources of difference: training apparatus, method of stimulus presentation, and extent of lesions. Thompson trained cats in the Brodgen-Culler wheel (as did Meyer and Woolsey) and used lesions that removed all auditory fields, thus being larger than the minimally effective lesion of Meyer and Woolsey and considerably larger than those of Butler et al. The Butler et al. method of stimulus presentation was employed (see Figure 11.18). Following bilateral removal of auditory cortex the animals easily relearned the discrimination. Since apparatus and lesions were comparable to those of the Meyer and Woolsey study, and stimulus presentation and results (relearning) were comparable to those of Butler et al., it must be concluded that method of training is the crucial variable. A subsequent group of animals were trained in a procedure analogous to that used by Meyer and Woolsey, except that more comparison stimuli were given (see Figure 11.18). Following lesion they were completely unable to relearn the discrimination. The animals were then switched to the ongoing background stimulus method of Butler et al., and exhibited immediate and perfect frequency discrimination. They were then switched back to the previous method and again were unable to learn the discrimination. Thus animals with the *same* lesion both could and could not discriminate frequency, depending on the method of training used. Clearly the discrimination of tone frequency, per se, is not the crucial factor; the nature of the learning task appears to be far more important. Goldberg and Neff (1961) also showed relearning of frequency discrimination with the ongoing background stimulus method, using lesions that were in some instances even larger than those used by Thompson.

Because frequency discrimination can still be learned by animals with all auditory cortex removed, it has been suggested that subcortical mechanisms may mediate the discrimination (Neff, 1961). A recent study has shown that frequency discrimination is permanently lost and cannot be relearned, even by the ongoing background stimulus method of Butler et al. if sufficiently large cortical lesions are made (Thompson, 1964). The effective lesion removed essentially all cortex posterior to area SI, including SII, and all auditory field, the posterior association areas, and the visual cortex. Unambiguous interpretation of these results is difficult; such massive cortical lesions may well have general or nonspecific effects that in turn could conceivably interfere with the possible subcortical mediation of frequency discrimination that might occur when only auditory cortex is removed. Alternatively, the posterior association areas might play a crucial role in frequency discrimination when the ongoing background stimulus method of training is used. The issue will only be clarified by further research.

Although animals with all auditory cortex removed can learn frequency discrimination with the change from background stimulation technique, their behavior is markedly different from normal animals in many situations in which tone frequency is a relevant cue. One case in point is stimulus generalization across frequencies. If normal cats are trained until they respond most of the time to a given tone, and then tested to tones of different frequency, they tend to respond less the more different the test frequency is from the training frequency, i.e. they exhibit a generalization *gradient*. An example of the stimulus generalization gradient to tone frequency is shown in Figure 11.19 (dashed line). Normal cats were trained (shock avoidance) to respond to a tone of 250 cps and separate subgroups were then tested without shock to octave multiples of the training tone. Note that the curve (expressed as percent response relative to the training tone) decreases rapidly from 500 cps to reach zero at 2000 cps. However, animals trained and tested in the same manner after total bilateral ablation of all auditory cortex respond equally to all test frequencies (solid line in Figure 11.19, Thompson, 1962). More recently, Randall (1965) has obtained comparable results using a quite different method of training and testing. Thus auditory operates do not respond differentially to tone frequency in generalization tests. Since animals with the same lesions can be trained with other procedures to discriminate frequency, the effect is not due to a breakdown of the discrimination process as such. It appears that the cortical lesions can differentiate between generalization and discrimination behavior.

The data given in Figure 11.19 suggest that the auditory cortex may play a rather crucial role in the development of the stimulus generalization gradient for frequency. A recent theoretical analysis (Thompson, 1965) suggests that if a few minimal assumptions are made concerning the number of neurons in the auditory cortex activated in common by the training tone (i.e. 250 cps here) and test tones, the behavioral frequency generalization gradient exhibited by normal animals (dotted line in Figure 11.19) can be accurately predicted from response

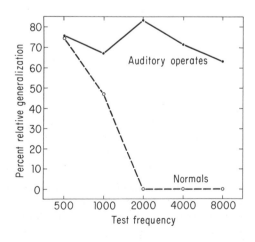

Figure 11.19. Effect of removing auditory cortex on frequency stimulus generalization in cats. Following lesions animals show total generalization to all test frequencies. (From Thompson, 1962)

characteristics of the auditory neurons. This is illustrated in Figure 11.20. The dots indicate strength of behavioral generalization plotted against distance along the auditory cortex (arrows indicate locations of cells most responsive to the various test stimuli). A theoretical equation was developed from the neurophysiological data of Hind et al. (1961a) predicting behavioral frequency generalization. The straight line in Figure 11.20 is the plot of this equation. Agreement between the theoretical equation and the actual behavioral data is surprisingly close.

There is evidence suggesting that the more ventral portions of the auditory cortex may play a particular role in some of the more complex aspects of discriminations involving frequency. A study by Diamond and Neff (1957), using shock avoidance training in a double grill box, indicates that ablation of the ventral auditory regions in cat severely impairs discrimination of tonal patterns. Thus if the discrimination is between 2 tones of different frequency, A and B, in two sequences such as $A B A$ versus $B A B$, the discrimination is not relearned after lesion (see Figure 11.21). Control lesions involving only the more dorsal portions of the auditory response fields do not cause permanent loss of the ability to relearn the pattern discrimination. Neff and Diamond (1958) suggest that one function of the more ventral portion of the auditory cortex is to provide a mechanism for short-term retention such that, in a group of auditory signals

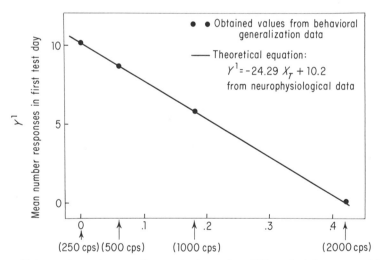

Figure 11.20. Prediction of auditory frequency stimulus generalization behavior from neurophysiological data on single cell response characteristics in area AI of the cat. Dots represent obtained behavioral data and the straight line is the theoretical equation, obtained from purely electrophysiological data. (From Thompson, 1965)

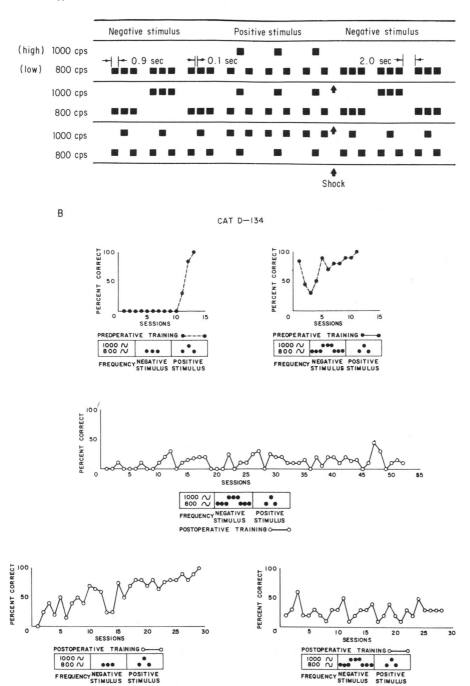

Figure 11.21. Effect of ablation of ventral temporal cortex of cat on tonal "pattern" discrimination. **A**, method of stimulus presentation. **B**, example of behavioral data. Prior to lesion, the animal was able to discriminate tonal *frequency pattern*. After lesion, this task could not be relearned; however, intensity pattern could be discriminated. (From Diamond and Neff, 1957)

temporally arranged, the first will leave an aftereffect in the central nervous system with which neural activity set up by succeeding signals may interact. In addition to having implications for tonal pattern discrimination this important study by Diamond and Neff is one of the few neurobehavioral experiments showing clear differentiation between effects of removing different portions of the auditory cortex (i.e. ablation of *A*I has no effect but ablation of ventral regions has a marked effect).

Localization of the sounds in space appears to be another aspect of behavior that is somewhat impaired by lesions of the auditory cortex. Neff et al. (1956) presented cats with a semicircle of food boxes and trained the animals to go to the box from which a sound came. Following the ablation of the more dorsal portions of the auditory cortex, the accuracy of localization was markedly reduced. Although the animals could relearn to localize to some extent, the localization was always poor following lesion. A recent study by Masterton and Diamond (1964) evaluated the effect of auditory lesions on discrimination of small time-differences in a stimulus presented to both ears. Thus a click would be presented to the right ear a fraction of a second before or after a click to the left ear. Human subjects, when given this kind of stimulus presentation, report that the sound appears to come from one side or the other side of the head. Masterton and Diamond reported that following total bilateral ablation of all auditory cortex animals are completely unable to relearn differential response on the basis of this type of sound localization cue. They suggested that ability to localize sounds in space may be totally lost following complete removal of all auditory cortex. However, a study by Thompson and Welker (1963) showed that this need not be the case. Cats were simply given stimuli through either of two loud speakers placed on opposite sides of the animal's head. The orienting response of the cat, a rapid head turning toward the speaker producing the sound, was rated. Following total bilateral removal of all auditory areas, the animals, although significantly poorer in performance, were still able to localize relatively well. It would appear that here, too, method of testing or training is an important variable in assessing the behavioral losses resulting from removal of auditory cortex. Interpretations of the effects of various lesions upon auditory discriminations have differed, particularly with regard to tasks in which frequency is the cue (Axelrod and Diamond, 1965; Goldberg and Neff, 1961; Neff, 1961; Thompson, 1960; 1965). There appear as yet to be no crucial experiments which distinguish between the alternative theoretical analyses.

Visual cortex: electrophysiological analysis

Correlation of visual function with the striate area of the occipital lobe has been known for nearly a century (see Fulton, 1949b). Detailed anatomical studies (Brouwer and Zeeman, 1926; Clark and Penman, 1934; Minkowski, 1913) indicated that there is a receptotopic representation of the retina on the primary visual cortex (area *V*1). For example, if a restricted region of *V*1 is destroyed, a corresponding restricted region of the lateral geniculate body degenerates. If this same region of the lateral geniculate body is destroyed, ganglion cells in a restricted portion of the retina degenerate. The gross organization of the projection of the retina on the visual cortex can be determined by such retrograde degeneration analysis. The synaptic relay of the axon terminals of retinal ganglion cells on cells in the lateral geniculate body is one of the places in the CNS where transneuronal degeneration occurs. Consequently, lesions of restricted portions of the retina sometimes produce restricted regions of degeneration in the visual cortex. Results from this method have been consistent with the picture obtained in retrograde degeneration studies.

The anatomical relations of projection from visual field to retina to visual cortex are rather complicated in mammals. In lower vertebrates such as the frog there is complete crossing at the chiasm, so that all input to the right eye (right visual field) goes to the left brain, and vice versa (Figure 11.22). Such animals

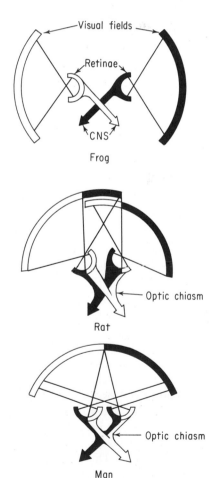

Figure 11.22. Degree of binocularity of visual projections to cortex for different species. In frog the optic tracts are completely crossed; the left visual field projects entirely to the right optic lobe and vice versa. In the rat there is some crossing, with a degree of binocular vision. In man the degree of "mixing" is virtually complete; most of the visual field is binocular.

have no binocular vision. In lower mammals like the rat or rabbit, there is partial overlap of the visual fields from the two eyes. Here there is incomplete crossing at the optic chiasm. About 80 percent of the left retina and 20 percent of the right retina project to the right visual cortex. The projection from the two retinas overlap, so that perhaps 30 percent of the visual area has input from both eyes and hence can mediate binocular vision (see Figure 11.22). In dog and cat there is about 80 percent overlap, so that they have considerable binocular vision. Primates, including man, have virtually total binocular vision; the left half of each retina projects to the left visual cortex and the right half of each retina projects to the right visual cortex (see Figure 11.22). This means, of course, that the right cortex receives input from the left visual field, and vice versa. Ablation of the left visual cortex eliminates all visual input from the entire left half of the visual field of both eyes.

Pioneering electrophysiological studies by Marshall and colleagues (Marshall and Talbot, 1940; Marshall, Talbot, and Ades, 1943; Talbot and Marshall, 1941; Thompson, Woolsey, and Talbot, 1950) established the existence of retinotopic projection to the visual cortex in rabbit, cat and monkey. The basic technique involved light flash stimulation of the retina using a small point source of light on a perimeter. This is simply a circular frame that permits the light to be focused on any portion of the retina. Gross evoked responses to this type of flash stimulus can be mapped on the striate cortex in the barbiturate anesthetized animal. Results of these experiments established a clear " point-to-point " representation of retinal regions on the occipital cortex. Cortical representation of the foveal area is relatively large, occupying nearly half of the primary visual cortex. This is to be expected since the fovea, although only a small region of the retina, is the central focal point of the eye, and mediates detail vision (i.e. it is the region of maximum visual acuity).

Results of the early evoked response studies indicated a rather fine degree of localization. A small discrete stimulus to a given location on the retina produced evoked responses in a small corresponding region of VI. However, as noted, the fovea has a relatively greater area of cortical projection; the amount of cortex devoted to retinal regions decreases as a function of distance away from the fovea on the retina. The fine degree of retinal projection to the visual cortex was recently challenged by Doty (1958). He reported that point sources of light activate wide regions of visual cortex. Subsequent analysis (see discussion by Doty and Whitteridge, pp 246–247 in Jung and Kornhuber, 1961) has resolved this apparent discrepancy. Doty used a light flash in background darkness, which can result in considerable diffusion of light to the retina. Studies showing good localization have used a light flash in dim background illumination or a spot of light reflected from a screen. Further, Doty included long latency-(50–100 msec) evoked responses in his analysis. These are much more widespread and diffusely organized on the cortex under some conditions than are the short latency primary evoked responses. There appears to be general agreement today that a rather precise point-to-point projection of the retina on the cortex exists.

As in other sensory regions of the cortex, the application of microelectrode techniques has provided important new data about the organization of sensory information at the cellular level. Particularly striking are the studies by Hubel and Wiesel (Hubel, 1960a; Hubel and Wiesel, 1959; 1962; 1963a; 1965). They recorded extracellular single nerve cell responses in the primary visual cortex to a variety of stimulus conditions in either unanesthetized cats, using a chronically implanted microelectrode holder, or in lightly anesthetized and paralyzed cats. Small patches of visual forms were projected on a screen directly in front of the animal's head.

Hubel and Wiesel found a high degree of organization or analysis involved in the kinds of stimuli that will activate cells in the visual cortex. At this point it is worth recalling the organization of receptive fields for ganglion cells in the retina and cells in the lateral geniculate body discussed in Chapter 10. In general, these cells have simple and more or less concentric receptor fields and can be activated or inhibited by discrete light flash to portions of the receptor fields. Most commonly, stimulation of the central portion of the field induces cell firing ("on" discharges), and in the peripheral portion inhibits activity or causes discharges when the stimulus is turned off ("off" discharges). Illumination of the entire receptor field usually activates cells, as does diffuse light flash to the entire visual field. In marked contrast, most of the cells in the visual cortex do not respond at all to large or diffuse spots of light. While cortical cells do have receptive fields, their organization can only be detected by a very small and discrete spot of light.

In general, the receptive fields of cells in the visual cortex are not concentric or circular but tend instead to be rectangular or "edge shaped." An example of such a receptive field is shown in Figure 11.23A. In addition to shape, the orientation of the receptive field, and movement of the appropriate shape across the field, are crucial variables. Figure 11.23B illustrates the importance of orientation. The cell fires when the stimulus rectangle is at a particular orientation. Figure 11.23C shows that for this movement of a stimulus rectangle in one direction through one angle is the most effective stimulus. The rectangular shapes of receptive fields are analogous to "edges." In more general terms, cells of the visual cortex respond to edges or boundaries of particular shapes, sizes, positions, and orientations, and often only if they move in particular directions. Hubel and Wiesel differentiate between "simple" and "complex" receptive fields. Simple fields are those whose response to form could be predicted from the asymmetric regions of excitation and inhibition. The properties of complex fields could not be so predicted. In general, complex fields differ from simple fields in that a stimulus is effective whenever it is placed in the field, provided that the orientation is appropriate. Simple fields require the stimulus to have a specific location as well.

Another striking finding by Hubel and Wiesel was the existence of a columnar organization in the visual cortex. If the microelectrode penetrates through the cortex in a path perpendicular to the surface (i.e. at right angles), all the cells

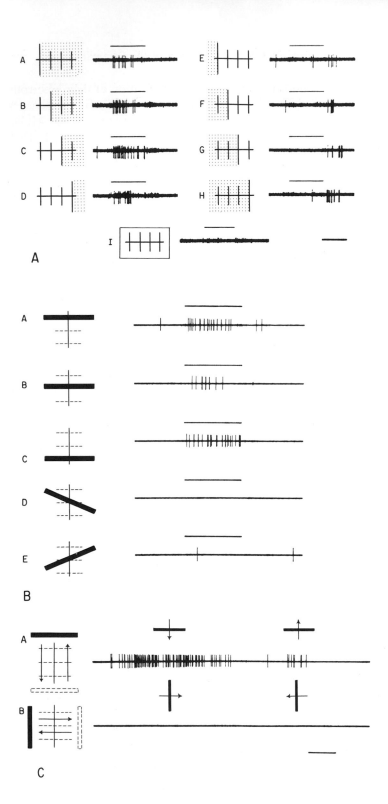

in that penetration will respond only to a stimulus edge of the same orientation. Different columns of cells respond to stimuli having different orientations. A small region of the retina will be projected to each square millimeter of cortex. Within that area of cortex are many different columns of cells, each column having cells responding to a different stimulus orientation. This vertical columnar organization is somewhat analogous to that seen in the somatic sensory cortex, except that there are fewer types of columns in the latter (eg, touch, joint movement and pressure). There are a great many different types of columns in the visual cortex that are responsive to different stimulus orientations. Furthermore, the neural organization required for this columnar "abstraction" of stimulus orientation in the visual system occurs at the cortex. No such organization is found for cells of the lateral geniculate body. As Hubel and Wiesel put it (1965) "far from being a mere aggregation of cells with common characteristics, the column emerges as a dynamic unit of function."

The reader has undoubtedly been struck by the many similarities between responses of the frog optic nerve fibers described by Lettvin and his colleagues (see Chapter 10) and responses of the cortical visual cells of the cat. In both cases, the cells respond to objects, shadows and movements in the visual field in ways that cannot be predicted from responses to diffuse light flash. Indeed, the characteristics of stimuli that are effective in activating cells are those that are often said to be mediated by "higher" processes such as "perception." Perhaps the most fundamental importance of these experiments is that they remove much of the mystery from "perception." Abstract aspects of stimulus quality are coded by single nerve cells and do not require mysterious gestalt fields, a "scanning sensor," or a "man-within-a-man" to do the perceiving. The transformations of stimulus characteristics from retina to cortex are the results of neural interconnections, and are often predictable from the elementary response properties of the receptive fields (as in the "simple" cells of Hubel and Wiesel). Perception of visual form appears to be a direct result of the structure of the cells; it is built in.

The major difference between the frog and the cat lies in the level at which the transformations take place. In the frog the processing occurs in the retina, whereas in cat much of the processing takes place in the cortex. Hubel and Wiesel contrast the visual systems of the two animals as follows.

◄────────────────────────────

Figure 11.23. Examples of types of visual stimuli that will activate cells in the primary visual cortex. In all three cells (i.e. 11.23A, **B** and **C**) the stimulus patterns are shown in the left (and also above in **C**) and the cell discharges on the right. The horizontal line above each spike discharge base line (in **A** and **B**) indicates a stimulus presentation. Horizontal bar in lower right (in **A** and **B**) is 1 sec time calibrations. **A**, example of an "edge detector" cell. Labels a–h indicate responses of the cell to a stimulus edge placed in different locations (no edge in i). **B**, example of an "orientation detector" cell. Labels a–e indicate responses of the cell when the stimulus bar is presented in different orientations. **C**, example of a "direction of movement detector" cell. The cell fires a great deal when the stimulus bar moves down and very little when it moves up (a) and does not fire at all when the bar moves from left to right or right to left (b) over the same region of the retina. (From Hubel and Wiesel, 1962)

"At first glance it may seem astonishing that the complexity of third-order neurones in the frog's visual system should be equalled only by that of sixth-order neurones in the geniculo-cortical pathway of the cat. Yet this is less surprising if one notes the great anatomical differences in the two animals, especially the lack, in the frog, of any cortex or dorsal lateral geniculate body. There is undoubtedly a parallel difference in the use each animal makes of its visual system: the frog's visual apparatus is presumably specialized to recognize a limited number of stereotyped patterns or situations, compared with the high acuity and versatility found in the cat. Probably it is not so unreasonable to find that in the cat the specialization of cells for complex operations is postponed to a higher level, and that when it does occur, it is carried out by a vast number of cells, and in great detail." (1962, p. 150.)

A great many interesting correlations have been observed between the behavior of cells in the visual cortex of the cat and various human psycho-physical phenomena by Jung and his many collaborators at Freiburg University (see Jung, 1958; 1961; Jung and Kornhuber, 1961). Patterns of response in many cortical visual cells appear predictably related to such phenomenon as brightness, flicker fusion, after-images, simultaneous contrast, and binocular rivalry. To take a specific example, there is a regular temporal sequence of after-images reported by human subjects exposed to a brief light flash. There is a very brief dark interval, followed by a brief (20-millisecond) after-image, then about 100 milliseconds of dark, followed by a dimmer 150-millisecond after-image, then a longer dark interval (about 300 milliseconds), and finally a long lasting dim after-image (this last is the most commonly observed "after-image"). Certain cells in the cat visual cortex discharge during all of the periods of after-image, but not during the "dark" intervals.

An interesting aspect of Jung's work concerns the influence of nonvisual stimulation on behavior of cells in the cat visual cortex. As Hubel and Wiesel reported, many cells will not fire to diffuse light. Jung reports that some of these cells can be activated by stimulation of the vestibular receptors or by electrical stimulation of the midline thalamic nuclei. Cell response latencies to such "inadequate" stimuli are much longer than are visual responses of cells activated by visual stimuli, so the effects are likely indirect, possibly by altering excitability in the visual system. In addition, such nonvisual stimuli can influence response patterns of cells that fire to visual stimuli. The critical flicker fusion point (CFF) is a good example. If the flicker frequency of a flickering light is increased, the light is reported by human subjects to become a steady nonflickering light at a certain critical frequency. This CFF ranges from 5 to 50 per second depending on such things as brightness, area of retina stimulated, and so forth. Cells in the visual cortex of the cat show corresponding "CFFs" (defined as the frequency at which the cell stops firing after every flash and begins to fire irregularly). Electrical stimulation of the midline thalamus or the ascending reticular formation is often followed by an increase in the cellular CFF in cat. Jung draws a parallel with the human psycho-physical studies suggesting that behavioral CFF is increased by "attention" or "arousal."

There has been very little work on the possible cortical mechanisms concerned with color vision. Gross cortical-evoked responses elicited by light flash do differ in some of their characteristic as a function of the stimulus wavelength (Lennox and Madson, 1955; Madson and Lennox, 1955). Perhaps the clearest difference has to do with evoked response latency, which of course reflects conduction time (and therefore probably afferent fiber size). In cats, response latencies are shortest to red, intermediate to yellow, and longest to blue and green.

A very careful and comprehensive microelectrode study of single nerve-cell responses in the visual cortex of the monkey (Lennox-Buchthal, 1962) indicates that more than half of the cortical cells that respond to light do so with restricted spectral responsiveness. Cells of this type are driven by only one of five filters transmitting 450, 515, 555, 587 and 640 mμ. Thus many cortical cells are highly tuned to certain wavelengths of light. There seems to be no close correspondence between the patterns of discharge of cortical neurons and those of thalamic neurons in response to colored light. We noted earlier (work of DeValois and associates, see Chapter 10) that lateral geniculate body cells in the monkey were of several types, " on " cells responding to only one color, " on and off " cells responding to one color but being inhibited by another, and so forth. Cells studied in the cortex seem to show primarily simple " on " responses to flashes of colored light. Furthermore, light intensity had no effect on the discharge characteristics of such cells; all intensities of the effective wavelength induced one or two spikes. Finally, the patterns of spectral sensitivity for cortical cells are rather different than are those of geniculate neurons. Lennox-Buchthal suggests that these differences may reflect basic coding processes that occur in the cerebral cortex.

ADDITIONAL VISUAL AREAS. In Talbot and Marshall's (1941) original study of the retinotopic organization of VI in cat, they also discovered a second visual area (VII). This region is immediately adjacent to area VI and contains a second layout of the half retinas (i.e. the left visual cortex has a binocular representation of the two left retinas in area VI and another such representation in area VII). The areas appear to be mirror images of one another. This same organization was found for the rabbit visual cortex by Thompson, Woolsey, and Talbot (1950).

A recent study (Hubel and Wiesel, 1965) suggests that there may be three separate visual fields on the occipital cortex of the cat (see Figure 11.24). Each of these three areas appears to have essentially complete representation of the half retinas. Hubel and Wiesel worked out the retinotopic organization of the three visual areas using microelectrode recording of single cell activity. In addition, they very carefully analyzed the histological appearance of the cortex in the three areas. Their results would seem to constitute a real triumph for histology. Since the time of Brodmann, visual cortex has been subdivided into three regions: area 17 (the striate or " primary " visual area), and areas 18 and 19, the latter two being termed the " prestriate " visual areas. Hubel and Wiesel found an *exact* correspondence between physiologically defined area I and histologically defined area 17, between area II and area 18, and between area

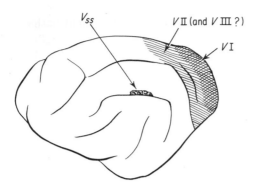

Figure 11.24. General locations of the visual fields of the cortex of the cat (facing left). V_{ss} stands for the visual field lying on the dorsal bank of the suprasylvian sulcus.

III and area 19. Although the physiological definitions of the visual areas in the primate have not yet been extended beyond areas I and II (see Cowey, 1964), it is possible that three areas corresponding to histological regions 17, 18, and 19 may be found. On the other hand, careful gross evoked response analysis of the visual cortex of the cat by Woolsey and associates has revealed no indication of a third visual area (i.e. VIII) (Woolsey, personal communication). The existence of a third retinal projection to the visual cortex of the cat is thus a matter of dispute at present.

It appears that much of the lateral geniculate body degenerates when the striate area (VI = area 17) is removed. However, definition of area 17 has not always been consistent. Nonetheless, it is probable that direct projections from the lateral geniculate body to areas 18 and 19 are considerably smaller than the projection to area 17. Hubel and Wiesel found that small lesions made in area 17 of the cat resulted in circumscribed regions of afferent fiber degeneration in areas 18 and 19. A lesion to either hemisphere leads to bilateral regions of degeneration. Thus pathways relay from each area 17 to both areas 18 and 19.

The visual stimulus properties that will activate cells in areas 18 and 19 are of considerable interest. Most of the cells studied in VII and about half the cells in VIII were of the type called "complex" by Hubel and Wiesel (see above). Some cells in VII were "hypercomplex" and many cells in VIII were either "hypercomplex" or "higher order hypercomplex." Hypercomplex cells not only require a given orientation for a stimulus lying within a visual field but also a given *length* of stimulus line (complex cells do not require a specific length). Some higher order hypercomplex cells respond to given length lines at either of two orientations (these might be called "angle" or "corner" perceivers). Examples of the behavior of a hypercomplex cell are shown in Figure 11.25. The reader is urged to consult Hubel and Wiesel's paper (1965) for details. It is likely that their findings will play a very fundamental and significant role in our ultimate understanding of visual "perception."

Marshall, Talbot, and Ades (1943) described an additional visual area lying in the medial suprasylvian sulcus in cat (V_{ss}, see Figure 11.24). This was subsequently studied in some detail by Clare and Bishop (1954), who showed that it

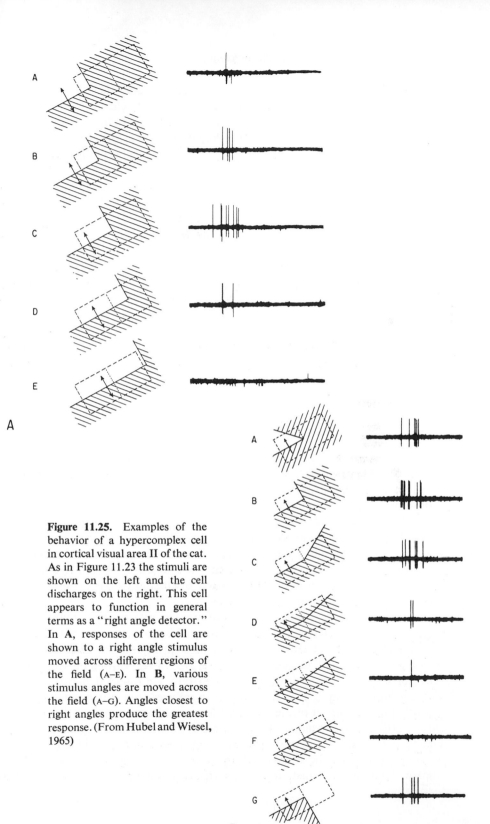

Figure 11.25. Examples of the behavior of a hypercomplex cell in cortical visual area II of the cat. As in Figure 11.23 the stimuli are shown on the left and the cell discharges on the right. This cell appears to function in general terms as a "right angle detector." In **A**, responses of the cell are shown to a right angle stimulus moved across different regions of the field (A–E). In **B**, various stimulus angles are moved across the field (A–G). Angles closest to right angles produce the greatest response. (From Hubel and Wiesel, 1965)

received projections both from the primary visual area and via stimulation of the optic nerve. Results of anatomical studies suggest that cells in the most medial portion of the lateral geniculate body, or lying just medial to the lateral geniculate body, may project to this cortical field (Polyak, 1927; Vastola, 1961). Hubel and Wiesel found discrete regions of afferent fiber degeneration in the V_{ss} field following small lesion in VI, thus confirming the physiological interconnections described by Clare and Bishop. Although the region has been characterized as an " auditory-visual " association area because it adjoins auditory cortex, evoked response analysis suggests that there are no interactive functions between auditory and visual evoked responses (Thompson, Smith, and Bliss, 1963). The significance of this fourth visual area is as yet obscure.

The principle of multiple sensory projection fields on the cerebral neocortex appears to hold for the somatic sensory, auditory and visual systems. There are four or more receptotopically organized cortical fields for each modality. The findings by Hubel and Wiesel suggest that the additional visual areas may subserve more complex " perception " functions. Although it is perhaps somewhat premature to assert this generalization for the additional cortical areas of the somatic sensory and auditory systems (recall, however, the role of ventral auditory cortex in tone pattern discrimination, see above and Diamond and Neff, 1957), such a view suggests a great many research possibilities.

Visual cortex: neurobehavioral analysis

The effects of ablations of visual cortex on visual discrimination behavior seem relatively clear. Learned responses to the presence of light, and discriminations based on amount of light, can be relearned to normal preoperative levels following bilateral ablation of the striate cortex, although there is generally marked impairment of performance immediately after lesion (Lashley, 1931, 1935). Meyer (1958) demonstrated that such tasks are not even impaired if the operations are done in two stages (i.e. one hemisphere at a time), so long as some type of visual stimulation intervenes between lesions. We will examine this intriguing experiment in more detail in our discussion of the "consolidation" theory of learning in Chapter 17.

In contrast to response to light, per se, discriminations of stimulus patterns (e.g. circle, square, triangle) cannot be relearned by rat, cat or primate following total ablation of the striate cortex, with subsequent total degeneration of the lateral geniculate body. Lashley (1931, 1935, 1939, 1942) carried out an extensive series of studies on such discriminations in rats. He found that pattern vision was not impaired by lesions outside the visual area, but was permanently lost following total removal of the area. A rather striking finding was that if only a small portion of the visual cortex remained (1/60 of the lateral geniculate body intact), pattern and brightness discriminations were retained. This finding has been confirmed for the monkey (Harlow, 1939) and the cat (Fischman and Meikle, 1965). In contrast, the tree shrew, a more primitive mammal, does exhibit good pattern vision after total bilateral ablation of the striate cortex (Snyder, Hall, and Diamond, 1966).

Klüver (1936, 1937, 1942) has shown that the monkey cannot relearn visual pattern discriminations after removal of the striate cortex. His monkeys were able to discriminate large versus small visual stimuli; but when brightness was adjusted so that each stimulus emitted the same total luminous flux, the discrimination could not be relearned. In other words, cortically blind monkeys can discriminate total amount of light, but not brightness, per se (which is *not* the same as total luminous flux), or visual form independent of amount of light. Klüver also reported that color discrimination was permanently lost following lesion.

Interpretations of lesion studies, particularly insofar as they relate to various cortical visual fields, are severely complicated by the changing definitions of the cortical fields. Some investigators have used the criterion of maximum amplitude evoked responses to define the area. As Doty (1958) noted, the largest evoked responses to flash stimulation are outside the striate area. In fact they are in area VII as defined by Hubel and Wiesel. In the recent study by Fischman and Meikle (1965), showing that visual intensity discriminations were lost but could be relearned following lesion, it appears that essentially all of VI and VII were removed, but only a portion of VIII was included.

Doty (1961) has reported striking recovery of function following ablation of visual cortex in newborn cats. The lesions removed areas VI and VII. Adult animals with comparable lesions cannot relearn pattern discriminations. However Doty's infant operates, when grown, could in some instances discriminate visual forms. This finding is consistent with the marked recovery of function following ablation of cortex in infant animals reported for other systems. Doty further reported that if the infant lesions also included cortex of the middle and posterior suprasylvian sulcus (remainder of areas VIII and V_{ss}) relearning did not occur. Interpretation of his infant striate lesion effect may be complicated by the fact that some intact cells were subsequently found in the lateral geniculate body. However Wetzel, Thompson, Horel, and Meyer (1965) similarly found that visual pattern discrimination was essentially normal in cats with total bilateral ablation of visual areas I and II in infancy. Adult operates were unable to learn the discrimination.

Methods of training and methods of stimulus presentation appear to be of some importance in determining effects of visual area lesions, as was the case with auditory lesions. The most common method of training animals in differential visual intensity discrimination is to have them choose between one of two doors or stimulus cards of different brightness. The animal must respond to one and inhibit response to the other. Typically the discrimination is lost and must be relearned. However, Wing (1946) trained dogs to lift their forelimb when the brightness of a stimulus patch was briefly increased above a constant background level. Under these conditions, ablation of visual cortex did not result in even a temporary loss of the discrimination. These results are somewhat analogous to the findings of studies on the effects of removing auditory cortex on frequency discrimination (see above).

Several studies have investigated effects of lesions removing only the lateral occipital cortex of the monkey. This would remove the foveal projection and about eight degrees of retinal visual angle around the fovea. Such lesions reduce the CFF (Mishkin and Weiskrantz, 1959) and impair visual acuity (Weiskrantz and Cowey, 1963), but do not appear to impair wavelength discrimination (Butter, Mishkin, and Rosvold, 1965).

In the studies discussed above, the lesions were planned to remove all or portions of the primary striate area (VI). It has been suggested that the prestriate areas (histological areas 18 and 19) may also play a crucial role in learning to discriminate visual form (Hebb, 1949). Extensive removal of prestriate cortex in monkey appears to produce surprisingly little impairment of pattern discrimination learning (Lashley, 1948).

Studies by Sperry and Myers and their associates have shown that the corpus callosum, the great band of fibers interconnecting the two cerebral hemispheres, can play a very significant role in the transfer of visual learning. Myers (1955) had found that if the optic chiasm is midsagittally sectioned, so that all input from the left eye goes to the left brain and all input from the right eye to the right brain (see Figure 11.22), visual tasks learned with one eye occluded are performed at the learned level when the learning eye is occluded and the other eye used (this is often termed *interocular* transfer). Visual information was thus able to transfer from one hemisphere to the other. Sperry, Stamm, and Miner (1956) and Myers (1956) showed that if the callosum was also sectioned prior to training there was no subsequent transfer when the initial training eye was occluded and the previously occluded eye trained. The animal had to relearn the task completely. An interesting observation in the experiment by Sperry et al. was that the learning curves for the two eyes in a single cat are much more similar than curves for different cats. Studies by Meikle and Sechzer (1960) and Meikle (1960) have shown that while near threshold brightness discriminations do not transfer, simple, suprathreshold brightness discriminations do indeed transfer. Impairment in transfer of learned tasks has also been found for somesthetic discriminations following callosal section, although the literature is less conclusive (Stamm and Sperry, 1957; Glickstein and Sperry, 1960). Meikle, Sechzer, and Stellar (1962) compared leg flexion shock avoidance conditioning and conditioned respiratory changes after callosum section, using a vibratory tactile conditioned stimulus. Interestingly, the leg flexion response showed no transfer, but the respiratory response showed considerable transfer.

A more recent experiment by Sechzer (1964) has complicated the picture for visual transfer. Her experiment was identical to that of Myers (1956) except that the cats were given both food reward and shock avoidance training on the visual discrimination. In agreement with Myers, animals that had prior section of the optic chiasm and the corpus callosum showed no interocular transfer when tested in the food reward situation (used by Myers). However, these same animals showed very good interocular transfer in the shock avoidance situation.

Clinical studies on humans who have suffered damage to the visual areas of the cortex have provided much useful information (see Teuber, 1960). The extent of damage in clinical studies (usually by tumor, injury, or cerebrovascular accident) is impossible to determine. Most patients do not come to autopsy, so the extent of damage cannot be measured. In the visual system the degree of damage to visual area 17 (or the geniculate projection to it) can be measured rather precisely by the use of a perimeter. The visual field defects (called scotomas) seem to correspond exactly with the retinal projection. By shining a small light on different portions of the retina, the exact extent of retinal blindness can be determined.

In general, patients with even quite large scotomas can correctly perceive visual form. Although a large portion of the retino-cortical system is nonfunctional, they are able to utilize the intact remnant of the system very well. Teuber describes two complementary cases, one with essentially total bilateral elimination of the visual fields except for the foveas, and another with total elimination of the central and foveal regions. Both patients could perceive visual forms. If a portion of the form was projected on the nonfunctional part of the retina, the patient responded as though the form were complete.

On the other hand, even relatively moderate lesions of the primary visual system seem to cause some impairment in a variety of tasks. For example "hidden figures," in which line drawings are concealed by embedding them in patterns of lines, are much more difficult for such patients to see. However, brain damage outside the visual areas causes equal impairment in the task. This type of deficit seems to be a general effect of brain damage rather than a specifically visual impairment.

CORTICAL REPRESENTATION OF THE CHEMICAL SENSES

TASTE.   As noted in our earlier discussion of the taste pathway (Chapter 10), the cortical representation of taste lies in the somatic sensory area I region having representation of the tongue. Microelectrode recordings from single cells in this region of the cortex have shown that some single cells respond to taste stimulation but not to touch or temperature stimuli. Still other units show convergence of tactile, thermal, and taste impulses (Pfaffmann, 1957). Lesions of this "taste" region of the cortex produce marked deficits in the taste discrimination behavior of rats measured by preference of water over quinine solution (Benjamin, and Pfaffmann, 1955). In the primate, Bagshaw and Pribram have shown that insular and other surrounding regions of temporal cortex must be included in addition to the tongue representation of SI to produce elevation of taste thresholds (1953). Taste representation in the cerebral cortex lies within the somatotopically organized tongue and throat region of somatic sensory area I (see Figure 11.9).

OLFACTION.   There appears to be no representation of the olfactory receptors on the cerebral neocortex. The primary central projection of the olfactory bulb is on older structures, the prepyriform area and the para-amygdaloid region in the base of the cerebrum (Chapters 11 and 15). Stimulation of the olfactory bulb can influence ongoing cortical EEG activity, but this effect appears to be indirect rather than the result of direct sensory projections to cerebral neocortex (Adey, 1959).

Suggested readings

Bard, P. (Ed.) *Medical physiology*. St. Louis: Mosby, 1956 (Chapter 75).

Harlow, H. F., & Woolsey, C. N. (Eds.) *Biological and biochemical bases of behavior*. Madison: University of Wisconsin Press, 1958.

Rosenblith, W. A. (Ed.) *Sensory communication*. New York: Wiley, 1961.

CHAPTER 12

THE NEURAL CONTROL OF MOVEMENT: I. SPINAL REFLEX MECHANISMS

V irtually all the measurable overt behavior of organisms consists of muscle movements. Walking, fighting, writing, and talking are simply sequences of skeletal muscle contractions and relaxations. Since psychology is the study of behavior, it is really the study of muscle movements. It is obvious that much more abstract categories of behavior may be more meaningful; if we wish to understand a novelist we read his novels rather than recording his finger movements while he is writing the novels. Nonetheless, muscle movements form the basis of all the higher order aspects of behavior. In this chapter we will see that even the "simple" reflex patterns of movement produced by the spinal cord can resemble the behavior of the intact organism. Reflex mechanisms can dramatically alter the probability that a given response will occur, even in the absence of any overt movements. The behavior of the spinal animal can appear as "purposive" as that of the whole animal. An understanding of the nature of muscle activity and the reflex control of movement exerted by the spinal cord would seem to be of value for all psychologists interested in the behavior of organisms.

THE NEUROMUSCULAR SYSTEM

The structure and actions of muscle

In terms of structural characteristics there are three general types of muscle tissue: striated, smooth, and cardiac (see Figure 12.1). Smooth muscle and cardiac muscle are under the control of the autonomic efferent portion of the nervous system and striated muscle is controlled by the somatic efferent portion

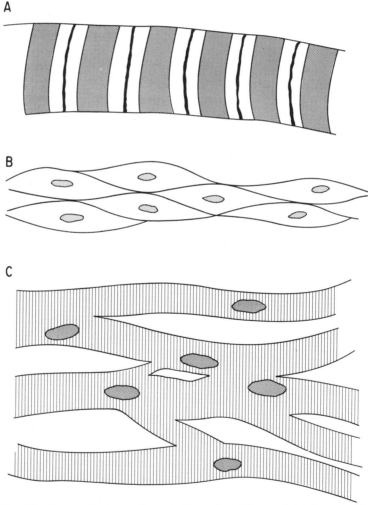

Figure 12.1.   The three major types of muscle fibers: **A**, striated or skeletal muscle; **B**, smooth muscle; **C**, cardiac (heart) muscle.

of the nervous system (see Chapter 4). Furthermore, smooth and cardiac muscle continue to function after all neural control is eliminated, while striated muscle is useless after nerve section. Biologists sometimes classify striated muscle activity as "voluntary" and smooth and cardiac muscle activity as "involuntary." Although these terms often carry surplus meanings, they can be approximately defined in operational terms. For example, we might use the label "voluntary" for all muscle actions a person can make upon request. Using this criterion we would include some smooth muscle actions as voluntary (i.e. bladder control) and some striated muscle responses as involuntary (i.e. postural adjustments) but there is a general correspondence.

It is common to differentiate two types of striated muscles: fast and slow. Fast muscles contract rapidly (7.5 to 40 msec contraction time) and are those most involved in the rapid movements of behavior like eye movement and limb contractions. Many of the deeper lying striated muscles that act to extend the limbs, particularly those involved in adjustments of posture, are slow (90 to 120 msec contraction time). In some mammals (e.g. cat) slow muscles appear red due to the greater concentration of myoglobin, a substance in muscle similar to the hemoglobin of blood, which stores oxygen for use during muscle activity. Fast muscles in the cat are pale or "white" in appearance.

In gross appearance muscle seems to be made up of many small fibers all running the length of the muscle. The fibers range in diameter from about 0.01 to 0.1 mm in man, and no individual fiber is longer than about 12 cm. If the muscle is shorter than this length all fibers run the entire length; if it is longer, individual fibers attach to other fibers along the muscle. The gross muscle attaches to the bone at each end by tendons or fascia of very tough connective tissue. Each muscle fiber is a separate entity but not necessarily a single cell, there being a number of cell nuclei in each fiber. Individual fibers viewed under a microscope have a characteristic striated appearance, due to the regular sequence of dark bands along the fiber.

Striated muscle fibers are of two types, *extrafusal* and *intrafusal*. The extrafusal fibers are the ones that actually do the contracting when the muscle contracts. The intrafusal fibers contain special sensory receptors, the stretch or spindle organs, to be discussed later. The microstructure of an extrafusal muscle fiber is shown in Figure 12.2. Each fiber is composed of many columns of fibrils, each column containing many fibrils, and each fibril is composed of a bundle of filaments. The filament is the smallest structural subdivision of the muscle fiber and has a diameter of about 150 Å. The muscle filament consists mostly of two proteins, *actin*, with a molecular weight of 57,000, and *myosin*, with a molecular weight of about 600,000. The combination of these two proteins is called actomyosin. Actomyosin can be extracted from muscle by placing the muscle in a salt solution for a long period of time. Englehardt (1939) first showed that if the rather viscous actomyosin so extracted was squirted out through a small opening into water (in the same general way that nylon threads are made) it solidified into a fiber. If this synthetic "muscle" fiber is treated with

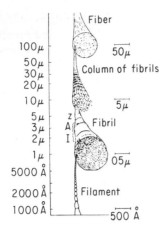

Figure 12.2. The microstructure of a skeletal muscle fiber. Each fiber is composed of many columns of fibrils and each fibril is composed of many filaments, each of about 1000 Å. An average muscle fiber may contain as many as 10 million filaments. (From Buchthal and Kaiser, 1951)

ATP (biological energy source) the fiber will contract. Actomyosin thus appears to be the active contractile substance of muscle.

The energy metabolism of striated muscle activity is of some interest. Under resting conditions the ATP formed by *oxidative* metabolism of carbohydrates (see Chapter 5) is ample to sustain the basal metabolic functions of muscle fibers. However, this source is entirely inadequate to handle the vast amounts of biochemical energy required for the strong and rapid contractions that are the primary function of muscles. Two additional energy-producing mechanisms exist in muscle. A great deal of energy is stored in the form of *phosphocreatine*. Upon demand, this substance is converted by an anaerobic process to ATP. In addition the muscle fibers have the ability to manufacture ATP from glycogen by an anaerobic process that yields lactic acid as the end product. As you may recall from Chapter 5, lactic acid can be further metabolized only by oxidative processes. This is accomplished in the liver. The muscle lactic acid is conveyed to the liver via the blood stream and there converted to blood glucose, which returns to supply glycogen to muscle for further metabolism into ATP and lactic acid. This recycling process, diagramed in Figure 12.3, is often referred to as the *Cori*

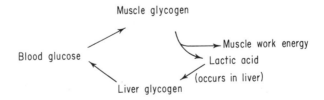

Figure 12.3. The Cori cycle. The lactic acid that accumulates in muscle during work is transported by the blood stream to the liver, where it is converted to glucose, passes via the blood stream to muscle, where it is converted to glycogen and " burned " to yield work energy and lactic acid.

cycle. The "oxygen debt" of a sprinter is the oxygen required to convert lactic acid formed during the race into glycogen. In contrast to striated muscle, virtually all the energy requirements of smooth and cardiac muscle are supplied by oxidative metabolism.

A given muscle can do only two things, contract or relax. Actually most muscles normally exhibit some intermediate level of contraction. Total relaxation is usually seen only in the paralyzed muscle. The effect of a muscle contraction depends on how the muscle is connected across bone joints. Two common types of limb muscle connections are shown in Figure 12.4. The *extensor* muscle is connected across the joint so that contraction of the muscle causes extension (straightening) of the limb. The *flexor* muscle is connected so that contraction causes flexion or contraction (bending) of the limb. Essentially all joint movements are controlled by both types of muscles. (There are, of course, other types

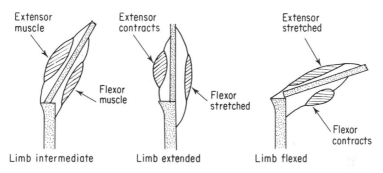

Figure 12.4. Reciprocal actions of flexor and extensor muscles. When the limb is extended the flexor is stretched and the extensor contracted. During flexion the flexor contracts and the extensor is stretched.

of muscle actions as well, e.g. lateral and rotational movements of limbs.) Each muscle or set of muscles acting in one manner is balanced by another set acting in the opposite manner. This is often referred to as *reciprocal* control. Muscles that act in an opposite fashion are called *antagonists*; those that act to produce the same type of movement are called *synergists*.

There are actually two different types of muscle contraction. Those discussed above in terms of limb movements are generally called *isotonic*; during contraction the muscle tension is relatively constant and the limb moves. The other type of muscle contraction is *isometric*; the muscle tends to change its degree of tension without actually moving the limb or changing its own length (exercises currently in fad that do not involve actual movement are thus termed isometric exercises). Isometric contractions are crucially involved in the control of posture. If two antagonistic muscle groups both contract to the same degree, there may be little movement of the limb and the contractions will tend to be isometric.

If one group contracts more than the other, both muscles will move and the contraction will tend more to be isotonic. In more general terms it is worth noting that changes in the isometric contraction strength of muscles can increase or decrease the tendency or probability that the organism will make a given response without actually producing any overtly measurable movement or response.

The innervation of muscles

In the normal organism striated muscles are activated by nerve fibers. After the muscle nerve is cut, the muscle can no longer be activated. Each efferent nerve fiber to muscle branches and innervates several muscle fibers. The basic unit of action of the neuromuscular system is the *motor unit*, a single efferent nerve fiber coming from a single motor neuron, together with the muscle fibers it innervates. The innervation ratio (number of muscle fibers per nerve fiber) ranges from about 3 : 1 for small muscles concerned with fine movement control to over 150 : 1 for large muscles. A spike discharge conducted along the axon of a single motor neuron will travel out all the axon branches and activate all the muscle fibers receiving the branches. The whole set of muscle fibers acts as a unit. All of them contract or none of them contracts.

We have already discussed the transmission of activity from the nerve fiber to the muscle fiber across the neuromuscular junction (Chapter 8). When the nerve spike discharge reaches the nerve fiber terminal it releases ACh across the synaptic space. The ACh causes a breakdown of the ionic barrier of the muscle fiber membrane, which results in a propagated muscle action potential. As a result of the muscle action potential, the muscle fiber contracts (see Figure 12.5). The actual mechanism whereby a muscle action potential leads to muscle contraction is unknown. The *in vitro* biochemical observations described above showed that when ATP contacts the actomyosin of muscle filaments, the filaments contract. Furthermore, ATP causes actomyosin to contract *in vitro* only in the presence of the same concentrations of potassium and magnesium ions that are present in normal muscle *in vivo*. In like manner, the presence of sufficient calcium ions inhibits contraction both *in vitro* and *in vivo*. Actomyosin, and in fact myosin alone, has been shown to act as an ATP-ase; i.e. it acts like an enzyme to break down ATP. The inorganic ion effects on the ATP-ase action of actomyosin parallel their effects on the initiation of actomyosin contraction by ATP.

An attractive possibility for the initiation of muscle contraction would be that the muscle action potential causes a shift in one of the inorganic ions, perhaps a decrease in the amount of calcium or increase in potassium and magnesium. Unfortunately, Hill (1949) showed that the contraction begins too soon to be produced by an inward diffusing substance released at the muscle fiber membrane by the action potential. Huxley (1957) has suggested that there may be a conducting membrane within the muscle fiber that crosses and

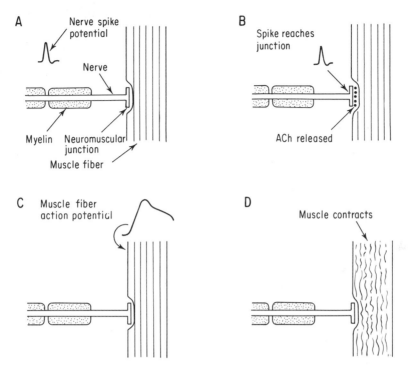

Figure 12.5.   Sequence of events involved in transmission across the neuromuscular junction. **A**, nerve action (spike) potential approaches junction; **B**, spike reaches junction and triggers release of ACh; **C**, ACh acts on muscle fiber to produce the muscle action potential; **D**, the muscle contracts.

recrosses the fiber at right angles to its length. A membrane-like structure does appear to exist within the muscle fiber, the so-called Z membrane which appears grossly as a part of cross-striations of muscle fibers. Huxley postulates that this Z membrane acts as an electrical conductor. This would permit ion shifts to occur directly at the filaments of the muscle fiber, and would make feasible the suggestion that such ion shifts could produce ATP activation and muscle filament contraction.

So far we have talked only about the innervation of muscle fibers by motor nerves. Muscles also have a variety of sensory receptors that send information to the CNS concerning the state of the muscle. In common with skin, small pain fibers come muscle tissue, many of which may be associated with blood vessels in the muscle. In addition there are two sorts of muscle receptors that are quite different from skin receptors: the *stretch receptor* or *spindle organ*, and the *tendon organ*. We will describe the special roles of these receptors later in the chapter. For now it is sufficient to note that they send information to the CNS concerning the initiation and degree of stretch of muscles and tendons. The spindle organs are of particular importance in that the afferent nerve fibers from them are the largest of the sensory afferents, the group Ia fibers. They make monosynaptic connections with the alpha motor neurons (neurons sending axons to the extrafusal muscle fibers), and are the fibers stimulated in the studies of monosynaptic excitation and disynaptic inhibition described in Chapter 7.

In closing this section it is perhaps well to re-emphasize the organization of peripheral nerves described in Chapter 4. Throughout their courses from spinal cord to muscles, skin and glands, most nerves are *mixed.* They contain both efferent fibers conducting to the muscles from the spinal cord and afferent fibers conducting to the spinal cord. They are segregated near the cord into the purely sensory dorsal roots and the purely motor ventral roots. Sensory fibers from muscle receptors enter into the dorsal roots, just as do all other sensory fibers. Peripherally, mixed nerves segregate into the cutaneous nerves, which contain mostly afferent fibers from skin receptors, and muscle nerves, which contain both the afferent and efferent nerve fibers of muscles. Consequently if a muscle nerve is stimulated electrically, both the afferent fibers from the muscle and the efferent fibers to the muscle will be activated. At the spinal cord there will be a sensory input via the dorsal roots and also an antidromic activation of the motor neurons via the ventral roots. If for experimental purposes we wish to prevent either of these results, it is necessary to cut the appropriate spinal roots.

SPINAL REFLEXES

Spinal reflexes are movements in response to stimulation mediated by the spinal cord of an animal after the cord has been severed from the brain. Such a preparation is called a " spinal animal." It is not uncommon for psychologists to ignore the study of spinal reflexes, or to pass over the subject lightly in order to treat of more "important" things like adaptive behavior, motivation, learning, "purpose," and so on. Actually the reflex behavior of the spinal animal is in many ways a prototype or simplified version of the behavior of the intact animal.

Psychologists are fond of subdividing behavioral events into the stimuli that go in, the complex central processes that occur, and the motor behavior that comes out. All three classes of events are well represented by the behavior of the spinal animal. The major difference is of course that the central events are a good deal less complicated. Nonetheless, the central events of the spinal cord range in complexity from the monosynaptic reflexes having only one synapse between incoming sensory fibers and output motor fibers to highly complicated multi-synaptic reflexes. The more complex spinal reflexes seem to exhibit many of the same kinds of higher order phenomenon usually attributed to the intact animal. Sherrington's (1947) description of the scratch reflex is a case in point:

In the dog a feeble electric current ("electric flea") applied by a minute entomological pin set lightly in the hair-bulb layer of the skin of the shoulder brings the hind paw of that side to the place, and with unsheathed claws the foot performs a rhythmic grooming of the hairy coat there. If the point lie forward (toward) the ear, the foot is directed thither, if far back in the loin the foot goes thither, and similarly at any intermediate spot. The list of such purposive movements is impressive.

As Sherrington has emphasized, the behavior of the animal is surely "purposive" and "motivated." The point is perhaps not so much that the spinal animal exhibits motivation and purpose, but rather that such terms may apply to both spinal and intact animals. The difference between the spinal cord and the brain is one of degree of complexity. There is no necessary reason why nerve cells of the spinal cord and the brain need be qualitatively different. Consequently, there is no necessary reason why behaviorally defined constructs like motivation and purpose should not apply to the behavior of the spinal cord as well as the brain. It is an interesting exercise to attempt definitions of such constructs for spinal reflexes. The degree of surplus meaning (meaning that cannot be operationally defined in reference to behavior) often attached to these higher order constructs soon becomes apparent.

The greatest advantage of the spinal animal is its relative simplicity. Its behavior is amenable to analysis in terms of central neural processes (i.e. in terms of synaptic interactions among neurons). Sherrington, who is perhaps the founder of modern neurophysiology, undertook his classical studies on spinal reflexes not because of any primary interest in the spinal cord per se, but rather because it offered some potential for analysis of basic neuronal processes and organization. Indeed he entitled his classic 1906 book *The Integrative Action of the Nervous System*. In the intact animal most complex central processes cannot easily be related to either sensory or motor events. In the spinal cord, on the other hand, muscle activity is usually to some extent predictable from sensory input, and central processes can be related to both sensory and motor events. Eccles' and others' elucidations of mechanisms underlying synaptic transmission in the nervous system were possible only because some neural aspects of reflex activity in the spinal cord (monosynaptic excitation and disynaptic inhibition) could be brought under direct experimental control. In short, the spinal cord can be viewed as a simplified model of the central nervous system, and spinal reflex behavior, a simplified model of the behavior of intact organisms.

Types of reflexes

There are many different ways to classify or group reflexes. One general type of classification has to do with the levels of the nervous system involved. If the afferent limb of a given reflex arc goes in one dorsal root and the efferent limb comes out the ventral root at the same level of the spinal cord, the reflex is called *segmental*. If more than one segment is involved, (e.g. in one or more dorsal roots and out several ventral roots) the reflex is termed *suprasegmental*. Reflexes involving the brain as well as the spinal cord are called *supraspinal*.

In this chapter we will restrict our discussion to spinal reflexes. As indicated earlier, the experimental preparation used to study spinal reflexes is the spinal animal, in which the spinal cord has been severed from the brain. Such animals can be prepared either acutely or chronically. It is not too difficult to maintain a chronic spinal dog or cat for a period of months. Actually, when studying segmental reflexes or reflexes that are restricted to a few segments, the most common procedure is to transect the spinal cord in the middle of the back. The posterior or caudal half of the spinal cord mediates reflexes of the hind limbs. The dorsal and ventral roots concerned with the hind limb of the cat and the dog are quite long and easy to dissect out for stimulation and recording. The "posterior spinal" animal has other advantages as well. When the cord is severed from the brain at the level of the neck, there is a marked drop in blood pressure and respiration becomes difficult. These effects do not occur when the transection is made in the lower thoracic spinal cord.

Perhaps the simplest way to classify reflexes is in terms of the type of sensory stimulation involved. In very general terms we can stimulate skin (by touch, pinching, crushing, electric shock, etc.) or we can stimulate muscles. The kind of muscle stimulus most effective in eliciting reflex responses is a stretch. The simplest of all spinal reflexes is the muscle *stretch reflex* or myotatic reflex (a segmental reflex). If a muscle is stretched it reflexly contracts. The familiar analogue of this reflex in man is the "knee jerk" (actually a tendon jerk, the tendon just below the knee cap is tapped). The reflex is a rapid and vigorous extension of the leg. The knee jerk reflex per se would seem to play an eminently trivial role in behavior. Actually it is simply an artificial example of the stretch reflex, which is the primary reflex determining the direction and degree of on-going tension in muscles. The stretch reflex is the basis of the reflex neural control of posture and locomotion. An example of the stretch reflex in the cat is shown in Figure 12.6A.

The *flexion reflex* is the most common type of response to stimulation of the skin. As illustrated in Figure 12.6B, painful stimulation of the hind limb evokes marked flexion (contraction) of the limb away from the stimulus. The flexion reflex involves both segmental and suprasegmental components. This type of reflex has often been called a nociceptive or defensive reflex, and is one of the most common responses used in shock escape or avoidance conditioning studies with intact animals. Extension of the opposite hind limb often accompanies flexion of the stimulated limb. This is the *crossed extension reflex* diagramed in Figure 12.6B. The flexion reflex generally requires a strong or painful stimulus, particularly in the acute spinal animal. However, in the chronic spinal preparation, firm but nondestructive pressure on the hindpaw may elicit both flexion and crossed extension.

In the high spinal animal, where the cord has been severed from the brain, a variety of more complex suprasegmental reflexes can be elicited. The description of the rather elaborate and "purposive" scratch reflex quoted above from Sherrington summarizes the capabilities of the preparation, particularly in the chronic state. An example of the *scratch reflex* is illustrated in Figure 12.6C. If

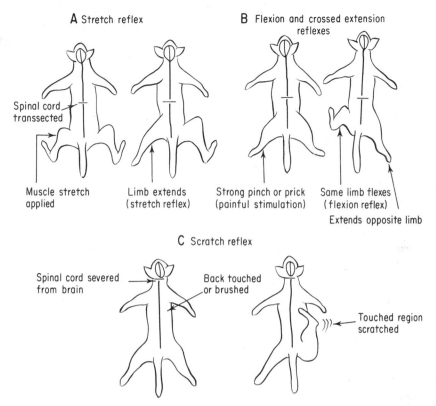

A Stretch reflex

B Flexion and crossed extension reflexes

Spinal cord transsected

Muscle stretch applied

Limb extends (stretch reflex)

Strong pinch or prick (painful stimulation)

Same limb flexes (flexion reflex)

Extends opposite limb

C Scratch reflex

Spinal cord severed from brain

Back touched or brushed

Touched region scratched

Figure 12.6. Examples of spinal reflexes. **A,** the stretch reflex is segmental and monosynaptic; **B,** flexion and crossed extension are polysynaptic and involve several segments; **C,** the scratch reflex is suprasegmental and polysynaptic.

the upper back is tickled or scratched lightly, the hind limb on the same side will reach up and scratch *the stimulated region* of the skin.

The reflexes considered above have been described in terms of movements of the leg rather than in terms of the actions of muscles or muscle groups. When a limb extends, extensor muscles contract and flexor muscles relax or stretch. When the limb flexes, just the opposite occurs. Remember that all limb movements are under reciprocal control. Thus in the stretch reflex it is necessary to activate extensor muscles and inhibit flexor muscles. In the flexion reflex, extensor muscles are inhibited and flexor muscles are activated. There is a dual excitatory and inhibitory control of the muscle actions involved in the movements. In terms of neural control, the motor neurons activating muscles have *reciprocal innervation*: each motor neuron can be excited or inhibited from a variety of different sources.

In the next section we will examine experimental investigations of the synaptic basis of reflex actions. Because reflexes are often classified in terms of synaptic mechanisms, it is worth giving a brief overview here (see Table 12.1). The stretch reflex involves *monosynaptic* (one synapse in the CNS) excitation of the motor neurons going to the extensor muscle that has been stretched and to synergistic extensor muscles. It also involves disynaptic (two synapses in the CNS) inhibition of the flexor muscles that act antagonistically to the stretched extensor muscle. Flexion reflexes involve rather general polysynaptic (more than one synapse) excitation of limb flexor muscles and polysynaptic inhibition of extensor muscles. Crossed extension is mediated by polysynaptic excitation of extensor muscles of the opposite limb and polysynaptic inhibition of the flexor muscles of the opposite limb.

It is impossible to describe the synaptic basis of reflex actions without some consideration of the types of sensory inputs involved. The sensory control of reflex actions will be discussed at greater length later in the chapter. The largest afferent fibers, group Ia, come from muscle spindle organs (stretch receptors), have monosynaptic excitary connections with motor neurons controlling the extensor muscles and exert disynaptic inhibitory control of flexor antagonist muscles. The next largest group of fibers, group Ib, come from the tendon organs. They act only through polysynaptic connections to motor neurons, and in terms of extensor muscles, tend to inhibit motor neurons to the stimulated extensor muscles and to other synergists, and tend to activate antagonistic muscles. All skin afferent fibers are the smaller group II, III and IV, and together with similar fiber groups from muscles tend to excite flexors and inhibit extensors of the stimulated limb, and have just the opposite effect on the opposite limb. These rather complex relationships will become much clearer after we have considered the synaptic basis of reflex actions.

The synaptic basis of reflex actions

The dorsal roots, you may recall, contain all the afferent (sensory) nerve fibers entering the spinal cord. These come from many different kinds of receptors or receptor functions: light touch, deep pressure, pain and temperature, joint position and movement, muscle stretch or relaxation, etc. They go to many different types of systems and destinations within the spinal cord and brain. The ventral roots contain all outgoing nerve fibers from the motor neurons of the spinal cord to muscles and glands. Figure 12.7 illustrates a typical experiment, taken from a classic study by Lloyd (1943). A dorsal root is stimulated electrically and the electrical response of the ventral root recorded. To avoid complications resulting from the feedback systems from muscle receptors let us assume that both dorsal and ventral roots have been cut distal to the electrodes. The recording electrode is bipolar, with the ventral root crushed over the distal electrode to yield a monophasic response. In a monophasic recording, the size of the nerve response (actually the area under it) is directly proportional to the number of fibers activated (see Chapter 3). With this type of recording

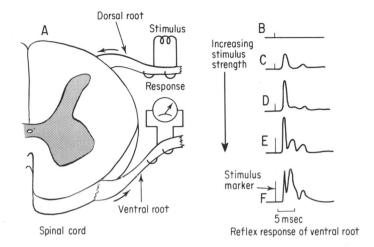

Figure 12.7.   **A**, schematic diagram of an experiment measuring the ventral root reflex. **B–F**, ventral root monophasic response to an increasingly strong dorsal root stimulus (indicated by height of stimulus marker). Note that the second hump appears in **D** and increases to **F**, but that no early hump occurs before the hump seen in **C**. The initial hump is the monosynaptic reflex. (From Lloyd, 1943)

arrangement, the electrical response is simply an envelope or sum of all the individual spike discharges from various ventral root nerve fibers.

The ventral root reflex response is shown for increasing intensities of stimulation in portions B–F of Figure 12.7. Several things can be noted. At the weakest stimulus at which a clear response is elicited (C) there is a sharp initial spike having a latency of about 2–3 msec, followed by some later low amplitude activity. As the stimulus is increased the initial spike increases in amplitude rapidly to reach a maximum stable amplitude (D, E and F). There are only slight changes in the later responses from C to D. Further increases in stimulus intensity cause the later portions of the response to increase gradually until at least one portion grows as large as the initial spike (F), and at least two peaks separate out (F). The simplest hypothesis to account for the various responses would be that the initial spike represents activation of afferent nerve fibers having low thresholds and only one or two synapses to the motor nerve fibers, and that later components represent afferent nerve fibers having higher thresholds and more synapses. Thus the initial response reaches a maximum at much weaker stimulus intensities than do the later components, indicating that all of its elements are being activated by the relatively weak stimulus. This type of experiment suggests that the early component of the response is monosynaptic and later components polysynaptic, but does not prove it.

The proof of this hypothesis was developed in a very ingenious experiment by Renshaw (1940). The basic experimental set up is illustrated in Figure 12.8A. Instead of dorsal root stimulation a bipolar stimulating electrode (S) has been inserted into the intermediate grey matter of the cord in a region above the locus of the motor neurons. A weak stimulus here will not excite motor neurons directly but might stimulate neurons having synaptic connections to the motor neurons. The first components of the response activated by the weak stimulus ought to result from synaptic actions of neurons that have synaptic connections with the motor neurons whose responses are recorded at *R*. You may recall (Chapter 7) that the cell body—and more specifically the axon hillock—has a much lower discharge threshold than the nerve fiber itself. As the stimulus intensity is increased, we ought eventually to stimulate the motor neurons directly by current spread from the stimulating electrode. In Figure 12.8A these situations are schematically indicated. The weak stimulus activates neurons within the dotted circle *a*, and a stronger stimulus can activate the motor neurons directly when the field has increased to *b*. Various control maneuvers can demonstrate that the stimulus is in fact directly activating the motor neuron. Responses recorded from the ventral root in this experiment are shown in Figure 12.8B–G. Over a wide range of relatively weak stimuli we can activate only a longer latency response. Then with increasing intensity a much shorter latency response occurs, and grows larger while the later response becomes smaller. The time from the stimulus to the onset of the first response is 0.1 msec,

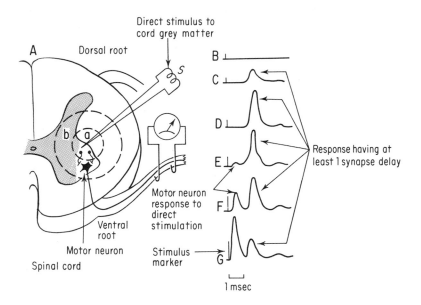

Figure 12.8.   **A,** experimental arrangement used by Renshaw to demonstrate monosynaptic transmission. **B–G,** ventral root response to increasingly strong electrical stimuli delivered directly to the grey matter of the cord. The response seen at **C** represents monosynaptic activation of the motor neurons (electrical field **A** in the cord) and the earlier response first seen at **E** is direct electrical activation of motor neurons when the stimulus field has increased (field *b* in cord) to include the motor neurons (see text). (From Renshaw, 1940)

exactly equal to the conduction time along the motor neuron axon to the recording electrode. The time from the first response to the second must then represent the time required to cross one synapse. The range of time falls between 0.5 and 0.7 msec.

If we now return to the kind of experiment shown in Figure 12.7, but insert a recording electrode where the afferent fibers of the dorsal root enter the cord (to measure convection time), we can compare the reflex response time with the " one synapse delay " time measured in the experiment of Figure 12.8. Such an experiment (Lloyd, 1943) gave an independent estimate of central conduction time of the order of 0.65 msec, in perfect agreement with Renshaw's value measured in Figure 12.8 as the time to cross one synapse. Therefore the initial response of the reflex must be monosynaptic, i.e. have only one synapse between the incoming afferent fiber and the outgoing motor nerve fiber. This synapse is of course made by the afferent fiber on the cell body of the motor neuron.

The experiment by Renshaw was described in some detail, not only because it is a classic, but because of the kinds of methods and thinking it illustrates. Currently, with microelectrodes and elaborate equipment, such demonstrations can be made more directly. The proof given by Renshaw of monosynaptic transmission is indirect, but nonetheless convincing. It hinges on the demonstration of the minimum delay at one synapse (Figure 12.8). If in fact there were two synapses between the stimulated and motor neurons, as the stimulus was increased three peaks would be seen in the response, one between the first and second large bumps. In fact there is a third but late response at the very end of the tracing that begins to develop at about the same time the later of the two large bumps does (trace E), indicating the presence of a disynaptic pathway as well. However there is no such response between the two large deflections, indicating that the two must represent direct and *monosynaptic* activation of the motor neuron. The fact that the second response gets smaller as the first gets larger (traces D, E and F) is consistent with this interpretation. Impulses activating the motor neuron monosynaptically arrive at the motor neuron later in time than direct electrical activation (which is instantaneous for all practical purposes). Thus they arrive while many motor neurons are still absolutely or partially refractive from direct activation. The more that are activated directly the more will be refractory to the monosynaptically conducted activation. Hence the two responses will tend to have an inverse relationship. Remember that for the most part the same motor neurons are activated by both types of stimuli.

The significance of the several different responses in the ventral root reflex (Figure 12.7) is not limited to the fact that the first is monosynaptic and the later components polysynaptic. In addition the various afferent fibers going to mono- and polysynaptic connections in the spinal cord have differing functional characteristics and come from different places. Since nerve discharge threshold is inversely related to size, the largest afferent fibers have the lowest thresholds. As indicated in Figure 12.7, the monosynaptic response reaches its maximum long before the polysynaptic components do. The largest afferent fibers thus appear to be the ones having monosynaptic connections to motor neurons. These fibers come exclusively from muscle, and are termed muscle *afferents*. Sensory nerves from skin receptors have exclusively polysynaptic reflex connections to motor neurons in the cord, and are of smaller diameter than muscle afferent fibers.

These facts can be illustrated by a simple and straightforward experiment (Lloyd, 1943). Nerves that connect either from skin (cutaneous nerves) or from muscle are stimulated electrically. A skin nerve will contain mostly afferent fibers, especially close to the skin regions innervated by it. A muscle nerve, on the other hand, will have both muscle afferent fibers and outgoing motor nerve fibers to the muscle. Stimulation of a muscle nerve will also cause *antidromic* (backward) conduction along the motor nerves to the ventral roots and motor neuron cell bodies, which would complicate the recording. The ventral roots distal to the recording electrodes are cut to eliminate such antidromic responses. Now if we stimulate the muscle nerve, all ventral root responses must be reflex responses to incoming sensory activation. With weak stimuli *only the short latency monosynaptic response is seen in the reflex response.* As stimulus strength is increased, the later polysynaptic humps are seen in the record. In contrast, no matter how hard we stimulate a cutaneous nerve, we can never obtain the initial monosynaptic response, only the later polysynaptic components.

In summary, all afferent fibers having monosynaptic connections with motor neurons in the spinal cord come from muscle receptors (muscle nerves). Afferent fibers from skin receptors have only polysynaptic reflex connections to motor neurons.

The properties of synaptic transmission discussed in the previous chapters can help us to understand the more general behavioral phenomena of reflex responses mediated by populations of neurons. We will discuss facilitation of monosynaptic reflexes first and then generalize our discussion to include di-synaptic inhibitory reflexes and polysynaptic reflexes. Facilitation, exemplified by spatial or temporal summation, is easily handled in terms of generation of EPSPs on motor neurons. A very important concept here is that of the *subliminal fringe*. Some years ago Lloyd (1943) demonstrated that suprathreshold electrical stimulation of the group Ia afferent fibers always influences the motor neurons on which they make monosynaptic connections, even though this influence may not appear in the ventral root discharge. For example, a weak stimulus may not cause any motor neurons to fire. However, if a stronger test stimulus is applied to group Ia fibers from a synergist muscle (this can also be accomplished by subdividing a dorsal root into branches and stimulating them separately) the ventral root response is larger when both stimuli are given at the same time than when the test stimulus is given alone. The weak stimulus does not cause motor neurons to fire but does induce subthreshold EPSPs in many motor neurons. In like manner, the strong test stimulus does not simply cause spike discharges in some of these motor neurons; it also produces subthreshold EPSPs in others. The two stimulus effects add together (spatial summation) to produce spike threshold EPSPs in some of the motor neurons, and a larger ventral root response

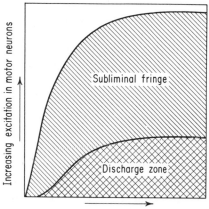

Figure 12.9. Graph showing the subliminal fringe effect in monosynaptic excitation. No matter how strong a single input stimulus delivered to the spinal cord is, a large proportion of excited motor neurons will not reach discharge threshold. (From Lloyd, 1943)

occurs. The motor neurons that exhibit subthreshold stimulation to either stimulus are said to be in the subliminal fringe. All of the motor neurons influenced by a given nerve, incidentally, are said to be in the motor neuron " pool " of the nerve.

The relative sizes of the subliminal fringe and the actual spike discharge zone as a function of stimulus strength are diagramed in Figure 12.9. A most important factor illustrated by this diagram is that no matter how strong a single shock delivered to the afferent neurons is, there will always be a significant percentage of neurons that are subliminally excited. In fact a maximum stimulus to a nerve will yield the greatest subliminal fringe. It may be presumed that the afferent terminals on these from the input nerve are insufficient to cause EPSPs of spike threshold amplitude. If another input which shares some of these neurons in the subliminal fringe is stimulated at the same time, the EPSPs will summate to discharge threshold and a very much larger reflex response will result than from either stimulus alone. Because of the subliminal fringe effect, it is even possible to select two stimuli—neither of which alone will yield a measurable reflex response—which together will produce a large response. Many motor neurons of the subliminal fringe for a given afferent nerve input connect to muscle groups closely related to the muscle from which the afferent nerve originated. These act as *synergists*: they tend to produce the same over-all response as does the original muscle.

Reflex inhibition is a logical extension of the phenomenon of IPSP generation. A given input nerve having monosynaptic excitatory connections to a motor neuron pool will also have inhibitory connections through inhibitory interneurons to motor neurons activating antagonistic muscles. If such a system is stimulated and the excitability of the antagonistic muscle neurons tested by using an input nerve having monosynaptic excitatory connections to them, the test output reflex is diminished in size over a period of about 4 msec. Maximum inhibition is obtained when the inhibitory volley precedes the excitatory test volley by about 0.5 msec, about the time that would be required to cross the additional synapse of the interposed interneuron (Lloyd, 1943). Although there is still some disagreement concerning the existence of interneurons mediating all instances of reflex inhibition, the evidence favoring this hypothesis seems quite strong (Eccles, 1964). In considering reflex inhibition we should also note the Renshaw cells, activated by recurrent collaterals from motor neuron axons, which act back to inhibit the same and neighboring motor neurons (Chapter 7). These presumably act in part as a damping system which will prevent over-excitation of muscles by "runaway" motor neuron discharge.

It is important to keep in mind that excitatory and inhibitory "subliminal fringe" effects reflect convergent EPSP and IPSP generation. Monosynaptic excitation of an extensor motor neuron by group I afferents from two different extensor muscles means that each input evokes monosynaptic EPSPs in the cell. Analogously, disynaptic inhibition of a motor neuron by two inputs means that both evoke IPSPs in the cell. Actually, the patterns of convergence are rather more complex than this simple characterization would suggest. Eccles, Eccles, and Lundberg (1957a) investigated convergence of monosynaptic excitation to many different groups of alpha motor neurons from a wide variety of muscles in the limbs of the cat. *Homonymous* excitation (excitation of motor neurons from a muscle controlled by the same motor neurons) was generally but not always greater than *heteronymous* excitation (excitation of motor neurons from muscles not controlled by the motor neurons). Synergists always exhibited convergence, but sometimes muscles not usually regarded as synergists showed heteronymous excitation. R. M. Eccles and Lundberg (1958) examined convergence patterns of group Ia afferent synaptic actions (monosynaptic excitation and disynaptic inhibition) on motor neurons of hip and knee muscles in the cat. In general reciprocal Ia inhibition was found between extensors and flexors acting at the same joint (i.e. antagonists). However, there was excitation from knee flexors to hip extensors, Ia inhibition to hip flexors from knee extensors, and other complex interconnections. A summary of their findings is shown in Figure 12.10. It illustrates the complexity of even the simplest reflex patterns.

The interactions described above are the result of group Ia afferent nerve fiber activation. Far more complex patterns can, of course, occur with poly-synaptic reflexes. Group Ib afferents, for example, induce di- and trisynaptic excitation and inhibition. Thus, flexor motor neurons often receive Ib excitatory actions from antagonist extensors, from extensors operating at a different joint, and in some cases from flexor muscles operating at different joints (Eccles, Eccles, and Lundberg, 1957b). In addition, there are a variety of complex poly-synaptic reflex actions of group II, III, and IV afferents. Finally, reflex actions produce *presynaptic* inhibitory affects on many afferent fiber groups. The reflex machinery of the spinal cord is not simple. (See Lundberg, 1966, for a discussion of integration in reflex pathways.)

In more general terms, polysynaptic reflex facilitation and inhibition may be presumed to work in a generally comparable manner to monosynaptic reflexes.

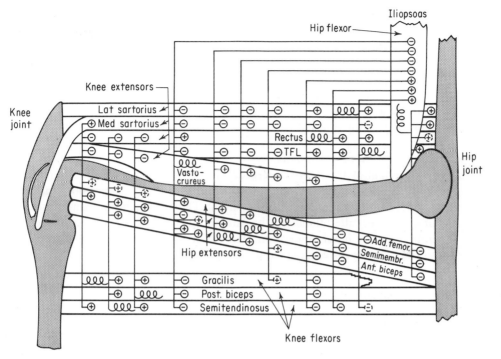

Figure 12.10.   Drawing summarizing the distribution of heteronymous monosynaptic excitatory actions ⊕ and disynaptic inhibitory actions ⊖ evoked by stimulation of group Ia afferents (indicated by ℓℓℓ) from hip and knee muscles in the cat. Occasional or weak actions are denoted by hatched circles. (From R. M. Eccles and Lundberg, 1958)

The obvious difference lies in the fact that several synapses are interposed between stimulus and response, rather than only one, thus allowing for much greater complexity of interaction. The time courses of facilitation and inhibition are considerably longer than for monosynaptic reflexes. In addition the reflex connections are more diffuse. Strong skin stimulation almost anywhere on the foot or leg activates essentially all muscles participating in the leg withdrawal response and inhibits most leg extensor muscles. Polysynaptic reflexes are characterized by longer duration effects and much greater amplitude variability than monosynaptic reflexes.

Sensory control of reflex activity

The experiments described above illustrate fundamental aspects of spinal cord reflexes and some of the methods used to study them. These and many other procedures have given us rather complete information about the various sensory nerve fiber groups, their receptor origins and central terminations, and the roles they play in spinal reflexes. The reader may find it somewhat difficult to abstract the more fundamental concepts in the brief survey given below of this complex and detailed literature. There are two very important and basic aspects to the sensory control of reflex activity. One is the fact that sensory receptors in the muscles and tendons transmit rather complete information to the CNS concerning the state of the muscles—the degree of tension, the rapidity, extent, direction, and duration of changes in tension, etc. The other basic point is that a type of motor neuron in the spinal cord (the gamma motor neuron) exerts *motor control on the sensory receptors in muscles*. The gamma motor neurons do not produce direct changes in muscle tension, but instead modify the degree of activity of certain of the sensory receptors in muscles. In a sense this action is opposite to the traditional reflex. Instead of sensory input determining motor output, motor output determines sensory input. The sensory input from muscles of course induces alterations in the motor output as well, which in turn will modify sensory input, and so on. The system represents a rather complex and elegant example of feedback control.

Sensory information from muscles

The sensory nerve fiber groups and their receptor origins and central terminations are summarized in Table 12.1 (modified from Mountcastle, 1956). With the exception of pain fibers, most muscle afferents are fast conducting group I or group II. For skin afferents, touch and pressure are group II (and groups III and IV to a lesser extent); but pain and temperature are the slower group III and IV fibers. There are two fiber groups subserving pain, one faster (group III, or *A* delta in the old terminology) and one very slow (group IV, or old group *C*). In terms of reflex connections in the cord, group I fibers participate either in monosynaptic or disynaptic reflexes, whereas group II, III and IV fibers all participate in more complex polysynaptic reflexes, the most common being the leg flexion withdrawal reflex. Remember that these are only the reflex connections of the various fiber groups. They also connect to the many afferent pathways of the spinal cord that convey all aspects of sensory information to the brain.

Little is known about the more complex polysynaptic reflexes. However, a great deal has been learned in recent years about the mono- and polysynaptic reflexes of the muscle afferent fiber groups. These reflexes are striking examples of feedback systems in the central nervous system. In Table 12.1 you will note that for group I and group II three different types of muscle receptors are listed, annulospiral and flowerspray for spindle organs, and the Golgi tendon organs. Before we describe these in detail, it is worthwhile to review the structural organization of skeletal muscle. Figure 12.11 illustrates a few of the muscle bundles making up a given muscle. They are attached at each end to bone by tendons composed of very tough connective tissues. Individual muscle bundles are of two types, the regular muscle bundles made up of *extrafusal* fibers, which are the contractile elements of the muscle (see Figure 12.1), and the *spindle*

TABLE 12.1.   CLASSIFICATION OF DORSAL ROOT FIBERS

Classification of nerve fibers	Range of fiber size and velocity	Receptor origins	Effective stimulus	Central destinations and/or reflex actions*
Group Ia (A-alpha)	12 to 20 microns 70 to 120 m/sec	Muscle: Annulospiral endings of muscle spindle	Stretch: Low threshold	Motorneurons of muscle of origin, synergists and antagonists. Alpha motorneurons: Monosynaptic excitation of muscle of origin and synergists, and disynaptic inhibition of antagonists.
Group Ib (A-alpha)	12 to 20 microns 70 to 120 m/sec	Muscle: Golgi tendon organs	Stretch: Slightly higher threshold	Motorneurons of the muscle of origin, and its synergists and antagonists. Alpha motorneurons: Polysynaptic excitation and inhibition.
Group II (A-beta and gamma)	5 to 12 microns 30 to 70 m/sec	Muscle: Flowspray endings of muscle spindle	Stretch: Low threshold	Polysynaptic: Inhibition of extensors and facilitation of flexors throughout the limb. Stretch-evoked flexion withdrawal reflex. The action is identical, regardless of the afferent discharge.
		Skin: Touch-pressure	Mechanical deformation of skin	Polysynaptic: Excitation of flexors and inhibition of extensors throughout the limb. Flexion withdrawal reflex. Contralateral component is the crossed extensor reflex.
Group III (A-delta)	2 to 5 microns 12 to 30 m/sec	Muscle: Unknown ? pain receptors	? Destructive	
		Skin: Pain, fast ? cold, heat, touch?	? Destructive temperature change	Polysynaptic: From either muscle or skin these afferents produce excitation of flexors and inhibition of extensors throughout the limb. Flexion withdrawal reflex. Contralateral component is the crossed extensor reflex.
Group IV (C-fibers)	0.5 to 1.0 micron 0.5 to 2.0 m/sec	From muscle and skin Pain—slow touch?	Destructive	

* Only the spinal reflex destinations and actions are indicated here. All nerve fiber groups send complete information to the brain as well.
SOURCE: Modified from Mountcastle (1956)

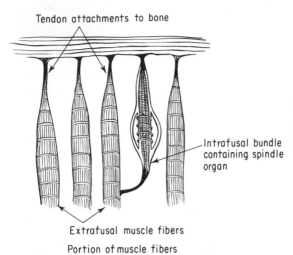

Tendon attachments to bone

Intrafusal bundle
containing spindle
organ

Extrafusal muscle fibers

Portion of muscle fibers

Figure 12.11. Anatomical arrangement of extrafusal (contractile) muscle fibers and an intrafusal muscle bundle containing a spindle organ.

organs, each consisting of several *intrafusal* fibers. The spindle organs are found intermingled with regular muscle bundles throughout muscles, and are attached to tendons or to regular muscle bundles. They always lie *parallel* to the regular muscle bundles. These spindle organs have been known for many years, but a clear appreciation of their significance has only been attained in recent years through the work of such scientists as Matthews, Kuffler, Hunt, Granit, and others. Although the intrafusal fibers of the spindle organ are muscle fibers and do contract, they contract very weakly and contribute nothing to the overall pull of the muscle, which is due entirely to contraction of the extrafusal fiber bundles.

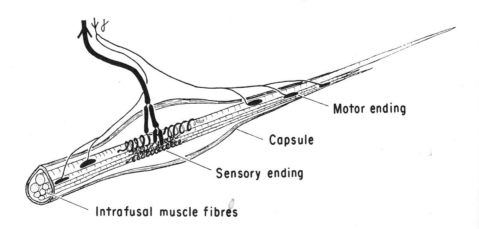

Motor ending

Capsule

Sensory ending

Intrafusal muscle fibres

Figure 12.12. Enlarged view of the muscle-spindle organ showing the motor nerve end plates on the intrafusal fibers and the sensory endings leading to the sensory nerve fiber (heavy line). (From Barker, 1962)

The intrafusal fibers of the spindle are innervated by a special type of motor neuron called the γ (gamma) motor neuron. Motor neurons innervating regular contractile muscle fibers are termed α (alpha) motor neurons.

Both the annulospiral and flowerspray *afferent* fiber terminals are found in the enlarged central region of the spindle. The annulospiral fibers encircle the inner region of the spindle, and the flowerspray endings are distributed close by in clusters along the sides in this same region (Figure 12.12). The annulospiral fibers are all group Ia—the largest and most rapidly conducting, whereas the flowerspray fibers are all slower group II (see Table 12.1). The central connections and reflex functions of these two types of afferent fibers are quite different, and they respond in a somewhat different manner to muscle contractions or relaxation. Hence we will refer to them as group I afferents and group II afferents, and to both as spindle afferents, in discussing muscle actions.

The other type of muscle receptor of importance here is the Golgi tendon organ. This is simply an afferent nerve fiber whose terminals lie in the tendon joining muscle and bone. The terminals proliferate in the tendon fibers close to the muscle-tendon junction (see Figure 12.13).

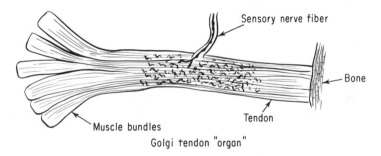

Figure 12.13.   Schematic drawing of the Golgi tendon organ. Nerve fibrils of the sensory nerve fiber are distributed to the tendon fibers. (After Patton, 1960)

In physical terms the tendon organs are in *series* with the muscle bundles. They stretch when the muscle contracts, because the muscle exerts pull on the tendon attachments when it contracts. In like manner if the muscle is stretched by a passive pull (as when antagonistic muscles are contracting) the tendon organ will also be stretched. However, the tendon organ has a relatively high discharge threshold and is not activated if moderate resting tension exists on a muscle. Hence only a fairly rapid change in the muscle tension, either a contraction or a relaxation, will cause a burst of activity in the fibers from the Golgi tendon organ. This is illustrated in Figure 12.14, in which the small spikes on the baseline indicate discharge in the afferent nerve fiber from the tendon organ. The tendon organ does have a slow spontaneous firing rate under constant tension, as indicated.

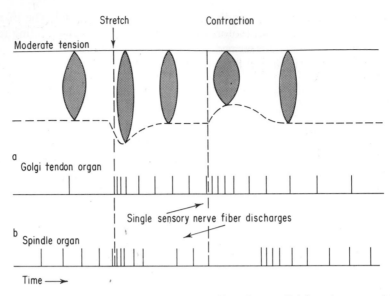

Figure 12.14. Response patterns of sensory nerve fibers from a Golgi tendon organ (a) and a spindle organ (b) to stretch and contraction of a muscle (After Granit, 1955)

The spindle organ, on the other hand, is connected in *parallel* with the muscle bundles. When they contract, tension on the spindle organ is reduced with consequent reduction of spindle afferent activity. When the muscle is stretched, the spindles are also stretched and hence activated. The spindle afferents have a moderately high spontaneous discharge rate, higher than the Golgi organ fiber rate when the muscle is under a given amount of constant tension. Furthermore, *the rate of spontaneous firing of spindle afferent fibers is directly related to degree of muscle tension*. While this relation is direct, it is not linear; with high tension the firing rate is less than would be expected from a straight line relationship. Thus muscle tension is coded in terms of the discharge frequency of the spindle afferent fibers. These effects are illustrated in Figure 12.14.

While the two types of spindle receptors and afferent fibers (group I and group II) both signal degree of muscle tension, they do differ in terms of just what aspects of muscle tension are coded. In particular, the group I afferents signal both the instantaneous *length* of the muscle and the *velocity* at which it is being stretched, while the group II afferents signal mainly the instantaneous *length* (Jansen and Matthews, 1962). Matthews (1964) has illustrated this difference vividly in the diagram shown in Figure 12.15. Note that while both group I (primary) and group II (secondary) afferents do code degree of "resting" stretch, they differ in terms of responses that occur while the muscle is actually stretching or contracting. The primary or group I fibers code the actual speed of stretch, whereas the secondary or group II fibers code the instantaneous length. Matthews puts it this way.

All these stretches may be resolved into separate static and dynamic components. Thus another way of describing the findings of Figure 12.15 is to say that the primary ending gives a large response to the dynamic component of a stimulus over and above its response to the static component, whereas the secondary ending does not. This *dynamic response* of the primary ending is most easily studied by measuring the change in discharge which occurs at the beginning and at the end of a period of stretching at constant velocity, as in Figure 12.15.

If we consider the actions of the tendon and spindle fibers together, rather complete information is transmitted to the CNS about the state of muscles. Suppose a muscle is under moderate tension. The Golgi tendon fibers will fire at a slow steady rate and the spindle fibers at a somewhat faster steady rate. If the muscle tension is suddenly increased and held at a high level, the Golgi fibers will show a brief burst of activity and then return to the slow spontaneous rate, whereas the spindle fibers will give a rapid burst and then stabilize at a higher rate. If the muscle tension is reduced, the Golgi fibers will again show a brief discharge, but the spindle fibers will cease firing briefly and then stabilize at a lower rate. *The Golgi fibers signal change in muscle tension and the spindles signal the degree, direction, and rate of change.*

What significance do these patterns of afferent activity have for reflex responses? First let us consider the group I afferents from annulospiral endings on spindles. These have direct monosynaptic excitory connections on the α motor neurons controlling the muscle and inhibitory connection through interneurons on the motor neurons to antagonistic muscles. Taking the patellar tendon reflex (knee jerk) as an example, a brief stretch resulting from a tap to the tendon increases group I activity, which causes contraction of the muscles extending the leg and relaxation (i.e. inhibition) of the flexor muscles. The leg

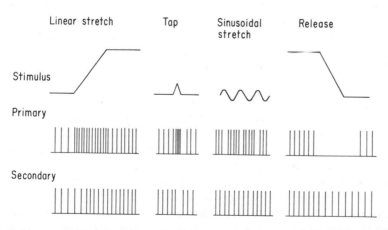

Figure 12.15. Response patterns of primary (Group I) and secondary (Group II) gamma afferent fibers to various types of mechanical stimulation (indicated on top row). (From Matthews, 1964)

thus extends briefly. The tendon organ activity, on the other hand, tends to work in an opposite fashion. A strong stretch or contraction of the muscle activates group I fibers from the tendon organ; these fibers have inhibitory connections through interneurons on the motor neurons to the muscle involved. In addition, antagonistic muscles are excited. Hence the over-all response tends to resist contraction of the muscle.

If we use a feedback analogue (cf. Patton, 1960b), the group I annulospiral fibers are a positive feedback system leading to an increase in activation following activation, whereas the group I Golgi fibers are a negative feedback system leading to a decrease in activation following activation. The balancing of these two systems results in very nice control over the degree of muscle tension. The group II flowerspray fibers from the spindle organs tend generally to inhibit extensors and facilitate flexors through polysynaptic pathways. Consequently they tend to oppose the action of the Ias for extensors but parallel the actions of the Ias for flexors. In a sense they increase the probability or readiness of flexion withdrawal reflexes (i.e. defensive reflexes). The group II spindle afferents tend in general to *excite flexor* motor neurons, whether their endings lie in flexor or extensor muscles.

The gamma motor neuron

As if the system were not already sufficiently complex, an additional mechanism must also be considered, the *gamma motor neuron*. Remember that these motor neurons of the spinal cord activate and cause contraction of the intrafusal fibers of the spindle organ. As first shown by Leksell (1945), increasingly intense electrical stimulation of the ventral root (containing all motor neuron axons) yields an initial graded response of the peripheral muscle nerve which reaches a maximum (alpha motor neuron fibers). With still stronger stimuli, a later bump develops, indicating activation of smaller, higher threshold, slower conducting fibers (gamma motor neuron fibers). Muscle contraction reaches a maximum with the maximum alpha response and does not increase further with gamma activation. Further experiments demonstrated that after blocking of alpha fiber activation (and consequently muscle contraction), activation of gamma fibers still caused increases in spindle *afferent* activity. Thus gamma motor neurons cause contraction of the spindle muscle fibers, which in turn stretch and activate the spindle afferent fibers. These of course in turn play back on the alpha motor neurons to the muscle to cause changes in muscle tension.

The next point to consider is what kinds of afferent stimuli will activate the gamma motor neurons. The picture that emerges is actually rather simple. Spindle and tendon afferents do not appear to influence gamma motor neuron activity directly. The most effective reflex stimuli altering gamma motor neuron activity are light touch, pressure and pain mediated by group II, III and IV fibers, primarily from skin receptors. The overall effect of such stimuli, particularly when applied to the foot, is to increase gamma efferent activity to ipsilateral

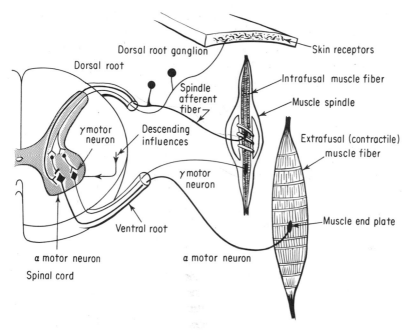

Figure 12.16.   Summary diagram of the gamma (γ) motor neuron system (see text)

flexors and decrease it to ipsilateral extensors. This in turn increases gamma afferent activity from flexors (and decreases from extensors), which increase excitation of the flexor alpha motor neurons (and decreases for extensors). Just the opposite occurs for gamma activity to muscles of the opposite leg. The net effect of this is to increase the probability of flexion for the ipsilateral limb and decrease the probability of flexion for the opposite limb. A summary diagram illustrating the ipsilateral interrelations is shown in Figure 12.16. It has been suggested that in reflexes the gamma motor neuron system acts in such a way as to maintain a sensory message from the spindles proportional to the amount of external stretch, even under changing conditions of muscle contraction (see Patton, 1960). Thus when a reflexly contracting flexor muscle shortens, the spindle activity—which otherwise would be reduced—is maintained by the increased gamma activity of the spindle muscle fibers.

We have spoken of the gamma motor neurons as if they were all of one kind. Actually recent evidence suggests that there may be two different types of gamma motor neurons (Boyd, 1962; Matthews, 1964). Although there is as yet no unanimity of opinion regarding this possibility (see Barker, 1962, for a dissenting opinion) it is sufficiently intriguing to merit some discussion. The diagram in Figure 12.17 illustrates the difference as conceptualized by Boyd. Histologically there are two different types of spindle muscle fibers. Both are innervated by group I and group II afferents, although the nuclear-chain fibers appear to have

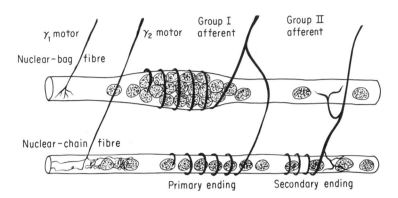

Figure 12.17. Hypothetical differentiation of gamma motor neurons into two different structural and functional types. (From Boyd, 1962)

a greater investment of the group II afferents. Boyd postulates that the larger gamma$_1$ motor fibers go only to the larger nuclear-bag type fibers and the smaller gamma$_2$ only to the nuclear-chain fibers. (Incidentally, a still further complication is the recent indication that some alpha motor neurons may innervate muscle spindles; Bessou, Emonet-Denand, and Laporte, 1963.)

There is good physiological evidence that two different types of gamma motor nerve fibers exist. If individual gamma efferent fibers are stimulated when the muscle fiber itself is at rest, no particular differences are seen in the responses of spindle afferent fibers. It is probably for this reason that the view has become well established that there is only one kind of gamma efferent fiber. However, Jansen and Matthews (1961, 1962) demonstrated that if the muscle were actually *being stretched*, stimulation of different individual gamma efferent fibers produced one or the other of two quite different types of responses in the afferent fibers. In brief (see Matthews, 1962; 1964) there seem to be *static* gamma efferents and *dynamic* efferents. Whereas the muscle is being stretched, stimulation of the *static* fibers abolishes the normal dynamic response of the group I spindle afferents (see above) so that they behave like group II spindle fibers. However, stimulation of *dynamic* gamma efferent fibers increased the response of the group I afferents to the dynamic stimulus while stretching, and increased the amount of change in frequency of discharge at the beginning and end of the dynamic phase of stretching—i.e. while the muscle was actually being stretched. It is as yet not clear whether physiologically defined dynamic gamma efferents correspond to the anatomically defined gamma$_1$ endings and static efferents to gamma$_2$ endings, or the other way around (see Matthews, 1964). These recent findings emphasize once again the very considerable degree of complexity possible in the central control of afferent information from muscle.

The gamma system has a general significance that extends beyond its role in spinal reflex activity. A number of descending pathways from the brain and upper regions of the spinal cord exert excitatory and inhibitory control on the gamma motor neurons (see Chapter 13). Thus many higher control systems can exert influence on muscle tension without necessarily causing direct contraction or relaxation of the contractile muscle fibers. By increasing or decreasing the degree of contraction of the muscle spindle fibers, the degree of spindle afferent activity, and hence contractile muscle fiber response probability, is altered. This occurs to some extent independently of the state of actual muscle fiber contraction. A great deal remains to be learned of the detailed functions and significance of the gamma system; it is an area of vigorous and extensive research at present.

The complex and elaborate sensory feedback systems from muscles would seem to suggest that controlled movements might be rather crucially dependent upon such feedback. Indeed, it has been known for many years that if all the dorsal roots conveying sensory information from one arm of a monkey are cut, the animal simply does not use that arm. However recent observations (Taub et al., 1965) indicate that a striking degree of movement control can develop if all sensory information from *both* arms is abolished. Such monkeys can learn to move an arm to a particular extent to avoid shock (to ear), even when viewing of the arms is prevented. Thus a learned arm movement can develop in the complete absence of *all* sensory information regarding the position and movement of the arm. Monkeys with total bilateral section of *all* dorsal roots in the spinal cord can move about, climb, and generally exhibit a striking degree of movement control. The extent to which such nonsensory control of movement is built into the nervous system, or whether it is learned during the course of development, remains to be determined.

Spinal reflex " Plasticity "

Anyone who has undertaken research on spinal reflexes can testify to the perhaps surprising fact that they are extremely variable, never being completely under the control of the experimenter. The spinal cord and its reflexes are far from a simple machine yielding an output entirely predictable from the input. Such variability is minimized when recording intracellularly the monosynaptic response from a single cell. However, when a reflex from a population of motor neurons with shifting subliminal fringe elements and other complexities is studied, certain population characteristics emerge. Whenever variability and complexity are such that "emergent" properties develop, it is possible that more complex aspects of behavior such as modifiability or learning can take place.

We will consider here two examples of "plastic" or relatively long lasting, reversible behavioral changes in spinal reflex response strength: *post-tetanic potentiation* (PTP) and *low frequency depression* (LFD). These phenomena have been obtained both for monosynaptic reflexes and polysynaptic reflexes. Our discussion will emphasize studies of monosynaptic reflexes because we have some understanding of the synaptic processes involved. Both PTP and LFD can be

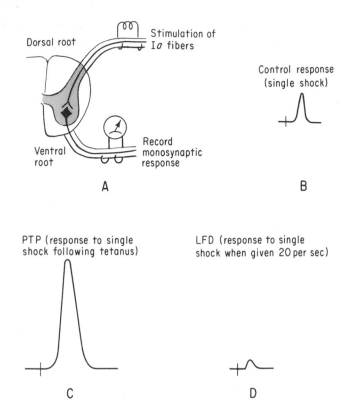

Figure 12.18. **A,** experimental arrangement used to show monosynaptic post-tetanic potentiation (PTP) or low frequency depression (LFD). **B,** amplitude of monosynaptic ventral root response to a single shock stimulation of the dorsal root (control response). **C,** PTP: enhanced response to single shock following high frequency (i.e. 500/sec) stimulation of the dorsal root for several seconds. **D,** LFD: depressed amplitude of response to individual shock when given at a rate of about 20/sec.

demonstrated by the experiment illustrated in Figure 12.18A. The group Ia afferent fibers (either of a nerve or a dorsal root) are stimulated electrically and the monosynaptic component of the ventral root response recorded. If a single electrical stimulus pulse is delivered at a rate of about once every 20 seconds, the monosynaptic ventral root response will remain constant in amplitude (Figure 12.18B). If this same stimulus is then given at a very high frequency (e.g. 500/sec) for a few seconds and the response is then tested every 20 seconds, the monosynaptic response will show a striking *increase* (Figure 12.18C) in amplitude that lasts for a period of minutes (PTP). If the initial 1/20 sec-stimulus frequency is simply increased to an intermediate frequency (say about 20/sec) the amplitude of the monosynaptic response *decreases* and stabilizes at a lower amplitude (LFD) (Figure 12.10D).

POST-TETANIC POTENTIATION. In Lloyd's initial demonstration of PTP he stimulated the group Ia afferent fibers in a peripheral nerve (the gastrocnemius nerve) at the slow rate of 1/2.4 sec to determine the initial or control amplitude of the monosynaptic ventral root reflex response. He then presented the same stimulus at a rate of 555/sec for 12 seconds, and then returned to the 1/2.4 sec-stimulus. There was a marked and prolonged increase in the amplitude of the monosynaptic response, which lasted for several minutes (see Figure 12.19). Curtis and Eccles (1960) have demonstrated comparable long lasting increases in the amplitudes of EPSPs recorded from individual motor neurons. This is a very long time compared to the few milliseconds duration of the EPSPs itself. Eccles and McIntyre (1953) found that if the dorsal roots were sectioned distal to the ganglia several weeks before the experiment, the PTP effects would last for an hour or more. Reversible increases in the amplitude of a reflex response that will last for minutes or hours after a few seconds stimulation would seem to be of considerable significance in terms of the possible synaptic basis of changes in the behavior of the intact animal.

Recently, Spencer and Wigdor, 1965 (and Spencer in personal communication) have shown that PTP may last for several hours in the "normal" acute spinal cat (i.e. without any prior surgical procedures such as the dorsal root section in Eccles and McIntyre's experiment). The crucial factor appears to be the *duration* of the high-frequency tetanizing stimulus. Results of their experiments are shown in Figure 12.20. In the upper graph the tetanizing stimulus lasted 7 minutes; monosynaptic PTP lasted about 12 minutes. In the lower graph, conditions were identical except the tetanizing stimulus was given for 20 minutes. Monosynaptic PTP lasted for more than two hours! The open circles in the lower graph compare the equivalent monosynaptic reflex for the

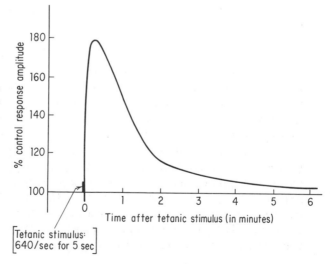

Figure 12.19. The time course of monosynaptic post-tetanic potentiation (PTP) plotted in terms of percent of the normal response amplitude with no tetanic stimulus. (From Lloyd, 1949)

% control response amplitude

Time after tetanic stimulus (in minutes)

Tetanic stimulus: 640/sec for 5 sec

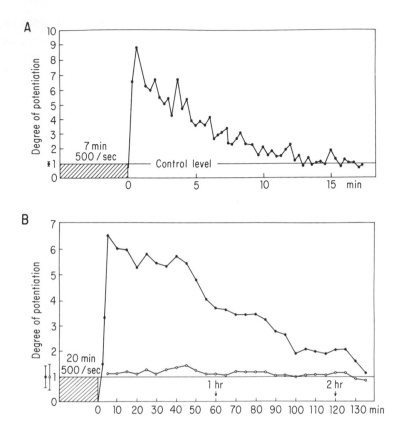

Figure 12.20. Monosynaptic PTP as a function of duration of tetanus. Shocks delivered to muscle afferents and responses recorded from ventral roots. **A,** PTP lasted about 12 min after a 7 min tetanus. **B,** PTP lasted approximately 2 hrs after a 20 min tetanus. Open circles are control data from hindlimb opposite to the potentiated side. (From Spencer, personal communication)

hindlimb opposite to the potentiated side, thus showing that the general excitability of the animal did not change during the experiment. As Spencer notes, it is perhaps suggestive that the tetanus producing a very long lasting increase in excitability is of the same approximate duration as the so-called "consolidation time" in learning. (The consolidation hypothesis is discussed in Chapter 17; for now it is sufficient to note that it is the supposed time after a learning trial required for "reverberating neural activity initiated by the trial" to establish some sort of permanent trace in the brain.) Thus a process like that responsible for PTP might conceivably be one of the neural mechanisms underlying learning.

Lloyd (1949) found that direct changes in the motor neurons themselves could not account for the potentiation effect because antidromic tetanic stimulation via the ventral roots produced no potentiation. He postulated that the presynaptic terminals of the afferent fibers became hyperpolarized after tetanization, thus leading to increased activation of the motor neurons (the resting membrane potential would be more negative; hence spike potentials would cause a greater shift in membrane potential at the afferent terminals with a corresponding increase in the release of transmitter substance, as diagramed in Figure 7.16). More recently Eccles and Krnjevic (1959) recorded intracellularly from the presynaptic terminal fibers and demonstrated that hyperpolarization developed following tetanizing stimuli which had the same time course as reflex PTP. Eccles et al. (1962) induced the same effects by applying hyperpolarizing currents to the cord. These data are all in accord with Lloyd's hypothesis.

Polysynaptic PTP has been observed in many experiments (see review by Hughes, 1955). Wilson (1955) showed that a very much lower frequency of tetanus (25/sec) was effective with polysynaptic reflexes. The synaptic basis of polysynaptic PTP is not well understood. It seems that interneuron participation in the reflex must be involved because polysynaptic PTP can be seen when one dorsal root is tetanized and another used to test the increase in reflex response strength. The two dorsal rootlets share no afferent fibers in common, so the increase that is obtained must involve interneurons activated by both rootlets (Wilson and Vernier, 1955).

Polysynaptic PTP appears to resemble reflex sensitization. In the flexion reflex of the spinal cat, for example, a brief tetanizing stimulus causes an increase in the amplitude of the flexion reflex that may last for many minutes (Thompson and Spencer, 1966; Spencer, Thompson, and Nielson, 1966a,b,c). The effect is somewhat analogous to sensitization in conditioning experiments (see Hilgard and Marquis, 1940). We will consider this point further in our discussion of the neural basis of learning in Chapter 17.

LOW FREQUENCY DEPRESSION.   If single shocks to group Ia afferent fibers are delivered at a faster rate than about 1/20 sec, amplitudes of the first few monosynaptic ventral root reflex responses decline and stabilize at a lower level (Jefferson and Schlapp, 1953; Lloyd and Wilson, 1957). Over the range of about 1/20 sec to 50/sec the stabilized response amplitude decreases as the stimulus frequency increases. When the stimulus is stopped and interposed only occasionally to test response amplitude, the response is found to return rapidly to its initial amplitude. The amount of decline in monosynaptic reflex response strength as a function of stimulus frequency is illustrated in Figure 12.21. Curtis and Eccles (1960) showed that the same kind of depression effect as a function of stimulus frequency occurs in the amplitudes of monosynaptically evoked EPSPs in individual motor neurons. Because the effect is not associated with any postsynaptic inhibitory actions on motor neurons, it is believed that, like PTP, the processes responsible for the depression are pre- or subsynaptic rather that postsynaptic (i.e. they occur prior to the motor neuron itself).

A depression of the monosynaptic reflex resulting from events separated in time by as long as 15 seconds is quite a different order of magnitude than the

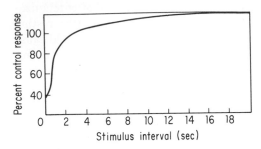

Figure 12.21. Degree of monosynaptic low frequency depression as a function of time between repeated stimuli. (From Lloyd and Wilson, 1957)

duration of IPSPs or presynaptic inhibition. A phenomenon somewhat analogous to monosynaptic low frequency depression is the habituation commonly seen in polysynaptic reflexes. Prosser and Hunter (1936) showed that brief trains of shocks to the hindlimb of the chronic spinal rat given 1/10 sec produced gradual but marked decrease or habituation of the flexion reflex. Recovery took place over a period of minutes. Habituation of the flexion reflex in the acute spinal cat is easily obtained (see Spencer, Thompson, and Nielson, 1966a,b,c; Thompson and Spencer, 1966). Although the synaptic mechanisms involved in reflex habituation (i.e. " polysynaptic LFD ") are not known, it may be that processes in interneurons analogous to the pre- or subsynaptic effects seen in monosynaptic LFD may be involved. This point will be elaborated in Chapter 17.

Here then are two relatively long-term reversible alterations in spinal reflex behavior as a result of stimulation; an increase following rapid stimulation and a decrease following slower stimulation. These kinds of changes may seem somewhat remote from learning, but they do indicate that rather long term reversible changes can be induced in even the simplest of neural systems, the monosynaptic reflex arc. If satisfactory analogues to normal behavioral phenomena such as habituation and learning could be established in the neurally isolated spinal cord, the very considerable knowledge and analytic techniques developed for spinal reflex functions could be brought to bear on these fundamental problems in the neuronal bases of behavior. We will examine several approaches to this basic question in the final chapter of the book (Chapter 17).

Suggested readings

Bard, P. (Ed.) Medical physiology. St. Louis: Mosby, 1956 (Chapters 61, 62, 63, 64, 67, 68, 69 and 70).

Granit, R. (Ed.) *Nobel symposium I. Muscular afferents and motor control.* New York: Wiley, 1966.

Granit, R. *Receptors and sensory perception.* New Haven: Yale University Press, 1955.

Eccles, J. C., & Schadé, J. P. (Eds.) *Physiology of spinal neurons.* Amsterdam: Elsevier, 1964.

Matthews, P. B. C. Muscle spindles and their motor control. *Physiol. Rev.*, 1964, **44**, 219–288.

Ruch, T. C., & Fulton, J. F. (Eds.) *Medical physiology and biophysics.* Philadelphia: Saunders, 1960 (Chapters 3, 4, 5, and 6).

13

THE NEURAL CONTROL
OF MOVEMENT:
II. BRAIN MECHANISMS

All striated muscle movements are controlled by the motor neurons of the spinal cord and cranial nerve nuclei. Sherrington termed the motor neurons the "final common path" of movement. All brain processes which are to influence movement must do so by acting ultimately on the motor neurons. In the preceding chapter we stated (and perhaps overstated) that spinal reflexes can accomplish a good many "purposive" behaviors. However, it is well to emphasize that spinal reflexes are responses to externally applied stimuli. The behavior of the intact animal is a great deal more than response to immediate external stimulation. The acute spinal animal tends to remain inert unless stimulated. The normal animal is hardly inert; his behavior is generally spontaneous and anything but predictable. The much increased complexity of behavior of the normal animal over the spinal animal must in the last analysis be accomplished by the higher regions of the brain exerting control over the final common path, the motor neurons.

The degree of complexity of control over movement exerted by the various regions of the brain was well described by William James in 1890. His analysis was based on simple acute experiments in which the brain of the frog was sectioned at different levels and the reflex behavior of the animal observed.

The types of reflexes exhibited by the spinal frog are not too different from those of the spinal dog or cat described in the preceding chapter. The acute spinal frog is unable to crawl or swim. If the section is made just above the medulla and cerebellum, rather clumsy crawling, jumping and swimming do occur. If the brain is cut at the junction of the midbrain and diencephalon locomotion becomes quite normal both on land and water. The animal croaks when pinched, and turns over when placed on his back. If the cerebral hemispheres alone are removed, the behavior of the frog appears at first glance to be normal. However there is one striking difference: the behavior of the decerebrated frog is not very spontaneous. William James draws this distinction in the following classic passage:

> Thus far, as aforesaid, a person unfamiliar with frogs might not suspect a mutilation; but even such a person would soon remark the almost entire absence of spontaneous motion—that is, motion unprovoked by a *present* incitation of sense. The continued movements of swimming, performed by the creature in the water, seem to be the fatal result of the contact of that fluid with its skin. They cease when a stick, for example, touches his hands. This is a sensible irritant towards which the feet are automatically drawn by reflex action, and on which the animal remains sitting. He manifests no hunger, and will suffer a fly to crawl over his nose unsnapped at. Fear, too, seems to have deserted him. In a word, he is an extremely complex machine whose actions, so far as they go, tend to self-preservation; but still a *machine*, in this sense —that it seems to contain no incalculable element. By applying the right sensory stimulus to him we are almost as certain of getting a fixed response as an organist is of hearing a certain tone when he pulls out a certain stop.
>
> But now if to the lower centres we add the cerebral hemispheres, or if, in other words, we make an intact animal the subject of our observations, all this is changed. In addition to the previous responses to present incitements of sense, our frog now goes through long and complex acts of locomotion *spontaneously*, or as if moved by what in ourselves we should call an idea. His reactions to outward stimuli vary their form, too. Instead of making simple defense movements with his hind legs like a headless frog if touched, or of giving one or two leaps and then sitting like a hemisphereless one, he makes persistent and varied efforts at escape, as if, not the mere contact of the physiologist's hand, but the motion of danger suggested by it were now his spur. Led by the feeling of hunger, too, he goes in search of insects, fish, or smaller frogs, and varies his procedure with each species of victim. The physiologist cannot by manipulating him elicit croaking, crawling up a board, swimming or stopping, at will. His conduct has become incalculable. We can no longer foretell it exactly. Effort to escape is his dominant reaction, but he *may* do anything else, even swell up and become perfectly passive in our hands.

The kinds of movement control described above for various levels of the frog brain are to some extent simplified, and not necessarily directly applicable to the mammalian brain, particularly in the long-term chronic preparation. Nonetheless, James' analysis depicts rather graphically that higher levels of the nervous system seem to be concerned with increasingly more complex aspects of movement control.

The reader will probably find the number and complexity of the various brain structures concerned with movement described in the course of this chapter somewhat bewildering, to say the least. It is well to remember that all of these systems can act only by influencing the activity of motor neurons, and the only effects of these influences are increases (excitation or facilitation) or decreases (inhibition or decreased excitation) in motor neuron activity. Although all control of movement must influence the final common motor neurons, there are many different *ways* that descending pathways can exercise this influence. The most direct method of control is by actually inducing depolarization (i.e. EPSPs) or hyperpolarization (i.e. IPSPs) in the motor neurons. In primates, one descending pathway from the cerebral cortex (pyramidal tract) does seem to have a direct monosynaptic excitatory action on spinal motor neurons. However, many influences, both excitatory and inhibitory, activate interneurons in the spinal cord which in turn induce hyperpolarizations or depolarizations in the motor neurons.

A more indirect method of influencing the excitability of alpha motor neurons is by controlling the activity of gamma motor neurons. An increase in gamma motor cell activity causes contraction of the intrafusal muscle fibers, which increases the activity of the spindle afferent fibers. These in turn synapse back to activate the alpha motor neurons, as described in Chapter 12. We encountered still another indirect method of alpha motor neuron control in our discussion of the efferent control of sensory input (Chapter 10). Descending pathways can exert presynaptic inhibition on incoming afferent fibers that activate and/or inhibit motor neurons. There are a great many other possibilities. One descending pathway might, for example, inhibit activity of the interneurons that normally mediate excitatory actions on motor neurons from another descending pathway. Another system might inhibit interneurons that normally mediate a descending inhibitory influence, and so on. Regardless of how indirect the synaptic mechanisms of action may be, all motor systems must ultimately influence the activity of motor neurons.

A number of brain structures are characterized as having predominantly motor functions. In a sense, any systems connecting to the final common motor neurons can be said to have motor functions, including the sensory Ia afferent fibers terminating monosynaptically on motor neurons. The English neurologist Hughlings Jackson asserted many years ago that the basic function of the nervous system is movement. In a very real sense, all areas of the brain are concerned with relating sensory input and endogenous activity to the movements that comprise behavior. However, some structures seem to be "more equal than others" in the control of movement.

It is common to distinguish two types of motor systems: *pyramidal* and *extrapyramidal*. The pyramidal system is a tract that descends from the cerebral cortex to the spinal cord without interruption to act on motor neurons. Many of the cell bodies of the pyramidal tract fibers lie in the motor cortex and their axons, descending to the spinal cord, make up the tract. The extrapyramidal system may be considered to be everything else that exerts influence on the motor neurons (grouped here under the headings of basal ganglia, cerebellum

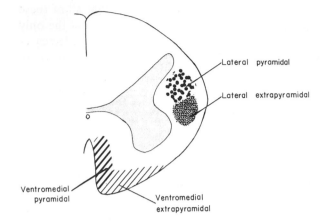

Figure 13.1. General locations of the lateral and ventromedial pyramidal and extrapyramidal pathways in the spinal cord (only right half of cord shown).

descending reticular formation, and vestibular system). There is considerable disagreement concerning the organization and functions of the extrapyramidal system and whether or not it can even be called a system.

Fortunately, at the level of the spinal cord the distinction between pyramidal and extrapyramidal pathways is fairly clear (see Figure 13.1). Basically, there is a pyramidal pathway and an extrapyramidal pathway on each side of the spinal cord. These are shown for one side of the cord in the oversimplified diagram of Figure 13.1. Each of these pathways has two tracts, one lying lateral and one ventromedial. The lateral portion of each pathway tends to supply motor neurons lying more lateral in the spinal grey, and the ventromedial portion supplies the more medially placed motor neurons. We can conceptualize these simply as the pyramidal pathway and the extrapyramidal pathway of the spinal cord. In terms of connections with motor neurons, there seems to be a tendency for the pyramidal tract to act on the alpha motor neurons. Some extrapyramidal influences appear to act indirectly on alpha motor neurons, e.g. by controlling the activity of the gamma motor neurons.

As a final oversimplification, we might characterize the pyramidal system as controlling rapid and precise movements of the extremities, of the type often called *skilled movements*. The rather ambiguous term "voluntary" has also been used to describe movements under control of the pyramidal tract. The influences of the extrapyramidal systems seem more concerned with alterations in response tendency, ranging in complexity from gross postural adjustments to subtle and as yet poorly understood control of movement.

The pyramidal tract

The pyramidal tract is composed of fibers passing through the *pyramids*, large pyramid-shaped fiber bundles in the medulla. The cell bodies of the pyramidal fibers lie in the cerebral cortex and the fibers end in the spinal cord (although many axon collaterals are given off by the pyramidal tract at sub-cortical levels. Cajal, 1899). The fibers of the pyramidal tract are the longest single fibers in the mammalian central nervous system, extending for some 2 feet in man and 30 feet or more in the whale. The pyramidal tracts are predominantly crossed: the tract originating in the left cortex, for example, descends on the left side to the lower medulla, crosses to the right at the *decussation* of the pyramids, and descends on the right side of the spinal cord. In primates there is also an uncrossed portion comprising about 20 percent of the pyramidal fibers which descends to the ipsilateral portion of the spinal cord (see Figure 13.2).

A number of early studies (see the review by Lassek, 1954) concluded that all pyramidal fibers originated from the giant Betz cells in the fifth layer of the motor cortex. This conclusion was based primarily upon retrograde degeneration evidence: section of the pyramidal tract resulted in degeneration of all giant Betz cells but other cells were not observed to degenerate. Recent evidence has shown that this conclusion is not valid. Almost 40 percent of the pyramidal fibers

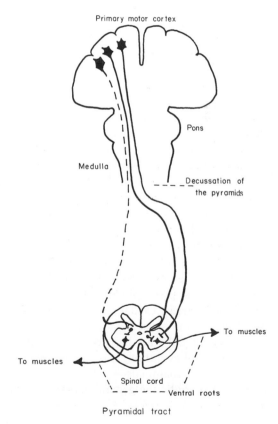

Figure 13.2. Schematic diagram of the pyramidal tract. Although most of the fibers cross in the medulla (decussation of the pyramids) some descend ipsilaterally (dotted line).

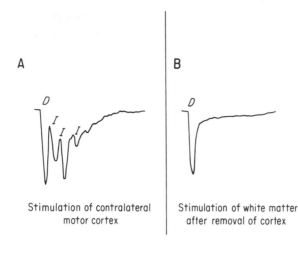

A

B

Stimulation of contralateral motor cortex

Stimulation of white matter after removal of cortex

Figure 13.3. A, gross evoked response recorded from the pyramidal tract to electrical stimulation of the motor cortex. The *D* wave represents direct activation of cells projecting down the tract and the later *I* waves represent activity relayed through one or more synapses in the motor cortex before activating the pyramidal cells. (Negativity down). **B,** pyramidal response to electrical stimulation of the fibers of origin of the pyramidal tract after removal of the motor cortex. Note the *D* wave (as in **A**) but the complete absence of the later *I* waves. (From Patton and Amassian, 1960)

apparently originate in various regions of the cortex other than the motor area, including prefrontal, parietal, temporal, and occipital regions (Walberg and Brodal, 1953). Twenty percent more come from the postcentral gyrus (somatic sensory area I; Levin and Bradford, 1938). Thus only 20 percent to 40 percent of the pyramidal fibers originate in the primary motor cortex. Finally, it appears that only about 2 percent of all the fibers in the pyramidal tract come from the giant Betz cells in the motor cortex. These fibers, the largest myelinated fibers of the pyramidal tract, range in diameter from 10 to 22 microns and are about as numerous as are the Betz cells in the motor cortex (Lassek, 1954).

This description of the origin of the pyramidal tract is based entirely upon anatomical evidence. Physiological studies have generally indicated a more restricted cortical distribution. Woolsey and Chang (1948) stimulated the pyramids electrically and recorded the gross antidromic response evoked in the cerebral cortex. Such responses occurred over the primary motor and somatic sensory areas, supplementary motor cortex, and somatic sensory area II in cat and monkey. Patton and Amassian (1960) stimulated the cortex electrically and recorded the response of the pyramidal tract. They found a still more localized region of origin, limited essentially to primary motor and somatic sensory cortex. These results are not necessarily in conflict with the anatomical data, but rather suggest that the predominant input to the pyramidal tract of cells having low threshold electrical excitability is from a relatively restricted area of cortex. (See discussion of sensory motor cortex in Chapter 11.)

The pyramidal tract has occasioned interest because of its late appearance in the course of evolution. It is found only in mammals—being well developed in most higher mammals—and reaches its maximum elaboration in primates. These facts parallel the general characteristics of the phylogenetic development of the cerebral cortex, a not too surprising observation in view of the cortical origin of the pyramidal tract. Of particular interest is the fact that in primates some 10 to 20 percent of the pyramidal fibers terminate monosynaptically on spinal motor neurons (Hoff and Hoff, 1934). This means that they can exert direct excitatory actions on motor neurons. The remaining fibers end on cord interneurons, having only indirect connections with the motor neurons. In contrast, there appear to be no direct monosynaptic connections of pyramidal fibers on motor neurons in the cat (Chambers and Liu, 1961; Lloyd, 1941).

Electrical stimulation of the motor area of the cortex evokes a characteristic gross electrical response in the pyramidal tract. An example is shown in Figure 13.3A (Patton and Amassian, 1960). The first large positivity has been termed the *D* wave and subsequent deflections are called *I* waves. In Figure 13.3B the cerebral cortex has been removed and the stimulus applied to the underlying white matter. Only the *D* wave can now be evoked. The obvious conclusion from this experiment is that the *D* wave results from direct electrical stimulation of the cell bodies whose axons make up the pyramidal tract (note the essentially zero latency of the *D* wave). Later *I* waves then presumably represent subsequent activation of these pyramidal tract cells through synaptic pathways from other cortical cells which are also excited by the electrical stimulus (Patton and Amassian, 1960). Although Betz cells have many recurrent axon collateral fibers, the *I* waves have been shown not to represent activation via these fibers (Patton and Amassian, 1954).

The *relayed* pyramidal response was first described by Adrian and Moruzzi (1939). In cats anesthetized with chloralose, electrical shock to skin or peripheral nerves elicits a relayed evoked response in the pyramidal tract. The response is called "relayed" because it is a response of the efferent pyramidal path to *sensory* stimulation; it is relayed through the brain from input to output. Subsequent research has demonstrated relayed pyramidal responses accompanying the augmenting response, spontaneous spindle bursts of the sleeping or barbiturized animal, and under some conditions the recruiting response as well (Brookhart and Zanchetti, 1956; Purpura and Housepian, 1961; Denney and Brookhart, 1962). In other words, bursts of activity are relayed down the pyramidal tract simultaneously with these various types of cortical activity. Relayed pyramidal responses can be elicited by auditory and visual stimuli as well as tactile stimuli, in the chloralosed animal.

The significance of the relayed pyramidal response lies in part in the fact that it is an illustration of a mechanism whereby a variety of sensory stimuli and endogenous brain activity can exert control on the final common pathway of movement, the spinal motor neurons.

Electrical stimulation of the pyramidal tract elicits movements. Brookhart (1952) carried out a careful and comprehensive study of such effects in monkey. Surprisingly, a single shock to the pyramidal tract will not elicit muscular activity, in spite of the fact that some pyramidal fibers terminate monosynaptically on motor neurons. Repeated shocks (i.e. temporal summation) are necessary for movement. It appears that the larger fibers of the pyramidal tract are primarily concerned with control of the distal musculature (hands and feet) and the smaller fibers with control of the larger proximal muscles. Although single shock stimulation of the pyramidal tract does not elicit movements, such a stimulus can exert profound influences on movements, even in the cat, in which no direct monosynaptic connections to motor neurons occur. Lloyd (1941) studied this effect in the cat, using a spinal reflex to test the excitability of the motor neurons. As indicated in Figure 13.4, he stimulated Ia afferent fibers to the spinal cord (*a*) and measured the amplitude of the monosynaptic ventral root discharge (reflecting activity of alpha motor neurons). If the pyramidal tract (*b*) was stimulated prior to stimulation of the Ia afferents at *a*, the ventral root response was much increased, even though stimulation of the pyramidal tract alone did not evoke any ventral root discharge. In general, stimulation of

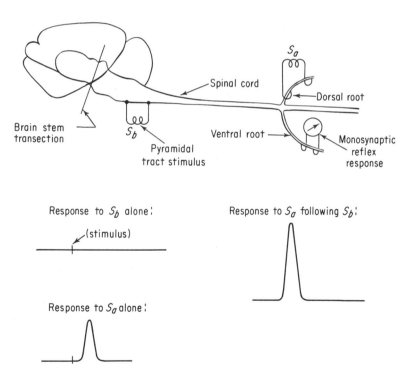

Figure 13.4.   Influence of the pyramidal tract on the excitability of spinal motor neurons. The experimental procedure is indicated above. Single shock stimulation to the pyramidal tract (S_b) does not produce any response in the ventral root. However, the monosynaptic reflex response to stimulation of the dorsal root (S_a) is markedly enhanced by prior pyramidal tract stimulation. (Based on Lloyd, 1941)

the pyramidal tract produced a facilitatory effect on the monosynaptic response, suggesting that the primary action of the pyramidal tract axons is facilitatory in nature.

More recently, Lundberg and Voorhoeve (1962) completed an extensive analysis of the actions of the pyramidal tract on spinal reflexes in the cat. They stimulated the sensory motor cortex and recorded intracellularly the responses of spinal motor neurons to stimulation of various reflex afferent systems, i.e. group Ia fibers, Ib fibers, and the "flexor reflex afferents" (higher threshold muscle and cutaneous afferents). Although they were stimulating sensory motor cortex rather than the pyramidal tract directly, all the effects they described were absent following section of the pyramids, hence the actions were pyramidal. In brief, they found that activation of the pyramidal tract produced facilitation of all spinal reflexes: excitatory and inhibitory paths from Ib afferents and from the flexor reflex afferents. In considering these results it is important to keep in mind the distinction between facilitation and excitation. The pyramidal tract acts to facilitate both excitatory and inhibitory spinal reflexes. The electrical stimuli to the sensory motor cortex in these experiments were too weak to produce any synaptic responses in the motor neurons themselves. Lundberg and Voorhoeve found that stronger stimulation of the motor cortex did produce synaptic actions on motor neurons. These were often mixed excitatory and inhibitory actions; however, there was a general tendency for excitation in flexor motor neurons and inhibition in extensor motor neurons.

The effects of pyramidal tract stimulation on reflex responses, described above, all occurred prior to the motor neurons, i.e. all actions occurred in the reflex paths, presumably on interneurons and/or primary afferent fiber terminals in the spinal cord. In this connection we might recall the presynaptic inhibition of cutaneous afferent fibers induced by stimulation of the sensory motor cortex (see Chapter 10; also Andersen, Eccles, and Sears, 1962; Carpenter, Lundberg, and Norrsell, 1962). Although presynaptic inhibition is an inhibitory rather than an excitatory effect, this does not imply that the pyramidal tract is exerting an inhibitory action. Carpenter, Lundberg, and Norrsell (1963) presented evidence indicating that the pyramidal action appears to be *excitation* of interneurons in the pathway that produces presynaptic inhibition of the afferent terminals. As far as other actions of the pyramidal tract on spinal interneurons are concerned, Lundberg, Norrsell, and Voorhoeve (1962) demonstrated monosynaptic excitation and disynaptic inhibition of interneurons by pyramidal stimulation.

The intracellular analyses of pyramidal tract actions described above all used the cat, where there are no direct monosynaptic pyramidal connections to motor neurons. As we noted earlier, there are a significant proportion of such connections in primates. Intracellular recordings from spinal motor neurons in primates have demonstrated such monosynaptic pyramidal connections for both hindlimb (Preston and Whitlock, 1961) and forelimb (Landgren, Phillips, and Porter, 1962 a,b) alpha motor neurons. As you may recall from our discussion of the motor cortex in Chapter 11, Phillips and his colleagues found that rather extensive and overlapping *colonies* of cortical pyramidal cells have mono-synaptic connections to given spinal motor neurons in the baboon. More recently Phillips and Porter (1964) compared monosynaptic pyramidal actions on motor neurons of distal (hand and forearm) and proximal (upper arm) forearm muscles. They found that the cortical pyramidal cell colonies projecting to motor neurons controlling distal muscles tended to occupy smaller cortical areas and induce larger monosynaptic actions than did those to motor neurons of proximal muscles. These findings have clear implications for the cortical-pyramidal control of fine hand movements:

> It is probable that such versatile but precise control (of the hand) depends in part on a special development of the monosynaptic corticospinal pathway to the motor neurons of the distal muscles of the upper limb. The directness of this pathway should increase the accessibility of hand motor units to the complex intracortical neuronal systems lying upstream of the corticofugal pyramidal neurons. (Phillips and Porter, 1964, p. 242.)

Earlier the pyramidal tract was believed to mediate "voluntary" movement in man. Even if we substitute the phrase "skilled movements" for the term "voluntary" the clinical evidence is contradictory. A remarkable degree of ultimate recovery from bilateral section of the pyramidal tract has been reported. One patient is said to have played a Beethoven piano concerto following such an operation (Ruch, 1960) although the quality of the performance was not indicated. Tower (1935, 1936, 1940) completed extensive studies of the possible role of the pyramidal tract in movement control. She sectioned the pyramidal tract bilaterally in monkeys and chimpanzees, and observed the subsequent behavior of the animals for long periods of time following lesion. She found that movements of the extremities lost the finer qualities of aim and precision. During the course of execution of a movement they were not able to modify the movement smoothly. Skilled movements were very much more poorly performed. The selective destruction was of the "least stereotyped, most discrete, movements or elements in movement." Thus the fine control of individual muscles, the type of control characteristically exerted by the motor cortex, appears impaired after bilateral section of the pyramidal tract. Nevertheless, a surprising degree of movement control does return.

In this regard, it is worth recalling Lashley's experiments indicating that although the motor cortex (and therefore much of the pyramidal tract) is necessary for skilled movements, it plays no essential role in the *learning* or *retention* of particular sequences of movements. Monkeys were trained to perform skilled acts such as opening a puzzle box to obtain food. The motor cortex was then ablated. After the initial paralysis began to dissipate, the animals performed the correct sequence of responses necessary to obtain the reward. Their movements were clumsy and awkward, but nonetheless correct. The lesion did not interfere with the learned behavior sequence, only with the skilled execution of the necessary movements.

EXTRAPYRAMIDAL SYSTEMS

Cortical extrapyramidal system

There are efferent projections from several cortical areas, including the primary motor area, which are involved in movement control but are *not* carried by the pyramidal tract. These extrapyramidal projection fibers end in the basal ganglia and the brain stem (see below) (Jung and Hassler, 1960). Tower (1936) stimulated the cortex before and after section of the pyramids. After section, movements could be evoked which appeared to be rather complex, often resembling "integrated acts" rather than the simple muscle contractions characteristic of motor cortex stimulation in the intact animal. Inhibitory effects were also frequently seen. Thus if the cortical stimulus was given during the course of a reflex movement, the reflex movement was often reduced. In addition cortical stimulation often reduced the resting muscle tone.

The cortical localization of extrapyramidal movement control is in many ways similar to that of the intact cortical motor system. If repetitive electrical stimuli of several seconds duration are used, the pattern of movement represented on the motor cortex of the primate is similar before and after section of the pyramids (Lewis and Brindley, 1965).

Hongo and Jankowska (1967) studied the effects of stimulating sensory motor cortex on spinal motor neurons following pyramidal section in the cat. Both excitatory and inhibitory actions (i.e. EPSPs and IPSPs) were induced in spinal motor neurons. Excitation tended to predominate in flexor motor neurons, but both types of actions were common in extensor motor neurons. They also observed facilitation of spinal reflex actions on motor neurons and depolarization of presynaptic terminals of Group Ib and cutaneous afferent fibers (i.e. presynaptic inhibition). These effects are somewhat parallel to pyramidal actions on spinal motor neurons discussed above.

Cerebellum

This structure is one of the oldest in the phylogeny of the vertebrate nervous system, being well developed in reptiles and very well elaborated in birds. Its general functions are clearly motor in nature, although its detailed mechanisms of action are only now becoming understood. The over-all structure of the cerebellum is somewhat analogous to the cerebrum in that the cellular layers form a cortex covering the white matter and several deep nuclei. The cerebellum is typically highly convoluted in appearance, with considerable areas of cerebellar cortex buried in fissures. The general location of the cerebellum is dorsal to the brain stem and posterior to the cerebrum (see Chapter 4). In primates it is almost completely covered over by the occipital lobes of the cerebral hemispheres.

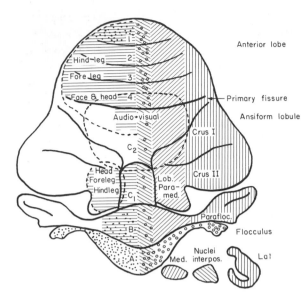

Figure 13.5. Sketch of the dorsal surface of the cerebellum indicating major anatomical subdivisions. Output from the cerebellar cortex to the three cerebellar nuclei (mediates, interpositus, and lateral) and to the vestibular nuclei (circles) shown on right. Major sources of input indicated on the left half (the two somatic sensory fields, and the auditory-visual area). Projections of the vestibular nuclei shown by dots. Both sides of course have both input and output. (From Ranson and Clark, 1959)

A generalized drawing of the dorsal surface of the cerebellum is shown in Figure 13.5, with the names of the larger subdivisions indicated. The anatomical relationships of the cerebellum are complex, and a knowledge of these relationships is necessary for a clear understanding of its functions. Such a discussion is well beyond the scope of this book; we will only attempt to convey here a few general aspects of cerebellar organization. Several excellent and detailed reviews of cerebellar anatomy and physiology are available (Jansen and Brodal, 1940; Larsell, 1951; Dow and Moruzzi, 1958; Brookhart, 1960).

In spite of the complex general anatomical relations of this structure, the histological organization of the cerebellar cortex is simple and strikingly uniform over the entire cerebellum (in contrast to the complexity of regional differentiation in the cerebral cortex) and in most vertebrates from reptile to man. As shown in Figure 13.6, cerebellar cortex consists of three layers, an outer layer of fibers

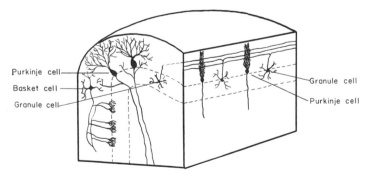

Figure 13.6. Histological organization of the cerebellar cortex. All output fibers from the cerebellum are Purkinje cell axons. (From Ranson and Clark, 1959)

and basket cells, a middle layer containing the large *Purkinje* cells, and an inner layer of granule cells. The Purkinje cells are efferent cells, sending axons out of the cerebellar cortex, and have immensely large and complexly branching dendritic trees (Figure 14.5). Most Purkinje cell axons terminate within the deep nuclei lying within the cerebellum. Cells of the flocculonodular lobe and some in the vermis send axons to the vestibular nuclei of the brain stem. Excluding this latter projection, however, all output of the cerebellar cortex is to cerebellar nuclei, which in turn project to many other regions of the brain (all of which, incidentally, are included in the pyramidal and extrapyramidal motor systems).

Anatomical subdivisions of the cerebellum have often been made in terms of the various lobes and lobules. However a classification by Jansen and Brodal (1942) made in terms of which cerebellar cortical regions project to the various cerebellar nuclei is relatively simple and appears to have some functional significance. In these terms (Figure 13.5) the subdivision is in the medial-lateral direction rather than anterior-posterior. The oldest (phylogenetically) part of the cerebellum is the flocculonodular lobe, projecting to the vestibular nuclei. The next oldest portion is the midline or medial region (vermis) projecting to the medial (fastigial) nucleus and vestibular nuclei. The intermediate portion projects to the nucleus interpositis, and finally, the lateral portion projects to the lateral (dentate) nucleus. It is the lateral portion of the cerebellum that has developed most markedly in mammals.

As with other neural structures, the cerebellum may be characterized in terms of its inputs, its internal organization, and its outputs. At least twelve separate afferent projection systems to the cerebellum have been described anatomically (Jansen and Brodal, 1954). We will list only a few of the inputs here. For many years it was believed that all afferent input to the cerebellum was from the vestibular and proprioceptive systems. However, in 1944 Snider and Stowell, using electrophysiological methods, demonstrated tactile, visual, auditory and visceral activation of the cerebellar cortex. The vestibular nuclei and some vestibular nerve fibers project to the flocculonodular lobe. The dorsal and ventral spinocerebellar tracts (both crossed and uncrossed) project primarily to medial and intermediate portions of the anterior lobe (Figure 13.5). Both of these pathways have only one synapse interposed (in the spinal cord) between the proprioceptive receptors of muscles, joints and tendons, and the cerebellum (see Chapter 4). There are comparable projections from the cranial nerve nuclei receiving somatic afferent input. In addition, there are cerebellar projections from the inferior olive, the pons, the reticular formation, the inferior and superior colliculi, and the red nucleus. In summary, essentially all varieties of sensory information appear to reach the cerebellum.

An extremely important aspect of mammalian cerebellar organization is its extensive interconnection with various areas of the cerebral cortex (Adrian, 1943; Hampson et al., 1952). The anterior lobe of the cerebellum projects to the primary motor area of the cerebral cortex via the lateral and interpositive cerebellar nuclei and the lateral ventral nucleus of the thalamus. Somatotopic

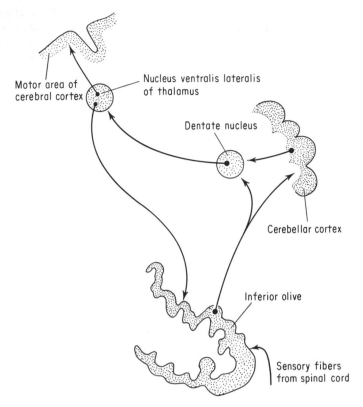

Figure 13.7. Schematic diagram of "feedback loop" involving the inferior olive and the cerebellum.

organization apparently exists between the anterior lobe and somatic sensory area I of the cerebral cortex, and between the posterior lobe and somatic sensory area II of the cerebral cortex. Thus electrical stimulation of the region of the anterior lobe that is responsive to left forepaw stimulation produces evoked responses in the forepaw area of SI on the cerebral cortex, stimulation of the cerebellar tail area on the posterior lobe of the cerebellum evokes responses in the tail area of SII on the cerebral cortex, and so on. The vermis and intermediate regions exhibit responses to auditory and visual stimuli and are functionally interconnected with the auditory and visual areas of the cerebral cortex. The extent to which the auditory and visual response areas of the cerebellum (which overlap almost entirely) have "receptotopic" organizations comparable to those of the corresponding areas in the cerebral cortex remains to be determined.

As noted above, the flocculonodular lobe and portions of the vermis project directly to the vestibular nuclei. The remainder of the cerebellar cortex projects, via the appropriate cerebellar nuclei, to the extrapyramidal motor portions of the reticular formation, the pons, midbrain, red nucleus, and the basal ganglia;

and to the motor cortex and pyramidal tract via the ventral lateral nucleus of the thalamus. One aspect of the anatomical organization of the cerebellum of particular importance is the fact that it is involved in a large number of *recurrent loops*. For example, after projecting down to the inferior olive via the red nucleus, there is a massive projection from the inferior olive back up to the cerebellum (see Figure 13.7). A number of such loops exist. To summarize once more, the cerebellum receives all varieties of sensory input, is interconnected with appropriate regions of the cerebral cortex, is involved in many circular loops, and projects to various portions of the pyramidal and extra-pyramidal motor systems.

The spontaneous electrical activity of the cerebellar cortex exhibits the same striking degree of uniformity which characterizes its histological organization. The typical electrocorticogram (i.e. spontaneous electrical activity recorded from the cortex) of the mammalian cerebellum consists of rapid 150 to 250 per sec waves of from 20 to 120 μV (Adrian, 1935; Dow, 1938) (see Figure 13.8). An

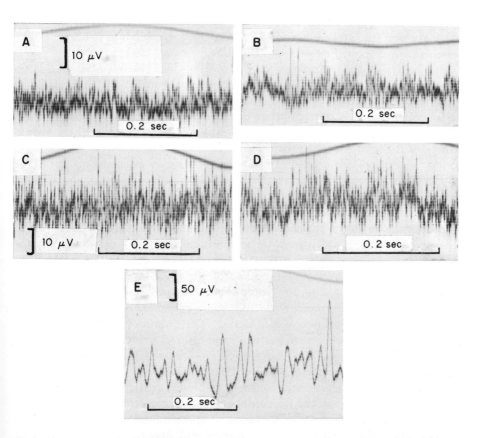

Figure 13.8. Comparison of grossly recorded spontaneous activity of cerebellar cortex (**A, B, C, D**) and cerebral cortex (**E**). Note that cerebellar cortical activity is very much faster than cerebral cortical activity. (From Dow, 1938)

essentially identical pattern of cerebellar activity has been recorded in fish, amphibians, reptiles and birds (see Brookhart, 1960). In addition, an 8 to 12 per second rhythm can be recorded in the barbiturized mammal (Snyder, 1954). An important feature of the fast wave is that it is locally generated, i.e. it persists after the cerebellar cortex is neurally isolated from the rest of the brain (Crepox and Fadiga, 1956). Extracellular single unit studies have shown that Purkinje cells fire spontaneously at high rates. These spontaneous firing patterns can be altered by a variety of afferent stimuli, drugs, etc. (Brookhart et al., 1950; 1951).

Output from the cerebellum can act through various brain stem relays to alter the excitability of both gamma and alpha spinal motor neurons. Granit and Kaada (1952) showed that stimulation of the vermal portion of the anterior lobe decreased afferent discharge from the muscle spindles, which in turn decreases muscle tone (there is a more extended discussion of this important experiment below in the section on the descending reticular formation). Stimulation of the intermediate portion of the anterior lobe has the opposite effect on gamma afferent activity, thus increasing the muscle tone. More intense stimuli can produce direct effects on alpha motor neuron excitability. Finally, electrical stimulation of the cerebellum can induce presynaptic inhibition in afferent fiber terminals (Carpenter, Engberg, and Lundberg, 1965).

In his careful and comprehensive review, Brookhart (1960) emphasized three important concepts derived from electrophysiological studies of the cerebellum. First, in the absence of controlled and purposeful stimuli, neurons of the cerebellar cortex are in a state of relatively high activity, probably close to their critical level of excitability. Second, this activity can be modulated by a wide variety of different inputs to the cerebellum. Finally, the outflow of cerebellar activity modulates the excitability of "key neurons in transmission pathways of the brain stem which receive their principal activation from the sensory sources or sources higher in the brain." (pp. 1258.)

Damage to all or to portions of the cerebellar cortex can produce a variety of deficiencies in motor behavior. Many of these are complex in detail; we will note here only a few which seem to be consistent with anatomical and physiological studies of the cerebellar organization. The two general types of deficits relate to the control of muscle tone and of the more rapid movements often termed "volitional." The terms "tonic" and "phasic" are often used to refer to these two types of muscular control. Tonic influences concern the ongoing or "resting" degree of muscle contraction. The extensor muscles involved in standing and other aspects of postural support are normally influenced in a tonic manner. The over-all levels of muscle tension or tone in these muscles are thus of crucial importance in posture. Phasic movements are the precise and rapid movements characteristic of the extremities, particularly the arm and hand in man. Damage to the flocculonodular lobe and vermis results in severe disorders of balance, corresponding to the interconnections of these regions with the vestibular nuclei (Dow, 1938; Chambers and Sprague, 1955). Damage to the medial anterior lobe increases extensor tone, particularly in subprimates, thus interfering with normal mechanisms of posture by producing a degree of extensor rigidity (see below). In man, a decrease in muscle tone is usually seen following damage to the more lateral portions of the cerebellum (Ruch, 1960). This is consistent with Granit and Kaada's data (see above) showing increased muscle tone following stimulation of this portion of the cerebellum.

Damage to the cerebellum in man produces a variety of deficiencies in the force, rate, direction, and steadiness of phasic movements. These seem to be predominantly the result of damage to the lateral and intermediate portions of the cerebellum, which have developed most in primates (Ruch, 1960). A simple movement such as touching an outstretched finger is slow to develop, overshoots the mark, and exhibits marked tremor. This tremor, incidentally, is called "intentional" in that it occurs during movement but not when the limb is at rest. Ablation and stimulation of the cerebellum thus tend to yield complementary (i.e. opposite) effects.

Readers who are somewhat familiar with servomechanism theory may have noted that the kinds of deficits seen after cerebellar damage are of the type commonly seen when a servomechanism, either mechanical and/or electromechanical, begins to dysfunction. Recent and current studies of the cerebellum have emphasized the fact that it is involved in a number of feedback loops and may be characterized in many ways as a servomechanism (see Figure 13.7) (Brookhart, 1960; Granit and Kaada, 1952). Although highly complex, it may well be susceptible to mathematical analysis in terms of servomechanism theory.

Basal ganglia

The functions of the basal ganglia in mammals are relatively obscure. They seem to have something to do with the control of movements and are commonly included as a part of the extrapyramidal motor system. Anatomically, the term basal ganglia usually refers to the *caudate* nucleus, the *putamen*, and the *globus pallidus*, three large nuclear masses embedded in the subcortical white matter of the cerebral hemisphere. The amygdala has sometimes been included as well, but it has much more intimate relations to the structures of the limbic system, and will be considered in that context (Chapter 15). The structures of the basal ganglia have direct connections to three nuclear masses lying in the general region of the midbrain and lower diencephalon: the *subthalamic* nucleus (corpus Luysi), the *substantia nigra*, and the *red nucleus*, and to the brain stem reticular formation as well.

The major interconnections of the basal ganglia, cerebral cortex, thalamus, and brain stem nuclei are shown in Figure 13.9A. Cell bodies from the motor region of the cerebral cortex send axons to the three basal ganglia, as well as to the reticular formation. The intralaminar thalamic nuclei also send direct projections to the three basal ganglia. The globus pallidus appears to be the major "switchboard" nucleus of the basal ganglia, interconnecting with the putamen, caudate, thalamus, red nucleus, substantia nigra, subthalamic nucleus, and the

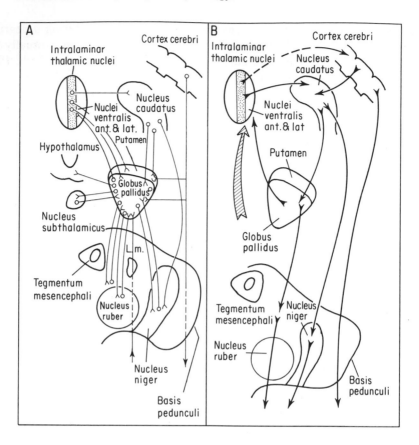

Figure 13.9.   **A,** schematic diagram of the anatomical connections of the basal ganglia, thalamus, cortex, and brain stem. **B,** schematic of the major functional relations of the basal ganglia (From Laursen, 1963)

reticular formation, and sends fibers to the hypothalamus. The major *functional* interactions (i.e. interrelations established by electrophysiological studies) of the basal ganglia and other structures are emphasized in the simplified schematic diagram of Figure 13.9B (from Laursen, 1963). A variety of sensory and nonspecific inputs feed into the intralaminar thalamic system and from there and elsewhere to cerebral cortex and basal ganglia and to the reticular formation, red nucleus, and substantia nigra.

   The basal ganglia are the major forebrain structures in lower vertebrates such as reptiles and birds, in which there is little cerebral cortex. In these forms they apparently serve as the highest brain regions, presumably controlling the most complex aspects of behavior. It is commonly stated that in birds the basal ganglia control flying. However, following ablation of the striatum in pigeons locomotion and flight appear unimpaired. On the other hand, the absence of spontaneity noted by James in the decerebrate frog is also evident in the hemispherectomized pigeon. "Spontaneous" flight is rare "he manifests no hunger ... and ... fear seems to have deserted him." (See Zeigler, 1964, for further discussion.) In mammals the basal ganglia are relatively smaller, being overshadowed (and covered) by the cerebral cortex. The results of lesion and stimulation experiments on the basal ganglia can be summed up in one word: inconclusive.

One particular response to electrical stimulation of the caudate nucleus, the "arrest reaction," has been described in numerous experiments (e.g. Mettler et al., 1939). Whatever movements the animal is making at the time of stimulation cease and the animal holds his position, much like a still picture in a movie. Head turning and "searching" responses, and more long lasting generalized inactivity have also been reported to follow caudate stimulation (Hassler, 1956; Hess, 1948; Akert and Anderson, 1951). Recent studies by Laursen (1963) suggest that at least the arrest portion of the caudate response is the result of electrical stimulus spread to the adjacent fibers of the internal capsule (containing afferents and efferents of the cerebral cortex). When care was taken to prevent such stimulus spread, no arrest reaction occurred, although head turning was still elicited. However, this interpretation is not entirely satisfactory, because in an early study Rioch and Brenner (1938) were able to obtain inhibition of movement by caudate stimulation in a cat after total decortication with subsequent degeneration of all efferent fibers from the cortex.

Rioch (1942) reported that there was essentially no difference in the observed gross behavior of cats with decortication and those with decortication plus removal of basal ganglia, implying that the latter structures have no fundamental role in motor behavior independent of the cerebral cortex. Later, Wang and Akert (1962) reported that ablation of basal ganglia plus cortex does appear to produce more severe deficits in motor behavior than decortication alone. In more behaviorally oriented studies, deficits have been found in delayed response learning and auditory and visual discrimination after lesions in the caudate nucleus of monkey (Rosvold et al., 1958; Battig, Rosvold and Mishkin, 1962). Laursen (1963) reports more rapid extinction of avoidance conditioned responses in cats following bilateral lesions of the globus pallidus.

Several clinical syndromes occur in man following damage to the basal ganglia, the best known being Parkinson's disease. This condition is characterized by a resting tremor and some degree of rigidity. It appears to be due to lesions in the basal ganglia and substantia nigra. *Athetoid* movements (slow twisting motions of hand or foot) and *choreiform* movements (quick, jerky motions) are associated with lesions of the caudate and putamen. These conditions are difficult to reproduce in animals, and the reasons why damage to the basal ganglia should produce them in man seem rather obscure (see Ruch, 1960).

Descending reticular formation

In 1946 Magoun and Rhines reported that both inhibitory and facilitatory effects on reflex contractions of skeletal muscles could be obtained by stimulation of the reticular formation. They inserted stimulating electrodes in the brain stem reticular formation in chloralose anesthetized animals and tested the effects of repeated electrical stimulation of the reticular formation on muscle responses evoked by a variety of other means: stretch reflex elicited by muscle tap, flexion reflex to pinch of the foot, responses to electrical stimulation of the motor area of the cerebral cortex, etc. The inhibitory region, lying in the ventro-medial portion of the medulla, inhibited such responses as the knee jerk, the flexion reflex, decerebrate rigidity (see below) and movements elicited from electrical stimulation of motor cortex. The region having facilitatory effects on these responses lay more lateral and extended up to the midbrain.

Subsequent work (Sprague and Chambers, 1954; Gernandt and Thulin, 1955) has shown that these two separate areas are not purely excitatory or purely inhibitory. Both kinds of effects can be obtained from both areas. Sprague and Chambers (1954), for example, used unanesthetized decerebrate animals and animals with chronically implanted recording electrodes. They reported that generalized facilitation or inhibition to reticular stimulation could not be obtained in the normal animal, but were seen in the physiologically more depressed decerebrate animal. For the most part they could elicit reciprocal facilitatory and inhibitory effects on muscle actions. Stimulation of the medial reticular formation tended to yield ipsilateral flexion and extensor inhibition, and a contralateral extension and flexor inhibition. Stimulation of the lateral reticular formation tended to yield just the opposite patterns. In their normal-waking animals with implanted electrodes they found some intriguing "integrated" behavior sequences of the whole animal to stimulation of the reticular formation. The entire postural substratum of "going to sleep" was produced in one experiment—the animal circled, curled up, and assumed the prone sleeping position. Their finding of reciprocal control of muscle actions is of course reasonable in terms of reciprocal innervation; a stimulus which inhibits an extensor muscle, for example, generally excites a flexor muscle. However, lesion studies indicate that over-all inhibitory effects may predominate in the caudal region and facilitatory effects in more rostral areas (Lindsley, Schreiner, and Magoun, 1949; Schreiner, Lindsley, and Magoun, 1949).

The elegant experiments of Granit and his colleagues (see particularly Granit and Kaada, 1952) have shown that some influences of the descending reticular system on muscle activity are mediated primarily by the gamma motor neuron system rather than by direct effects upon the alpha motor neurons. Their experiments merit description. Granit and Kaada recorded spike discharges of single fibers in hindlimb dorsal roots. By means of a variety of physiological criteria they were able to distinguish gamma afferents (sensory fibers from muscle spindles) from other muscle afferent fibers. Afferents from the gastrocnemius muscle (an extensor) were usually employed. Using either anesthetized (Dial-chloralose) or decerebrated cats they delivered repetitive electrical stimuli to the reticular formation, the *intralaminar* thalamic nuclei, the hypothalamus, the cerebellum, the motor cortex, and the caudate nucleus, and noted the effects of such stimulation on gamma afferents and efferents. Electrical brain stimuli were always adjusted so as to be too weak to elicit *any* activity in alpha motor neuron axons. This was proved in control experiments by putting the muscle under a constant tension and showing that the weak brain stimuli effective in controlling gamma activity produced no measurable change in actual muscle tension. Granit and Kaada obtained most of their data from gamma afferent fibers, which reflect activity in the gamma motor neurons. In some experiments direct recordings were obtained from gamma motor neuron axons, i.e. gamma efferents, in the ventral roots. These behaved in the same manner as did the gamma afferent response to brain stimulation.

The results of stimulating the reticular formation were quite consistent with the gross changes in muscle actions reported earlier by Magoun and Rhines (1946). Electrical stimulation of the cephalic parts of the reticular formation, ranging from the anterior portion of the medulla to the midbrain and the intra-laminar thalamic nuclei, usually caused marked *increases* in gamma fiber activity. Examples of such increases in the firing rates of two gamma afferent fibers are shown in Figure 13.10. The solid line is an instance of *after discharge*. The fiber continues to fire at an increased rate for many seconds after the electrical stimulus is turned off. The other fiber illustrates *recruitment*: the firing rate

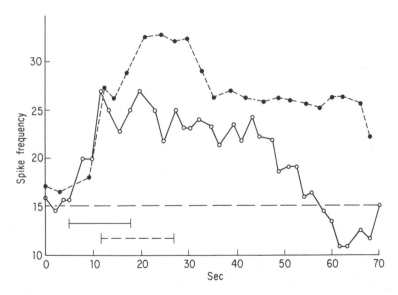

Figure 13.10.   Increase in the discharge rates of two gamma afferent fibers following electrical stimulation (horizontal bars just above abscissa) of the rostral reticular formation. The unit shown by the solid line increases its discharge frequency during the initial portion of the stimulus; then remains relatively constant for some time (after discharge), and then declines slowly to control level. The dashed line shows a unit exhibiting "recruitment"; discharge frequency continues to increase as long as the stimulus is applied. (From Granit and Kaada, 1952)

continues to grow throughout most of the stimulus duration. Increases were also obtained following stimulation of the hypothalamus and caudate nucleus. Less regularly, increases were obtained from stimulation of the motor cortex, and the anterior lobe of the cerebellum.

Decreased activity in gamma fibers was commonly observed following electrical stimulation of the caudal portion of the reticular formation in the lower pons and the medulla. An example is shown in Figure 13.11. Here the muscle was first stretched by a constant load to produce a high rate of discharge in the gamma afferent fiber. Stimulation of the bulbar reticular formation (horizontal bar) produced immediate and virtually total inhibition of activity in the gamma fiber. Such depressive effects could also be obtained from stimulation of the anterior lobe of the cerebellum, and, less regularly, from motor cortex, the prefrontal cortex, and the amygdala.

In comparing these findings to those of Magoun and Rhines, and Sprague and Chambers, several points should be kept in mind. First, Granit and Kaada recorded activity of gamma afferent fibers from the gastrocnemius muscle, which

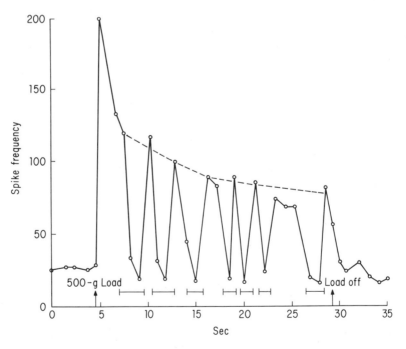

Figure 13.11. Suppression of gamma afferent activity by electrical stimulation of the caudal reticular formation. The gamma afferent fiber discharge frequency was first increased markedly by applying a strong load to the muscle (arrow). This high discharge rate was rapidly and reversibly abolished by electrical stimulation of the reticular formation (horizontal bars just above abscissa). (From Granit and Kaada, 1952)

physiologically speaking is an extensor muscle. Second, all experiments showing facilitation from rostral reticular stimulation employed virtually the same anesthetic condition as did Rhines and Magoun (chloralose). The decerebrate animal was used only in experiments showing depressive effects of caudal reticular stimulation. Their findings thus complement and extend the previous experiment on the gross muscular effects of brain stimulation. To summarize, stimulation of rostral portions of the reticular formation increases the gamma motor neuron activity (i.e. gamma efferents) to extensor muscles, which causes increased gamma afferent activity from these muscles. This in turn will tend to increase contraction of these extensors by monosynaptic actions on the alpha motor neurons controlling the extensor muscles. Electrical stimulation of the caudal portion of the reticular formation, on the other hand, causes a decrease in the activation of the gamma motor neurons, and hence ultimately on the muscles.

A final observation from Granit and Kaada's experiment is of interest in relation to the effects of brain stimulation on afferent information from muscles. Brain stimuli effective in modifying the actions of gamma afferent and efferent fibers had no influence whatever on activity of afferent fibers from the Golgi tendon organs of the muscles. To influence Golgi tendon afferents it was necessary to increase the brain stimulus strength to the point at which actual muscle contractions occurred. This would of course result in direct activation of the Golgi tendon receptors by muscle contractions.

During normal reflex actions the activity of gamma and alpha motor neurons is closely linked. In reflex responses to stimulation of the skin the gamma motor neurons have a lower threshold and begin firing sooner than the alpha motor neurons. Nonetheless there is a very close correspondence in the activity of the two. If the reflex involves excitation of gammas it also involves excitation of alphas, and vice versa. Coexcitation and coinhibition is precise in both types of efferents (Hunt, 1951; Granit, Job, and Kaada, 1952; Eldred and Hagbarth, 1954). This correspondence in behavior of the gammas and alphas, termed the *alpha-gamma linkage* by Granit (1955), is due not only to spinal reflex connections but involves supraspinal actions as well. In particular, if the anterior portion of the cerebellum is removed in a decerebrate cat, the alpha-gamma linkage is destroyed. Gamma activity is markedly reduced and in terms of reflex responses the animal appears to be an essentially "alpha" preparation—muscle actions are controlled only by the alpha motor neurons (see Granit, 1955). Granit suggests that these types of preparations cannot use their internal measuring instruments in the spindles in the normal way, because normal behavior is based on alpha-gamma linkage. To oversimplify, it appears as though there is a "gamma-alpha switch" in the anterior cerebellum that results in the closely parallel behavior of the two types of motor neurons.

You may recall from the previous discussion that the various extrapyramidal systems have connections with the brain stem reticular formation. It is in part through these connections in the inhibitory and facilitatory descending reticular systems that many extrapyramidal pathways exert their effects on motor neurons. Specifically, such functional connections have been shown for the basal ganglia (Garnot, 1944; Laursen, 1963), for extrapyramidal cortical efferents (Jung and Hassler, 1960), cerebellum (Gauthier, Mollica, and Moruzzi, 1956; Mollica, Moruzzi, and Naquet, 1953), and the vestibular nuclei (Gernandt and Thulin, 1952; 1953). In a very real sense, the descending reticular system appears to form a " final common path " for extrapyramidal influences on movement.

Vestibular system

The vestibular system is of course a sensory system, providing information to the CNS about the position and movement of the head. It is included in the discussion of motor systems here because of its profound and direct influence on posture and upon various reflex responses.

The gross anatomical appearance of the vestibular apparatus and cochlea are shown in Figure 13.12. The three *semicircular canals* lie in planes at right angles to one another and connect to the sac-like utricle. Each has an enlarged portion termed the *ampulla* which contains the hair cells (*cristae*). These are anchored at one end and project out into the fluid interior of the ampulla. Appropriate movements distort the hair cells, activating vestibular nerve fibers (see Figure 13.13). The two sac-like structures termed the *utricle* and the *saccule* (Figure 13.12) have regions of sensory epithelium termed maculi which contain receptor hair cells. They also contain granules of calcium carbonate. During appropriate positioning or movement the granules distort the hair cells, resulting in excitation of the vestibular nerve fibers (see Figure 13.13).

In general terms adequate stimulation of the semicircular canals results from rotation of the head around any axis. They may also be activated by cold water introduced into the external ear canal (caloric stimulation) and by direct electrical stimulation. The utricle on the other hand responds to the static position

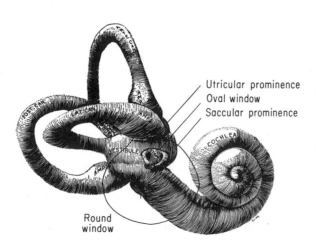

Utricular prominence
Oval window
Saccular prominence

Round window

Figure 13.12. Drawing of the gross anatomical appearance of the vestibular apparatus (semicircular canals, saccule and utricle) and the cochlea. (From Kreig, 1953)

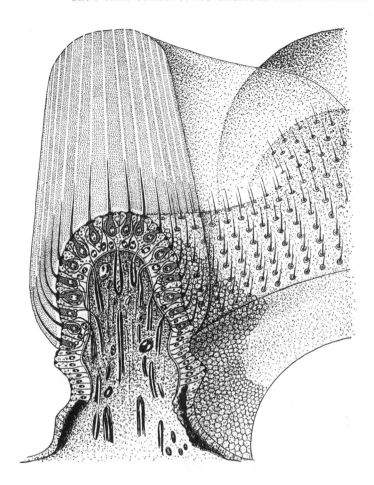

Figure 13.13. Schematic drawing of one half of a crista ampullaris, showing innervation of its epithelium. Thick nerve fibers forming nerve calyces round type I hair cells at the summit of the crista; medium caliber fibers innervating type I hair cells on the slope of the crista; medium caliber and fine nerve fibers forming a nerve plexus innervating hair cells of type II. The sensory hairs pass from the hair cells into fine canals in the cupula, which is separated from the epithelium by a narrow subcupular space. (From J. Wersäll, 1956)

of the head in space (gravitation pull), to centrifugal force, and to linear acceleration (Gernandt, 1959). The functions of the saccule are not well understood.

The vestibular nerve fibers have five separate nuclei as destinations in the CNS. We have already described projections from one vestibular nucleus to the flocculonodular lobe and vermis of the cerebellum. Other terminations are in the four remaining vestibular nuclei of the brain stem, three relaying to ascending systems and one relaying down the spinal cord to form the vestibulo-spinal tract. There are interconnections in the brain stem between the vestibular nuclei and the reticular formation. In addition to the reflex connections described below, the vestibular system projects upward to the cerebral cortex, both to a localized region (on the anterior suprasylvian gyrus in cat, see Kempinsky, 1951), and in a more diffuse manner to influence other areas of the cortex (see Jung, 1961).

The two major reflex systems controlling posture are the vestibulo-spinal tract and the ascending reflex pathways from the two vestibular nuclei through the medial longitudinal fasciculus to cranial motor nerve nuclei controlling muscles of the eyes and neck (see Figure 13.14). The latter system is concerned with various reflex responses of the head and eyes to vestibular activation. The vestibulo-spinal tract ends in spinal cord interneurons which influence the excitability of both alpha and gamma motor neurons. Vestibular control of the gamma motor neuron system is very potent. Both increases and decreases in the activity of gamma efferents and afferents of the spinal cord can be induced by stimulation of the vestibular nuclei, in a manner analogous to the effects of reticular stimulation described above (Andersson and Gernandt, 1956). A variety of complex postural reflex deficits result from damage to the vestibular system (see Gernandt, 1959).

INTERRELATIONS OF MOTOR SYSTEMS

We have already described some of the interrelations among various motor systems, particularly those of the extrapyramidal systems. It is important to

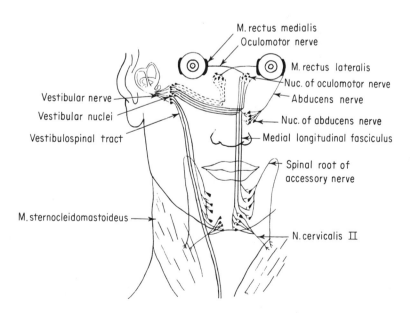

Figure 13.14. Vestibular reflex control of head movement (i.e. neck muscles) and eye movements. (From Ranson and Clark, 1959, as modified from Edinger)

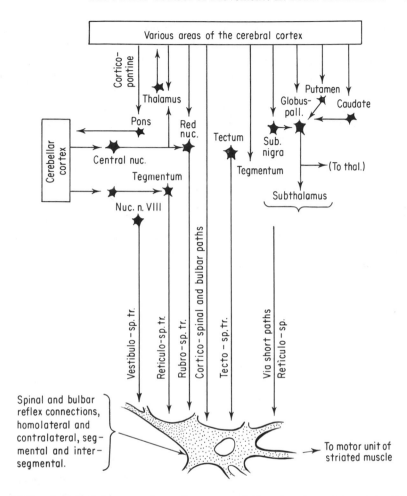

Figure 13.15. A few of the many descending systems influencing the activity of the "final common path," the spinal (or cranial) motor neuron. (From Ranson and Clark, 1959)

emphasize again that all motor effects ultimately converge on the alpha motor neurons of the spinal cord and brain stem which directly control the activity of muscles. Elucidation of the role played by the gamma motor neurons is an extremely important recent development. Many of the extrapyramidal systems exert their effects on alpha motor neurons indirectly through the gamma system (gamma motor neurons, muscle spindles, and returning muscle afferent fibers which synapse on alpha motor neurons). Such indirect routes permit higher regions of the brain to control the tendency to respond without actually producing muscle contraction or relaxation. This increases enormously the possibilities for subtle control of behavioral response probability. The diagram in Figure 13.15 summarizes a few of the many systems playing upon the alpha motor neuron, the final common pathway of muscle response.

In recent years there has been an increased emphasis on analysis of the neural mechanisms whereby descending systems exert their influences on the final common path, utilizing intracellular recordings of synaptic potentials from spinal motor neurons. Earlier in the chapter, for example, we reviewed experiments of this sort concerned with the actions of the pyramidal tract (e.g. Lloyd, 1941; Phillips and Porter, 1964; Lundberg and Voorhoeve, 1962). You may remember that the pyramidal tract has a general facilitatory influence on spinal reflexes, has monosynaptic excitatory connections to alpha motor neurons in primates, tends to induce polysynaptic excitation in flexor motor neurons and inhibition in extensor motor neurons, and induces presynaptic inhibition in group Ib and flexor reflex afferent fibers.

In considering the descending actions of various subcortical motor systems, particular reference must be made to the many elegant studies from Anders Lundberg's laboratory in Göteborg, Sweden. We will describe one experiment in some detail, partly to illustrate some of the methods used, and then review very briefly the results of studies on various descending systems. These experiments illustrate some of the physiological mechanisms whereby the descending systems diagrammed in Figure 13.15 act to influence the alpha motor neurons.

Engberg, Lundberg, and Ryall (1965) investigated the descending inhibitory actions of the brain stem reticular formation on transmission through interneurons of spinal reflex pathways. As we noted above (section on the descending reticular formation), stimulation of the ventromedial portion of the reticular formation in the medulla tends to produce inhibitory actions on spinal reflexes and on gamma motor neuron activity. The experiments by Engberg, Lundberg, and Ryall were concerned with the inhibitory action on the polysynaptic flexion reflex response to stimulation of the flexor reflex afferents (high threshold muscle and cutaneous afferent fibers). The general experimental arrangement is illustrated by the sketches in Figure 13.16. The experiment was done on cats that were decerebrated and decerebellated with spinal cord cut except for the dorsal part of the lateral pathways contralateral to the site of recording (middle drawing on right). High threshold afferent fibers from another muscle were stimulated to produce a polysynaptic inhibitory effect in an extensor motor neuron (intracellular recording electrode shown in lower right drawing). This polysynaptic reflex IPSP recorded from the extensor motor neuron is shown in upper trace (labelled "test"), recorded with a slow sweep speed (A-response is the sharp downward spike) and a fast sweep speed (B—this same IPSP is here spread out in time). The reticular formation was then electrically stimulated (upper right drawing) prior to stimulation of the reflex afferent fibers. The effect of this on the reflex IPSP is shown in the upper traces of the second row, labelled "brain stem + test" (D on slow sweep and E on fast sweep). Reticular stimulation induces a marked depression of the reflex IPSP of the extensor motor neuron.

So far the experiment has simply shown that the reticular formation can inhibit a reflex response (in this case an inhibitory reflex, the reticular effect is inhibition of inhibition). There are at least three different ways the reticular

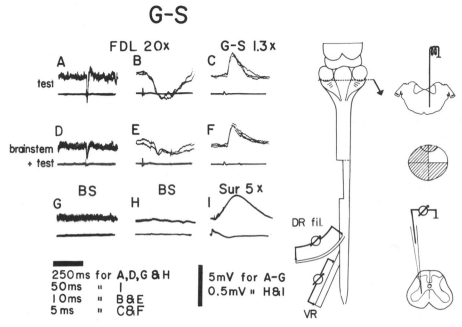

Figure 13.16. Inhibition from the reticular formation of transmission in the inhibitory pathway from the flexor reflex afferents to an extensor motor neuron. Drawings at right illustrate the experimental arrangement—electrical stimulation of reticular formation and afferent nerves with most of cord cut, and recording from single motor neuron and dorsal root filament (DR fil). See text for details. Upper trace of each pair **A–G** is the intracellular recording from an extensor motor neuron. Upper traces **H** and **I** are dorsal root potentials from the dorsal root filament. The lower trace of each pair is taken from the dorsal root entry zone and marks the entrance of the afferent nerve volley into the spinal cord. **A, B** and **C** are test responses (**A** and **B** at different sweep speeds to stimulation of flexor reflex afferents and **C** the monosynaptic group Ia response) and **D, E** and **F** are comparable responses following reticular shock. **G** indicates absence of response of cell to reticular shock alone, and **H** (from the DR fil) indicates absence of primary afferent depolarization to reticular stimulation. **I** shows such presynaptic inhibition of the same DR fil from Sural cutaneous nerve stimulation. Note the different time calibrations. (Taken from Engberg, Lundberg, and Ryall, 1965)

inhibition could act: (1) by producing synaptic actions on the motor neuron itself; (2) by inducing presynaptic inhibition in the afferent fibers of the reflex pathway; or (3) by acting to inhibit the interneurons involved in the reflex pathway. The first possibility was excluded by showing that reticular stimulation alone (upper trace in G) produced no postsynaptic response in the cell, and by showing that the reticular stimulation had no effect on the monosynaptic excitatory response of the cell (traces C + F, monosynaptic EPSPs induced in the cell by stimulation of the Ia afferents to the cell). The possibility of presynaptic inhibition was excluded by recording the dorsal root potential (" DR fil" in left drawing), an index of presynaptic inhibition, i.e. primary afferent depolarization. As indicated in trace H, there is no presynaptic inhibition acting on the primary afferent terminal fibers (trace I, for contrast, shows the marked presynaptic inhibition induced in these same fibers by stimulation of the sural cutaneous nerve). Consequently, the reticular action would seem to be on interneurons. In like manner they demonstrated reticular inhibition at the interneuron level of the polysynaptic *excitatory* response induced in flexor motor neurons by stimulation of the flexor reflex afferent fibers.

The various types of descending influences on spinal reflexes have been reviewed by Lundberg (1964; 1966; see also Grillner, Hongo, and Lund, 1966; Hongo, Jankowska, and Lundberg, 1965; Lund and Pompeano, 1965). To summarize very briefly, the *red nucleus* exerts excitatory actions on the interneurons of reflex pathways, particularly those from Ib and low threshold cutaneous afferents, but sometimes inhibitory actions on reflexes from high threshold reflex afferents, and induces presynaptic inhibition in Ib and cutaneous afferent fibers. *Deiter's nucleus* (vestibulospinal tract) induces monosynaptic EPSPs in extensor motor neurons and disynaptic inhibition in flexor motor neurons, and facilitates Ia inhibition from extensors to flexors. In terms of descending reticular actions, the *dorsal reticulospinal pathway* induces inhibition of excitatory and inhibitory paths from the flexor reflex afferents to motor neurons and primary afferents. Lundberg (1966) suggests that this pathway may play an important role in decerebrate rigidity (see discussion of this phenomenon on pp. 425–427). The *ventral reticulospinal pathway* acts to inhibit reflex elicitation of presynaptic inhibition on primary afferent fibers from flexor reflex afferents and Ia and Ib muscle afferents. Other brainstem effects include postsynaptic inhibition evoked in motor neurons by weak stimulation of a region lying somewhat ventral to the dorsal reticular pathway; monosynaptic excitation of flexor motor neurons from a dorsomedial region of the upper medulla; and monosynaptic excitation of *gamma* motor neurons from brainstem stimulation.

Posture and movement: levels of control

At the beginning of the chapter we cited William James' 1890 description of the motor capacities of frogs whose brains had been transected at various levels from spinal cord to cerebrum. The degree of increase in our understanding of supraspinal motor systems in the succeeding 75 years has in some ways been rather disappointing. A good deal more is, of course, known today concerning the general roles of many brain structures in the control of movement; some of this material was reviewed in the course of the present chapter. Nonetheless, we are still far from having a clear understanding of the kinds of neural mechanisms underlying the actions of the various brain structures that influence muscle actions. We are even less sure of the ways in which these systems interact upon one another to produce the complex integrated movements so characteristic of the normal animal. It is perhaps appropriate to end the chapter with a discussion of the motor capacities of the mammalian nervous system following transection at various levels. This may provide a somewhat clearer overview of the manner in which the various motor systems of the brain act together to control posture and movement.

One of the clearest effects of transecting the brain is the change in the tonic contraction of the limb extensor muscles involved in postural control. *Decerebrate rigidity* is a striking and easily observed syndrome following section of the brainstem. Limb extensor muscles are strongly contracted, producing extreme and rigid extension of the limbs, particularly the forelimbs. It is literally quite difficult to flex the forelimb of a decerebrate cat. Perhaps in part because of the very apparent changes in extensor rigidity attendant upon brain section, most analyses have employed this symptom. Our discussion will center around the degree of extensor rigidity induced by transecting the mammalian (particularly cat and dog) brain at various levels. We will use the terms "inhibition" and "facilitation" rather loosely to mean decreases or increases in the tonic strength of contraction of extensor muscles. If an inhibitory effect predominates, the forelimbs will be relaxed or flexed, if excitatory influences prevail, the forelimbs will be stiffly extended in front of the animal (see Figure 13.17).

The diagram of Figure 13.18, based on Lindsley et al. (1949), summarizes most of the gross regional brain influences on extensor alpha motor neurons that have been described in this chapter. Many of these effects were determined by experiments in which the regions were electrically stimulated. In brief, stimulation of parts of the cerebral cortex (1), basal ganglia (2), cerebellum (3), and caudal brainstem reticular formation (4) tend to inhibit contractions of extensor muscles. On the other hand, stimulation almost anywhere else in the brainstem reticular formation (5) facilitates or augments extensor muscle actions, as does stimulation of the vestibular nuclei (6). It should be emphasized that many of these actions are not "pure;" both facilitation and inhibition of extensor rigidity can be produced by stimulation of most of these regions. The diagram merely indicates the most commonly observed net or predominant effect.

THE SPINAL ANIMAL.   If the spinal cord is transected in a higher mammal a consistent sequence of events occurs. First *spinal shock* develops, with all spinal

Figure 13.17.   Typical posture of the cat in decerebrate rigidity. Note the marked and rigid extension of the forelimbs, the forward extension of the neck, and the extension of the tail. (From Pollock and Davis, 1930)

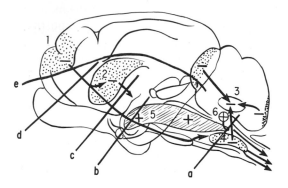

Figure 13.18. Diagram of the major sources in the brain of facilitation (+) and inhibition (−) of extensor muscle tone. See text for discussion. (After Lindsley, Schreiner, and Magoun, 1949)

reflexes being much reduced or absent. This is not surgical shock; subsequent transection below the level of the first section produces no evidence of spinal shock (Sherrington, 1906). The effect seems due to the removal of all descending influences from the brain. The period of spinal shock varies directly with phylogenetic level, lasting a few minutes in cat and several weeks in man. The mechanisms of spinal shock are not well understood.

After spinal shock has worn off a characteristic hyper-reflexia slowly develops, particularly for flexion reflexes. These become exaggerated and may develop into "mass reflexes" involving generalized contraction of all flexors. Extensor muscles and reflexes, on the other hand, generally remain less active than in the normal animal. Chronic spinal animals can stand if placed, but are unable to right themselves or to walk (Bazzet and Penfield, 1922). To summarize, the net effect of removing all brain control areas is partial inhibition of extensor reflexes, implying that the over-all influence of higher regions tends to be somewhat excitatory. The same effect is seen even if transections of the brainstem are made up to the level of line *a* of Figure 13.18.

DECEREBRATE RIGIDITY.   If the brainstem is transected anywhere between lines (a) and (b) in Figure 13.18 the characteristic syndrome of decerebrate rigidity develops (Sherrington, 1906). If the section is made anterior to the vestibular nuclei (6) and posterior to the anterior end of the midbrain (i.e. below line (b)), the predominately facilitatory influence of the brainstem reticular formation results in strong extensor rigidity. Removal of the inhibitory influences of the cerebellum (3) further augments the degree of extensor rigidity. Such an animal cannot right itself or walk.

There is an interesting interrelation between decerebrate rigidity and spinal transection displayed in the so-called *Shiff-Sherrington* reflex (Sherrington, 1906). If the spinal cord of a decerebrate animal is sectioned midthoracically (below the level of spinal outflow controlling the forelimbs) the degree of extensor rigidity in the forelimbs *increases*. This presumably results from interruption of ascending reflex influences in the spinal cord that normally exert a net inhibitory action on extension of the forelimbs.

HIGH DECEREBRATION.   If the brainstem is transected above the anterior portion of the midbrain (between lines (b) and (c)) marked decerebrate rigidity does not develop. Chronic midbrain animals do exhibit righting reflexes, can walk, and are even able to run and climb (Bard and Macht, 1958). However such activities require several weeks to re-establish themselves. These animals exhibit a milder form of decerebrate rigidity, but only when at rest. During phasic movements such as walking, the extensor rigidity is suppressed.

The differences between high decerebrate and decorticate animals (lines (d) and (e)) are surprisingly few. After total removal of neocortex alone, however, motor behavior such as walking and running are immediately present, in contrast to the long recovery periods necessary for the high decerebrate. If a decorticate animal is held suspended it will exhibit marked extensor rigidity. Such rigidity is less prominent in the decorticate than in the high decerebrate preparation when the animal is normally resting. Part of the difficulty in assigning specific functions to the basal ganglia results from the lack of clear differentiation between the decorticate and the high decerebrate states. Results of the study by Wang and Akert (1958) do suggest that locomotion is more severely impaired by decerebration than by decortication.

The description of brain influences on posture and movement reviewed above presents what might be termed the classical view of the regional organization of motor systems. The "salami" technique of slicing the brain at various levels has many obvious limitations. In the normal animal, it is the complex interactions of all the different systems that produced the smooth and integrated sequences of movements we call behavior. The approach in terms of cellular analysis exemplified by the experiments of Granit, Lundberg, Phillips, and others described in this chapter, in which responses of a particular type of neuron involved in the control of muscle actions are studied in relation to many different brain influences, utilizing the very powerful techniques of intracellular analysis, would seem to provide a rather basic understanding of the neuronal organization underlying motor actions. This approach is being extensively employed in current research on the organization and functions of motor systems. It is to be hoped that the rather disparate collection of motor "systems" described in this chapter can someday be integrated in terms of the basic neuronal organization underlying their actions.

SUGGESTED READINGS

Bard, P. (Ed.) *Medical physiology*. St. Louis: Mosby, 1956. (Chapters 71, 72, 76.)
Field, J. (Ed.) *Handbook of physiology. Section I: Neurophysiology*. Vol. II. Washington, D.C.: American Physiological Society, 1960.
Granit, R. (Ed.) *Nobel symposium I. Muscular afferents and motor control*. New York: Wiley, 1966.

14

THE ASCENDING RETICULAR ACTIVATING SYSTEM

The study of the organization and possible functions of the ascending reticular activating system (ARAS) has had an enormous impact on psychology. The discovery that electrical stimulation of the reticular core of the brainstem could produce the EEG pattern of arousal in the cerebral cortex (Moruzzi and Magoun, 1949) opened up many new areas of investigation of brain function and behavior, ranging from studies of coma and sleep to analysis of the physiological and behavioral correlates of alerting, attention, and even motivation. The ARAS appeared to provide the "missing link" between the classical sensory systems of the brain and many nonspecific behavioral phenomena subsumed under headings like "alertness," "attention," "arousal," "sleep," etc. that seem to be related to sensory activation but not necessarily to any specific type of stimulation.

Many of the anatomical characteristics of the brainstem reticular formation have been known for some time. Cajal described it in 1909 as a ventral core of neural tissue extending from the spinal cord to the thalamus composed of intermingled cell bodies and fibers having the appearance of a "reticulum" (network). The reticular core is surrounded by the long ascending fibers and systems of the classical sensory

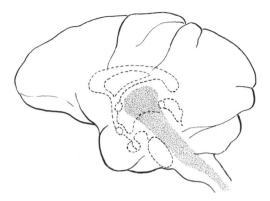

Figure 14.1. General location of the reticular formation (shaded area) lying within the brainstem and diencephalon.

pathways and the descending motor pathways. The general location of the reticular formation within the brain is sketched in Figure 14.1.

In an early paper, Allen (1932) noted that embryological and anatomical characteristics of the reticular formation indicated that it very likely serves general functions of inhibition, excitation and integration of brain activity, a remarkable prediction in the light of subsequent research. Phylogenetically it is a very old system, developing in the embryo from cells that are " left over " after the sensory and motor systems of the brainstem are formed. In lower vertebrates it is relatively undifferentiated. Allen noted that it receives many axons from the principal sensory and motor pathways. We will examine the anatomical organization of the reticular formation in more detail later in the chapter.

Physiological analysis of the ARAS really began with Bremer's now classical observation in 1935 concerning the effects of transection of the brainstem on EEG sleep. If the brainstem of the cat is completely transected at the level of the midbrain, a rather special set of symptoms resembling normal sleep develop. Such an animal displays a permanently "sleeping" cortical EEG; high voltage relatively slow (8–12/sec) sleep spindles appear continuously (see Figure 14.2). You may recall from Chapter 9 that during light or intermediate levels of sleep, both cat and human EEGs—recorded from the cortex or the scalp—show a predominance of spindles and slow waves. Bremer termed this preparation the *cerveau isolé*. The level of brain section used in the *cerveau isolé* cuts off all afferent cranial nerve inputs to the brain except I and II (olfactory and visual), and interrupts all motor outputs of the brain except some control of eye movement.

Because most sensory input cannot reach the portion of the brain above the level of section, and this portion of the brain can no longer control muscle activity, most behavioral measures of the state of the brain (i.e. whether it is asleep or awake) above the level of section are simply not possible. One sign of sleep in the normal cat that can be mediated by the isolated forebrain of the *cerveau isolé* is pupil diameter. The pupil of the normal sleeping cat is constricted to a narrow slit. The same is true of the pupil in the *cerveau isolé* cat (see Figure

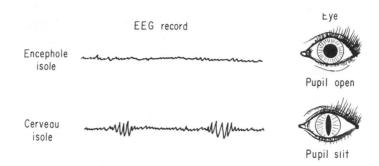

Figure 14.2.   Comparison of cortical EEG and pupil size in the *encéphale isolé* (brain separated from the spinal cord) and the *cerveau isolé* (midbrain transected) in the cat. The low voltage fast EEG arousal pattern and open pupil of the *encéphale isolé* are characteristic of the normal waking animal and the synchronized EEG spindles and slit pupil are characteristic of the normal sleeping animal. (Based on Bremer, 1935, 1937)

14.2). Thus the cortical EEG pattern and the pupillary reflex of the *cerveau isolé* resemble those of the normal sleeping animal.

If the normally sleeping cat or man is aroused or awakened, the sleep spindle pattern of the EEG suddenly disappears, and is replaced by a pattern of rapid, low voltage activity. This latter EEG pattern is variously termed EEG arousal, EEG alerting, alpha blocking, desynchronization, low voltage fast activity, etc. (see Chapter 9). The EEG arousal pattern persists as long as the organism is awake and alert. Bremer attempted to induce EEG arousal in the *cerveau isolé* by strong sensory stimulation of the available sensory inputs (olfactory and visual). He found that only a brief and feeble EEG arousal could be induced, even by very strong stimuli. The arousal effect did not outlast the arousing stimulus.

Bremer's discovery of the *cerveau isolé* was of great importance in terms of the then prominent view that sleep resulted from a withdrawal of sensory stimulation. Because the transection used in preparing the *cerveau isolé* removes most sensory input that normally goes to the brain, it is a natural assumption that the forebrain permanently sleeps because there is insufficient sensory input to arouse it. To test the relative importance of somatic sensory stimulation from the body in controlling sleep, Bremer developed another preparation in which he transected the brainstem at the point at which the brain joins the spinal cord (see Figure 14.2). Section of the CNS at this level eliminates sensory input from the body but preserves all inputs of the cranial nerves, including somatic sensory input from the face and head via the fifth cranial nerve. This preparation, termed the *encéphale isolé* by Bremer, exhibited EEG and pupil signs comparable to those of the normal animal. When the EEG showed the sleep spindles and the pupils are slit, sensory stimulation induced long lasting EEG arousal and dilation of the pupil (see Figure 14.2). In the absence of stimulation both EEG and pupil measures showed alternate periods of "waking" and "sleeping" similar to those of the normal cat. Consequently, elimination of sensory input from the body did not appear to be a crucial factor in the permanently "sleeping" EEG of the *cerveau isolé*.

The above interpretation of Bremer's experiments was prevalent until the publication, in 1949, of Moruzzi and Magoun's now famous study of reticular activation. They delivered electrical stimuli to the brainstem reticular formation of chloralose anesthetized or *encéphale isolé* cats. Relatively high frequency stimulation (100–300/sec) of the reticular formation produced immediate and often long lasting EEG arousal. An example of this finding is shown in Figure 14.3. The stimulus (horizontal bar below the EEG records) was delivered while the EEG showed typical sleep spindles. There is an immediate transition to the low voltage fast activity characteristic of EEG arousal.

The results of Moruzzi and Magoun's experiments immediately suggested a new explanation for Bremer's *cerveau isolé* experiment. The reticular formation rather than the classical sensory pathways might be the source of EEG arousal. Because both are transected in the *cerveau isolé*, the issue could only be settled by destroying the sensory pathways in isolation or the central reticular core of the brainstem in isolation. Lindsley, Bowden, and Magoun (1949) and Lindsley, Schreiner, Knowles, and Magoun (1950) performed these crucial experiments. They found that animals with lesions limited to the classical sensory pathways exhibited normal behavioral sleep-wake cycles with appropriate EEG activity— spindles during sleep and arousal when awakened and alert (see Figure 14.4). On the other hand animals with reticular lesions tended to be stuporous after lesion and exhibited only a spindling EEG (see Figure 14.4). Short duration EEG arousal could be induced in these reticular lesioned animals by strong sensory stimulation but the arousal did not persist after the stimulus was removed. This is comparable to the short duration EEG arousal reported by Bremer for the *cerveau isolé*. It thus appears that cortical EEG arousal is mediated by the reticular core and not by the classical sensory pathways. Consistent with both the lesion and the stimulation studies reported above, studies using normal animals

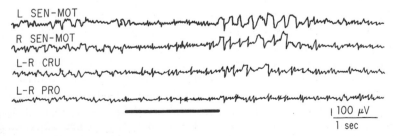

Figure 14.3. Cortical EEG arousal produced by rapid electrical stimulation of the brainstem reticular formation (horizontal bar). The four traces were recorded from different regions of the anterior portion of the cortex. (From Moruzzi and Magoun, 1949)

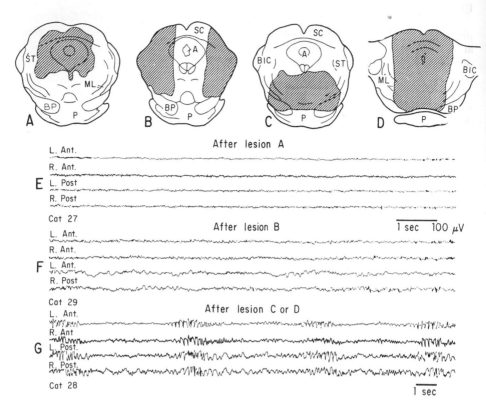

Figure 14.4. Effects of various brainstem lesions (above) on the cortical EEG. Lesions of the dorsal midbrain (**A**) or classical sensory pathways (**B**) do not produce a sleeping EEG but lesions involving the reticular formation (**C** and **D**) produce a sleeping EEG. Abbreviations: BP, basis pedunculi; M, medial lemniscus; P, pons; A, cerebral acqueduct; BIC, brachium of the inferior colliculus; SC, superior colliculus. (From Lindsley, Bowden, and Magoun, 1949)

with implanted electrodes have noted that behavioral alerting appears to occur when the reticular formation is electrically stimulated (see French et al., 1960).

The one remaining loose end in the reticular story as we have described it concerns the manner in which peripheral stimuli get to the reticular formation in order to produce cortical EEG arousal. Electrophysiological studies demonstrated that gross evoked responses could be recorded from the reticular formation to all modalities of peripheral stimulation (French et al., 1952). Furthermore, responses evoked by different kinds of stimuli interact with one another (Bremer and Terzuolo, 1954). For example, if a light flash is presented and followed after a short time by a tactile stimulus, the evoked response to the tactile stimulus is much reduced. This type of interference effect of different kinds of stimuli on one another suggests that the various stimuli are activating one and the same system, i.e. the reticular formation is activated by all types of stimuli in a nonspecific manner. In addition, it was shown that electrical stimulation in certain regions of the cortex produced EEG arousal in the reticular formation (Bremer and Terzuolo, 1954; Segundo et al., 1955; French et al., 1955), suggesting the existence of reciprocal connections. The evoked response studies thus indicated that all manner of stimuli, including electrical stimulation of the cortex, could activate the reticular formation. Anatomical evidence available then was consistent with the view that the various classical sensory pathways sent axon collaterals to the reticular core of the brainstem.

At this point it is perhaps well to summarize the classical view (circa 1956) of the organization and functions of the ascending reticular activating system (ARAS). The ARAS was believed to consist of a multisynaptic nonspecific system acting on the cortex. The well-known summary diagram by Magoun of the organization of the ascending reticular formation in the monkey is shown in Figure 14.5. Classical sensory pathways are shown projecting into the reticular formation as well as to specific sensory areas of the cortex. The reticular formation in turn projects diffusely to thalamic, hypothalamic, and cortical regions. Activation of the ARAS by sensory stimuli or direct electrical stimulation produces cortical EEG arousal. The role the ARAS was believed to play in sleep is well summarized in a review by Moruzzi (1964):

In 1956 everyone was convinced that behavioral sleep was constantly and necessarily associated with EEG synchronization. One knew that both EEG and behavioral arousal were due to a *phasic* barrage of ascending reticular impulses, which probably

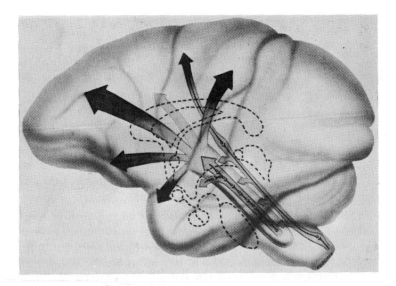

Figure 14.5.   Lateral view of the monkey brain (facing left) showing the ascending reticular system receiving collaterals from the somatic afferent pathway in the brainstem and projecting diffusely to the cortex. (From Magoun, 1954)

disrupted the slow cortical rhythms by desynchronizing the activity of the thalamic pacemaker (Moruzzi and Magoun, 1949). These facts and the study of the effect of midbrain tegmental lesions had led to the conclusion that behavioral wakefulness and EEG activation were due to a *tonic* flow of ascending reticular impulses. Sleep was regarded as a passive phenomenon, due to absence of wakefulness (see Kleitman, 1929, 1939). Behavioral alertness and EEG activation were present whenever the tonic flow of ascending reticular impulses was above a critical level required for the maintenance of wakefulness. Vice versa, the animal succumbed to sleep whenever the tonic discharge of the ascending reticular system decreased below such a critical level. The withdrawal or any striking reduction of the diffuse reticular facilitation led then to a fall of the cerebral "onus," which was regarded as the cause of all the EEG and behavioral manifestations of sleep.

Finally, mention must be made of "activation" theory, which attempts to relate generalized arousal or activation level to the variables of human performance (Duffy, 1962; Malmo, 1959). In particular, an inverted "U" shaped function obtains between performance and induced or assumed level of activation in many situations (Malmo, 1959).

Subsequent status of the ARAS

It is almost axiomatic in the field of brain function and behavior that whenever a clear picture relating a given structure to particular functions emerges, additional research will tend to complicate and obfuscate that picture. Such has been the fate of the classical view of the ARAS. However, in the somewhat detailed accounting of the problems with the classical view that follows, it is well to keep in mind that the original observations of Moruzzi and Magoun, namely that activation of the ARAS produces cortical EEG arousal, still stands, as do many of the other experimental results that led to the classical view. It is the interpretation of these experiments that has been altered by the newer information.

Anatomical organization

The three major anatomical characteristics of the classical ARAS, namely collateral afferent input from ascending sensory pathways, conduction of activity through a long multisynaptic system within the ARAS, and diffuse anatomical organization of the ARAS, have all been questioned. As far as collateral input from sensory systems is concerned, there appears to be no collateral input to the ARAS from the medial lemniscus (i.e. the primary somatic sensory pathway conveying touch and pressure information from the body to the brain, Brodal, 1957). Instead, the spinothalamic tract (pain, temperature, and diffuse touch) actually relays through a portion of the ARAS on its course to the thalamus (Nauta and Kuypers, 1958). The visual system apparently projects to the reticular formation via relays from the superior colliculus rather than from axon collaterals of the retino-cortical system (Brodal, 1957). However, there is anatomical evidence for axon collateral input to the reticular formation from the auditory system, and from the trigeminal (face) portion of the lemniscal system (Brodal, 1957). In sum, information from major sensory systems does reach the ARAS, but the types of information do not necessarily include all those conducted in the classical sensory pathways, and they do not necessarily reach the ARAS by afferent collaterals.

There are at least two major ascending output pathways in the ARAS that are composed of long axons uninterrupted by synapses (Nauta and Kuypers, 1957). One of these ascends throughout the length of the brainstem. It contains many axons originating in the reticular formation of the pons and medulla, and projects to a variety of subcortical structures including the periaquaductal gray, superior colliculus, the intralaminar thalamic nuclei, and subthalamus. In addition, fiber systems originating in the ventral mesencephalon project to the hypothalamus, medial septal nucleus, and to nuclei of the basal ganglia. Some cells within the reticular formation have been found to send widely branching axons both rostral and caudal for considerable distances, ending in multiple branchings to other cells (Scheibel and Scheibel, 1958; see Figure 14.17). There are also very small cells, presumably having short processes.

Finally, the anatomical organization of the reticular core of the brainstem is far from diffuse. Olszewski and Baxter (1954) noted some 98 histologically distinguishable reticular nuclei! Brodal (1957) has demonstrated that some of the regions can be differentiated in terms of projections and connections. First, there are three nuclei of the brainstem reticular formation that project to the cerebellum. These are topographically distinct and separate from the major reticular formation. Second, the medial reticular regions tend to be concerned with efferent influences upon both spinal cord and higher brain structures. Lateral regions are those receiving the bulk of projections from the specific sensory pathways. Third, the rostrally projecting neurons of the medulla and pons tend to lie more caudal than the caudal projections. Finally, the medial efferent portion of the system is differently organized at different levels of the brainstem.

While these anatomical findings contrast with earlier views of the structural organization of the ARAS, they do not necessarily contradict the classical view of the *functional* organization of the ARAS. Cortical EEG arousal could be mediated by a continuous axon pathway as well as by a multiple synapse short axon pathway. Indeed, Magoun has presented physiological evidence for a rapidly conducting reticular projection to the cerebral cortex that bypasses the thalamus entirely. All major sensory modalities do project to the ARAS, even if some types of information within a given modality do not. A multiplicity of definable nuclei within the ARAS might tend ultimately to simplify rather than contradict the story, particularly in view of Brodal's more general groupings in terms of the organization of efferent projections from the reticular formation.

ARAS influences upon the EEG

Perhaps the greatest difficulty with the classical view of the ARAS is the relatively uncritical identification of cortical EEG arousal with behavioral arousal, and cortical EEG synchronization (spindling) with behavioral sleep. Relations between EEG and behavioral measures are by no means this clear-cut. Special procedures can often dissociate the two types of measures. For example, administration of atropine (a drug whose peripheral action is to block transmission at ganglia in which epinephrine is the transmitter substance) yields an animal who behaviorally is perfectly awake and alert, yet whose EEG is one of permanent sleep (Wikler, 1952; Bradley, 1958).

It could be argued that the atropine effect is an artificial condition not relevant to the normal animal. A much more significant disparity between EEG and behavioral measures occurs during deep sleep (Dement and Kleitman, 1957; Jouvet, 1962). It has been shown in both cat and man that during a sleep period the EEG will alternate between the ordinary EEG spindle or synchronization sleep and a phase in which it appears identical to the EEG arousal pattern (see Figure 14.6). During the EEG arousal periods of sleep, the eyes exhibit characteristic rapid eye movements. A natural assumption would be that during the "EEG arousal" phase the animal is on the point of waking up. However in both cat and man a stronger sensory stimulus is required for behavioral awakening during the "EEG arousal" sleep phase than during the "EEG spindle" sleep phase. A weaker stimulus given during the EEG arousal sleep phase will change the EEG to the spindle sleep pattern, whereas the same stimulus given during the EEG sleep spindle pattern may awaken the animal. In other words, in terms of behavioral criteria, EEG arousal sleep is deeper than EEG spindle sleep. It is for this reason that EEG arousal sleep has been called *paradoxical sleep*. We will consider paradoxical sleep further in our discussion of sleep and waking, at the end of this chapter. For now it is sufficient to note that it has resulted in a breakdown of the previous view that EEG arousal necessarily means behavioral arousal.

Dissociation between behavioral and EEG signs of arousal has also been produced by lesions. Feldman and Waller (1962) showed that extensive bilateral destruction of the posterior hypothalamus in cats resulted in permanent behavioral somnolence or coma; however cortical EEG arousal could be induced by repetitive (100/sec) electrical stimulation or peripheral stimulation without

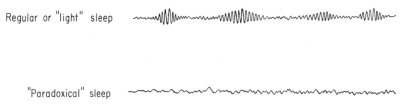

Regular or "light" sleep

"Paradoxical" sleep

Figure 14.6. Diagram comparing cortical EEG tracings during "light" sleep (spindling or synchronization) and during deep or "paradoxical" sleep (low voltage fast activity). The pattern during paradoxical sleep is very similar to the normal waking EEG.

any accompanying behavioral arousal. Interestingly, the EEG arousal lasted a maximum of only four minutes after cessation of stimulation, a much shorter time than EEG arousal following comparable stimulation in the intact cat, which would seem to indicate that the mechanisms producing EEG arousal were altered although not abolished by the lesions. Nevertheless, the most important finding of their experiment, the dissociation of EEG and behavioral signs of arousal, seems quite clear.

Recent experiments concerned with the effects of brainstem transection on the spontaneous cortical EEG have complicated the original dichotomy between the spindling *cerveau isolé* and the aroused *encéphale isolé*. In the course of a systematic investigation of the effects of transections made at many different levels of the brain stem, Rossi and Zirondoli (1955) noted that whenever the transection was *above* the input of the trigeminal nerve (fifth cranial nerve conveying tactile and pain information from the face and head), the cortical EEG pattern became the typical spindling activity of the *cerveau isolé*. Because the fifth nerves enter the brain stem of the cat at about the middle of the pons, this would be a low *cerveau isolé*. However, if the transection were made posterior to the fifth nerve input, just slightly more caudal in the pons, the typical aroused cortical EEG of the *encéphale isolé* developed.

The results of Rossi and Zirondoli's experiments suggest that afferent input conveyed by the fifth nerve may be crucial in the maintenance of cortical EEG arousal. Such a possibility is not at all unreasonable. In most earlier experiments utilizing the *encéphale isolé* (which, remember, shows EEG arousal) the animal is anesthetized with ether in order to sever the spinal cord from the brain and expose the cerebral cortex. Local anesthetics are then administered to all cut skin edges and the ether *withdrawn*. In spite of local anesthetics, the painful pressure exerted by the stereotaxic holder (i.e. ear bars), may still be present. In other words, under the best circumstances the *encéphale isolé* animal is bound to experience some pain or discomfort and this most certainly should cause cortical EGG arousal.

Roger, Rossi, and Zirondoli (1956) demonstrated that fifth nerve input indeed played a crucial role in the cortical EEG arousal pattern of the *encéphale isolé*. In acute experiments they found that after severing the spinal cord from the brain, the typical cortical EEG arousal of the *encéphale isolé* preparation could be converted to the spindling cortical EEG of the *cerveau isolé* merely by severing the fifth nerve. In chronic experiments they destroyed the fifth nerve and, several days later, severed the spinal cord. Again, the "detrigeminalized *encéphale isolé*" showed the spindling cortical EEG. These experiments suggest an entirely different interpretation of the role of the reticular formation in cortical EEG arousal, namely that it simply mediates painful stimulation.

Fortunately for the reticular story, experiments in Moruzzi's laboratory at Pisa have shown that under certain circumstances it is possible to produce the typical EEG arousal pattern of the *encéphale isolé* by a brain stem transection just anterior to the zone of entrance of the fifth nerve in the pons (Batini et al., 1959).

This is the so-called "mid-pontine pretrigeminal animal." Because the section is anterior to the fifth nerves, all pain input is abolished and the cortical EEG arousal cannot be due to painful stimulation. However, transection of the brainstem at a level just slightly higher than that used to produce this preparation yields the typical *cerveau isolé* with cortical spindling (i.e. the findings of Rossi and Zirondoli). Consequently, it would appear that a restricted region of the pontine reticular formation just anterior to the fifth cranial nerve input plays a rather crucial role in cortical EEG desynchronization. Moruzzi (1964) has tentatively identified the crucial structure in the mid pons as the *nucleus reticularis pontis oralis*.

In reviewing the many brainstem transection studies, Moruzzi (1964) has distinguished five different preparations. Two different types of measures have been used: EEG activity (synchronized or desynchronized) and eye movements. The latter has been used by the Italian workers as an independent index of behavioral wakefulness. If the eyes will follow with vertical eye movements an object crossing the visual field, and if the pupil (of the cat) dilates when a dog or mouse is presented, then the eye movements are said to indicate wakefulness. This rather ingenious measure is perhaps the only behavioral index available concerning the functional status of the portion of the brain *above* the level of transection, particularly with high midbrain lesions. Vertical eye movements are controlled by the third and fourth cranial nerves, which exit from the rostral midbrain. Consequently, if the section is posterior to the anterior portion of the midbrain, vertical eye movements will be controlled by the forebrain. Furthermore, visual input cannot affect activity below the transection (the optic nerve input is anterior to all levels of section). Hence any eye movements that are stimulus-controlled must themselves be controlled by input-output relations above the transection. (It is important not to confuse these ocular signs of wakefulness with the rapid eye movements of the paradoxical sleep. These latter movements are quick shifts of the eyes unrelated to visual stimulation and are a characteristic sign of deep or paradoxical sleep.)

The five types of brainstem preparation are summarized in Figure 14.7. The *precollicular* transection (1) is made at the anterior level of the midbrain and disconnects the entire brainstem from the cerebrum. The cortical EEG is entirely dominated by synchronization (spindles and slow waves). Ocular signs of wakefulness are irrelevant here, because all motor control of the eyes is below the level of section.

The *postcollicular* transection (2) is the classical low *cerveau isolé* of Bremer. The EEG is characterized by spindles separated by long interspindle lulls of low voltage fast activity (see Figure 14.7 and also Figure 14.8). Although control of vertical eye movements by the cerebrum is possible with this transection, there are no ocular signs of wakefulness. This preparation differs from the precollicular animal in showing considerably longer periods of EEG desynchronization between spindle bursts. Interestingly, much of this low voltage fast activity seems to be the result of input from the visual system. Visual stimulation is not

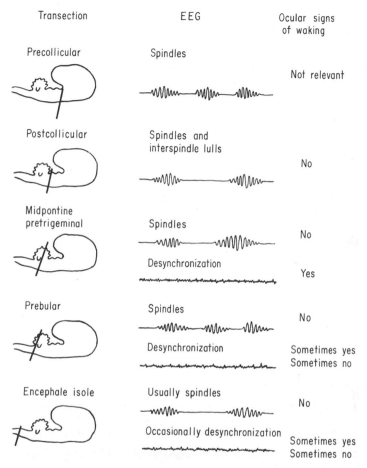

Figure 14.7. Effects of transecting the brainstem at various levels on cortical EEG activity and on eye movements in response to visual stimulation (see text).

the critical factor however. The typical EEG shown in Figure 14.8A is the same whether the animal is in an ordinary lighted room or in total darkness. You may recall from Chapter 10 that there is pronounced discharge of the optic nerve fibers even when the eye is in total darkness (so-called "dark-discharge"). This dark discharge can be reversibly abolished by temporarily occluding the blood supply to the eye. Figure 14.8B shows the effect of this procedure on the cortical EEG activity of the postcollicular animal. Much of the low voltage fast activity disappears and the EEG now resembles the precollicular animal. Figure 14.8C shows recovery following restoration of the normal blood supply to the retina (Bizzi and Spencer, 1962). This observation, incidentally, fits very nicely with Granit's suggestion that spontaneous activity in sensory systems may play a role

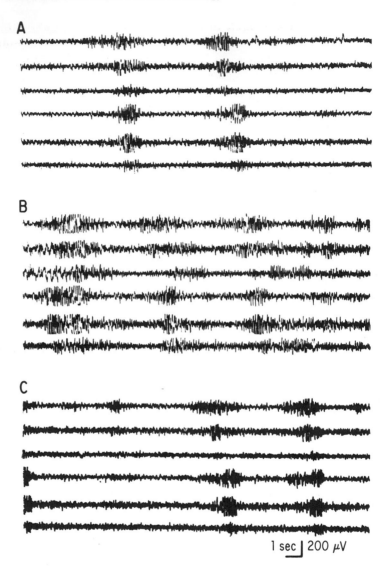

Figure 14.8. Effect of retinal ischemia (occluding of blood supply to eye) on the cortical EEG of the acute post collicular transected cat. **A**, control record. **B**, record after three minutes of retinal ischemia (note increase in spindles and background activity). **C**, after the retinal blood supply is restored the cortical EEG returns to the control pattern. (From Bizzi and Spencer, 1962)

in general level of activation of the reticular formation (see discussion of spontaneous activity in sensory systems in Chapter 10).

The *midpontine pretrigeminal* transection (3) was described above. The section is made just anterior to the entry zone of the fifth cranial nerves in the pons.

The EEG shows alternate periods of desynchronization and synchronization. During periods of EEG synchronization there are no ocular signs of wakefulness. Low voltage fast desynchronization of the EEG is usually accompanied by ocular signs of wakefulness. Suppression of retinal dark discharge reduces the amount of EEG desynchronization in this preparation (Arduini and Hirao, 1959) but both synchronization and desynchronization are seen after chronic deafferentation of the olfactory and visual inputs (Batini, Palestini, et al., 1959).

Jouvet (1962) has reported on two animals having *prebulbar* transections (4). Most of the pons lies above the level of section. These animals resemble the midpontine pretrigeminal preparation in showing periods of EEG synchrony and EEG desynchrony. During synchrony, ocular signs of wakefulness are absent. However EEG desynchrony may be accompanied by signs of wakefulness or by the absence of such signs. In terms of these two measures the prebulbar animal resembles the intact animal.

Finally, recent studies of the "*encéphale isolé*," (5), in which the spinal cord is severed from the brain, indicate that if care is taken to avoid all painful stimulation (i.e. animal's head removed from the stereotaxic head holder) there is a striking tendency to exhibit EEG synchrony and the ocular signs of sleep (Ho et al., 1960). These findings agree with the earlier experiments of Rossi and Zirondoli (1955), and Rodger, Rossi, and Zirondoli (1956) described above.

There is as yet no unanimity of opinion concerning the interpretation of these rather complex results of brainstem transection. Perhaps the simplest hypothesis would be to assume that different regions or "centers" exist which exert influences of some kind or another on the state of the cortical EEG and the ocular signs of wakefulness. Thus structures above the midbrain might produce only EEG synchrony and no ocular wakefulness. The "activating region" just anterior to the fifth nerve entry in the pons might produce both EEG desynchronization and ocular signs of wakefulness. Regions in the lower pons and medulla might act to produce cortical EEG desynchrony without ocular signs of wakefulness. Finally, the net balance of these symptoms might yield a predominately "sleeping" cortex in the "*encéphale isolé*." As we will see later in our discussion of sleep, Moruzzi (1961, 1964), Magoun (1963), and Jouvet (1961, 1962) have developed theories of this general type to account for the neural mechanisms of sleep and wakefulness.

Microelectrode studies of the ARAS

In the course of this book we have repeatedly observed that microelectrode recording of activity from single nerve cells has led to major changes in our understanding of the organization of various neural systems. The ARAS is no exception. For example, gross evoked response studies cited earlier in the chapter had shown that all types of stimuli would evoke responses in the ARAS. Consequently, it was believed that the ARAS was activated in a nonselective and nonspecific manner by sensory stimuli. Microelectrode experiments have shown that few if any individual neurons in the ARAS are influenced by all types of stimulation.

Scheibel, Scheibel, Mollica, and Moruzzi (1955) completed an extensive microelectrode study of approximately 1000 neurons in the bulbar and mesencephalic regions of the reticular formation in the cat, using a variety of sensory stimuli. Most of the animals they used were decerebrate (*cerveau isolé*) or *encéphale isolé* preparations, and the stimuli employed included somatic sensory (skin tap, shock to sciatic nerve, shock to muscle afferent nerves, etc.), autonomic (shock to vagus nerve), auditory (click), electrical shock stimulation of the sensory motor areas of the cerebral cortex and the auditory area of the cerebral cortex, and finally, polarization (steady dc current of about 1 mA) of the anterior lobe of the cerebellum. This last method appears to have a profound effect on

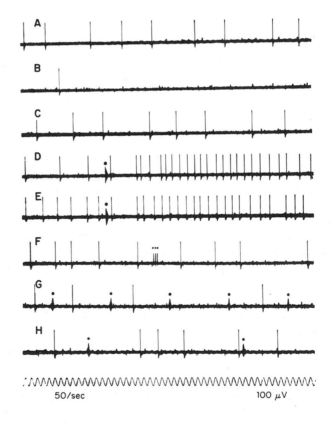

Figure 14.9. Spike discharges recorded extracellularly from a single cell in the midbrain reticular formation. This cell is influenced by cerebellar polarization and sciatic stimulation, but is unaffected by vagal nerve or auditory stimulation. (Synchronous stimuli indicated by dots). **A**, spontaneous activity. **B**, inhibition of activity by cerebellar polarization. **C**, normal activity after cerebellar polarization. **D** and **E**, increased discharge frequency to stimulation of the ipsilateral sciatic nerve. **F**, stimulation of the vagus nerve is without effect. **G**, and **H**, auditory click stimulation is without effect. (From Scheibel, Scheibel, Mollica, and Moruzzi, 1955)

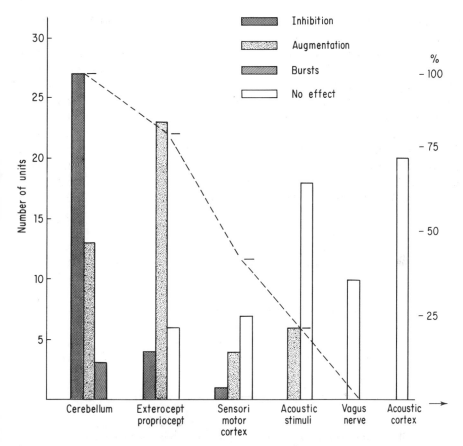

Figure 14.10. Summary of the results obtained by Scheibel et al. (1955). Histograms indicate number of reticular cells that could be influenced (i.e. inhibited, augmented, or made to fire in bursts) or not influenced by various types of stimuli. Dashed line illustrates relative over-all degree of influence exerted by the stimuli. (Scheibel, Scheibel, Mollica, and Moruzzi, 1955)

the activity of reticular cells and was used as the major method of identifying cells belonging to the reticular formation. Typically, only cells showing spontaneous activity in the absence of stimulation were studied. In terms of effective stimuli, there were two major classes of cells: those responsive to only somatic sensory stimulation, and those responsive to only auditory stimulation. Some units responded to both classes of stimuli and some units responded to both these classes of stimulation and to stimulation of sensory motor cortex as well. *No units responded to vagus nerve stimulation or stimulation of the auditory cortex.*

An example is shown in Figure 14.9 of a cell responsive to cerebellar polarization (as were all cells in this study by definition) and sciatic nerve stimulation, but not to vagal and acoustic stimulation. Note that in this instance the cerebellar influence is inhibitory and the sciatic nerve influence is excitatory. A summary histogram (Figure 14.10) shows the relative effectiveness of the various types of stimulation, and the relative preponderance of the kinds of influences exerted on the cells. These results might be characterized as follows (always remembering that some influence from cerebellar polarization defines the cells as reticular): some types of stimulation (vagus nerve and auditory cortex) have no influence on discharge characteristics of reticular cells. Most cells are responsive to all varieties of peripheral somatic sensory stimulation, and a few to stimulation of the sensory motor cortex. A few cells respond to all types of stimulation (of course excluding vagus nerve and auditory cortex). To simplify these results still further, in terms of peripheral stimuli that were at one time or another effective, most cells responded to somatic sensory stimulation, some cells responded only to auditory stimulation, and a few cells responded to both.

The problem of identifying any given cell in the brainstem as belonging to the ARAS is a formidable one. A microelectrode is pushed blindly into the general region of the reticular formation of the brainstem, a small diameter structure containing many different neural systems. Even if histological controls demonstrate that the microelectrode was indeed in the anatomically defined reticular formation (as was done in the study by Scheibel et al.) the cells might belong to the descending reticular system rather than the ARAS. A variety of physiological techniques can be used; none of these is very conclusive. Scheibel et al. employed the criteria of response to dc polarization of the cerebellum. Although this maneuver influences many cells in the reticular region of the brain stem there is no *necessary* reason why it should influence *all* ARAS cells or *only* ARAS cells.

Another method of identification that has been suggested is to define cells in the reticular region of the brainstem as belonging to ARAS if they show increased spike activity when the cortical EEG shows desynchronization, and reduced activity during EEG synchronization. This type of cellular behavior would of course be predicted by the classical view of the ARAS function. Such a criterion obviously begs the question and would result in extremely biased samples of cells. Actually, it appears that many brain stem reticular cells do not exhibit this neat correspondence with the cortical EEG.

One somewhat puzzling feature of neurons in the reticular formation is that many cannot be influenced by sensory stimuli or by electrical stimulation of the cerebellum or cerebral cortex. Several studies have shown that even in the unanesthetized animal, of the neurons whose spontaneous activity was examined, some 50 percent of the pons and 65 percent of the midbrain could not be influenced by any type of stimulation (Palestini, Rossi, and Zanchetti, 1957; Mancia, Michelse, and Mollica, 1957). In these experiments only the overall level of discharge frequency, or gross changes in pattern such as bursts *vs* continuous firing, were studied. Amassian and Walter (1958) analyzed the temporal patterns of spike discharges of cells in the reticular formation to peripheral stimuli. They were able to distinguish the influences of different types of sensory stimulation on cells activated by several types of stimulation in terms of measures like latency and interspike intervals. It may be that these more complex measures would have demonstrated subtle sensory influences on the cells described as unresponsive in the studies noted above.

One of the more striking findings of microelectrodes studies of cells in the reticular formation is the fact that discharge patterns of many cells do not correspond to the cortical EEG. Mollica, Moruzzi, and Naquet (1953) did observe midbrain reticular cells whose activity was markedly increased when the cortical EEG pattern was shifted from synchrony to desynchrony by cerebellar stimulation. However, the EEG arousal pattern lasted much longer than the increased reticular cell activity. The same phenomenon was observed by Machne, Calma, and Magoun (1955) for units of the rostral midbrain and intralaminar thalamic nuclei. (Note: these thalamic nuclei are sometimes termed the rostral or diencephalic component of the reticular formation; we will discuss them further in the section on the " Diffuse Thalamic System " later in the chapter.) These authors observed several different patterns of cellular activity. One category of cells yielded burst discharges during interspindle lulls (i.e. during periods of

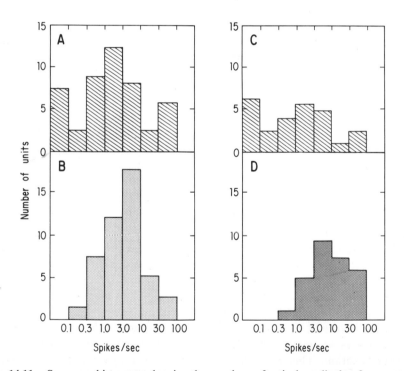

Figure 14.11.   Summary histogram showing the numbers of reticular cells that fire spontaneously at various frequencies under various conditions. **A**, activity of 50 cells during quiet waking. **B**, same cells as **A** during behavioral sleep with EEG synchronization (slow waves and spindles). **C**, activity of a different group of 28 cells during quiet waking. **D**, same cells as **C** during sleep with low voltage fast EEG (paradoxical sleep). Note increased activity of cells during paradoxical sleep compared to waking. (From Huttenlocher, 1961)

EEG arousal). The firing pattern of another group of cells seemed to have no relationship to the cortical EEG. Still another category of cells fired trains of spikes during EEG arousal. Some neurons exhibited all of these different patterns at different times.

A careful quantitative analysis of the discharge characteristics of midbrain reticular cells during sleep and waking was completed by Huttenlocher (1961) using normal cats with chronically implanted microelectrodes. Some rather striking regularities were observed in neuron behavior. The majority of cells exhibited slow spontaneous discharges (less than 15/sec) when the animals were behaviorally awake and had EEG desynchronization. During behavioral sleep with EEG synchronization (spindles and slow waves) most of these cells increased their firing rates. A smaller number of cells exhibited high spontaneous rates during behavioral and EEG wakefulness; these slowed during behavioral and EEG synchrony sleep. In contrast, virtually all of the units studied during both wakefulness and behavioral sleep with EEG desynchrony (i.e. paradoxical sleep) approximately doubled their discharge rates during paradoxical sleep. These results are all summarized in Figure 14.11.

The results of Huttenlocher's experiment would seem to pose problems for the classical view of the ARAS. The majority of reticular cells seem more active during slow wave sleep than during wakefulness. It has been suggested that Huttenlocher may not have been recording cells of the ARAS, because the ARAS should be strongly depressed during sleep. However any such objection would seem to presuppose the very kind of information that Huttenlocher was attempting to obtain. As noted above, the use of any such criteria to identify reticular cells would seriously bias the results. Unless satisfactory quantitative data to the contrary can be obtained, Huttenlocher's results would appear to complicate the classical interpretation of the functions of the ARAS.

Pharmacological properties of the ARAS

A number of rather interesting pharmacological effects have been described for the reticular formation. A very dramatic finding is the extreme sensitivity of cells in the reticular formation to epinephrine (adrenalin). Paul Dell and his associates in Paris have shown that intravenously injected epinephrine in doses as low as 5 μg/kg can induce cortical EEG arousal in a spindling preparation (Bonvallet, Dell, and Heibel, 1954). They used the low cerveau isolé cat (transection 2 in Figure 14.7), a preparation that exhibits marked spindling. Injection of low dosages of epinephrine was followed in about 20 sec by cortical EEG desynchronization. This EEG arousal pattern is initially accompanied by a transient increase in blood pressure. However, the EEG arousal outlasts the blood pressure effect by a considerable time. The EEG effect does not appear due to direct action of epinephrine on the cerebral cortex; the injection has no effect on the spindling EEG of the high cerveau isolé (transection 1 of Figure 14.7), in which the reticular formation is severed from the forebrain (i.e. some reticular formation must project to the forebrain before the arousal effect of epinephrine can be obtained).

In a more direct demonstration of the reticular action of epinephrine, Bonvallet, Hugelin, and Dell (1956) neurally isolated the mesencephalic portion of the reticular formation by transecting the brain at both the anterior and posterior ends of the midbrain, and recorded the behavior of single cells with microelectrodes. Following injection of epinephrine, some cells increase discharge frequency, others decrease the frequency of firing, and still others were unaffected.

It has been known for some time that cells in the respiratory "center" of the brainstem are directly sensitive to the concentration of CO_2 in the blood. If blood CO_2 becomes elevated they act to increase breathing. These centers are contained within the brainstem reticular formation. However Dell and associates have reported that blood CO_2 level also appears to influence the portions of the reticular formation concerned with cortical EEG arousal (Bonvallet, Hugelin, and Dell, 1955; Dell, Bonvallet, and Hugelin, 1954). Thus inhalation of CO_2, with a concomitant increase in blood CO_2, produces intensive-cortical EEG arousal and decreased blood CO_2 produces cortical EEG synchrony. Coagulation of the anterior portion of the midbrain reticular formation abolishes both CO_2 effects, thus suggesting that CO_2 acts on reticular cells.

One possible problem in these studies of epinephrine effects on the reticular formation is the recent observation that epinephrine appears to have great difficulty crossing the blood-brain barrier (Weil-Malherbe et al., 1959). It appears to require a matter of *hours* to get from the blood stream to the brain. Furthermore direct injection of epinephrine into the ventricles (thus by-passing the blood-brain barrier, see dicussion in Chapter 5) induces sleep in animals (McIlwain, 1955; Feldberg, 1964). It has been suggested that the supposed direct reticular actions of intravenously injectioned epinephrine may be due to its peripheral actions, which would result in increased barrages of afferent impulses to the brain (Feldberg, 1964).

There is some evidence to suggest that the reticular formation may itself release humoral substances into the blood stream that can act both locally and on distant regions such as the cerebral cortex. Ingvar and associates (see Ingvar, 1955; 1958; Ingvar, Krakau, and Söderberg, 1957) have obtained evidence suggesting that electrical stimulation of the reticular formation may cause local release of compounds that can exert actions on the cerebral cortex. A slab of cortex was neurally isolated by undercutting but its blood supply via pial vessels maintained intact. Electrical stimulation of the reticular formation produced, after a few seconds, EEG arousal in the cortical slab.

The pharmacological studies described above all have been concerned with the possible effects of substances that are normally present in the brain. There are a wide variety of studies of the actions of various drugs and chemicals on the reticular formation and related structures. It is not feasible to survey this extensive literature here, but many of the observations have been summarized

Figure 14.12. Diagram showing possible sites of action for various drugs within the central nervous system: (1) reticular formation, (2) diffuse thalamic projection system, (3) afferent collaterals to reticular formation. Barbiturates might act directly on (1), cholinergic drugs on (2), and chlorpromazine and LSD-25 on (3). (From Bradley, 1958)

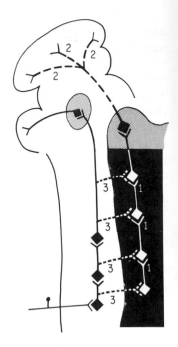

▨ Thalamic nuclei

■ Reticular formation

—— Specific afferent pathways

– – – Diffuse projection systems

······ Afferent collaterals

by Bradley (1958), (see Figure 14.12). In general, barbiturates appear to depress the reticular formation while amphetamine ("benzedrine") has an excitant action (i.e. such drugs may act on area 1 in Figure 14.12). Cholinergic drugs (such as acetylcholine, astropine, and physostigmine) do not appear to act directly on the reticular formation, but instead may influence the diffuse thalamic system (i.e. may act on area 2). Finally, some tranquilizers such as chlorpromazine may depress, and certain psychotomimetics such as LSD-25 may excite, the afferent inputs to the reticular formation (i.e. may act on areas 3). This schema, while highly speculative and based on rather extended inferences from the experimental literature, does summarize suggestions from a large variety of psychopharmacological experiments. There is as yet little evidence concerning the synaptic mechanisms whereby these hypothetical actions take place.

Neurobehavioral studies of the ARAS

In terms of its behavioral implications, the most significant early experiment on the ARAS was that by Lindsley, Schrainer, Knowles, and Magoun (1950), showing that lesions of the reticular formation produced permanently sleeping animals. More recently, other experimenters have questioned the results and interpretations of this study. Because of their very considerable behavioral significance, these experiments deserve careful consideration.

Lindsley et al. prepared four cats with electrolytic reticular lesions at different levels: the junction of the pons and midbrain, the rostral midbrain, the hypothalamus, and the junction of the hypothalamus and thalamus. None of these animals survived longer than 25 days and all remained continuously comatose until death. Sensory stimulation could induce cortical EEG arousal, but it seldom outlasted the stimulus for more than a very few seconds and was not accompanied by any marked behavioral signs of arousal. Two animals sustained lesions of the periaquaductal gray; one remained sleepy for about one week following lesion and then recovered, and the other showed normal sleep and waking the day following lesion. Finally, two animals received large bilateral lateral midbrain lesions eliminating all the classical sensory pathways, but sparing the reticular system. They exhibited normal sleep-waking behavior (with appropriate EEG activity). One of these animals exhibited compulsive walking, but otherwise their symptoms were no more than would be expected from interruption of the sensory input conveying auditory and somatic sensory information to the brain. These animals were studied for two months and then sacrificed.

The extent of neural destruction of the animal with the midbrain reticular lesion is shown in Figure 14.13A. Note that it appears to invade slightly the medical lemniscus (somatic sensory pathway), and the brachia of the superior colliculus (probably involved in visual function). There is thus total destruction of the reticular system plus some damage to sensory pathways.

A similar experiment was completed on monkeys by French and Magoun (1952) with lesions limited to the ARAS. Of nine lesion animals, four sustained extensive destruction of the midbrain reticular formation and all four died the day of surgery. One monkey had a smaller lesion placed in the caudal midline thalamus and exhibited normal behavioral sleep and waking following the lesion. Another animal appeared comatose immediately after lesion but regained " purposive" eye movements and, by this measure, appeared to have normal sleep and waking cycles, although remaining paralyzed until death on the twenty-third day. The lesions in this animal spared the reticular formation but destroyed the basis peduculis and basis pontis (motor tracts). The remaining three monkeys had partial lesions of the midbrain reticular formation. Two of them survived less than 18 days and remained comatose. The third animal had a less extensive lesion, and could be behaviorally aroused for very brief periods. This animal did not die and was ultimately sacrificed.

If we limit our consideration to the reticular system itself, Lindsley et al. prepared two cats with extensive reticular lesions (posterior and anterior levels of the midbrain). Both died within 22 days after lesion and, behaviorally speaking, remained totally comatose. French and Magoun prepared six monkeys with extensive midbrain reticular lesions. Four died on the day of surgery, and the other two died within 18 days of surgery, remaining completely comatose until death. One monkey had partial reticular lesion and remained moderately comatose. It is clear that large reticular lesions appear to produce very drastic effects. The animal is not simply drowsy or unattentive, he is totally " out," remaining completely comatose and unresponsive to stimulation. The fact that all large lesion animals died within a month of surgery suggests that rather drastic physiological malfunctions developed.

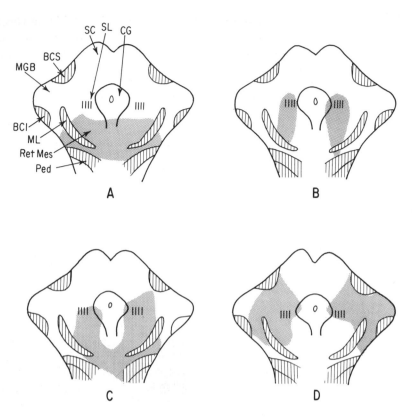

Figure 14.13. Approximate lesions in several studies in which effect of destroying the midbrain reticular formation (**A, B,** and **C**), or the classical sensory pathways (**D**), on sleeping and waking behavior was examined. **A,** animals comatose until death (Lindsley et al., 1949) **B,** animals regained normal sleep—wake cycle (Adametz, 1959). **C,** animal regained normal sleep—wake cycle (Doty, Beck, and Kooi, 1959). **D,** animals were very unresponsive to sensory stimuli but were not comatose (Sprague, Chambers, and Stellar 1961). Note marked variability in the three reticular lesions and the overlap of the reticular (**A, B, C**) and classical sensory (**D**) lesions. (**B** cl, brachium of the inferior colliculus; BCS; brachium of the superior colliculus; CG; central grey; MGB, medial geniculate body; ML, medial lemniscus; Ped, cerebral peduncle; Ret Mes, mesencephalic reticular formation; SC, superior colliculus; SL, spinal lemniscus.)

In these experiments the entire lesion was made in one operation. More recently Adametz (1959) prepared 15 cats with large bilateral midbrain reticular lesions in one stage, and 12 with equally large lesions done in two stages, one side at a time, allowing three weeks between the two operations (see Figure 14.13B for the lesion). The lesions were made longitudinally on each side of the midbrain and appeared to spare the most medial ventral portion of the midbrain reticular formation. Of the 15 single-stage lesion animals, all but one died within 30 days and all remained seriously comatose for this period. The one animal that survived began to recover on the thirty-fifth day and by two months after lesion exhibited a normal sleep and waking cycle and moved about relatively normally, albeit clumsily. This animal "attended" to mice; in fact he caught and ate them quickly and purposively.

In striking contrast to the one-stage lesion animals, all 12 cats with two-stage lesions were awake and alert both after the first and second stages of the operation. They exhibited *normal sleep-wake cycles*, could eat unaided, and appeared virtually normal in all aspects of behavior. Yet these animals had nearly total midbrain lesions as large as those in the single-stage group, in which all animals were totally comatose after lesions!

Adametz interprets his results as supporting the old concept of *diaschisis*. This term was first suggested by the nineteenth-century neurologist Von Monakov; it refers to a kind of "neural shock" following massive damage to the nervous system. Thus large single-stage lesions produce much more diaschisis than two-stage lesions, and recovery of function is much poorer. As far as Adametz's experiment is concerned, diaschisis is of course just another word that describes his results, and as an explanatory construct is somewhat circular (i.e. the animals with one-stage lesions were severely impaired because they were severely impaired). More important from the point of view of this discussion is the fact that the two-stage lesion animals recovered so well. Actually, there were no behavioral measures in his experiment; the animals were simply observed.

In comparing Adametz's results with previous studies, it should be emphasized that the most medial portion of the reticular formation was spared in all of the animals described above. In three additional animals almost the entire midbrain reticular formation was destroyed in seven to eight stages at one level (stereotaxic A + 4). These animals did show some postoperative deficits in ability to stand and walk and had impaired sleep-wake cycles for the first week after surgery. Nonetheless, comparable lesions in one stage (three cats) produced totally comatose animals, all of whom died within 12 days.

Doty, Beck, and Kooi (1959) demonstrated that animals with extensive midbrain reticular lesions (electrolytic, done in one stage) could be maintained for long periods after lesion and exhibited marked recovery of movement, sleep-wake cycles, and even of EEG arousal. Using a hindlimb shock avoidance conditioning procedure (tone CS) they found that significant retention and/or relearning were possible after lesions. In general their lesions were somewhat incomplete, often sparing the most medial portion of the reticular formation (see Figure 14.13C). One animal appeared to have total destruction of the midbrain reticular formation. This animal died 21 days after lesion and remained comatose until death. Only a very fragmentary and infrequent conditioned response could be demonstrated (six feeble "conditioned" leg twitches out of 45 trials on the eighteenth postoperative day). In summary, incomplete reticular lesions produced transitory coma with considerable recovery, both in terms of general behavior and in terms of conditioning performance.

In a somewhat similar study, Kreindler, Unghar, and Volanskii (1959) were able to obtain comparable recovery of function and reconditionability of dogs with large bilateral electrolytic lesions in the posterior midbrain reticular formation. Their lesions appeared to spare the most medial portion of the reticular formation at that level (thus resembling those of Adametz, Figure 14.13B). In general, the conditioned response was relearned approximately three weeks after lesion, and gross behavioral deficits tended to show improvement at about this time.

Feldman and Waller (1962) prepared cats with extensive bilateral lesions in the midbrain reticular formation that spared the most medial portions and the periventricular gray. They reported that such lesions were followed not by somnolence, but rather by "sluggish" behavior. The animals fed themselves, attended to auditory and visual cues and showed alternation of sleep and wakefulness. The EEG records showed spontaneous shifts from slow, high-voltage activity to fast low-voltage activity which correlated only approximately with behavioral arousal. On the other hand, animals with extensive bilateral lesions of the *posterior hypothalamus* were unresponsive to sensory stimuli, exhibited virtually continuous somnolence, required tube-feeding, showed no spontaneous movements, and could not be behaviorally aroused. These latter findings are similar to the results of early experiments by Ransen (1939) showing that posterior hypothalamic lesions produce permanent somnolence or coma. Feldman and Waller made the important additional observation, noted earlier in the chapter, that the permanently somnolent hypothalamically lesioned animals showed cortical EEG arousal to reticular and peripheral stimuli that was not accompanied by behavioral arousal.

All of the experiments discussed above have followed up the observations of Lindsley et al. on reticular lesions. Sprague, Chambers, and Stellar (1961) have completed an extensive analysis of the effects of destroying the classical sensory pathways of the midbrain on behavior in the cat. The animals were studied in a wide variety of both observational and learning situations utilizing all types of stimuli, for periods of up to two and a half years following either unilateral or bilateral electrolytic lesions. The extent of the typical bilateral lesion is shown in Figure 14.13D. Note that in addition to destruction of the classical ascending sensory pathways, there is some invasion of the reticular formation, and extensive undercutting of the superior colliculus. After bilateral lesions the animals showed marked tactile, auditory, proprioceptive, nociceptive (pain response), gustatory, visual, and olfactory deficits. They were mute, exhibited no rage or aggression, showed little sexual behavior, and little response to normally aversive situations. Much of their waking activity consisted of "aimless, stereotyped wandering, and apparent visual and olfactory searching, hallucinatory in nature and very difficult to break into."

In interpreting their results, the authors point out that the visual deficits (often amounting to virtual blindness on one side of the unilateral lesioned animal) are probably due to undercutting of the superior colliculus. The olfactory deficits were unexpected. All other sensory deficits are of course to be expected. The most significant findings of the experiment concern the general debility of the animals, and the very striking changes in emotional behavior. As the authors point out, the absence of affect and lack of interest in sex shown by the animals resemble the behavior of the totally neodecorticate animal (Bard and Mountcastle, 1947). Indeed these effects are much more marked than in animals in which only sensory receiving areas of the cortex are removed, Sprague et al. interpret their results in terms of a massive sensory deprivation of the neocortex, and draw parallels to the sensory deprivation literature.

Sprague, Chambers, and Stellar prepared two animals with reticular lesions; one with a limited lateral reticular lesion on each side, and one with an extensive bilateral lesion destroying all medial reticular formation. The limited lesion produced no observable effects. The more extensive lesion produced coma that lasted for about one month. Subsequently the animal slowly recovered most behavioral functions, but tended to remain drowsy unless stimulated. It was hyperexcitable in response to painful stimulation and performed poorly on learning tasks.

Several reasonably consistent syndromes appear to emerge from this reticular lesion literature. First, massive one-stage bilateral lesions of the midbrain reticular formation produce severe coma and death. If the lesion is made in several stages, the animal can be kept alive and exhibits considerable recovery of gross functions. Smaller one-stage bilateral lesions, particularly those sparing the most medial portion of the midbrain tegmentum, produce severe but transitory coma, with partial recovery of gross function and learning abilities occurring about a month after lesion. Similar lesions made in two stages result in little gross behavioral impairment. Still smaller lesions, even if made in one stage, appear to produce few symptoms. The coma and death resulting from large one stage reticular lesion is not too surprising, incidentally. Fibers and cell nuclei concerned with a host of crucial physiological regulatory mechanisms (body temperature, respiration, metabolism, etc.) are embedded in the brainstem reticular formation and are likely to be damaged by massive lesions.

The considerable recovery of function shown with long term postoperative care following relatively large reticular lesions, or after large lesions made in several stages, demonstrates that the bulk of the midbrain reticular core is not an *absolutely essential structure* for behavioral sleep and waking, learning ability, emotional reactivity, or even of gross aspects of "attention" behavior. However, the residual deficits of such animals suggest that the reticular core may normally play an important role in many of these functions.

It is difficult to assess the relative importance of the reticular formation and the classical sensory pathways for normal behavioral functions. Most large reticular lesions have also invaded the sensory pathways, and large sensory lesions tend to invade the reticular formation. The kinds of deficits reported by Sprague et al. after destruction of the sensory pathways are not unexpected. Indeed, prior to the discovery of the ARAS most authorities would probably have predicted that they would occur. Attentive and affective behavior ought to be impaired if sensory input is virtually wiped out. On the other hand, it is clear that the classical view of the ARAS as the neural substrate of behavioral arousal and wakefulness must be modified. The ARAS appears to play some role in these functions, but the exact nature of that role seems as of this writing to be somewhat obscure.

It was observed in early experiments that activation of the reticular formation, either by external stimuli or direct electrical stimulation, produced EEG arousal and behavioral arousal (Lindsley et al., 1950; French et al., 1953). Upon stimulation a normally sleeping animal will open his eyes, raise his head and look about. These observations led to the well-known hypothesis that behavioral alerting or attention is mediated or controlled by the ARAS. Surprisingly enough there have been few attempts to test this hypothesis experimentally. The lesion studies reviewed above do not provide much evidence regarding *attention*; the most obvious effect of large lesions is total coma, which would seem to be much more than simple "inattention."

Perhaps the most direct attempt to evaluate the attentional role of the ARAS is an experiment done by Fuster (1958) in Lindsley's laboratories (see also Lindsley, 1958). Normal monkeys with stimulating electrodes implanted in the reticular formation were trained to discriminate between two objects. The objects were on a tray in front of the animal and were lighted only briefly by a tachistoscopic device. The monkey was required to reach through a trap door under the correct object (one object was always correct and the other incorrect) to obtain a reward. Both the number of correct responses and the latency of response were recorded, as functions of the duration of the tachistoscopic light. This procedure was repeated both with reticular stimulation and without reticular stimulation. The results on one animal are shown in Figure 14.14. If the ARAS is stimulated during the discrimination the animal makes a significantly greater percentage of correct responses and also has a significantly shorter reaction time.

If only reaction time were improved it might be argued that the major effect of reticular stimulation was to increase muscle tone, perhaps via the descending reticular system. However, the significant improvement in correct choices demonstrated that something more is occurring. Fuster's results have been interpreted as indicating that during reticular stimulation the animal attends more closely to the situation. Such interpretations are to some degree ambiguous. A variety of central processes might be influenced. For example, the animal's general drive level might have been increased (see discussion by Brown, 1961). Nonetheless, Fuster's experiment is one of the few demonstrations that direct electrical stimulation of the reticular formation can significantly improve behavioral performance. In view of their potential significance it is to be hoped that his observations will be replicated and extended to other behavioral situations.

Lansing, Schwartz, and Lindsley (1959) carried out an interesting analogue of Fuster's experiment in humans. They recorded the EEGs from normal subjects and measured the reaction times (finger movement) to a visual stimulus.

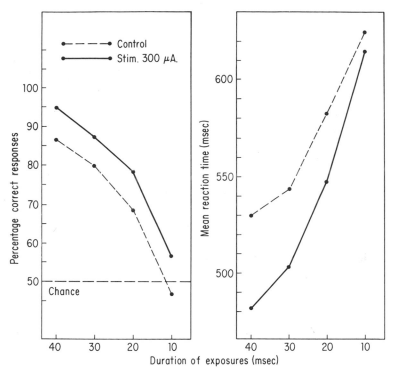

Figure 14.14. Performance of a monkey (percent correct responses and reaction time) on an object discrimination task both during electrical stimulation of the reticular formation (solid lines) and in the absence of such stimulation (dashed lines). (From Fuster, 1958)

Two different conditions were used, an alerted condition in which a preliminary warning click was presented before the flash, and a nonalerted condition with no click. In both conditions the stimulus was given both during alpha waves and during EEG arousal. The experimental design and the results are indicated in Figure 14.15. In the nonalerted condition there was no difference between alpha present and alpha absent conditions of light presentation (mean reaction time 280 msec). However, in the alerted condition, with a brief forewarning the reaction time was reduced to 250 msec and with a long forewarning period it was shortened to 206 msec. In the latter condition alpha blocking occurred between the warning and the light stimulus. Lindsley (1958) suggests that in this experiment reticular activation produced by previous instructions and sensory stimuli may be analogous to Fuster's direct electrical stimulation of the ARAS.

Electrical stimulation of the reticular formation does not always improve performance. Indeed one of the more common results of such stimulation is avoidance behavior. Olds (1960) has found, in his well-known electrical self-stimulation experiments, that when the stimulating electrode is in the reticular formation the animals frequently stop pressing the lever. Delgado, Roberts, and Miller (1954) have shown that electrical stimulation of the mesencephalic

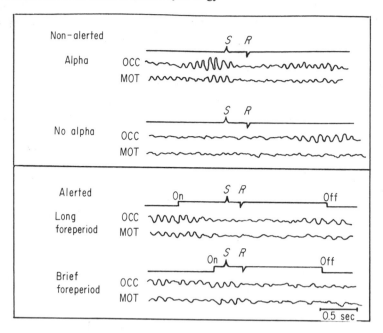

Figure 14.15. Human finger reaction times as a function of presence or absence of alpha and presence or absence of a forewarning alerting signal. There is no difference in the nonalert groups, but the long forewarning group is superior to the brief forewarning group in the alerted condition. (From Lansing, Schwartz, and Lindsley, 1959)

reticular formation in cats elicits fear responses. In fact these responses can serve as a punishment in training hungry cats to avoid food!

The possibility that electrical stimulation of the reticular formation is, in some ways, equivalent to a peripheral sensory stimulation is a basic problem in interpreting such experiments. Indeed the study by Delgado, Roberts, and Miller was done to illustrate this point. The reticular stimulus acted just like peripheral shock in serving as a negative reinforcement. In Fuster's experiment, both reaction time and correct responses might be equally improved by moderate electrical stimulation of the foot rather than the reticular formation. That this can indeed occur was well demonstrated many years ago in the classical studies by Muenzinger (1934). Rats given moderate electric shock for *correct* choices in a T-maze learning situation with food reward learned considerably better than rats given no shock. Proponents of the arousal or activation theory of ARAS function can counter with the point that if painful stimulation produces the same effects as reticular stimulation the effect is mediated by the ARAS. This in turn can be countered by the experiments of Sprague, Chambers, and Stellar indicating that it was extremely difficult to produce behavioral alerting or activation in animals with sensory pathways cut but reticular system mostly intact. Furthermore, several lesion experiments reviewed above reported that animals with fairly extensive reticular lesions do exhibit behavioral arousal, and even EEG arousal. In short, the evidence supporting the view that the ARAS plays a special role in the mediation of behavioral arousal and alerting is by no means consistent or compelling.

A major difficulty with the classical theory of the ARAS concerns the fact that there is no consistent relationship between EEG "arousal" (desynchronization) and behavioral arousal. One of the simplest ways to produce a dissociation between EEG activity and behavior is to administer atropine. Following moderate doses (15 mg/kg) the EEG becomes strongly synchronized, showing the typical spindling and slow waves of sleep, even though the animal remains behaviorally awake. In fact, strong sensory stimulation cannot produce EEG arousal after atropine administration. Bradley and his associates (1964) completed a rather careful evaluation of the behavioral state of atropinized rats. They measured the EEG to insure that the atropine-induced EEG synchrony was present in all cases. Three separate behavioral experiments were done: Shock avoidance responses to a bell, differential responding to a bell versus the buzzer, and maze learning. In all cases there were no differences between animals given atropine and control animals given saline, even though the atropine groups showed total EEG synchrony during the experiments and the saline groups did not. Thus the marked EEG synchrony produced by atropine appears to have no influence whatever on performance in these three behavioral situations.

A brief summary of the extent to which the classical view of the ARAS has been modified by the more recent literature surveyed above is perhaps in order. First, the reticular formation is by no means diffuse, either in its anatomical or its functional organization. Different regions can be subdivided in terms of their anatomical appearance, their inputs and their outputs. Single neurons in the ARAS are by no means activated by all sensory stimuli. In fact, some types of sensory stimuli do not appear to influence the ARAS at all. As repeatedly noted above, cortical EEG arousal and behavioral arousal are not concomitant; either can occur without the other. There appear to be at least two different regions of the ARAS that can produce cortical EEG arousal, the anterior region more associated with waking and the posterior region with deep sleep (see below). Discharges of single cells in the ARAS do not correlate at all well with the notion that cortical EEG arousal indicates a greater degree of neural activity in the ARAS. Finally, it would seem that sleep-wake cycles and "attentive" behavior can occur in animals with virtually complete destruction of the ARAS and that animals with lesions limited to sensory pathways may be much impaired in alerting and "attentive" aspects of behavior. To assert that the ARAS has any clear or paramount unitary function would seem at present to be somewhat premature.

THE DIFFUSE THALAMIC SYSTEM

During the course of our discussion of the reticular formation we have included mention of the diffuse or midline thalamic nuclei. Some authors have

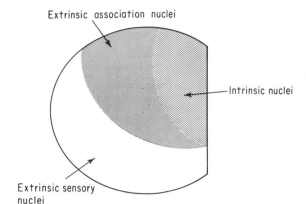

Extrinsic association nuclei

Intrinsic nuclei

Extrinsic sensory
nuclei

Figure 14.16. Schematic diagram of a cross section through the left thalamus indicating the general locations of the three functionally differentiated types of thalamic nuclei.

simply included this medial portion of the thalamus as a part of the brainstem reticular activating system. However, it has sufficiently special properties to justify a separate treatment. First and most obviously, it is a part of the thalamus rather than the brainstem. You may recall from our discussion of the thalamocortical relation in Chapter 11, that the thalamus can be separated into three different types of nuclei (see Figure 14.16). The most lateral regions are the sensory specific extrinsic nuclei, relaying primary sensory information to sensory areas of the cortex. The second group of thalamic relays, the extrinsic association nuclei, lie more medial than the specific sensory regions. They receive all their input from other thalamic regions and project rather discretely to association fields of the cerebral cortex. Finally, the intrinsic nuclei lie in the most medial and midline location in the thalamus. They do not appear to have any *direct* projections to cerebral neocortex. Anatomically, the intrinsic thalamic nuclei correspond to the physiologically defined diffuse thalamic nuclei.

One of the major sources of input to the intrinsic thalamic nuclei is the brainstem reticular formation. Anatomical studies, using both retrograde degeneration and terminal degeneration methods, have demonstrated the existence of several pathways arising in the bulbar reticular formation that terminate in various regions of the intrinsic thalamic nuclei, periaquaductal gray of the midbrain, and in the hypothalamus. The striking diagram in Figure 14.17 of the ramifications of a single reticular neuron illustrates these ascending projections (Scheibel and Scheibel, 1958). This neuron was reconstructed from a sagittal Golgi stained section from a two-day old rat. The cell body lies in the nucleus reticularis magnocellulars, a nucleus of the reticular formation at the level of the pons. One axon descends to the spinal cord and the other ascends to terminate in many regions of the intrinsic thalamic nuclei, and the other regions noted above.

Before considering the functional aspects of the diffuse thalamic system in detail, a brief overview of the reasons why it is often included in the ARAS would perhaps be of value. First and foremost, it appears to be the region of the brain that acts as a "pacemaker" to induce rhythmic spindling or alpha activity in the cerebral cortex. In the precollicular brainstem preparation (Figure 14.7), where all of the reticular formation below the level of the diffuse thalamus is separated from the forebrain, the cortex exhibits continued EEG synchrony. Alternatively, destruction of the diffuse thalamic nuclei in an otherwise intact animal abolishes cortical EEG spindling. Repetitive electrical stimulation of the diffuse thalamic nuclei at rates of about 8–12/sec evokes large cortical waves, called recruiting waves, that closely resemble spontaneous spindle waves in the cat. Moruzzi and Magoun (1949) showed that high-frequency stimulation of the bulbar reticular formation abolished the recruiting waves produced by slow thalamic stimulation as well as abolishing spontaneous cortical spindling. Furthermore, stimulation of the diffuse thalamic nuclei on one side at 8–12/sec induces recruiting waves in the diffuse thalamic nuclei of the other hemisphere, and reticular activation also blocks these. In other words reticular activation can act to block the EEG synchrony resulting from stimulation of the diffuse thalamic nuclei either at the cortex or at the thalamus, or both.

Morison and Dempsey (1942) and Dempsey and Morison (1942a, b) first discovered and analyzed the cortical *recruiting response* to electrical stimulation of the thalamus. Using cats, they found, with 8–12/sec stimuli (the approximate frequency of spontaneous spindling), a very characteristic repetitive response that followed the stimulus frequency in certain regions of the cerebral cortex (see Figure 14.18). They termed it a "recruiting response" because the first few waves grew progressively larger or "recruited." As indicated in Figure 14.18 the cortical recruiting response to thalamic stimulation is primarily a surface negative potential which follows the stimulus and grows in amplitude during the first few stimuli. The thalamic regions which elicit the cortical recruiting

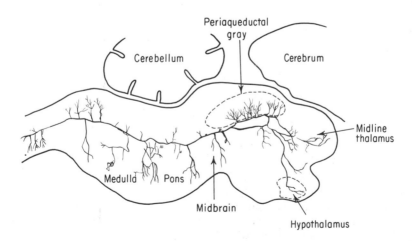

Figure 14.17.   Drawing of a sagittal Golgi section of a two-day old rat, showing the axon branches of a *single* reticular cell. (From Scheibel and Scheibel, 1958)

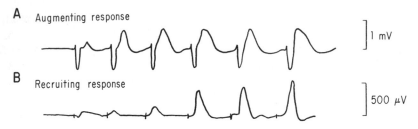

Figure 14.18. Gross surface cortical recordings of augmenting and recruiting responses (negative up). Note that the recruiting responses are almost entirely negative. (From Brookhart and Zanchetti, 1956)

response are indicated in Figure 14.19. These are the physiologically defined *diffuse thalamic nuclei,* and as noted earlier, they correspond closely to the anatomically defined intrinsic thalamic nuclei.

Morison and Dempsey found that stimulation of almost any portion of the diffuse thalamic system would yield cortical recruiting responses over wide areas of the cortex. More recently it has been shown that maximal recruiting responses are found in certain areas of the cortex, particularly association areas and the somatic sensory-motor field (Starzl and Magoun, 1951; Starzl, Taylor, and Magoun, 1951). Dempsey and Morison had earlier demonstrated that spontaneous EEG spindling activity has a cortical distribution similar to that subsequently found for the recruiting response. The significance of the recruiting response lies in large part in its similarity to spontaneous spindling activity, the simplest hypothesis perhaps being that cortical spindling is "driven" from the diffuse thalamic system. Spindle waves can also be recorded from the diffuse thalamic nuclei (Dempsey and Morison, 1943), as can recruiting waves in one portion of the diffuse thalamic nuclei to an electrical stimulus delivered to another portion of the diffuse thalamus. Destruction of these thalamic nuclei abolishes cortical spindling and the cortical recruiting response to thalamic stimulation.

If a specific sensory relay nucleus in the thalamus is stimulated electrically at 8–12/sec a somewhat different type of cortical activity, termed the *augmenting* response, develops (see Figure 14.18). Suppose, for example, that the ventrobasal complex relaying somatic sensory information to the somatic sensory receiving area of the cerebral cortex is stimulated repetitively. A cortical response develops and grows in amplitude with repeated stimuli (i.e. augments). However, this response differs from the recruiting response in several ways. It is localized to the cortical somatic sensory receiving area; it has a different appearing waveform (large surface positive component); and a different depth distribution in the cortex (see Figure 14.18). In fact the augmenting wave resembles the recruiting response only in that the first few waves grow in amplitude.

Our current understanding of the diffuse thalamic system is due in large part to the careful and extensive studies by Jasper and his colleagues (see Jasper's

1960 review). It appears that *recruiting* responses are not entirely restricted to association and somatic sensory-motor areas of cortex (although they are largest in these regions), and that there is a kind of region to region correspondence between the place stimulated in the diffuse thalamic system and the cortical region showing spindling. There is some disagreement concerning the extent to which recruiting responses can be obtained from sensory fields of the cortex (see Starzl and Magoun, 1951). However, Hanberry and Jasper (1953) report that recruiting responses appear to be obtainable from primary sensory cortical areas after total destruction of the appropriate primary sensory relay nuclei in the thalamus. Thus small "recruiting" responses are reported to occur in auditory cortex to diffuse thalamic stimulation after destruction of the medial geniculate body.

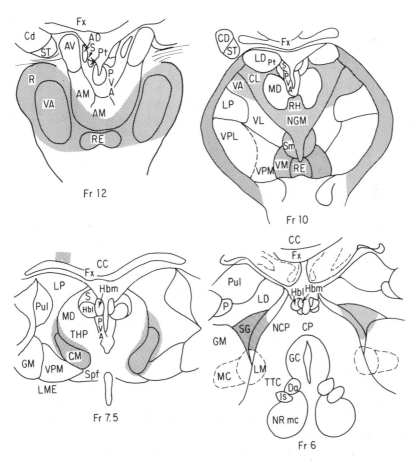

Figure 14.19. Sections through the thalamus at various stereotaxis planes (Fr) showing the extent of the diffuse thalamic system (stippled area). (From Jasper, 1960)

The pathways mediating cortical recruitment from thalamic stimulation have not yet been definitely established. There appear to be two major routes, one passing anteriorly through n. ventralis anterior of the thalamus, another via relays in the reticular nucleus of the thalamus (not to be confused with the reticular formation of the brainstem). Destruction of ventralis anterior abolishes cortical recruiting (however, EEG arousal produced by high-frequency activation of the same midline thalamic structures that yield recruiting is not affected by this same lesion (Weinberger, Velasco, and Lindsley, 1965). The reticular nucleus is a thin sheet of cells that surrounds almost the entire thalamus and projects to widespread areas of the cortex with a kind of region-to-region specificity (Rose, 1952). This reticular nucleus degenerates completely after ablation of all cerebral cortex. With total neocortical ablations, incidentally, the diffuse thalamic nuclei exhibit some retrograde degenerative changes but by no means entirely degenerate (Jasper, 1958). It may be that they have sustaining but not essential projections to the neocortex (see discussion in Chapter 11). Recent evidence suggests that the projection pathways from diffuse thalamus to cerebral cortex may include a relay through anterior limbic regions of the orbital cortex. Velasco and Lindsley (1965) reported that both recruiting responses (from thalamic stimulation) and spontaneous spindling in the cerebral cortex were totally abolished following bilateral ablation of the orbital cortex in cat.

Morison and Dempsey (1942) first speculated that projections to the cerebral cortex mediating the recruiting response involve a special type of cortical afferent fiber termed the unspecific afferent fibers to sensory projection areas, which terminate in layer 4. Evidence is not yet conclusive on this point.

Interest has centered on the neural mechanism producing the progressive increase in the response amplitude of the first few recruiting waves. Extracellular microelectrode recordings of activity from cortical cells during the development of the recruiting response from thalamic stimulation have indicated that the initial small waves always occur before single nerve cell spike discharges occur. This implies that the grossly recorded waves are not the result of spike discharges but rather are the events leading up to spike discharge (Li et al., 1956, a, b). They most likely represent summed graded postsynaptic membrane potentials in cortical cells. It was noted earlier that cortical IPSPs have about 10-msec duration. If cells developed these IPSPs synchronously, they could most easily be discharged by electrical stimulation every 100 msec or so (i.e. at the frequency of about 10/sec), the frequency of optimal recruiting and also of spontaneous spindling. In line with this speculation, Purpura and Shofer (1963) have recorded intracellularly from neurons in the diffuse thalamic nuclei during electrical stimulation of other regions of the diffuse thalamic system (remember that stimulation of one portion of the diffuse thalamic system produces recruiting responses in other portions of the system). They found that there were clusters of spikes which occurred at the end of each 100 msec IPSP. The spikes grew in number during the first few recruiting stimuli. Examples of their findings are shown in Figure 14.20. The upper tracing (A) shows the grossly recorded cortical

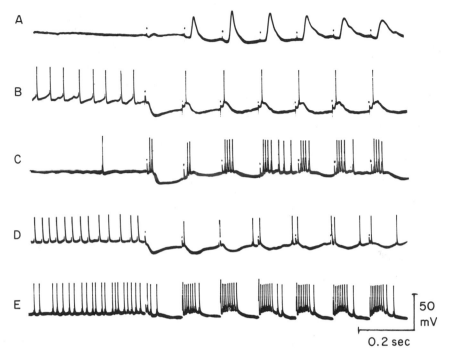

Figure 14.20.   Intracellularly recorded responses of single thalamic neurons during 7/sec stimulation of midline thalamus. Note that spike discharges tend to cluster immediately after each stimulus (short lines with dots above); and that IPSPs (the downward baseline shifts) develop following each response burst and last until the next stimulus. (**A** is gross surface record.) (From Purpura and Shofer, 1963)

recruiting response to thalamic stimulation and the lower traces (B and C) show intracellular records from two cells in the diffuse thalamic nuclei. In trace B, the cell fires spontaneously prior to stimulation. During stimulation, note that the firing pattern of the cell becomes synchronized and discharges once during each stimulus. Furthermore, note that immediately following the stimuli and the nerve spike discharges there are prolonged IPSPs. The cell shown in C exhibits little or no spontaneous discharging but shows a spike discharge immediately following the first electrical stimulus to the thalamus. In the following response there is a marked IPSP, which decreases following subsequent stimuli. There is a marked increase in the number of spikes that are discharged by successive stimuli. In other words, the behavior of this cell illustrates the recruitment effect. D and E are cells having spontaneous discharge rates that become synchronized by the repeated stimulus. Thus it would seem that the firing of cells in the thalamus activated via stimulation of the diffuse thalamic system, and possibly cortical cells as well, may be synchronized or recruited or timed by the intervening IPSPs following the cellular discharge.

In some ways the influences of the diffuse thalamic system and the ARAS on cortical EEG activity appear to be reciprocal. As noted above, cortical recruiting elicited by low-frequency thalamic stimulation can be blocked by higher frequency electrical stimulation of the ARAS. Magoun (1963) has emphasized the opposite influences of these two systems, suggesting that the ARAS mediates arousal and alerting, and the diffuse thalamic system mediates depression of cortical excitability and sleep. However, in many ways the actions of these two systems appear to be parallel rather than reciprocal. Destruction of the diffuse thalamus produces coma, but of a less profound nature than that produced by reticular lesions (Jasper, 1960). Cortical EEG arousal is easily produced by high frequency stimulation of the diffuse thalamic system (Jasper, 1960). It has been shown that both behavioral sleep and behavioral arousal can be produced by slow or fast stimulation through the same electrode implanted in the diffuse thalamic nuclei (Akimoto et al., 1956). The EEG arousal response from thalamic stimulation is very short-lived (a few seconds) in contrast to reticular arousal, which may last for many minutes. In this connection we might recall the experiment by Lindsley et al. (1950) showing that only short duration arousal could be induced in animals with reticular lesions. As noted above, lesions of ventralis anterior block recruiting but not arousal to stimulation of the midline thalamus (Weinberger et al., 1965).

Sharpless and Jasper (1956) have suggested that there may be a basic functional differentiation between the thalamic and reticular components of the activating system. In an experiment on habituation of the EEG arousal response they recorded the EEG activity in normal sleeping cats using implanted cortical electrodes. They were able to differentiate between a phasic or short duration component of EEG arousal, which was very resistant to habituation, and a tonic or long-lasting EEG arousal which rapidly habituated. The phasic response could be abolished by severing the classical auditory pathways at the collicular level but not by bilateral destruction of the auditory areas of the cortex. They suggested that it was mediated by the nonspecific thalamic nuclei. This would be consistent with the observations of Lindsley et al., that only short duration arousal is induced in animals with reticular lesions. The tonic EEG arousal then would be mediated by the reticular formation of the brainstem. The conclusions of Sharpless and Jasper were as follows:

It is evident that if the activating system is to play an important role in the waking animal, alerting the central nervous system and compelling attention in the presence of novel and biologically important stimuli, it must be sensitive to slight changes in the quality of stimuli impinging on the organism's receptors. Moreover, it must be capable of producing rapid but brief shifts in the reactivity of the central nervous system. Our evidence indicates that only the diencephalic component of the activating system has these properties. The more caudally situated reticular system is capable only of crude differentiation between stimuli and produces long-lasting persistent changes in the level of reactivity. The properties of the brainstem reticular system, therefore, are well-suited to the maintenance of wakefulness over long periods of time, but ill-adapted to the sudden and brief changes in reactivity that must occur in response to highly specific stimuli if the animal is to meet the demands of its waking environment.

SLEEP AND WAKING

In this section we will attempt to integrate the many observations and ideas concerning sleep and waking that have been mentioned above. The problem of definition looms large in any discussion of sleep. We have attempted to distinguish between EEG activity and behavioral signs of sleep. However, even if sleep is defined by behavioral measures, we are faced with the problem of a multiplicity of measures that do not always agree with one another. Indeed, many of the current debates concerning sleep seem to result from a lack of agreement over what measures to use. Commonly, the organism is relatively inactive during sleep. Various types of changes in muscle tone, blood pressure, heart rate, eye movements, verbal response to stimuli, and so on, may occur in different "stages" of sleep. There is no agreement, incidently, concerning the number and characteristics of sleep stages. In this discussion we will sidestep the problem of definition and assume a general idea of the difference between sleep and waking.

Investigations of sleep deprivation suggest that sleep is a biological necessity for mammals. Animals die and men become severely disturbed if sleep is withheld long enough. Observations of this sort led to the very old hypothesis that sleep is produced by the actions of various chemical fatigue or sleep "toxins" that accumulate during waking. Early experiments provided some suggestive evidence for this hypothesis. Thus, Legendre (1910) and Pieron (1906) kept one group of dogs awake for long periods of time, extracted cerebrospinal fluid from them and injected it into rested dogs. The rested dogs "fell asleep." More recent repetitions of this experiment (e.g., Ivy and Schnedorf, 1937) indicate that the effect is probably the result of trauma—sleep induced in rested animals in this way is accompanied by fever.

Surprisingly enough, there is as yet no satisfactory evidence favoring the existence of any sleep substances. Indeed, most evidence is against this hypothesis. Thus Siamese twins with a common blood circulation have different sleep rhythms. This is true not only of twins joined after their circulations have passed through their liver (where some elimination of toxic substances could occur), but even when they have a completely shared circulation (Alekseeva, 1958).

A great many factors influence sleep, particularly in humans, including social conditions, the 24-hour day, time the sun is up, and so on. These factors, which are thoroughly discussed in Kleitman's text (1939), are not of direct concern here. We are limiting consideration to the immediate neural precursors, or most direct causal factors, involved in producing sleep or waking. The two major theoretical alternatives to the chemical toxin theory of sleep might be called the *afferent input* and *neural centers* theories. Bremer elaborated the afferent input idea in relation to his brain stem transection experiment. There is no question but what level of sensory input is a crucial factor in sleep. An organism subjected to painful stimulation is not likely to go to sleep. Actually the more recent experiments on the *encéphale isolé* tend to support Bremer's notion, even though the results do not agree with his initial observations. If the spinal cord is severed from the brain and *all sources of pain eliminated*, the EEG shows almost continuous synchronization. On the other hand, the observation of Sprague, Chambers, and Steller that animals with most primary sensory pathways severed at the midbrain level show relatively normal sleep-waking cycles, indicate that other factors also must play a significant role.

Contemporary theories of sleep have emphasized the view that active neural centers are crucial in determining sleep and wakefulness. We have considered the role of the ARAS in sleep and waking at some length already. To review, high-frequency electrical stimulation of the ARAS induces both EEG arousal and behavioral awakening in a sleeping animal. High brainstem transection produces a permanent, synchronized EEG, and large lesions of the midbrain reticular formation produce a synchronized EEG and a behaviorally comatose animal. Moruzzi's midpontine pretrigeminal preparation, with brainstem section just above the fifth nerve entry in the pons (which eliminates all pain input), exhibits relatively normal sleep-waking cycles in terms of EEG patterns and ocular signs of wakefulness. Thus it would appear that a limited region of the pontine reticular formation acts as a "wakefulness center," maintaining more rostral regions of the brain in a waking state.

The diffuse thalamic system, while related to the ARAS, appears to play a somewhat opposite role in sleep. Slow stimulation of this structure produces EEG signs of sleep—spindling and slow waves. Interestingly, Akert, Koella, and Hess (1952) have shown that behavioral sleep can be induced in normal waking cats by slow repetitive electrical stimulation (5–10 sec) of the diffuse thalamic system. Perhaps consistent with this are the observations of Pompeiano and Swett (1962) that slow repetitive stimulation of peripheral nerves appears, at least under some conditions, to induce natural sleep in cats.

The observations summarized above have led some investigators to the theory that the ARAS is the active waking center and the diffuse thalamic system is the active sleep center. Magoun (1963) summarized this view as follows:

If the inferences drawn from these many conclusions are correct, it is now possible to identify a thalamo-cortical mechanism for internal inhibition, capable of modifying activity of the brain partially or globally, so that its sensory, motor, and higher nervous functions become reduced and cease. The consequences of the action of this mechanism are the opposite of those of the ascending reticular activating system for internal excitation (Magoun, 1963). The principle of reciprocal innervation proposed by Sherrington (1906) to account for spinal-reflex integration would additionally appear relevant to the manner in which these two higher antagonistic neural mechanisms determine the alternating patterns of brain activity manifest as wakefulness and light sleep.

There is a kind of unwritten assumption in much of the EEG literature to the effect that the low voltage fast activity of cortical EEG arousal represents an increase in neural activity over the spindles and slow waves of EEG synchrony. As Eccles has pointed out (1961), it may be that desynchronized waves represent at least two different phenomena operating at different times to give the same over-all EEG, one with intense activity of cells out of phase, and another with diminished activity of cells out of phase. All that is really known is that EEG synchrony probably reflects *phasic* activity of many cells and EEG desynchrony does not.

Evarts (1961) completed a study of the behavior of single nerve cells in the visual cortex of the normal unrestrained cat, using chronically implanted microelectrodes. He compared cellular behavior in the awake condition and in slow-wave sleep. Of 90 units, 48 had higher spontaneous discharge rates during sleep

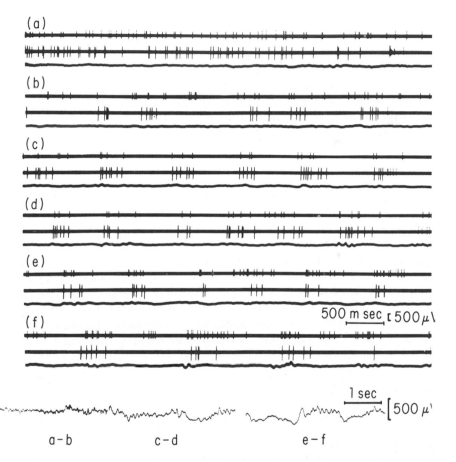

Figure 14.21. Onset of sleep in 2 neurones of the cat's motor cortex. After a brief aroused state, (a), the records (b–f) were taken at 2-second intervals during progressive drowsiness and final sleep showing "sleep spindles" of 12–13 per second in the EEG (samples of higher amplification from simultaneous EEG records are shown in the bottom row). Both neurones change their discharge pattern during sleep to a periodic grouped activity with longer pauses. They slow their average frequencies from around 12 per sec in arousal to 3–9 per sec in falling asleep, but neurone 1 speeds up again in (f) to the original frequency of (a) with a different pattern of grouped discharges. The neuronal groups are mostly concomitant with the "sleep spindles" of 12 per sec developing progressively from (d–f). (From Creutzfeldt and Jung, 1961)

than during waking and 42 had higher rates during waking. In the waking animal the degree of variability in discharge rates is higher than in the sleep state, but the mean rate of discharge was slightly *lower*. In this connection, we may recall Huttenlocher's results from cells in the reticular formation (Figure 14.11) showing essentially the same findings for waking and slow-wave sleep, with a significant increase in cell discharge rate during paradoxical sleep. Multiple simultaneous microelectrical recordings of neurons in the cortex and thalamus (Verzeano and Negishi, 1961; Creutzfeldt and Jung, 1961) indicate that during slow-wave sleep the more or less random discharge frequencies of cortical cells tend to group into periodic bursts of activity, separated by longer pauses. This tendency toward increased grouping in slow-wave sleep is illustrated in Figure 14.21. In sum, what little single cell data exists suggests that over-all amount of neuron activity is greatest in deep paradoxical sleep, next in slow-wave sleep, and least in the behaviorally awake state. Discharges tend to be synchronized more in slow-wave sleep than in the waking state or paradoxical sleep. These findings would seem to raise some difficulties for conventional interpretations of the gross EEG responses in sleep and waking.

Paradoxical sleep

The view that the behavioral state of sleep or waking results from a reciprocal balance of the reticular waking and thalamic sleep centers has been complicated in recent years by the discovery of paradoxical sleep, a discovery that has added a new and important dimension to our understanding (Dement and Kleitman, 1957; Dement, 1958; Jouvet, 1962; Rossi, 1963; Hubel, 1960b). As noted earlier, it is termed paradoxical because the EEG pattern is desynchronized as in a waking animal. Paradoxical sleep develops after slow-wave sleep, and the two will alternate during a night's sleep. In fairly deep "slow-wave" or EEG-synchrony sleep the EEG record may suddenly shift to that of an aroused, alert, waking EEG pattern, even though the organism remains asleep in terms of behavioral criteria. An example of the onset of paradoxical sleep in the cat is shown in Figure 14.22. Concomitant with the sudden occurrence of EEG arousal are rapid eye movements, a marked decrease in muscle tone of the neck musculature, decreases in heart rate, blood pressure, and other physiological changes. The various non-neural physiological indices of paradoxical sleep are extremely important because they provide a set of criteria in addition to EEG changes. If experimental procedures are carried out on the nervous system, which prevent the appearance of cortical EEG changes (i.e. brainstem transection), these other measures can still be used to define the occurrence of paradoxical sleep.

One of the most intriguing aspects of paradoxical sleep is that it appears to be associated with dreaming (Aserinsky and Kleitman, 1955; Dement and Kleitman, 1957; Dement, 1958). This fact was determined simply by waking human subjects when they were exhibiting the paradoxical sleep "syndrome"

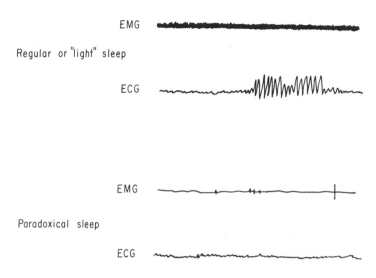

Figure 14.22.   Activity of the neck muscles (EMG) and cerebral cortex (ECG) during light sleep and paradoxical sleep in the cat. (From Rossi, Favale, Hara, Giussani, and Sacco, 1961)

and asking if they were dreaming. First reports indicated that dreaming was only associated with paradoxical sleep and not with slow-wave sleep. More refined behavioral measures have complicated this picture somewhat. If care is taken to rate the degree and complexity of the reported dream, a substantial amount of dream activity is reported after wakening from slow-wave sleep (Kamiya, 1961). Nevertheless, there is significantly more dreaming associated with paradoxical sleep.

Several lines of evidence indicate that paradoxical sleep is behaviorally a deeper stage of sleep than slow-wave sleep. First, more intense stimuli, either sensory or reticular, are necessary to waken an animal from paradoxical sleep than from slow-wave sleep (Hubel, 1960b; Rossi et al., 1961; Jouvet, 1962). Furthermore, as noted earlier in the chapter, if stimuli are not strong enough to waken an animal from paradoxical sleep they may induce slow-wave sleep. A direct transition from wakefulness to paradoxical sleep has never been observed (Hubel, 1960). A much more complete relaxation of neck and other antigravity muscles during paradoxical sleep is also consistent with this view. In characterizing paradoxical sleep as deeper than slow-wave sleep, Moruzzi (1964) points out that in comatose and barbiturate anesthetized animals, only slow-wave sleep is exhibited, and yet these animals are behaviorally much " deeper " than the normal animal is in the paradoxical phase of sleep. This suggests that normal paradoxical sleep episodes are actively produced by neural structures that are prevented from acting on the cortex by midbrain transection or barbiturate anesthesia.

If this argument for an active production of low-voltage fast EEG (i.e. paradoxical) sleep is valid, then it ought to be possible to produce it by electrical stimulation of the brainstem. This has in fact been demonstrated (Rossi et al., 1961; Jouvet, 1962). The results of the experiment by Rossi et al. are shown in Figure 14.23. Part A shows the normal spontaneous onset of low-voltage fast sleep in the cat. In Part B, electrical stimulation of the brainstem reticular formation during slow-wave sleep awakens the animal. However, the same

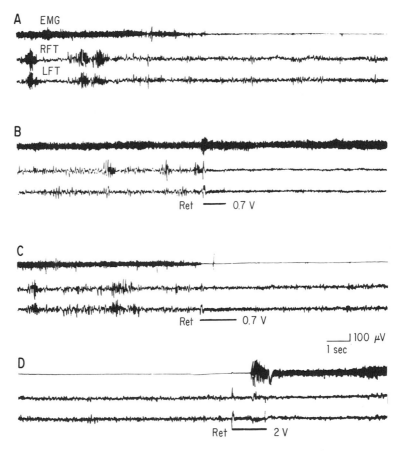

Figure 14.23. Opposite effects of high frequency electrical stimulation of the reticular formation (horizontal bar labeled "Ret") during different stages of sleep in the cat. Tracings are from neck muscles (EMG), and frontal to temporal regions of the right and left hemispheres of the cerebral cortex (RFT, LFT). **A**, spontaneous shift from light to paradoxical sleep. **B**, during light sleep reticular stimulation awakens the animal both behaviorally and in terms of EEG measures. **C**, during a somewhat deeper stage of light sleep reticular stimulation shifts the animal to paradoxical sleep. **D**, much stronger reticular stimulation awakens the animal. (Rossi et al., *op. cit.*)

stimulus given when the animal is in a slightly deeper phase of slow-wave sleep produces paradoxical sleep (Part C). Finally, as shown in Part D, a very much stronger reticular stimulus is necessary to waken the animal from paradoxical sleep than from slow-wave sleep. In interpreting these records, remember that when the neck muscle activity is great (thick EMG base line) and the EEG shows low-voltage fast activity, as in the right portions of B, the animal is behaviorally awake. When the EMG activity is large and the EEG shows spindling, as in the left portions of A, B, and C, the animal is in slow-wave sleep. Finally, when the neck muscle activity is markedly reduced (thin EMG) and the EEG shows low voltage fast, as in the right half of C and the left half of D, the animal is in paradoxical sleep. In summary, it is possible to induce deeper paradoxical sleep by electrical stimulation of the brainstem reticular formation when the animal is in the light slow-wave stage of sleep.

In analyzing the regions of the brain involved in paradoxical sleep, Jouvet (1962) has made ingenious use of the neck muscle, blood pressure, and heart rate indices, together with EEG measures from the brainstem. His findings suggested that there is a portion of the lower pons, in the region of the nucleus *reticularis pontis caudalis*, that plays a crucial role in the development of the cortical paradoxical sleep. The cortex in turn is said to control the brainstem signs of slow wave sleep; after decortication he reported only paradoxical sleep symptoms in the brainstem. Jouvet and Michel (1959) have suggested that this pontine reticular region projects to the cortex outside the reticular formation in a presumed limbic-midbrain circuit. Thus electrolytic lesions of the midbrain reticular formation are reported to abolish the low-voltage fast cortical EEG that normally results from sensory or lower reticular stimulation, but not the same low-voltage fast cortical EEG activity during paradoxical sleep. Alternatively, lesions of the "limbic-midbrain" circuit abolish the cortical EEG arousal pattern of paradoxical sleep but not the cortical EEG arousal that is associated with behavioral wakening. Rossi et al. (1963) have questioned this latter observation. They were unable to abolish the low-voltage fast cortical EEG of paradoxical sleep by destruction of the "limbic-midbrain" circuit.

A final complication is added by studies in Moruzzi's laboratory showing that electrical stimulation of the reticular formation at the caudal portion of the brainstem, in the medulla, can induce cortical EEG *synchrony* (Magnes et al., 1961). In fact, they were able to obtain EEG spindling by slow (5–12/sec) stimulation and EEG arousal by fast stimulation (26/sec) through the same electrode. Moruzzi has suggested that this medullary center may act to inhibit the EEG activation region of the middle pons.

A summary schema for the neural control of sleep, based on the hypotheses of Moruzzi (1964), Jouvet (1962), and Magoun (1963) is illustrated in Figure 14.24. The diffuse thalamic system (a), acts on the cortex to produce EEG synchrony and behavioral sleep. The reticular activating system (or more specifically the nucleus *reticularis pontis oralis*) (b) acts on the cortex and the diffuse thalamus to produce EEG and behavioral arousal. Jouvet's region (c), possibly

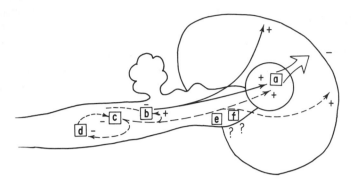

Figure 14.24. Hypothetical schema of some of the brain "centers" involved in the control of sleep and waking. (a) diffuse thalamic system; (b) reticular activating system; (c) Jouvet's reticular region; (d) reticular synchronizing region of medulla; (e) and (f) waking and sleeping centers of the hypothalamus. (Based on Moruzzi, 1964; Jouvet, 1962; Magoun, 1963)

the nucleus *reticularis pontis caudalis*, acts directly on both higher and lower regions of the brain to produce EEG arousal and behavioral deep sleep. Finally, the reticular synchronizing region of the medulla (d) acts to induce cortical EEG synchrony, possibly by inhibition of the actions of b and/or c.

One structure that has been left out of this discussion so far, and in fact has been rather ignored in recent theories of sleep, is the hypothalamus. Many years ago, Ranson reported that hypothalamic lesions often produce long-lasting or permanent coma (1939). Feldman and Waller (1962) have more recently confirmed and extended these observations. Furthermore, in a most important experiment, Nauta (1946) reported that a relatively localized lesion in a somewhat different region of the hypothalamus produced permanent wakefulness in rats! These two hypothalamic regions are indicated as (e) and (f) in the schema of Figure 14.24. A final complication is the recent evidence indicating that EEG and pupil signs of sleep can be induced by repetitive stimulation of vagal afferent nerves, particularly those from the carotid bodies, and of the tractus solitarius in the brainstem (Bonvallet and Allen, 1963; Bonvallet, Dell, and Hieble, 1954).

It should be obvious to the reader that the diagram in Figure 14.24 is highly speculative, and in no sense to be regarded as proven. A great many assumptions are involved. Indeed many students of brain function tend to reject theories based on the concept of "active neural centers." They would probably point out that the number of such centers believed to control sleep has increased from two in 1960 to four or six in 1966, and in all probability will increase to 10 or 20 in a few years. Skeptics might suggest that in fact there are no neural "centers" controlling sleep, but rather that all regions of the brain interact in producing sleep or waking, and any given region may function in a given way depending on a great many other things.

Suggested readings

Jasper, H. H. (Ed.) *Reticular formation of the brain.* Boston: Little,Brown, 1958.

Moruzzi, G. Reticular influences on the EEG. *EEG clin. Neurophysiol.*, 1964, **16**, 2–17.

Rossi, G. F., and Zanchetti, A. The brain stem reticular formation: anatomy and physiology. *Arch. ital. biol.*, 1957, **95**, 199–435.

Wolstenholme, G. E. W., and O'Connor, M. (Eds.) *The nature of sleep.* Ciba Foundation Symposium, London, 1960. Boston: Little,Brown, 1961.

CHAPTER 15

CEREBRAL CORTEX: ASSOCIATION AREAS AND BEHAVIORAL RELATIONS

W e discussed the organization and possible functions of the sensory and motor areas of the cerebral cortex in some detail in Chapter 11. There is a good deal of neocortex that is neither sensory nor motor, particularly in higher mammals. These regions of cortex, sometimes called the "association" areas, have expanded enormously in phylogenetic development of mammals. There is virtually no association cortex in the rat, but in man the bulk of the cortex is "association" rather than sensory or motor (see discussions in Chapters 4 and 11). In this chapter we shall take a brief look at the electrophysiological organization and possible behavioral roles of these cortical regions, and then survey the recent but rapidly growing literature concerned with relating cortical activity to behavioral variables like habituation, attention, and learning. The reader may feel that we have been somewhat arbitrary in dividing the cortex between two quite different sections of the book. We have. It is quite possible that "association" areas of the cortex are no more integrative in functions than are sensory and motor fields, although the term "association" (probably a misnomer) would suggest otherwise. However, it was felt that the reader will gain a clearer understanding of the topics covered here after exposure to the previous material.

Association areas of the cerebral cortex

In the late Nineteenth and early Twentieth centuries a kind of "switchboard" theory of cortical function was popular. Sensory information was believed to project to sensory fields of the cortex, relay directly to association areas where it was "associated, integrated, and evaluated," and then relayed to motor cortex to control movements. It was assumed that subcortical systems, other than those concerned with autonomic activity, served primarily to get information to the cortex and movements from it. Many years ago Lashley (1950) disposed of any rigid interpretation of this type by showing that severing the motor cortex from sensory areas by deep vertical cuts appeared to have no effect at all on an animal's behavior. In other words, *cortical-cortical* connections between sensory, association, and motor areas do not seem of crucial importance in cortical function. Indeed, there is a striking paucity of direct anatomical connections from most other areas of the cortex to the motor cortex. Nonetheless the phrase "association cortex" has stuck, and is widely used today.

Electrophysiological activity in association cortex

One of the classical preparations used to study cortical responses evoked by sensory stimulation, and muscle movements evoked by electrical stimulation of the cortex, has been an animal deeply anesthetized with a barbiturate (usually "Nembutal," a commercial brand name for sodium pentobarbital). With this anesthetic condition a given type of sensory stimulus evokes responses over a rather limited region of cortex, e.g. a click evokes responses only in the auditory region of the cortex, a flash only in the visual region of the cortex, and so on. These are the primary sensory cortical fields. In like manner electrical stimulation of the cortex evokes muscle movements only when a rather limited anterior region of cortex, the "motor" cortex, is stimulated. Relatively large regions of the cortex do not yield sensory evoked responses, nor will stimulation of them produce movements. These are the so-called "silent" or association areas of the cortex. The relative amount and location of such "association" cortex is shown for the cat and monkey in Figure 15.1.

Actually these regions of "silent" cortex are of course not electrically silent; in fact several types of activity tend to occur predominantly in certain areas of the association cortex. Figure 15.2 indicates approximate regions of the cortex (of cat) exhibiting maximum spindling responses, recruiting responses, responses to electrical stimulation of the midbrain reticular formation (in the chloralosed animal), and so-called "nonspecific association" evoked responses. Spindling activity, you may recall from Chapter 14, is the spontaneous 8–12/sec waves occurring in "bursts" that are characteristic of the sleeping, barbiturized or *cerveau isolé* cat, and appear to be under the control of the midline thalamic nuclei. Recruiting responses resemble spindle bursts except that they are evoked

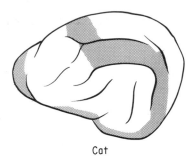

Cat

Figure 15.1. Relative amount of "association" or "silent" cortex (stippled) and sensory and motor cortex (open) in cat and monkey.

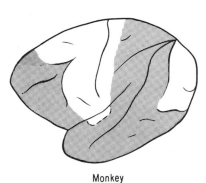

Monkey

by repeated electrical stimulation of the midline thalamus (see Chapter 14). Nonspecific association evoked responses are described further below. All these types of activity tend to predominate in certain portions of association and motor areas (compare Figure 15.1 and 15.2). It would seem that these regions of cortex

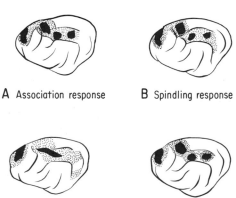

A Association response   **B** Spindling response

C Recruiting response   **D** Response to reticular stimulation

Figure 15.2. Relative cortical distributions of: **A**, association responses evoked by peripheral stimuli; **B**, spontaneous spindling; **C**, recruiting responses to repetitive electrical stimulation of the diffuse thalamic nuclei, and **D**, evoked responses to single shock stimulation of the mesencephalic reticular formation in cat. (Based on Dempsey and Morison, 1942; Starzl, Taylor, and Magoun, 1951; Buser and Borenstein, 1957; and unpublished observations by Phillips, Thompson, and Denney) may represent focalized projections from nonspecific systems of the brain (see, for example, discussion by Lindsley, 1961).

The relative appearance and characteristics of primary sensory and " non-specific association" evoked responses are schematized in the drawings of Figure 15.3. Responses in association areas and in the primary auditory cortex to auditory (A), visual (V) and tactile (T) stimulation are compared for barbiturized, chloralosed and unanesthetized cats. In the Nembutalized animal there are no evoked responses to any stimuli in association areas; however, in the auditory area there is a clear primary evoked response to click, but no responses

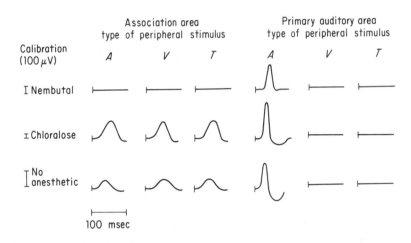

Figure 15.3. Schematic drawings of the types of evoked responses recorded from primary auditory and association areas of the cerebral cortex to auditory (S), visual (V), and tactile (T) stimuli in various anesthetic conditions in the cat. Note the varying amplitude calibrations on the left (bar height always equals 100 microvolts). Stimuli are a click (*A*), a light flash (*V*), and a shock to the paw (*T*).

to the other types of stimuli. In the chloralose anesthetized animal, on the other hand, all types of peripheral stimuli evoke rather comparable looking responses from the same region of association cortex (see Figure 15.4). In the auditory area the evoked response to click stimulation is larger than was the case in the Nembutalized animal, but its other characteristics are quite similar. Again there are no responses on the auditory cortex to visual or tactile stimulation. This modality specificity of response in the primary auditory cortex holds for other sensory areas as well. Only light flash evokes responses in the primary visual cortex and only tactile stimulation evokes responses in the primary somatic sensory cortex, both with Nembutal and with chloralose.

Evoked responses recorded from the association cortex in the normal waking animal appear quite similar to those obtained with chloralose. Responses

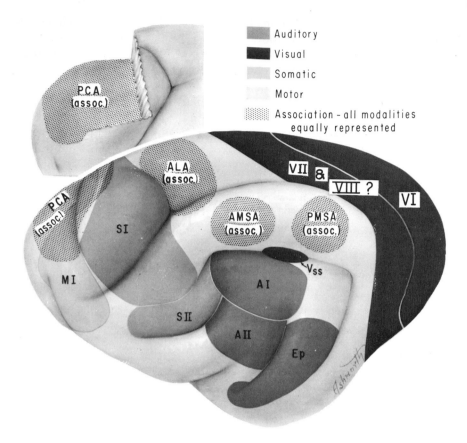

Figure 15.4. Primary and association evoked response regions of the cerebral cortex of the cat. Primary areas are modality specific, but association responses are evoked by all types of stimuli. VI, VII and VIII, V_{ss}, visual areas; AI, AII, Ep., auditory areas; SI, SII, MI, sensory-motor areas; PCA, ALA, A, SA, PMSA, association response areas. (From Thompson, Johnson, and Hoopes, 1963)

are seen to all modalities of stimulation and they all have a similar appearance. Note, however, that the voltage calibration scale is quite different here. The absolute response amplitudes of association responses evoked in the unanesthetized animal are ten to twenty times lower than in the chloralose state. In the auditory cortex the response to click has a very similar appearance to primary responses obtained with chloralose and Nembutal, but again is very much lower in amplitude. As in the other conditions, the primary sensory areas seem to be modality specific; only a click evokes a response in the auditory cortex. The very much lower amplitudes of cortical evoked responses in the normal waking animal than in the anesthetized preparation seem to be a consistent finding for all types of evoked activity.

In view of the rather striking differences in the electrical behavior of cortical association response fields with chloralose and with Nembutal, a few words are perhaps in order concerning anesthetic effects. Both substances are anesthetics in the sense that the animal is completely comatose and does not respond to painful stimulation. However, skeletal and autonomic reflexes are more vigorous with chloralose; thus it is often the anesthetic agent of choice in studies of cardiovascular reflexes. Skeletal muscle reflexes of the chloralosed animal are such that with light doses almost any type of sudden sensory stimulation produces a vigorous muscular twitch or seizurelike clonic response. This latter observation has led some investigators to be rather dubious concerning the "normalcy" of the CNS with chloralose. On the other hand, reflex activity is so much reduced with Nembutal that some investigators feel dubious about CNS organization as revealed by the Nembutalized animal. It is clear that neither agent produces a normal CNS. Alternatively, it is likely that sensory projections revealed under these conditions do reflect actual neural pathways in the brain. In terms of synaptic mechanisms, results of neurophysiological studies reviewed in Chapter 8 suggest that barbiturates reduce several aspects of neuron excitability, whereas chloralose appears, among other things, to enhance presynaptic inhibition.

Amassian (1954) was the first to report evoked association responses in the cortex of the chloralosed cat. He observed these responses to tactile stimulation in an association area lying posterior to somatic cortex and anterior to visual cortex (area ALA in Figure 15.4). Subsequent experiments reported evoked responses in several cortical association areas of the cat to tactile, auditory, and visual stimulation (Albe-Fessard and Rougeul, 1955; Buser, Borenstein, and Bruner, 1959; Thompson and Sindberg, 1960). Tactile input was shown to be convergent, in the sense that stimulation of different areas of the body gave responses in the same region of the cortex (Albe-Fessard and Rougeul, 1955). Similarly, stimulation of different regions of the cochlear nerve produced "auditory" association responses in the same regions of the cortex (Thompson and Sindberg, 1960). Acute ablation of primary auditory and visual areas of the cortex did not abolish cortical association responses to these types of stimuli (Buser et al., 1959). In fact, if the auditory cortex was totally ablated bilaterally several months before the experiment, cortical evoked association responses to auditory stimuli were normal in appearance, even though the medial geniculate body (the thalamic auditory relay nucleus) was totally degenerated on both sides (Thompson and Sindberg, 1960). If all cortex of one hemisphere is removed and all cortex of the other hemisphere except the association response regions also removed, the remaining association area islands still exhibit evoked responses to auditory, visual, and tactile stimuli (Thompson, Johnson, and Hoopes, 1963). Consequently, cortical-evoked association responses cannot be due to activity relayed from other areas of the cortex.

Convergence of sensory projections to association response areas is not limited to different types of input within a given modality. The distribution of evoked responses within these regions appears identical for auditory, visual, and tactile stimuli (see Figure 15.4). Several portions of the posterior "silent" cortex exhibit these responses, as does a frontal region overlapping the motor cortex, at least in the cat.

At this point it is well to reemphasize the problem of definition and usage of terms employed to describe cortex that is neither sensory nor motor (see also the discussion in Chapter 11). The phrase *association cortex* is used here (and by most other people) to refer to essentially all neocortex that is neither primary sensory nor motor. Some portions of this association cortex exhibit the so-called nonspecific evoked association responses. The latter *by no means* includes all association cortex, particularly in the primate. Various anatomical criteria, such as architectonic analysis of cortical histology and retrograde degeneration analysis of thalamic projection fields to the cortex, are frequently used to define or locate a particular region of association cortex. For example, in the primate, a portion of the prefrontal association cortex is labeled area 9 on the basis of its histological appearance (it is also termed a portion of the frontal granular cortex). Area 9 is also the cortical projection field for the dorsomedial nucleus of the thalamus. Finally, the effects of cortical damage on behavior are used to define a region of the cortex. Thus removal of cortical area 9 has often been reported to lead to hyperactivity and impairment of delayed response in primates. Unfortunately there is no easy guide for the student to the particular definition of association areas that may be used. In this text "association cortex" refers to all neocortex that is neither primary sensory nor motor.

The data described above concerning nonspecific evoked association responses were all obtained using the chloralosed cat. Evoked responses having similar appearances (but much lower amplitudes) in association regions have been obtained for tactile, auditory, and visual responses in the curarized but unanesthetized cat (Buser and Borenstein, 1959). Similar-appearing cortical responses to tactile stimulation were also obtained in normal animals with chronically implanted recording electrodes (Albe-Fessard et al., 1960). In more recent experiments on normal unanesthetized cats with chronic electrodes, it has been shown that at least on the middle suprasylvian gyrus of the cat (areas AMSA and PMSA in Figure 15.4), evoked association responses to all three types of sensory stimulation have the same relative distribution as in the chloralosed animal (Shaw and Thompson, 1964a). Indeed, association responses of the normal waking cat are similar in most characteristics to those of the chloralosed animal (see Figure 15.3), except that they are of much lower amplitude and somewhat more extensively represented on the cortex than with anesthesia.

Microelectrode studies of single cell responses in cortical association response areas have generally noted considerable sensory convergence. Thus Buser and Imbert (1961) reported that the majority of cells in the anterior response field (PCA in Figure 15.4) responded to all modalities of stimulation employed. They compared the effects of chloralose, and of curare but no anesthesia, on responses of single cells. In the chloralosed animal, of 100 cells studied in the anterior response field, 92 responded to all types of sensory stimuli (tactile stimulation of several regions of the body surface, auditory clicks, and light flashes), and 8 responded only to somatic sensory stimulation. In the curarized animal, a somewhat small proportion were completely nonspecific in their responses. Thus, of 100 cells in the anterior response field, 64 were completely polysensory in the sense that they responded to all types of stimulation, and 36 responded only to somatic sensory stimulation. Examples of polysensory cells studied in the chloralosed animal, and in the unanesthetized, curarized animal, are shown in Figures 15.5 and 15.6.

Shimozano et al. (1963) compared responses of cells in the suprasylvian association area (AMSA and PMSA in Figure 15.3) in the curarized unanesthetized state and with chloralose. They found a marked degree of convergence of different types of stimuli. Many cells could be activated by light flash, peripheral somatic sensory stimuli, and electrical stimulation of several regions of the brain

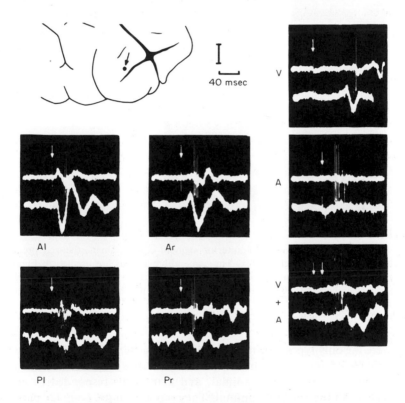

Figure 15.5. Polysensory neuron of right perisigmoid cortex under deep chloralose; no spontaneous firing; negative deflection upward for microelectrode recording. Typical responses to somesthetic stimulation of each limb, anterior or posterior, left or right (Al, Ar, Pl, Pr), to a flash (V), a click (A), and a closely spaced flash and click (V + A). Lower trace, activity from pontine pyramidal tract, recorded with a bipolar concentric electrode (tip distance, 0.5 mm) in right pyramidal tract. (From Buser and Imbert, 1961)

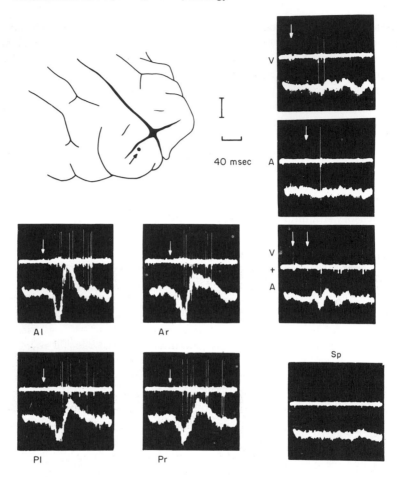

Figure 15.6. Polysensory neuron of anterior sigmoid cortex. Unanesthetized preparation, immoblized under curare; right cortex. The same abbreviations are used as in Figure 15.5. No spontaneous activity, as shown in the figure in the lower right-hand corner (Sp). Calibration, 100 μv (upper channel) and 200 μv (lower channel). Lower trace, pyramidal tract activity. (From Buser and Imbert, 1961)

(these were the only types of stimulation used). In general the findings are similar to those of Buser and Imbert, in that virtually all cells responded to all types of stimulation in the chloralosed animal, and many cells responded to all types of stimulation in the curarized animal. They reported more complex patterns of cellular activation in the curarized animal than in the chloralosed animal. In a similar study, Dubner and Rutledge (1964) recorded the activity of single nerve cells in both the curarized and chloralosed states from a small region on the middle suprasylvian gyrus. They found cells that were responsive to all types of sensory stimulation (they used somatic sensory, auditory, and visual) and other cells that were responsive only to visual stimulation. As in the experiment by Shimozano et al. they report rather complex patterns of interaction and response by many cells in this region of the suprasylvian gyrus to different types of stimulation. Bental and Bihari (1963) studied responses of single cells in the suprasylvian gyrus of the normal unrestrained cat, using implanted microelectrodes. They employed auditory and visual stimulation, and found that a substantial proportion of the cells they studied could be activated by both types of stimulation. To summarize these microelectrode studies, it appears that a very substantial number of cells in the association response areas are activated by many or all types of stimuli employed. In addition, there are cells, particularly in the suprasylvian gyrus, which appear to be responsive to only one or a few types of stimulation and whose patterns of response appear to depend upon the particular conditions and type of stimulation.

All of the experiments discussed above on association response fields have used the cat. Evoked nonspecific association response areas are incompletely mapped for the primate cortex. Albe-Fessard et al. (1959) have described two such cortical fields responsive to somatic sensory stimulation in the monkey. In the cat, in which there is only an intermediate amount of silent cortex, much of this cortex does exhibit evoked association responses. However, in the primate there are still large regions that are neither sensory nor motor and do not exhibit association evoked responses. (In squirrel monkeys, at least, nonspecific polysensory "association" areas occupy only two limited regions of cortex, one on the dorsal portion of primary and supplementary motor areas, and the other posterior to the dorsal portion of area SI; unpublished observations from the author's laboratory.) In particular, the cortical regions described by many investigators as temporal, parietal, preoccipital, and prefrontal association areas (most of the shaded regions of the primate brain in Figure 15.1) do not exhibit evoked association responses. This, of course, does *not* mean that these regions do not exhibit neural activity. Spontaneous electrical activity can be recorded from all regions of the cortex of the waking animal. A microelectrode study by Jasper, Ricci, and Doane (1960) using chronically implanted microelectrodes, indicated that activity of many single neurons in temporal areas of the primate cortex respond in many different ways as a function of the stimulus conditions and behavioral state of the animal (see further discussion below). The existence of large areas of cortex in the primate that are not motor, and do not exhibit primary-, sensory-, or association-evoked responses, emphasizes our current limited knowledge of the electrophysiological organization of the association cortex. As will be seen below in our discussion of cortical lesion studies, the nature of association area function is among the most persistent and complex problems facing the student of brain and behavior.

Neurobehavioral analysis of association cortex

Most of our information concerning the possible functions of association cortex has come from studies of the behavioral effects of removing it. Association cortex, particularly in the primate, has been the favored target of assaults by physiological psychologists in recent years. There are well over 1,000 studies concerned with the behavioral effects of damage to the association cortex; any attempt to review this vast literature here would be impractical. Instead, we will take a very brief look at some of the generalizations that have been made concerning probable functions of the association cortex, together with a very few illustrative experiments. Comprehensive reviews of the animal literature may be found in Chow and Hutt (1953); Pribram (1960); Rosvold (1959); Warren and Akert (1964). Teuber (1961) has reviewed the human data.

The primate, particularly the rhesus monkey, has been the subject of choice in most lesion-behavior studies—it has a large amount of association cortex, and is readily adaptable to behavioral training and testing procedures. It might be well to describe the most common technique used for behavioral testing of primates, namely the Wisconsin General Test Apparatus (see Figure 15.7). This was developed and standardized by Harlow. The monkey remains in a cage facing the investigator. A stimulus tray in front of the animal can be pushed forward so that he can reach objects on it through the bars of his cage. The objects are placed over the food wells, one of which is baited with a raisin, peanut, or other reward. The experimenter can slide the tray back and interpose an opaque screen while baiting the wells. To take a simple example of discrimination learning, suppose the monkey is required to discriminate between a cube and a pyramid. The experimenter always baits the food well underneath the cube, but varies the relative positions of the two objects in a random fashion. The monkey soon learns to push the cube away to obtain the reward.

Behavioral tests that have been used extensively in evaluating effects of cortical damage include *discrimination learning*, particularly visual discrimina-

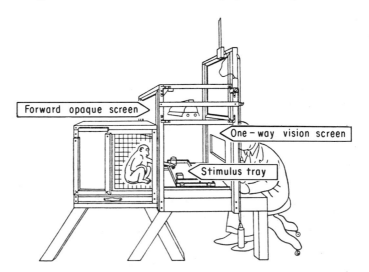

Figure 15.7. The Wisconsin General Testing Apparatus (WGTA) used to test monkeys in a variety of discrimination and learning problems. (From Harlow, 1958)

tions, *learning sets*, *delayed response*, and *delayed alternation*. We have just described the basic procedures for visual discrimination. The animal is required to respond to one object but not another. Learning set is an interesting "higher order" type of discrimination learning task (see Harlow, 1949). The monkey is given a long series of six trial tests on simple visual discriminations. Each test employs a different pair of dissimilar objects. Thus on the first test the animal is given six trials of training on two dissimilar objects, one of which is always correct. If his first trial response is to the wrong object, he has to wait until the next trial. After six trials on this pair of objects, he is given six trials on a different pair of objects, and so on. A normal adult human will generally solve the problem on the second trial of each test: no information is available telling which object is correct on trial one. If the correct object is first chosen, it will always be correct in the next five trials. If the incorrect object is chosen on the first trial the other object will always be correct on subsequent trials. Thus performance over a long series of such six-trial tests will always be about 50 percent correct on trial one and 100 percent on trials two to six. Rhesus monkeys (and small children) typically improve gradually on their trial two to six performance over a long period of time with a great many different test objects. This gradual improvement on trials two to six is what has been called by Harlow *learning set*.

The delayed response test was first developed by Hunter (1913). The method in common use today for primates is to bait one of two food wells while the monkey watches and then place two identical objects over the food wells and require the monkey to wait for varying periods of time, usually from 0 to 30 seconds, before pushing the tray within reach. An opaque screen is often placed in front of the monkey during the period of delay. In colloquial terms, the monkey has to "remember" which object the food is under. Delayed alternation is an elaboration of the delayed response test. On the first trial two identical objects are usually baited. After the monkey makes the first choice an opaque screen is interposed and only the object opposite the one chosen on the first trial is baited. If the monkey gets this correct, the opposite object is next baited, and so on. If the monkey chooses the incorrect object, he is required to repeat the trial until he eventually chooses that object. Varying periods of delay are used between successive choices in the delayed alternation test. Again, in colloquial terms, all the monkey has to do is "remember" which object the bait was under on the last trial and choose the opposite object on the next trial.

THE FRONTAL LOBES.   One of the most impressive aspects of the human brain is the relatively great size of the frontal lobes, particularly the cortex anterior to the motor area. Practically all conceivable functions have been attributed at one time or another to the frontal lobes, ranging from sensory-motor integration to higher thought processes, the will, emotions, and intelligence. There has been a tremendous amount of research on the possible behavioral functions of the frontal lobes; the recent symposium on *The Frontal Granular Cortex and Behavior* edited by Warren and Akert (1964) contains twenty chapters, each packed

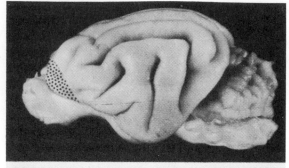

CAT

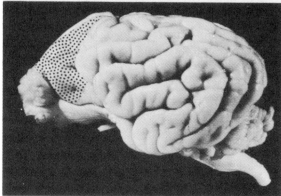

DOG

Figure 15.8. Relative locations of the frontal granular cortex in four mammals (brains *not* to scale). (From Warren and Akert, 1964)

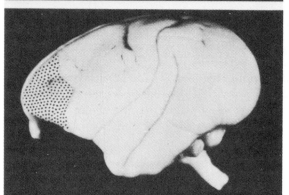

SQUIRREL MONKEY

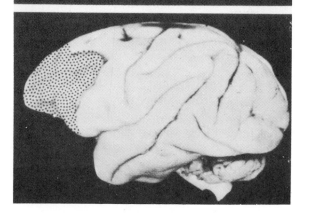

RHESUS MONKEY

with a great deal of new information, and a bibliography of over 600 references. (This author is tempted simply to refer the reader to that book; it is impossible to do justice to the material here.)

The locations of the frontal granular cortex (Brodmann's areas 7–12) are indicated in Figure 15.8, for cat, dog, squirrel monkey, and rhesus monkey, as determined by cytoarchitectonic methods. The relative amount of this frontal granular cortex increases from cat to rhesus, and is considerably greater still in man. A large portion—but not all—of the frontal granular cortex receives direct projections from the dorso-medial nucleus of the thalamus (Akert, 1964).

The most consistent and clear-cut behavioral deficit exhibited by monkeys after frontal lesions is severe and long-lasting impairment in delayed response performance. This was first demonstrated in the classic study by Jacobsen (1935) and has been confirmed in dozens of subsequent studies. A recent and carefully designed experiment by French and Harlow (1962) is typical. Monkeys were trained preoperatively in a simple delayed response task. At the start of a given trial an opaque screen was present in front of the animal. After raising the opaque screen, the experimenter placed a reward in one of two food wells and placed identical wooden blocks over the two food wells when the monkey had given some sign of attending to the reinforcement. Both food wells were immediately covered and five seconds allowed to pass. The object tray was then advanced and the monkey allowed to displace one block only and obtain (or fail to obtain) the reward. Preoperative performance of a group of four monkeys trained to criterion on this task is shown in Figure 15.9A. Data are plotted in

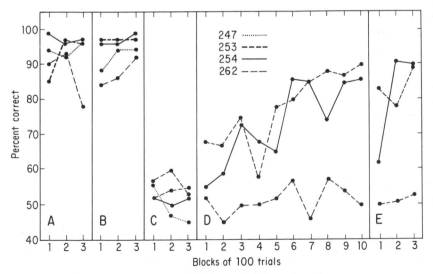

Figure 15.9. Performance of monkeys with lesions removing frontal areas 9 (done between B and C) on delayed reaction. **A,** last 300 trials of initial training. **B,** preoperative retests. **C,** early postoperative retests. **D,** interim postoperative retests. **E,** late postoperative retests. (From French and Harlow, 1962)

blocks of 100 trials; the performance shown is for the last 300 trials of training. Figure 15.9B illustrates retesting of these same animals after a period of six months has elapsed in which they were given no training. This control demonstrates that there is no forgetting of the performance during the six-month period. Between portions B and C of the Figure, animals all received bilateral ablations of area 9 of the prefrontal granular cortex. Their initial performance, shown in portion C of the Figure, is at a chance level for the first 300 trials. In portion D they are shown on intermediate postoperative test performance in over 1000 trials of training. As can be seen, there is significant improvement in the performance of some animals, but in no case do the animals recover to preoperative performance. Figure 15.9E, finally, illustrates the last of a very long series of postoperative training trials. Note that two animals are performing moderately well and one animal is still responding at chance level. This partial recovery of delayed response performance is obtained only after very extensive postoperative training; few studies have reported even this much recovery of function. The delayed response deficit following frontal lesions is unique to the frontal cortex—it does not occur if lesions are made in other regions of the cortex (Pribram et al., 1952; Pribram et al., 1955).

Another task that shows marked impairment after frontal lesion is delayed alternation. An example from an experiment by Stamm (1964) is shown in Figure 15.10. Four animals were trained preoperatively in the delayed alternation task. In this experiment, the animals faced a testing tray consisting of two rectangular boxes, each covered with an aluminum slide. By pushing the slide forward the monkey could find a peanut in the box. A sliding opaque panel was interposed between the monkey and testing tray between subsequent trials and the intertrial interval was approximately 7 seconds. Both boxes were initially baited and after the subject had retrieved a peanut from one box, the reward was placed in the opposite box. During subsequent trials, the box opposite to the one just previously rewarded was baited. When an error was made, the peanut remained in the same box for succeeding trials until it was found by the monkey. A correct response was scored when the animal shifted to the opposite box after it had obtained a reward, whereas repetitive responses to one side were scored as a single error.

Percent of correct responses in preoperative training and in postoperative relearning of the task is shown in Figure 15.10. Note that by 400 preoperative trials the animals had attained virtually perfect performance. They were then subjected to bilateral ablation of dorso-lateral frontal cortex. Following operation their performance was down to nearly a chance level and improved only very slowly, appearing to stabilize after a thousand trials at a slightly lower level than preoperative performance. Thus there is an initial total loss of the delayed alternation performance following frontal lesion, but after extensive retraining there is considerable recovery. Delayed alternation deficits also seem unique to the frontal lobes, other neocortical regions not being essential to the task. However, lesions in rhinencephalic regions and the caudate nucleus can also cause

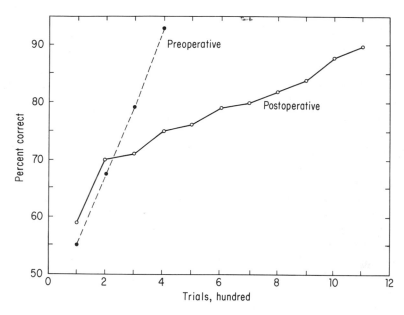

Figure 15.10. Percent correct performance by a group of monkeys on a delayed alternation task before and after frontal lesions. (From Stamm, 1964)

marked impairment in this task (Rosvold and Delgado, 1956; Rosvold, Mishkin, and Szwarcbart, 1958). The deficit in delayed alternation performance is perhaps somewhat less severe than is the case with delayed response performance following frontal lesions. If animals are trained in a variety of situations over a period of years following lesions, their ultimate performance on the delayed alternation tasks is comparable to that of normal animals (Leary et al., 1952; Warren et al., 1957).

Another commonly noted symptom following frontal damage in monkeys is a marked and long-lasting hyperactivity (Ferrier, 1886; French, 1959). Interestingly, this hyperactivity is exhibited only in a lighted room and not in darkness (Gross, 1963; Isaac and Devito, 1958). Unlike delayed response deficit, hyperactivity is by no means a universal symptom of frontal damage in monkeys. New world monkeys (e.g. squirrel monkey) exhibit no hyperactivity following such lesions (Lashley, 1948; Miles and Blomquist, 1960). Behavioral phenomena quite different from those discussed above in terms of the more conventional types of learning situations also seem to be impaired by frontal lesions. Thus, Brody and Rosvold (1952) have reported that frontal ablations produce an increase in the degree of aggressiveness of monkeys in social interactions with other monkeys. Furthermore, rhesus monkeys with frontal lesions seem to be less tolerant of frustration than are intact monkeys (Spaet and Harlow, 1943). On the other hand, frontal damage produces quite variable effects on frustration tolerance among chimpanzees, the differences between individual animals often being greater than the effects of lesions on them in changing their performance (Blum, 1948).

There has been a good bit of comparative work analyzing the effect of prefrontal ablations in dog and cat on a variety of tasks, particularly by Konorski and his many associates, and by Warren and associates. Lawicka and Konorski (1959) were able to demonstrate severe and chronic deficits in delayed response performance by dogs following ablation of frontal cortex. The apparatus they used is closely modeled on Hunter's original test of delayed response (see Figure 15.11). The dog is placed on the starting platform and the food trays are placed far from each other, separated by angles of 60 degrees from the starting platform. Food is placed in one of the three food trays and a buzzer sounded from the correct food tray only. The dog is held on the starting platform by the experimenter during the period of delay and, when released, required to run to the correct tray to receive food. If he goes to the incorrect tray first, he is not allowed to obtain food from the correct tray. They found that normal dogs were able to perform correctly with delays of *many minutes* even though a variety of distractions to the animal were interposed during the delay period. However, after bilateral ablation of the prefrontal cortex, the animals became severely incapacitated. Correct delayed responding seemed to depend on the animals maintaining a body orientation pointing toward the correct food tray. If its orientation was changed the operative animal was no longer able to go to the correct tray. This clear-cut and permanent deficit in performance was also demonstrated with cats, and has been extensively analyzed in subsequent work by Lawicka and Konorski (1959), Konorski (1961), Konorski and Lofka (1964). Konorski and his colleagues have also demonstrated a variety of deficits in conditioned response performance following prefrontal lesions in dogs. Particular kinds of deficits that are most pronounced are those involving conditioned inhibition, i.e. situations in which the animal has been conditioned to respond to one stimulus but not to another. Following lesion, animals typically seem to respond to both positive and negative stimuli. (This type of deficit, you may

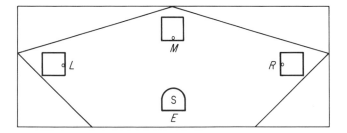

Figure 15.11. Delayed response testing apparatus for dogs used by Konorski. Animal is placed at *E* and one of the three boxes is baited. (From Konorski and Lawicka, 1964)

recall, also occurs following lesions of sensory cortex, see Chapter 11.) Brutkowski (1964) has recently completed a very extensive analysis of the effects of prefrontal lesions on conditioning and has suggested that the kind of response inhibition that is most impaired by frontal lesion might be termed inhibition of affective behavior, or drive inhibition.

Warren and associates have completed a very extensive series of experiments testing effects of prefrontal lesions in cats on most of the types of learning situations that have been used in primate investigations. He has found that prefrontal lesions impair retention but do not prevent postoperative solution of the double-alternation problem by cats (see Warren, 1964). Cats are impaired on delayed response following lesions but rather less so than are dogs or primates. In addition, a variety of discrimination learning deficits appeared to show up in cats following frontal lesions. However, these deficits all disappear after extensive postoperative training. He also finds that frontal cats are seriously and permanently impaired in discrimination reversal learning (in which objects that have been rewarded are subsequently not rewarded). A comparable deficit has also been reported in this kind of task by Settlage et al. (1948), in primates. Finally, Warren finds, as does Konorski, that neither dogs nor cats are hyperactive following frontal lesions. In this respect they are more like New World monkeys than Old World monkeys. The fact that carnivores resemble one type of monkey more than another type of monkey poses some difficulties concerning the role of the frontal cortex in hyperactivity.

Perhaps the most difficult aspect of attempts to understand frontal lobe function has to do with the inferred meanings of the various operative deficits. There is virtually unanimous opinion regarding the fact that ablation of prefrontal cortex in the primate leads to severe and long-lasting deficits in delayed response performance. However, there is virtually no agreement concerning the interpretation of this deficit. The initial conclusion that immediate or short-term memory resides in the frontal lobes has been questioned in a variety of ways. Delay does seem to play a rather general role in the frontal lobe syndrome. Mishkin and Weiskrantz (1958) showed that deficits were still present if, instead of making a delay between baiting the food well and the animal's response, the delay was introduced between the animal's response and delivery of the reward. However, Riopelle and Clurukian (1958), showed that frontal monkeys are successful on discrimination type tests even with very long intertrial delays. Pribram and Mishkin (1956) demonstrated in an ingenious experiment that frontal monkeys could learn a "go—no go" type delay task. Instead of two cups, only one was used. The cup was baited within view of the animal, and he was required to wait (no go) if the experimenter's hand was held over the cup, but to go (move the cup) if the experimenter's hand was not there. Consequently, immediate memory, as defined by this procedure, is not necessarily lost. French (1962; 1964) showed that if the stimulus and reward objects are spatially separated from one another in discrimination training where no delays are involved, frontal monkeys do much more poorly than do normal monkeys. All of these experiments serve to qualify the initial hypothesis that immediate memory is the basic function of the frontal lobes.

Pribram and associates have developed a comprehensive and ingenious series of experiments which seem to support the general notion that in frontal monkeys a given set of responses that had proved useful in the past tend to perseverate when reinforcement cue changes are introduced *between* problems, but that there is an increased tendency to shift to other types of responses when such changes occur *within* problems (see Pribram, 1960; 1964). Pribram interprets these findings within the context of formal problem-solving models (Newell et al., 1958). Finally, Harlow, Akert, and Schiltz (1964) have demonstrated that if the frontal granular cortex is removed in infant monkeys their subsequent performance on delayed response is virtually normal, in striking contrast to the marked impairment following lesions in older animals.

Another difficulty facing the student of frontal lobe function is the comparative data on the effects of lesions in animals and man. For many years it appeared that no symptoms of human frontal damage paralleled the classical deficits seen in monkeys. However, recent studies by Milner (1964) and Teuber (1964) have obtained deficits in frontal humans in tasks resembling some of those that show deficits in frontal animals. Thus Milner finds marked deficits in a delayed comparison task. Two brief stimuli in the same sensory modality are given 60 seconds apart and the patient required to state whether the two stimuli are the same or different (Konorski, 1959; Stepien and Sierpenski, 1960). On the basis of this and other types of task deficits she concludes that "in man, frontal lobe lesions are compatible with normal performance on many intellectual tasks. Nevertheless, it is possible to demonstrate a deficit after frontal lobectomy in situations requiring a constant shifting of response to meet changing environmental demands. Under such conditions, the patient with frontal lobe lesion seems unable to suppress his ongoing response tendencies whether spontaneous or experimentally induced, or to rid himself of perseverative interference of previous sensory events. The critical lesion for this loss appears to be dorsal-lateral rather than orbital."

Teuber presents considerable data indicating that many complex aspects of sensory-motor function are impaired in frontal man. Thus the ability to maintain correctly perceived upright position during changes in posture is severely depressed in frontal patients. Visual searching tasks, in which the subject has to engage in active visual searching to find an object embedded in a group of dissimilar objects, exhibits marked impairment. Teuber summarizes his conclusions as follows: "We have only to look at the forced movements of the hyperkinetic bifrontal monkey or the curious forced grasping and groping of human frontal lobe disease to be impressed at the need for an analysis of frontal symptoms that stresses the motor element. But it is a particular aspect of motor control that needs to be stressed: it is that aspect which may permit us to give a physiologic meaning to the forbidden concept of "voluntary" movement, in contrast to forced or reflex movement."

Interestingly, the so-called "typical" signs of frontal damage in man, such as changes in mood and attitude, i.e. euphoria, superficiality, facetiousness, and so on, seem to be relatively rare in cases in which the brain damage is limited to the frontal lobes (Teuber, 1964). However, one rather dramatic aspect of the "typical" frontal syndrome in man seems to be widely substantiated. This is the lack of responsiveness to chronic pain (see discussion by Barber, 1959). Indeed about the only current justification for performing lobotomy in man would appear to be relief of chronic incurable pain, such as that resulting from terminal cancer. When questioned, such patients generally report the presence of pain, but otherwise act as though it does not bother them, in spite of the fact that their pain thresholds are normal.

The posterior association cortex

Most studies on the behavioral functions of posterior regions of the association cortex have emphasized the temporal lobe. This is due in large part to the very dramatic findings of Klüver and Bucy (1937) indicating that total destruction of the temporal lobes in the rhesus monkey produces a variety of symptoms including some deficits they characterized as "psychic blindness." Their animals did not distinguish between edible and inedible objects (putting both in the mouth), were no longer afraid of stimuli such as rubber snakes that invariably produce intense fear reactions in normal monkeys, were abnormal in sexual behavior, and showed marked deficits in many types of visual discriminations. We will defer discussion of changes in emotional behavior to Chapter 16 and emphasize here the learning and performance deficits. Klüver and Bucy actually resected the temporal lobe, removing it entirely. This procedure includes a great deal more than just the temporal neocortex: rhinencephalic cortex, the amygdala, and portions of the hippocampus are removed as well. However, more recent experiments with lesions limited to cortical tissue have reproduced many aspects of the syndrome, including visual deficits and changes in response to fear-producing stimuli (Blum, Chow, and Pribram, 1950; Mishkin, 1951; Riopelle and Ades, 1951; Riopelle et al., 1958; Meyer, 1958). The visual deficit is particularly severe in pattern discrimination and color problems, but surprisingly enough may be minimal or nonexistent in object recognition and visual acuity tasks (Chow, 1951; 1952a; 1952b). The results are in marked contrast to the effects of large lesions of the lateral surface of the occipital cortex, which can produce marked visual field deficits and some decrease in acuity without significantly impairing pattern discrimination (Harlow, 1959; Settlage, 1939). On the other hand, impairment in delayed response performance, the *sine qua non* of the frontal animal, does not occur in the animal with temporal lesions.

Learning set performance seems to be rather severely impaired following temporal neocortical lesions. Riopelle et al. (1953) found that if temporal animals were trained on *learning set* problems, their initial performance was comparable to that of normal animals, but with practice the normal animals improved considerably more than did the temporals. Chow (1954) found that if the lesion was made after training it caused severe impairment in retention of learning set performance. Meyer (1958) completed an extensive analysis of this effect. Animals were well trained prior to lesion. He found that initial impairment in learning set performance following lesion was marked, but that there was some degree of recovery, and indeed one animal eventually reached preoperative performance levels. These results, together with the previous findings, would seem to suggest that temporal lesions produced their greatest effects in complex visual tasks.

Pribram (1954) has emphasized the fact that complex discriminations based on various types of sensory information are selectively impaired by lesions of differing location within the posterior association cortex of the primate, the effective locus depending upon the sensory modality. This regional specificity has been reported for visual (Blum et al., 1950; Chow, 1952; Mishkin and Pribram, 1954), somesthetic (Pribram and Barry, 1956; Wilson, 1957), auditory (Mishkin and Weiskrantz, 1958), and gustatory (Bagshaw and Pribram, 1953) discriminations. Pribram (see Pribram, 1958; Spinelli and Pribram, 1966) has suggested that these regionally distinct and modality specific effects might result from the association areas exerting their influences downstream via corticofugal afferent pathways (see Chapter 10) which could alter the functional activity of the primary sensory systems. Results of an interesting study by Spinelli and Pribram (1966) concerning the effects of long term electrical stimulation of posterior association cortex seem consistent with this view. A small, transistorized stimulator was implanted in a dental cement plug attached to the skull in monkeys. Stimulating electrodes were placed on the inferior temporal cortex, or the parietal center, or the precentral gyrus, in different groups of animals, and continuous low level electrical stimulation was given for periods of weeks. The group receiving infratemporal stimulation learned visual discriminations significantly faster than did the other groups. This finding is of course beautifully consistent with the fact that lesions of the infratemporal area, but not the other areas, impair visual discrimination learning.

Findings on humans in whom the temporal lobes have been removed or electrically stimulated are rather consistent with the other primate literature. First, damage or electrical inactivation of the *left* temporal lobe produces aphasia (loss of speech), particularly of speech comprehension (see Penfield and Rasmussen, 1950; Schiller, 1947). Milner (1954) studied a series of patients with *right* temporal lobe damage. She found striking and consistent impairment of complex visual discrimination tasks, particularly those in which attention has to be given to many aspects of a complex picture. Perhaps the best-known experiments on the human temporal lobe are those of Penfield and Rasmussen (1950). Electrical stimulation of the exposed temporal lobes in epileptic patients may produce complex auditory and visual hallucinations, and even " reactivate" memories. However, in terms of temporal lobe functions, it must be emphasized that such effects appear to occur only if the patient has an epileptic focus in the temporal lobe. In sum, it would seem that complex visual discrimination losses are the most consistent result of temporal lobe damage in all primates.

In considering the effects of lesions of the posterior association areas, mention should be made of studies using carnivores. Unfortunately, the homologies between primate and carnivore posterior association areas are not terribly clear. The deficits exhibited by cats on auditory pattern discrimination following ventral temporal lesions (Diamond and Neff, 1957; see discussion in Chapter 11) are reminiscent of some aspects of the temporal lobe syndrome in primates. Suprasylvian lesions in cats impair detour ("Umveg") learning (Warren, Warren, and Akert, 1961) and complex visual discriminations (Hara, 1962). Ablation of suprasylvian, anterior lateral and pericruciate areas prevents the subsequent development of sensory preconditioning (Thompson and Kramer, 1965). (Sensory preconditioning, first conclusively demonstrated by Brogden in 1939, involves presentation of paired tones and lights with no reinforcement training, followed by shock avoidance conditioning to light, followed by test to tone. Such animals respond more in the tone test than controls not given the light and tone paired in pretraining. It is termed *sensory pre*conditioning because the response to tone results from exposure to paired sensory stimuli prior to the reinforced conditioning training.) Auditory-visual conditional learning is seriously impaired by the same type of lesion (Thompson and Johnson, 1966). In this context it is of some interest that parietal and temporal areas of the monkey cortex have been implicated in similar conditional learning problems (Evarts, 1952).

Chow and Hutt prepared a summary diagram in 1953 of the types of deficits seen following lesions in the various regions of association cortex. This figure, modified somewhat in the light of more recent work, is shown in Figure 15.12. Delayed response, delayed alternation and conditioned inhibition deficits consistently result from frontal lobe damage. However, the occurrence of hyperactivity following frontal lesion seems to be very much species-specific. Complex visual, auditory, auditory-visual, and learning set problems seem most impaired by posterior associations lesions. These types of deficits are of course defined by the particular tests utilized in the various experiments. Inferences concerning

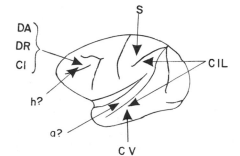

Figure 15.12. "Localization of function" in association areas of the primate cortex in terms of the results of lesion experiments. Abbreviations are: a, complex auditory; CI, conditioned inhibition, CV, complex visual discriminations; CIL, complex intersensory learning; DA, delayed alternation; DR, delayed response; h, hyperactivity; S, somesthetic discriminations. (Modified from Chow and Hutt, 1953)

underlying functions and processes mediated by the various regions of association cortex, and in fact all areas of the cortex are as yet a matter of debate.

CORTICAL ACTIVITY AND BEHAVIOR

Technological advances in recent years have made it feasible to study the relations between behavioral variables and cortical activity in the normal unrestrained animal (including man) using chronically implanted electrodes. Although this is a relatively new area, a great deal of experimental information is already available. It will probably be some time before the data can be adequately evaluated, replicated, and fitted into any kind of consistent theoretical schema relating cortical activity and behavior. Two major approaches that have been used are electrical stimulation of the brain (see reviews by Zeigler, 1957; Sheer, 1961) and the recording of electrical activity from the brain (see review by Morrell, 1961).

Electrical stimulation of the cerebral cortex

The now classical experiments by Loucks (1933, 1936, 1938), Loucks and Gantt (1938), and Brogdan and Gantt (1942) were among the first successful attempts to combine electrical stimulation of the brain with behavioral conditioning procedures. Loucks demonstrated that animals could easily be conditioned to respond to an electrical stimulus (conditioned stimulus) delivered through electrodes implanted in the auditory area of the cortex. He developed an ingenious procedure in which a small coil of wire was implanted underneath the skin, and the two ends of the wire placed on the surface of the cortex through holes drilled in the skull. When a stimulus was to be delivered, another coil of wire was placed over the imbedded coil on the surface of the head and current sent through the outer coil. By a transformer action current was induced in the coil embedded in the skull. (This method has the obvious limitation that it is not possible to measure the voltage or current being delivered to the brain.) Using shock avoidance leg flexion conditioning in the dog, Loucks and colleagues were able to demonstrate that if a repeated electrical stimulus was given to the auditory cortex, paired with shock to the foot, the leg flexion response became conditioned to electrical stimulation of the auditory cortex. More recently, Doty and colleagues (Doty, Rutledge, and Larsen, 1956; Doty and Rutledge, 1959; Doty, 1961b, 1965) and others have confirmed and extended these observations. Doty et al. (1956) showed that electrical stimulation of the dura (the membrane that covers the brain) without stimulation of the brain itself could serve as a conditioned stimulus (the dura has considerable pain innervation) in shock avoidance leg flexion conditioning. This finding raised the possibility that the earlier studies may have been dealing with a peripheral pain stimulus as the CS rather than with direct electrical activation of the cortex.

However, Doty and colleagues were able to show in addition that when all possibility of dura stimulation was eliminated by section of the fifth (trigeminal) nerve (the pain input from the dura goes through the fifth nerve) it was still possible to establish conditioned responses. They found that electrical stimulation of several regions of the cortex, including auditory, visual, somatic sensory and suprasylvian areas, could serve as the conditioned stimulus. The animal would learn to flex his leg upon presentation of the cortical stimulus.

In view of Penfield's work, it is not surprising that animals can be conditioned to electrical stimulation of the sensory cortex. Patients report buzzing sounds when the auditory cortex is electrically stimulated, light flashes when the visual cortex is stimulated, and tingling in the appropriate body regions when the somatic sensory cortex is stimulated (Penfield and Rasmussen, 1950). The brain stimulus apparently can serve as a conditioned stimulus in a somewhat analogous manner to a peripheral stimulus.

Conditioning studies using cortical stimulation have not in general established the degree of equivalence between peripheral and cortical stimulation. Doty and Rutledge (1959) showed that if animals are conditioned to respond about 60 percent of the time to electrical stimulation of the visual cortex, they will respond to either peripheral visual or auditory stimulation. This does not necessarily imply that electrical cortical stimulation may have more generalized effects than peripheral stimulation. Animals trained and tested with natural peripheral stimuli show similar generalization effects. Thus if initial training to a light CS proceeds only to the 60 percent response level, animals will respond to a tone in subsequent test trials; however, such cross-modal generalization does not occur if animals have received more extensive initial training (Pavlov, 1927; Thompson, 1959). Studies of generalization effects among different locations of cortical electrical stimulation seem consistent with this interpretation. Doty (1965) found that if monkeys were initially trained to respond 95 percent of the time (food reward or shock avoidance conditioning) to electrical stimulation of one point on the cortex, they tended not to respond to stimulation of other regions of cortex, *except* when both training and test electrodes were in the *same* primary sensory area (i.e. visual cortex). Even more specific effects were found by Grosser and Harrison (1960). They found that if care was taken to stimulate electrically two separate populations of cells in the visual cortex, rats well trained to one stimulus would not give generalized responses to the other. However, if the electrical stimulus intensity was increased so that overlapping populations of cells were stimulated in the cortex, behavioral generalization did occur. A great deal more research is needed to ascertain the extent of equivalence relations between peripheral stimulation and electrical stimulation of the sensory cortex.

It would seem that animals can be trained to respond to electrical stimulation of virtually any region of the cerebral cortex. In an extensive study of this problem in the monkey, Doty (1965) was able to establish conditioned responses to every location of cortical stimulation he used, including the prefrontal and

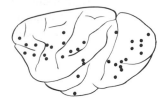

Figure 15.13. Locations (dots) of cortical electrodes used by Doty (1965) as conditioned stimuli in the monkey (Macaque). All were effective. (Redrawn from Doty, 1965, 1965a)

infratemporal association areas (see Figure 15.13). In addition, he found that animals could be trained to respond to stimulation of one location but to not respond to stimulation of another point (i.e. discrimination). If both electrodes were in the visual cortex, animals could discriminate between electrodes less than one mm apart. This finding is consistent with the Grosser and Harrison (1960) study described just above, and of course with the fact that animals can discriminate between peripheral visual stimuli that activate different areas of the retina (i.e. pattern discrimination). Much more unexpected is the finding that monkeys can also discriminate between electrodes placed close together in the so-called "silent" prefrontal association area of the cortex (Doty, 1965a).

The studies described above used brain stimulation as the CS in conditioning. Behavioral responses were evoked by a peripheral shock UCS. Several investigators have stimulated motor regions of the brain to elicit directly behavioral responses. The brain stimulus now serves as the UCS eliciting the UCR. The response is then conditioned to a peripheral sensory stimulus such as a tone or a light. Results of these experiments are somewhat inconsistent. Loucks (1936) was unable to establish a CR to a neutral stimulus using electrical stimulation of the motor cortex as the UCS. Brogden and Gantt (1942) were able to condition leg flexion to a sound using electrical stimulation of the cerebellar cortex. Doty and Giurgea (1958) reported success in establishing a conditioned response using electrical stimulation of the motor region of the cerebral cortex as the UCS. It is worth noting in this connection that the cerebellum and the motor cortex both have extensive sensory afferent projections. The threshold difference between evocation of movement and activation of sensory effects could explain the contrasting findings. Indeed, experiments by Lilly (1958) suggest that in a normal waking monkey movement threshold may be lower than "sensation" threshold to electrical stimulation of the motor cortex. Thus Loucks may have used a weaker stimulus than Doty and Giurgea. However, another report by Doty and Giurgea (1961) suggests that intertrial interval may be the crucial factor in these experiments.

In all of the experiments discussed above, electrical stimulation of the cortex was used as a *stimulus*; the cortical shock served to activate the neurons of the cortex. In a most ingenious experiment, Chow (1961) used cortical shock to reversibly *inactivate* the cortex. Repeated shocks of sufficient strength to induce electrical signs of after-discharge (epileptic-like electrical activity) in the visual cortex of monkeys were used. The animals were trained on visual discrimination problems both with and without paroxsymal cortical shocks. Animals not given electrical shocks learned the problem rapidly, but animals given cortical shocks during training exhibited no signs of learning. If well-trained animals were tested with cortical shocks present, their performance on the discrimination dropped to chance level. In other words, strong seizure-inducing shocks to the visual cortex act like a reversible lesion of the cortex, making it impossible for the animal to learn visual discriminations that normally require the intact visual cortex.

Electrical activity of the cerebral cortex

Study of the electrophysiological correlates of behavior has expanded tremendously in the past few years. Most work in this area does not date back beyond the early 1950s; yet a review article on the subject by Morrell (1961) lists well over 350 references. Three types of behavioral phenomena have been emphasized in most of this work: habituation, attention, and learning. In terms of studies relating electrical activity of the cerebral cortex to behavior, the two most commonly employed measures are EEG activity, particularly the EEG arousal response, and evoked responses.

HABITUATION. Behavioral response habituation is defined simply as a decrease in response as the result of repeated stimulation. It is usually distinguished from receptor adaptation (a decrease in receptor response to a constant stimulus), and from effector fatigue (a decrease limited to the muscle or gland responses). In other words, habituation is generally believed to be a central event. Behavioral response habituation is one of the most common facts of behavior. Virtually all responses elicited by stimuli decline with repeated stimulation (see the extensive review of habituation by Harris, 1943; also Thompson and Spencer, 1966). A common example is the orienting response. If a novel stimulus is presented suddenly, an animal (or man) typically orients toward the source of stimulus (i.e. points appropriate receptors toward it). A variety of changes in autonomic responses such as heart rate, GSR, respiration, etc. also occur (see extensive discussion by Sokolov, 1963). If the stimulus is repeatedly presented orienting responses rapidly decrease or habituate. Habituation is thus a frequent and easily observed change in behavior. Two procedures are commonly used to distinguish habituation from response decrements due to trauma, aging, or other more permanent processes. First, habituated responses spontaneously recover over time if the habituating stimulus is withheld. Second, if, after response to a given stimulus is habituated, a sudden extraneous stimulus is presented, the response to the initial stimulus appears to return to its initial level, i.e. it is "dishabituated." Some authors have characterized habituation as a simple type of "negative learning" (i.e. Hernández-Peón, 1960); certainly response habituation bears many resemblances to the extinction of a conditioned response.

Habituation is indeed a change in behavior as a result of training and thus fits within the general rubric of learning. However, most operational definitions of the various types of learning and conditioning specify a good deal more than simple response decrement. It is perhaps better to include habituation and other forms of changes in behavior within the more general category of *behavioral plasticity*, suggested by William James (1890) and more recently by Konorski (1948).

In early studies in both animals (Rheineberger and Jasper, 1937) and man (Knott and Henry, 1941) the EEG arousal response was observed to decrease upon repeated stimulation. The first investigation of this effect per se was the now classic study by Sharpless and Jasper (1956). Using repeated presentations of brief tones they found that cortical EEG arousal of the normally sleeping cat (recorded through implanted electrodes) becomes progressively shorter and finally disappears. After cessation of stimulation the arousal response exhibits spontaneous recovery over a period of minutes or hours. Furthermore, a strong sudden stimulus that differs markedly from the habituating stimulus will cause dishabituation of the EEG arousal to the original stimulus. One very interesting aspect of Sharpless and Jasper's experiment was the specificity of the EEG arousal habituation in terms of stimulus characteristics. If the EEG arousal response of the sleeping animal was habituated to presentations of a 500-cycle tone to the point at which no arousal at all occurred, a 1,000-cps tone would elicit strong EEG arousal. However, if a 600-cps tone was presented after habituation to the 500-cps tone, no EEG arousal occurred. In behavioral terminology this could be described as an auditory frequency generalization gradient for EEG arousal. In a more recent study. Appelbaum et al. (1959), noted a more restricted generalization gradient for EEG arousal as a function of tone frequency when using waking cats rather than sleeping animals. An example from Sharpless and Jasper's experiment is indicated in Figure 15.14. The human alpha blocking response, which resembles EEG arousal in the cat, has been shown to habituate to tactile, auditory, and visual stimulation by Sokolov and his associates in the Soviet Union (Sokolov, 1960). Experiments by Glickman (1958), Roig and Sommer-Smith (1959), and Glickman and Feldman (1961) have demonstrated that peripheral receptors are probably not involved in habituation of EEG arousal to sensory stimulation. They induced cortical EEG arousal by electrical stimulation through electrodes implanted in the midbrain reticular formation. Under these conditions habituation of EEG arousal occurred just as it did in earlier experiments using tones.

A number of investigators have reported *evoked response* habituation to various types of stimuli at most levels of the CNS, from first-order sensory nuclei to the cerebral cortex. The first experiment to report evoked response habituation was that of Hernández-Peón, Sherrer, and Jouvet (1956, 1957); they recorded responses at several levels of the auditory system to click stimulation. Trains of clocks were delivered once every two seconds for long periods of time and evoked responses of the cochlear nucleus, the midbrain reticular formation,

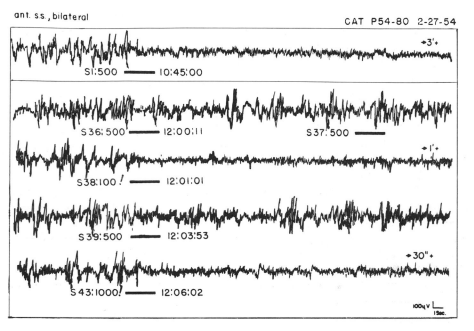

Figure 15.14. Cortical electrograms from the suprasylvian gyrus of a normal cat showing typical habituation of the arousal reaction to a 500-cycle tone after about 30 trials. In the first tracing the response to the first presentation of the 500-cycle tone is shown (SI: 500). The solid bar shows the duration of the stimulus followed by the time in hours, minutes, and seconds (10:45:00). In the second tracing is shown the 36th and 37th trials (S36 and S37). Then a novel tone of 100 cycles is presented in the 38th trial (S38:100!) followed by a repetition of the habituated tone (S39:500) and then another novel tone (S43:1,000!). The figures at the right above the EEG traces indicate the duration of the activation in each trial. (From Sharpless and Jasper, 1956)

and the auditory cortex were observed. The investigators reported that evoked responses at all levels of the auditory system exhibited marked habituation, i.e. evoked response amplitudes decreased markedly during the course of habituation training. An example of their findings for the auditory cortex is shown in Figure 15.15. Other investigators have reported similar findings for auditory evoked responses (Galambos, Sheatz, and Vernier, 1956; Gershuni et al., 1960). On the other hand, Worden and Marsh reported negative results. They have emphasized the importance of controlling stimulus intensity, of demonstrating statistically reliable changes in the response, and of other necessary control procedures not always observed in the studies listed above. Experiments satisfying all these methodological criteria have not in general found any consistent or significant evidence of habituation of auditory-evoked responses in the waking animal (Sharpless and Jasper, 1956; Marsh et al., 1962; Huttenlocher, 1961; Worden and Marsh, 1963).

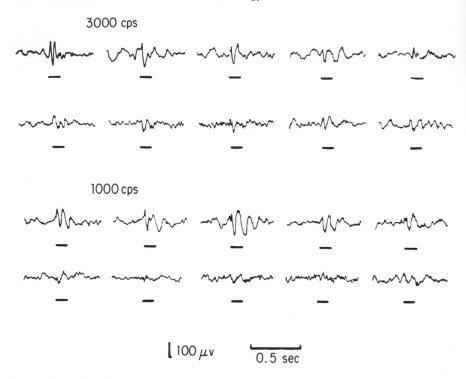

Figure 15.15. Auditory responses in cochlear nucleus. Both series show the decrement observed during 20 successive acoustic stimuli: the upper row are responses to the first 5 stimuli, and the lower row responses to the last 5 successive stimuli in each series. The upper series shows the decrement in response magnitude to a tone of 3000 cycles per second. The lower series shows the responses obtained immediately after, by changing the frequency of the tone to 1000 cycles per second. (From Hernández-Peón, Jouvet, and Sherrer, 1957)

An example of the findings of Worden and Marsh (1963) is shown in Figure 15.16. These data were obtained from the cochlear nucleus rather than the auditory cortex. While there is considerable variability in response amplitude there is no consistent or significant habituation of the evoked response amplitudes. More recently Marsh and Worden (1964) have observed a decline in cortical auditory evoked response amplitudes *when the EEG exhibited arousal,* even in the absence of any consistent response changes at the cochlear nucleus. Webster et al. (1965) reported a rapid initial decrease in the amplitude of sound-burst-evoked responses of the cochlear nucleus that occurred only during the first 30 seconds of stimulation if the sound (20 msec duration) was presented 1/sec or *faster.* No decreases occurred with slower rates of stimulation. (The experiments described above generally presented stimuli slower than 1/sec and examined responses over periods of many minutes or hours). The extent to which this very rapid frequency dependent response decrement can be included as an instance of habituation remains to be determined.

Recent experiments on cortical evoked association responses to auditory stimulation have shown that they do not habituate as a function of repeated presentations (Shaw and Thompson, 1964a; Thompson and Shaw, 1965). A click was presented every two seconds for 74 hours and the evoked association responses sampled at various times during that period. Although there were considerable changes in evoked response amplitude over time, they were not consistent and exhibited no over-all habituating trend.

Head position in the sound field has been shown to be powerful and consistent determiner of auditory evoked response amplitudes (Marsh, Worden, and Hicks, 1962). Contractions of middle ear muscles have been implicated in some studies of auditory evoked response habituation (Guzman-Flores et al., 1960) but denied by other workers (Moushegian et al., 1961). As the evidence stands at present, it is not possible to conclude that habituation of evoked responses to auditory stimulation in the auditory cortex, or for that matter in subcortical areas, is a consistent or reproducible finding.

There have been many reports of habituation of evoked responses from various regions of the visual system to repeated flash stimulation (Hernández-Peón et al., 1958; Palestini et al., 1959). These studies reported quite comparable findings to the early studies of auditory evoked response habituation, namely

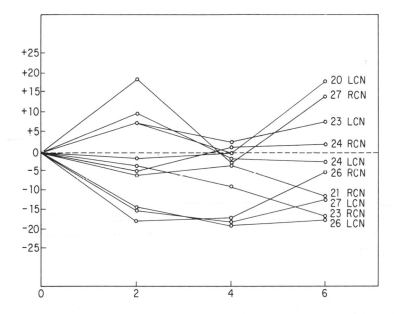

Figure 15.16. Changes in evoked potential amplitudes during a 6-hour habituation run are plotted as percentage changes from the initial (0 h) amplitude. Only bipolar recordings from the alerted animals are included. Each line on the graph represents data from one electrode pair identified by cat number. There is no evidence of habituation. Abbreviations. LCN: left cochlear nucleus. RCN: right cochlear nucleus. (From Worden and Marsh, 1963)

that repeated flash stimulation resulted in a consistent decrement in the amplitude of visual-evoked responses at the visual cortex and at lower regions of the visual system. However, pupil diameter apparently was not controlled in these experiments. Recent experiments by Hess (1965) indicate that pupil diameter is sensitively dependent on behavioral state. Studies utilizing an atropinized eye (atropine produces maximal dilation of the pupil and prevents pupillary constriction), together with an artificial pupil, to produce a constant pupil size have been unable to find consistent or satisfactory evidence of visual-evoked response habituation (Naquet et al., 1960; Affanni et al., 1962). A more recent study, however, does report visual evoked response habituation with controlled pupillary diameter (Garcia et al., 1963). As was the case with auditory evoked response habituation, the literature is replete with contradictory evidence and no consistent conclusions can be drawn at this time. As far as evoked responses to somatic sensory stimulation are concerned, Hernández-Peón et al. (1956) and Hernández-Peón (1960) reported habituation of cortical responses, but Santibeñez et al. (1963) reported no habituation of cortical somatic sensory evoked responses.

To summarize, the evidence for EEG arousal habituation is clear and consistent; it exhibits the same characteristics as does behavioral response habituation and has been obtained by all authors who have investigated it. Studies of evoked responses, on the other hand, permit only one safe generalization at present: there is as yet no agreement regarding the occurrence of evoked response habituation in sensory systems of the waking brain. Where habituation has been reported, it may be the result of decreases in effective stimulus intensity due to alterations in head position, middle ear muscle contractions, pupillary constriction, etc., an indirect result of changes in state of EEG arousal, or a genuine phenomenon. The issue can only be settled by further research.

ATTENTION.   Perhaps the most difficult aspect of research on the neural basis of attention is a satisfactory definition of "attention." Like so many terms in psychology, this word has been borrowed from everyday language and carries with it a good bit of surplus meaning. Ordinary usage of the word "attention" seems to imply some kind of active "focusing of the mind" or "concentration of awareness." Such definitions are clearly unsatisfactory from a behavioral point of view. It is not difficult to give an operational definition in any particular situation for attention; viz., an animal attends to a stimulus when he points his receptors towards it (a cat "looking" at a rat). In human experiments attention is more often defined by the verbal instructions given to the subject. He might be told to "listen to the tone" or "ignore the tone," or may be required to count the number of tones, and so on. The difficulty comes when we try to establish an inferred construct of "attention," particularly of *selective* attention, that will interrelate the different types of operational definitions to one another and to other behavioral constructs (see, however, the ingenious analysis of attention in terms of "observing responses" by Wyckoff, 1952). The reader is urged to consult the review by Deutsch and Deutsch (1963), the symposium on vigilence edited by Buckner and McGrath (1963), and the careful and extensive review by Mackintosh (1965) for discussions of current views of attention.

We examined the relation between EEG arousal and behavioral state at some length in Chapter 14. An early observation in studies involving electrical stimulation of the reticular formation was that when a normal resting or sleeping animal showing EEG spindling was stimulated, the EEG changed to the low voltage fast arousal pattern and the animal gave behavioral signs of arousal such as lifting up his head, opening his eyes, pricking up his ears, and looking about. This general type of observation has been reported in many studies. However, under a variety of other conditions (atropine, paradoxical sleep) there seems to be little correlation between EEG arousal and behavioral arousal. Nonetheless, when a sleeping animal is awakened, both EEG and behavioral arousal occur. In interpreting this correlation, it should be kept in mind that moderate shock to the foot, or for that matter any sudden intense stimulus, will produce the same parallel neural and behavioral events. The effects of reticular stimulation do not necessarily imply that activation of the reticular formation is the unique neural event underlying behavioral alerting.

A great many investigators have studied the relations between "attention" and sensory evoked responses recorded from various regions of the brain. Hernández-Peón, Scherrer, and Jouvet (1956) were the first to report that auditory evoked responses (recorded from the cochlear nucleus to click stimulation in their original experiment) decreased in amplitude when a cat looked at a mouse, smelled fish, or received a forepaw shock (see Figure 15.17). Similar depressions of auditory and visual cortical evoked responses were reported in subsequent studies when the animal was attending to another type or novel or distracting stimulus. Thus, the auditory evoked cortical response decreased when the animal looked at a mouse or smelled fish, and the visual evoked cortical response decreased in amplitude when the animal attended to a novel sound or odor (Hernández-Peón et al., 1957). On the basis of these intriguing findings Hernández-Peón postulated that when the animal attended to a given stimulus, input to other sensory modalities was filtered out or attenuated by peripheral gating mechanisms so that the animal could remain maximally sensitive to input from the attention evoking stimulus.

A possible conclusion from Hernández-Peón's hypothesis is that evoked responses from stimulation of the same modality as the attention arousing stimulus ought to increase in amplitude rather than decrease. Thus, if a cat is given a repeated click and is suddenly shown a mouse, click-evoked responses will go down, but the visual responses evoked by a light flash ought to go up. Horn (1960) tested this possibility in a very careful experiment. He recorded light flash evoked responses from the visual cortex of cats when resting and when watching a mouse. The flash-evoked response amplitude went down rather

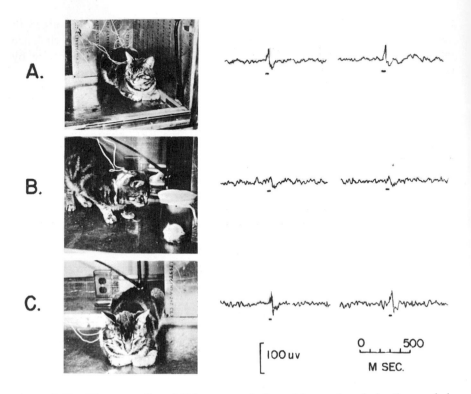

Figure 15.17. Direct recording of click responses in the cochlear nucleus during three periods; the photographs were taken simultaneously. Top and bottom, cat is relaxed; the click responses are large. Middle, while the cat is visually attentive to the mice in the jar, the click responses are diminished in amplitude. (From Hernández-Peón, Scherrer, and Jouvet, 1956)

than up when the animal looked at the mouse (see Figure 15.18). These findings suggest that all modalities of primary cortical evoked responses may decrease in amplitude when an animal attends to any type of novel stimulus.

Measurement of nonspecific evoked cortical association responses has provided further evidence against the hypothesis that attention involves selective depression of irrelevant stimulus modalities and augmentation of activity in the relevant modality (Shaw and Thompson, 1964b; Thompson and Shaw, 1965). Association evoked responses were recorded from the posterior middle suprasylvian gyrus of the normal unrestrained cat (area PMSA in Figure 15.4) to click, light flash, and forepaw shock stimulation. The effects of novel stimuli of all three modalities (sight of a white rat; growling sounds; air jet directed on fur of back) on the evoked responses were measured. Each modality of novel stimulus caused marked and significant depression of cortical association responses evoked by *all* modalities of stimulation. There was no modality selective effect of novel stimuli, but rather a blanket depression of responses evoked by all types of stimuli. This uniform depression of evoked association activity by novel stimuli would seem to suggest a common central mode of action rather than peripheral gating at each type of receptor input. However, the latter possibility cannot be conclusively ruled out.

If it can be assumed that cortical evoked association response amplitudes are inversely proportional to the degree of attention the animal pays to the response evoking stimulus, then the evoked response ought to increase when a stimulus is repeatedly presented (i.e. during habituation training). Numerous behavioral studies have been demonstrated that the degree of behavioral orienting to a stimulus decreases (i.e. habituates) when the stimulus is repeatedly presented (Sokolov, 1960; Robinson and Gantt, 1947). The behavioral orienting response of pointing the receptors towards a stimulus is the most widely accepted operational definition of attention in animals. Consequently, during the first few presentations of a novel stimulus the behavioral orienting response and, hence, "attention" to the novel stimulus will habituate. On the other hand, the cortical

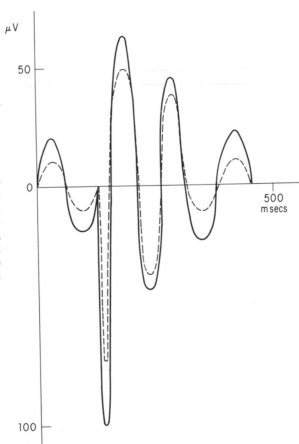

Figure 15.18. Diagrammatic representation of mean evoked response to flash recorded at the visual cortex in 5 unanesthetized cats. Continuous line, control response in relaxed animal; broken line, response as cat watched mouse. (From Horn, 1960)

evoked response amplitude, if it is indeed inversely proportional to degree of attention, ought to increase during the first few presentations of the novel stimulus.

Experiments measuring evoked cortical association responses have supported this hypothesis of an inverse relationship between evoked response amplitudes and attention (Shaw and Thompson, 1964b; Thompson and Shaw, 1966). Cats were given series of individual clicks through either of two speakers on opposite sides of a test cage. The degree of behavioral orienting response to the click was rated, and the cortical association response evoked by the click was simultaneously recorded on film. As shown in Figure 15.19, the behavioral orienting response decreased significantly over trials and the cortical evoked association response increased significantly over the same period of time. The degree of inverse correlation is high; a rank order correlation of −0.70 was obtained between the two variables. Thus, at least for association responses, there does appear to be an inverse relationship between degree of attention to a novel stimulus and the amplitude of the cortical response evoked by the novel stimulus.

Microelectrode studies of single cells in the auditory cortex of the normal unrestrained cat suggest that some cells may be selectively responsive only when the animal is attending. Hubel et al. (1959) reported that some cells in the primary auditory cortex, interspersed among those that regularly respond to tones of given frequency, do not normally respond to any type of stimulation. However, when the cat appeared behaviorally to be "paying attention" to a squeaking sound, these cells would fire. In other words, a given frequency would

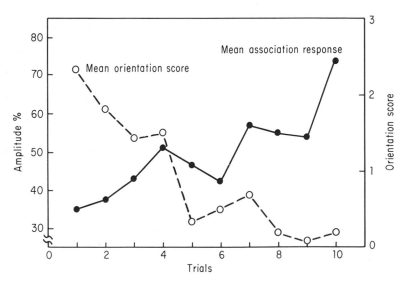

Figure 15.19.   Inverse relationship of cortical association responses and behavioral orienting responses to a series of click stimuli. (From Thompson and Shaw, 1965)

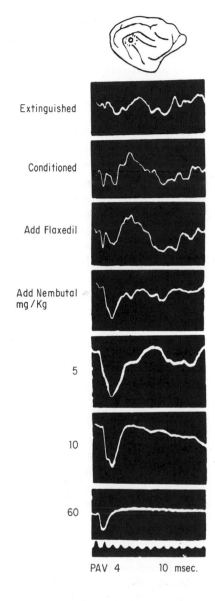

Extinguished

Conditioned

Add Flaxedil

Add Nembutal
mg / Kg

5

10

60

PAV 4   10 msec.

Figure 15.20. Example of a click evoked response recorded from the auditory center of a normal alert cat (top three traces), and the effects of an anesthetic on the response. " Extinguished " and " Conditioned " refer to various experimental procedures, and "Add Flaxedil" indicates little effect of paralyzing agent. (See also Figure 15.24). (From Galambos, 1960)

not fire the cell if the animal appeared to be inattentive, but would fire the cell if the animal appeared to be attending to the stimulus.

In the gross evoked response studies of attention reviewed above, the most common component of the cortical evoked response measured was the initial surface positivity. Examples of a typical gross evoked response from the auditory cortex to click stimulation, in the waking state (upper three tracings) and after Nembutal, are shown in Figure 15.20 (using the positive down convention). Note that there is an initial positivity, a subsequent negativity, then a positivity, and so on, and that the reponse is far more variable in the waking state than in the anesthetized state. Some investigators have emphasized that the later components of the primary sensory evoked response are much more labile and more related to behavioral conditions than is the initial positivity (Marsh et al., 1961). Many of the discrepancies in the "attention" literature could well be due to differences in just what aspect of the evoked response was measured (e.g. baseline to initial positive peak, or positive peak to subsequent negative peak, and so on).

Several investigations of brain responses in humans have indicated that the later components of the sensory evoked response are related to the state of "attention." In experiments of this type electrodes are simply placed on the surface of the scalp and a series of stimuli given. Each individual response contains too much electrical noise to be intelligible. However, a series of such responses are run through an average response computer, which "develops" the response embedded in the background noise. A great deal of caution is necessary in interpreting such averaged evoked responses from the scalp. Remember that the electrode is some distance from the cortex and can record any kind of electrical activity from the head and body. As an example, if scalp-evoked responses are recorded over the auditory area of the cortex to click stimulation, the response shows a short latency component that appears to be muscular in origin rather than neural (Bickford et al., 1963; Mast, 1963). This initial component can be predictably altered by changing the degree of tension of the posterior neck muscles.

Haider, Spong, and Lindsley (1964) investigated the effect of "vigilance" on the amplitude of average scalp evoked responses in humans to light flash. Subjects were given a series of flashes (1/3 sec), most of which were relatively bright, but with dim flashes occasionally interspersed. The vigilance task required the subject to push a key only when the dim flashes were presented. Figure 15.21A compares the average scalp-evoked response to the dim signal flash, both for series when the subject correctly detected the flashes as dim by depressing the key, and where the signal flashes are not detected. Most of the later components of the evoked response are considerably larger with correct detection than with incorrect detection.

Davis (1964) has described a somewhat similar kind of effect using tone-evoked responses recorded from the vertex of the scalp. His subjects were required to discriminate a small change in the intensity of a repeated tone. The tone was given four times in a row. The first presentation was a low frequency warning tone, and the second, third, and fourth tones were all of the same higher pitch and intensity except for a small increase or decrease in the intensity of the third tone. The subject had to determine whether the third tone was louder than the second tone. Examples of average evoked responses to a repeated series of the four tone pattern is shown in Figure 15.21B. Note that the later negative and positive components of the response are much larger to the tone whose intensity had to be discriminated. These findings seem consistent with those of Haider, Spong, and Lindsley described above.

A

Figure 15.21. A, computer-averaged evoked potentials for equal numbers of detected and missed signal stimuli by two subjects. Both subjects show evoked responses of reduced amplitude to the missed signals. (From Haider, Spong, and Lindsley, 1964) **B**, slow responses evoked by auditory stimuli and recorded from the vertex. Tone pips at about 70 dB hearing level were delivered at the start of each trace. The intervals, A–B, B–C, C–D, D–A, were all 2.5 seconds. Responses to 32 cycles were averaged. ΔI (3 dB) was added 10 times and also subtracted 10 times in the "decision" series. (From Davis, 1964)

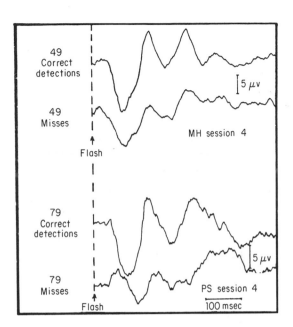

B

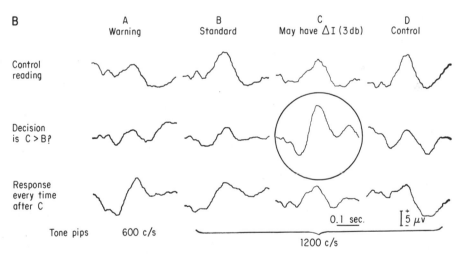

In a more recent experiment, Spong, Haider, and Lindsley (1965) have been able to show differential effects on auditory and visual average evoked responses. They recorded the visual response to light flash from the occipital region of the scalp and the auditory response to click from the temporal region of the scalp. Series of alternating flashes and clicks were given and the Ss required to attend to the flash and ignore the clicks or vice versa ("vigilance" in Figure 15.22), or to press a key for flashes or clicks ("pressing" in the figure) or to count flashes or clicks ("counting"). In the vigilance task the evoked response of the "attended

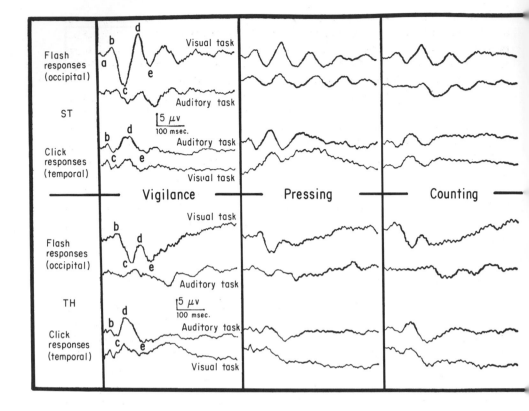

Figure 15.22. Computer-averaged cortical evoked potentials obtained from two subjects in response to flashes and clicks. The potentials were recorded from the occipital and temporal areas while the subjects performed visual and auditory tasks under three experimental conditions: vigilance, key-pressing, and counting. Flashes alternated with clicks throughout. Each trace is the averaged evoked response to 300 stimuli. Analysis time, 500 msec. Recordings: right occipital and temporal areas to left ear: negatively upward. (From Spong, Haider, and Lindsley, 1965)

to" modality is much enhanced compared with the response to the ignored stimulus, particularly for flash-evoked responses. This relative difference favoring the attended stimulus also appears in the other tasks when light flash is the stimulus. Results for click-evoked responses are much less clear-cut.

In summary, it would seem that two quite different kinds of evoked-response changes as a function of "attention" have been reported. Some authors have described a decrease in the initial positive component of the primary sensory evoked response, particularly in animal studies. The initial positive component of the evoked cortical association response to any type of stimulus is virtually abolished when an animal attends to any type of stimulus. On the other hand, the later components of primary sensory evoked responses recorded from the human scalp increase when the subject attends to a response evoking stimulus.

It might appear that the decrease in association evoked response amplitudes and the increase in the later components of the primary response are opposite or contradictory findings. However, this is not necessarily the case. Recent experiments have shown that electrical stimulation of certain regions of the brain can differentially influence cortical evoked primary and association responses. Krauthamur and Albe-Fessard (1965) report that a brief train of electric shocks delivered to portions of the basal ganglia can abolish cortical evoked association responses without altering primary evoked responses in chloralosed animals. Brief repetitive electrical stimulation of the frontal cortex, on the other hand, both abolishes the cortical evoked association responses and *markedly enhances* the later components of the primary evoked responses to auditory, visual, and tactile stimuli (Thompson et al., 1966). Thus a single maneuver can reproduce both types of attention effects: a decrease in association evoked cortical response amplitudes and an increase in the later components of primary sensory cortical evoked responses.

Learning: EEG alpha blocking

Investigations of the relations between electrical measures of brain activity and learning represent one of the most vigorous and rapidly growing fields in the study of brain and behavior. Indeed the neural basis of learning has long been considered by many to be *the* fundamental problem in physiological psychology. Most studies have been concerned with the electrical activity of the cerebral cortex, particularly with EEG arousal and evoked responses. Two quite different approaches to the problem have been used. The more direct but less common method has been simply to record brain activity during the course of a standardized learning experiment, usually either classical or instrumental conditioning. Much more frequently the brain activity itself has been used as the response to be conditioned. Thus if stimulus S_1 elicits some kind of neural activity such as EEG arousal, a neutral stimulus, S_2, is paired with S_1 until S_2 alone elicits EEG arousal. This latter method has been characterized as "sensory-sensory conditioning" or "neural conditioning" because no behavioral responses or measures are used; stimuli are presented and brain activity is recorded. We will use the somewhat neutral term "EEG conditioning" here.

EEG conditioning was first reported by Durup and Fessard (1935). They observed that when a camera shutter click had been paired with a light flash, the latter being used to induce EEG alpha block, the click alone could serve to block alpha activity. While there is not complete agreement concerning the comparability of EEG spindling in the cat or dog and EEG alpha in man (see discussion in Chapter 9), it is probably possible to compare "EEG arousal" in the experimental animal with "EEG alpha blocking" in humans. We will consider both animal studies in which EEG arousal was conditioned and human studies in which EEG alpha blocking was conditioned.

Durup and Fessard's procedure has served as the prototype for most subsequent experiments on EEG conditioning. A typical human experiment might be carried out as follows (see Figure 15.23). Subjects exhibiting good alpha activity are selected (usually about 1/3 of normal adults show clear alpha activity). During the experiment the various stimuli are presented only at times when the EEG shows clear alpha activity. The response to be conditioned is blocking of this alpha activity by the stimuli; the blocking appears as a sudden shift from alpha waves to the low voltage fast activity of EEG arousal. A steady or flickering light is commonly used as the UCS; presentation of the light during a period of EEG alpha activity produces alpha blocking. A tone is commonly used as the CS. One problem in EEG conditioning is the fact that intitially almost any type of stimulus causes alpha blocking. Thus the first few presentations of the tone CS alone will cause alpha blocking, the response to be conditioned to the tone! Consequently a series of habituation trials of tone presentation are always given before the conditioning procedure itself. The tone is repeatedly presented until it no longer causes alpha blocking. Tone is then paired with light for a series of trials, and the tone is then given alone in a series of test trials. Typically, with these procedures, after paired presentations of tone and light, the tone alone will cause alpha blocking in a large proportion of cases.

Many investigators have termed this result conditioning of the alpha blocking response. However, since the days of the early experiments on EEG conditioning, dissenting opinions have been voiced (Diamond and Chow, 1962; Knott, 1941; Lilly, 1958; Stern et al., 1961; Weiss, 1955). Certainly in terms of the traditional definitions of psychology, the prototype experiment described above is *not sufficient* to demonstrate conditioning. A common observation in early conditioning experiments was the occurrence of sensitization or pseudoconditioning (see discussion by Hilgard and Marquis, 1940). Whenever a strong UCS is first given many otherwise neutral stimuli will tend to elicit the response produced by the

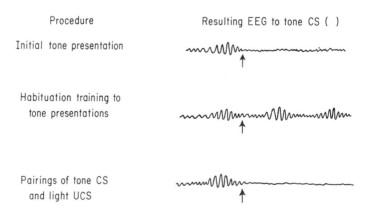

Figure 15.23.   Typical conditions used in human EEG "conditioning." A series of tones is presented, unpaired with light, until tone alone does not cause alpha blocking. Tone and light are then paired for a few trials until alpha blocking is again elicited by tone.

UCS. In GSR conditioning, for example, after a few strong shocks to the skin, most subjects will show palm sweating to any and all stimuli that are given. This sensitization does not depend upon pairing of the CS and UCS, and is probably due to an increased level of arousal or excitement of the subject resulting from the strong shock UCS. The essential aspect of conditioning is that the CS comes to elicit the "conditioned response" as a result of the *pairing* of the CS and the UCS.

The standard method used in traditional conditioning experiments to demonstrate that conditioning rather than sensitization occurred is to give a mixed or alternating series of CS and UCS presentations without actually pairing the two. This is often called a backward conditioning control group: the UCS is given before the CS in the series. Alternatively, a series of trials in which the UCS alone is presented has often been used to test the possibility of sensitization. Under either of these conditions, true conditioning does not occur. In the GSR example, if tone is alternated with skin shock, the GSR does not become conditioned to the tone. After a long alternating control series, the initial "excitement" produced by the UCS tends to habituate out, and the tone CS will not elicit a GSR. In the same way, a long series of skin shocks alone will not result in a conditioned GSR to tone. The initial excitement to the shock habituates out. However, if the tone and skin shocks are paired for a number of trials, then the conditioned GSR response to the tone does develop. To return to EEG conditioning, in order to demonstrate that the alpha blocking property acquired by the tone after pairing of tone and light is conditioning rather than sensitization, either a backward control group or a group given a series of UCS trials alone is necessary. Unfortunately the majority of experiments on conditioned alpha blocking have not used this rather crucial control group.

There were a number of rather thorough early studies on EEG conditioning; we might cite as examples the studies of Travis and Egan (1938), Knott and Henry (1941), and Jasper and Shagass (1941). We will discuss some aspects of Jasper and Shagass's experiment; it illustrates many of the typical findings of subsequent experiments. They used 24 male college students, all of whom were selected as showing good EEG alpha activity. Electrodes were glued to the scalp overlying the occipital region of the cortex. The CS (500-cps tone) was presented a few times in order to habituate alpha blocking. Tone was then paired with light, both stimuli lasting about 5 seconds, with tone beginning about 0.7 seconds before light. Occasional test trials of tone alone were interspersed. However, the conditioned alpha blocking could be seen in regular trials: the alpha blocking latency to light was about 0.5 seconds, and after pairing tone and light, the alpha blocking to tone appeared with about the same latency, 0.5 seconds. Thus conditioned alpha blocking to tone occurred before the onset of the light stimulus and could be idenified as such. They observed conditioned responses beginning in about the tenth trial of pairing. Trials were presented at irregular intervals to avoid temporal conditioned responses. Although no quantitative analyses were presented, they report that the conditioned response was not very stable, appearing in some trials but not on others. If the light was omitted after conditioning, and the tone presented alone, extinction occurred in as few as three trials.

It is of considerable interest in view of our discussion of sensitization that Jasper and Shagass ran backward conditioning control groups. If the light preceded the tone by several seconds and the two stimuli overlapped, backward conditioning was easily obtained. On the other hand, if the two stimuli did not overlap at all, no backward conditioning developed. Interpretation of this finding is unfortunately ambiguous. They required the Ss (subjects) to push a button whenever the tone was given in the backward procedure when it was not paired with light. In all other procedures (paired presentations) the subject was required to push the button when the *light* occurred. The differential effects of this motor response cannot be evaluated. Jasper and Shagass also described "temporal conditioning": if a 5-second light was presented at regular intervals, the alpha blocking response tended to occur even on trials when the light was omitted. In addition, they reported delayed and trace conditioned responses. One of Jasper and Shagass's most interesting findings was the establishment of a differential conditioned response. Subjects were first conditioned to show alpha blocking to a 500 cps tone. A 400 cps tone was then introduced without light and alternated with paired light—500 cps trials. Alpha blocking continued to the 500-cps tone but extinguished to the 400-cps tone.

In the time since Jasper and Shagass's experiment there have been in the neighborhood of 100 experiments reporting conditioned alpha blocking. Some of the better known experiments, in addition to those mentioned above, include Cruikshank, 1937; Jasper and Cruikshank, 1937; Motakawa, 1949; Morrell and Ross, 1953; Morrell and Jasper, 1956; Livanov and Poliakov, 1945; Jus and Jus, 1959; Gastaut, 1957; and Wells, 1959. Surveys of this literature may be found in Morrell (1961), Glaser (1963), Diamond and Chow (1962), and Delafresmaye (1961). In many of the experiments in which conditioned alpha blocking is reported, no backward control group was used to evaluate the possibility that sensitization had occurred.

A rather interesting variation of EEG conditioning involves attempts to condition the abnormal EEG activity of epileptic patients. Gastaut et al. (1956) reported some success in conditioning the spike-wave epileptic discharge pattern in two patients. However, in a more extensive investigation, Stevens (1960) was unable to condition spike-wave patterns elicited by photic driving. Stevens (1962) also attempted to condition such patients to respond to their own abnormal EEG activity. She found that as long as the patients could hear the auditory cue of the spike-wave pattern from the EEG machine (during spike-wave discharges the pen noise increases considerably) they could respond. However when this auditory cue was eliminated only one of the 10 subjects was able to respond to the occurrence of his own paroxsysmal EEG activity.

In evaluating the current status of EEG conditioning, several problems that are somewhat unique to this field must be considered. These might be listed as follows: (1) What strength of conditioning can be established? (2) Is it conditioning or sensitization? (3) What is implied by the fact that the response to be conditioned to the CS is initially elicited by the CS? and (4) Does the conditioned alpha response become better established with long-term training?

1. Concerning the strength of conditioned alpha blocking, most studies agree with Jasper and Shagass's observation that it is weak and variable. Shagass and Johnson (1943) obtained it in 6 of 12 subjects; Loomis et al. (1936) observed the effect only a few times; Travis and Egan (1938) found it in only 34 percent of stimulus presentation. In short, among the earlier experiments, in the few situations in which quantitative analyses were made, EEG conditioning was infrequent and variable. In a recent study designed to evaluate this aspect of the phenomenon Albino and Burnand (1964) concluded that "these experiments support the view of Knott (1941) that there is only tenuous evidence for conditioning of the alpha rhythm to tone."

2. In a recent carefully designed experiment, Milstein (1965) specifically evaluated the possibility that sensitization training will produce a "conditioned" alpha blocking response. Subjects were first habituated to a tone and then given 40 presentations of a light alone, and then tested to the tone during periods of alpha activity. Fifty-seven percent of the subjects gave 79 percent alpha blocking to the test tones. All subjects were then rehabituated to the tone and given 40 paired presentations of tone and light. They were again tested to the tone during periods of alpha. Now 57 percent of the subjects showed 88 percent alpha blocking responses. There is no significant difference between the initial light-only condition and the light-tone paired condition. A control group that was not given light but merely waited after tone habituation did not show alpha blocking to the subsequent tone, suggesting that light presentation was the crucial variable. The levels of sensitizated alpha blocking obtained by Milstein, in the initial condition in which light and tone were not paired, were actually higher than in many of the early experiments purporting to demonstrate conditioned alpha blocking. In short, Milstein's experiment provides rather suggestive evidence that "conditioned alpha blocking" may not be conditioning at all, but rather an example of sensitization.

3. Conditioned alpha blocking has often been questioned because of the necessity for initial habituation of the blocking response to tone CS. This criticism, per se, is probably less troublesome than the evidence indicating that conditioned alpha blocking may instead be sensitization. A great many types of conditioned responses are initially elicited to some degree or another by the CS prior to conditioning. This is particularly true for autonomic indices like the GSR, salivation and heart rate. However it also seems partially true for striated muscle responses, at least in the sense that the organism usually makes postural orienting responses to any new stimulus. Perhaps more crucial is the fact that in most conditioning experiments the CR gradually becomes larger or stronger than the initial unconditioned response to the CS. However, in alpha blocking, the response can get no smaller than to block completely. Hence it is usually not

possible to show an increase in the conditioned alpha blocking response over and above the initial blocking produced by the first presentations of the CS.

4.   Finally, there is the somewhat anomalous finding that as more and more paired tone-light conditioning trials are given, alpha blocking tends to become weaker rather than stronger (Knott and Henry, 1941). This observation would seem to be more consistent with the view that conditioned alpha blocking is really sensitization rather than conditioning.

In sum, if the EEG alpha blocking response to tone is habituated, and a series of paired tone-lights presented, the alpha blocking response to tone reappears, albeit somewhat variably. All studies are consistent in reporting this observation. However, if only a series of lights are presented instead of tone-light pairings the alpha blocking response also reappears. Consequently, it would seem that conditioned alpha blocking resembles sensitization more closely than it resembles conditioning. This is *not* to say that the phenomenon is uninteresting and undeserving of careful and extensive investigation. It is clearly a reversible change in the behavior of an index of neural activity as a result of experience or training. The degree and specificity of the changes that can be induced in alpha blocking, as exemplified in the careful and extensive study of Jasper and Shagass (1941), emphasize this point.

A number of experimenters have analyzed changes in EEG arousal during the course of actual behavioral conditioning (see review by Morrell, 1961). Beck, Doty, and Kooi (1958), for example, measured EEG arousal from several cortical areas in cats during leg flexion conditioning. The EEG arousal response to the CS (500-cps tone) was first habituated, as in human alpha blocking studies. Animals were then given bulbocapnine to reduce behavioral activity and increase the frequency of EEG spindling. A classical conditioning procedure was used: paired tone-shock presentations were given until the response occurred to the onset of tone. EEG arousal occurred in all cortical leads during the first few conditioning trials, long before the behavioral response developed. With over-training the EEG arousal response diminished, even though the behavioral CR (leg flexion) was maintained. Yoshii et al. (1958) obtained a similar rapid appearance of the habituated EEG arousal response in both salivary (to food) and leg flexion (to shock) conditioning procedures. However, they reported that the EEG arousal response was maintained throughout the course of behavioral conditioning. Chow (1961) completed an extensive and careful analysis of EEG arousal changes in the temporal lobe during learning of visual discriminations by monkeys. His findings were somewhat disappointing. Only transient EEG arousal occurred and only during the initial acquisition phase of the experiment. Morrell (1961) concludes on the basis of a survey of the literature that EEG arousal is more widespread on the cortex during initial stages of training and gradually becomes limited to the sensory cortical field of the CS (i.e. auditory cortex for tone CS) and also to the motor cortex if the CS serves to elicit a motor response.

The most general finding of such studies has been that EEG arousal occurs at the beginning of learning, but tends to disappear as learning proceeds. *There*

is no close correlation between the degree of EEG arousal and the degree of learning.
In this connection we might recall the studies of Bradley (see Chapter 14, and
Key and Bradley, 1959) in which animals with permanent EEG synchrony
(spindling), induced by prior administration of atropine, exhibited normal
learning in several types of learning situations. EEG arousal is not a necessary
concomitant of learning, nor is it very closely correlated with degree of learning
(see also Chow, Dement, and John, 1957).

Learning: evoked responses

The general picture of cortical evoked response changes associated with
learning resembles the EEG literature in many ways. Results of most studies
are consistent in indicating that on the first few paired CS–UCS conditioning
trials cortical evoked responses to the CS increase markedly in amplitude, at
least in situations in which the unconditioned stimulus is shock or other aversive
stimulation. As in EEG studies there have been two types of conditioning
procedures: "sensory-sensory" in which the evoked response amplitude itself
serves as the conditioned response, and conventional conditioning studies in
which evoked responses are also measured.

An experiment by Galambos, Sheatz, and Vernier (1956) was one of the
first to report conditioned changes in evoked responses, and is a prototype of
many subsequent experiments. Electrodes were implanted in auditory and visual
areas of the cortex and a variety of subcortical regions in cats. The animals were
given loud clicks once every 3 seconds for a period of days until the evoked
response was reported to have habituated. A series of about ten strong shocks
to the chest were then paired with clicks. Evoked response amplitudes increased
markedly. If the shocks were then withheld the response to click diminished to
the initial level. Examples of their data are shown in Figure 15.24. Repeated
series of conditioning and extinction were obtained. Conditioning was also
established in animals paralyzed with Flaxedil and artificially respirated. This
control rules out the possibility of muscular response artifacts in the data.

In extensive subsequent experiments, Galambos and colleagues have demonstrated the increase in evoked response amplitudes in cats after air puffs to the
face were paired with clicks in cats (Marsh et al., 1961). A careful statistical
analysis of the data indicated that during paired click-puff trials the evoked
responses to clicks in nonauditory structures (caudate nucleus, hippocampus,
field *H* of Forel, and intralaminar thalamic nuclei) increased more than did
responses in auditory cortex and subcortical auditory pathways. However,
responses from virtually all areas increased significantly during pairings.

There have been numerous experiments of this type in which the effects on
neural-evoked responses of pairing a response-evoking stimulus such as a click
or a flash with shock or other aversive stimulus have been studied. Historically
the first experiment in this field was probably done by the Soviet scientists
Artemyev and Bozladnova (1952). Some of the better known experiments, in
addition to those described just above, include Jouvet and Hernández-Peón

EXTINGUISHED CONDITIONED

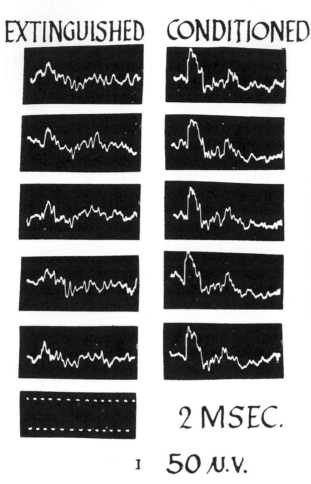

2 MSEC.

I 50 N.V.

Figure 15.24. Cochlear nucleus responses to successive identical click stimuli before ("extinguished") and after ("conditioned") application of three shocks to a cat. The increase in response magnitude after shocks as noted here was observed eight times in this animal. (From Galambos, Sheatz and Vernier, 1955)

(1957), Galambos (1958), and Beck, Doty, and Kooi (1958). The general consensus of such experiments is that when the click or other neutral response evoking stimulus is paired with shocks there tends to be an increase in the amplitude of the evoked response. In general, it is the later components of gross evoked responses, particularly cortical responses, that exhibit the greatest degree of change. It must be emphasized that in most experiments no attempts were made to ascertain whether the evoked response increase reflected a conditioning process or a sensitization process. The reader may consult Morrell (1961) and Galambos and Morgan (1960) for extensive reviews of the literature.

There are several experiments oriented more toward correlating the changes in neural evoked responses with measures of behavioral conditioning. There have been two general types of such experiments, one type using single conditioned stimuli to elicit single evoked responses in the brain, and the other using a repeated stimulus such as a flickering light to produce a train of responses. An example of the single stimulus method is experiment by Hearst et al. (1960). Monkeys with chronic recording electrodes implanted in a variety of brain regions were given several types of behavioral training procedures, including a simple operant response for food reinforcement, differential training using shock for negative reinforcement, and both negative and positive reinforcement operant discrimination procedures. The details of their experiments are rather complex. In general they reported that during the early stages of learning, particularly when negative reinforcement was involved, evoked responses were large. As learning became well established evoked response amplitude tended to decline. In operant training situations evoked responses declined to low levels.

In an interesting experiment by Buchwald, Halas, and Schramm (1966), the technique of integrating massed unit discharges (see Chapter 3) was employed to measure amount of nerve discharge activity during the course of conditioning. They implanted small (50μ tip) steel electrodes in several locations in the auditory pathway and cortex (a tone CS was used), in the somatic sensory pathway and cortex (they used a hindpaw shock UCS), and in the reticular formation, and recorded unit hash activity during classical conditioning of the hindlimb flexion reflex in normal cats. They reported that activity in response to the tone CS increased in the auditory system and reticular formation when the UCS was first given, and continued to increase during training. In contrast, little or no activity was present in the somatic sensory system in response to the CS prior to the appearance of overt conditioned responses. No backward conditioning controls were used to investigate possible sensitization effects in this situation.

John and Killam (1959) utilized a repetitive light flashing at a rate of 10/sec as a "trace label" to identify the occurrence of a CS-evoked repetitive response in various areas of the brain. Cats with electrodes in a variety of cortical and subcortical regions were conditioned to respond in an instrumental shock avoidance situation. John and Killam report that initial presentations of the flashing light alone caused repetitive neural responses at most electrode loci. With repeated presentations of the flashing light alone the responses tended to disappear in all areas, including the visual cortex. When shock avoidance training commenced, repetitive responses reappeared at most regions, including the cortex. As conditioning proceeded the repetitive response again began to wane in most areas.

Results similar to many of those described above have been obtained in a variety of other studies (Roitbak, 1960; Morrell, Noquet, and Gastaut, 1957; Grastýan et al., 1959; etc.). Further references may be found in Morrell (1961) and Galambos and Morgan (1960). At the risk of seeming repetitious, it must be emphasized that in most instances these experiments did not include control groups to evaluate the possibility that the neural response changes might reflect sensitization rather than conditioning. To take a simplified example, suppose an animal is trained to flex his leg to avoid shock whenever a click occurs. In view of the experiments cited above, it is likely that the click-evoked response of the auditory cortex will increase in amplitude in the first few pairings of click and shock. Then as the leg flexion response becomes well learned the click evoked response will diminish. What would happen if instead of pairing click and shock, shocks were given either just before or between click presentations? If the click-evoked response increased in amplitude in this backward control procedure, the increase would be an example of sensitization rather than conditioning. The fact that in most experiments cited above the evoked response amplitude declined as the behavioral response became well established would seem more consistent

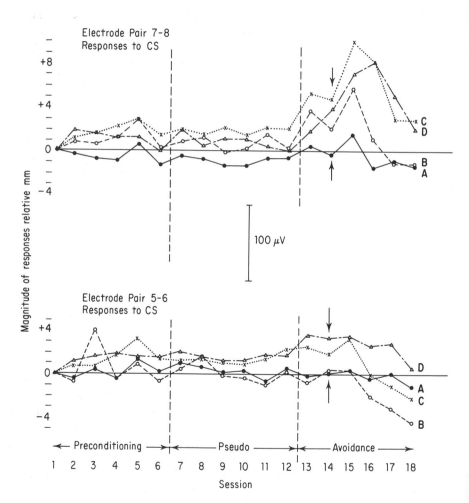

Figure 15.25. Changes in various components of evoked responses recorded from auditory cortex of the cat during preconditioning, pseudoconditioning, and avoidance conditioning. A, B, C and D represent the first 4 peak-to-peak measures of the auditory evoked response (see Figure 15.23). There are no consistent changes in response components in avoidance vs pseudoconditioning. (From Gerken and Neff, 1963)

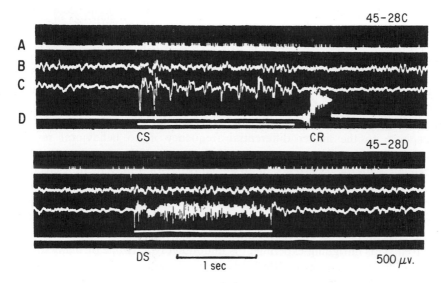

Figure 15.26.   Two records of the same single nerve cell in parietal association cortex. Above, unit firing is increased and driven by the CS; below, unit is inhibited by the differential stimulus. A, microelectrode data; **B**, surface record from parietal cortex; **C**, surface record from occipital cortex; **D**, EMG and switch signal (CR). (From Jasper, Ricci and Doane, 1958)

with a sensitization hypothesis than with a conditioning hypothesis. Several investigators have suggested that the cortical evoked response changes during conditioning may indeed reflect more a changing level of attention or arousal than an actual correlate of the learning process itself (see Diamond and Chow, 1962; Morrell, 1961).

A very carefully controlled experiment by Gerken and Neff (1963) provides rather strong support for the sensitization hypothesis. They trained cats in leg flexion shock conditioning to a sound. Both the CS (4000-cps click train) and a single click test stimulus were used to evoke responses recorded in the auditory cortex. Subgroups of animals were given presentations of the CS alone followed by avoidance conditioning, pseudoconditioning (control for sensitization) and classical conditioning (shock unavoidable). They found no systematic relationship between the magnitude of the cortical evoked response and the presence or absence of a conditioned response. During both conditioning training and pseudoconditioning control series the evoked response tended to increase comparably in amplitude (see Figure 15.25). In brief, the increase in evoked response amplitude was not a reflection of the conditioning procedure per se, but rather of the introduction of the aversive stimulus.

Jasper, Ricci, and Doane (1958; 1960) completed a very comprehensive study of single nerve cell discharges during the course of shock avoidance conditioning in monkeys. A flashing light served as the CS and hand shock as the UCS. The animal could avoid shock by withholding his hand when the light occurred. The monkeys were maintained in "living" chairs arranged in such a way that they could not reach the chronically implanted electrode equipment. Cell discharges from the motor cortex and the parietal cortex were studied during the development of a conditioned response and a differential response (shock avoidance for the 10/sec light but no shock for a higher frequency light flash). Cells studied in the motor cortex tended to increase their firing rates prior to and during the actual occurrence of a conditioned hand withdrawal. Cell activity did not change in response to the higher differential frequency if no behavioral response occurred. Thus, as might be expected, cell discharges of the motor cortex tended to correlate with the occurrence of an actual behavioral movement. Cells of the parietal cortex, in contrast tended to increase discharge rates during the CS period of the trial when a CR was given, but not during the actual occurrence of the CR (see Figure 15.26). On the other hand, they tended to be inhibited during presentation of the differential stimulus when no behavioral response was given. This intriguing experiment is undoubtedly only one of many to come in which the analytic power of the microelectrode approach is used to study the specific behavior of single cells in the brain during the course of learning.

CONCLUDING REMARKS

Much of our information about the possible functions of various cortical regions has come from lesion studies. This approach may be likened to determining the organization and functions of a complex piece of electronic equipment by smashing various portions of it with a hammer. It is necessary to be extremely cautious in drawing conclusions from lesion studies. Merely because a given type of behavior cannot be learned after ablation of a piece of cortex does not mean that the learning occurs in this region of the cortex. The brain is a complex system of interconnections. Some regions appear necessary for certain behavioral functions (i.e. visual area for pattern vision) but these behavioral functions would normally seem likely to involve a great many regions of the brain.

Lashley's classical search for the engram (1929) is an excellent illustration of the difficulty in localizing "centers" in the brain controlling particular types of behavior. He studied the effect of various cortical lesions on the ability of rats to learn three mazes of varying complexity. No single region of the cortex was more important than another, the critical variable being amount of cortex removed. The more cortex removed the greater the deficit, the amount of deficit being disproportionately great for complex mazes. These are approximate statements of his two principles of *mass action* (amount is crucial) and *equipotentiality* (region unimportant).

Lashley's results apply to complex learning involving multiple sensory cues. We noted above that a variety of tests involving single stimulus modalities or particular types of behavior (i.e. delayed response) are critically affected by lesions in certain regions of the cortex. It is difficult to jump from such statements to conclusions about the function of a given cortical region. A good example is the effect of removing auditory cortex on frequency discrimination (see Chapter 11). If one type of training procedure is used, frequency discrimination is permanently lost. It is easy to leap from this observation to the conclusion that the auditory cortex is essential for frequency discrimination, and to the final conclusion that the auditory cortex functions as a frequency discriminator. However, with another type of training procedure frequency discrimination is not impaired. The conclusion here might be that the auditory cortex has nothing much to do with frequency discrimination. Both conclusions are clearing wrong. The deficit is more complex than the category "frequency discrimination."

Strict adherence to operational definition is of considerable help in describing the results of brain-lesion studies. Thus we would not say that a given experiment demonstrates loss of frequency discrimination following lesion, but rather loss of frequency discrimination defined by a given method of training. Immediate memory loss following prefrontal lesions is another case in point. Immediate memory defined in terms of a certain set of conditions (delayed response testing with or without an opaque screen during delay, separation of test and reward objects, etc.) is impaired, not immediate memory in general. Terms like "frequency discrimination" and "immediate memory" are categories imposed on the experimental situation by the investigator. There is no reason to suppose that regions of the cerebral cortex function in terms of the arbitrary word categories of the English language.

The kinds of conclusions obtainable from lesion studies are very clearly of the *intervening variable* sort. Certain functions are hypothetically assigned to pieces of brain, and various lesion-behavior procedures used to test the validity of the hypotheses. The jump from operationally defined results to hypotheses is usually rather great (see discussion by Pribram, 1962). This level of intervening variable analysis is quite comparable to Hull's theoretical analysis of behavior, being only slightly more molecular (pieces of brain rather than the entire organism are related to behavior). The hypothetico-deductive method has been applied to lesion-behavior data only rarely (see however Pribram, 1960). Generally, theories of brain function based on lesion data are stated in rather descriptive terms taken from ordinary English. It seems likely that the over-all conclusions about brain function will remain somewhat unclear until more rigorous theoretical analyses are developed.

The rapidly growing body of literature concerned with relations between electrical activity and behavioral variables reviewed earlier in the chapter deserves some comment here. The considerable number of contradictory reports and ambiguous interpretations are probably more symptomatic of a new and vigorous field of research than indicative of any basic defect in the approach. It seems likely that in a very few years it will be possible to catalog the essential types of changes in the gross electrical activity of brain structures that accompany the various categories of behavioral phenomena. A more fundamental interpretive problem concerns the nature of the neuronal events and synaptic processes underlying these gross indices of brain activity. At present, it is not possible to determine with any degree of certainty what types of neurons and neuron processes behave in what ways to yield gross evoked responses or EEG activity, even under the best conditions. The positive component of a primary sensory evoked response, for example, may represent excitatory synaptic activity, inhibitory activity, or several different types of synaptic actions all summed together. It is to be hoped that both extra-cellular and intracellular microelectrode analyses of cortical neuron activity accompanying learning will be increasingly utilized in the future. A combination of gross and microelectrode approaches may well provide some necessary keys to the fundamental problems of brain function and learning.

It has been possible to draw a few general and admittedly imprecise conclusions concerning the probable functions of the cerebral cortex. Following Pavlov's dictum it was believed for many years that the cerebral cortex was the seat of all learning. However subsequent research has demonstrated that totally decorticate animals (dogs and cats) can learn (Bromiley, 1948; Lebedinskaia and Rosenthal, 1935). Such learning may even be of a relatively discriminable nature, i.e. differential response to a light and a sound (Bromiley, 1948). More complex learning does seem to require the cerebral cortex, at least in higher mammals (birds of course learn very well with essentially no cerebral cortex). Unfortunately there has been far too little research yet on the capacities of total decorticate mammals, particularly primates, for us to define the limits with any degree of precision.

Studies by Lashley, and by Sperry and colleagues, suggest that the functional organization of the cortex tends to be " vertical " rather than " horizontal," Thus, vertical cuts between sensory and motor regions appear not to impair behavior at all (Lashley, 1950). Similarly, cross-hatched vertical cuts made through the visual cortex do not affect visual pattern discrimination (Sperry et al., 1955). These findings are consistent with electrophysiological studies showing that vertically arranged regions of cortex are activated by given kinds of stimuli. Mountcastle's demonstration of columnar representation for submodalities of somatic sensory stimulation in the somatic cortex is a striking example of this vertical organization (see discussion in Chapter 11).

Recent microelectrode studies of sensory cortex have raised the possibility that earlier attempts to correlate detailed cytoarchitechtonic parcellation of cortical areas with behavioral functions may have been dismissed too cavalierly. Thus Hubel and Wiesel (1965) found that in the visual cortex of the cat, cells in areas 17, 18, and 19 tend to respond to progressively more complex aspects of visual stimuli (see discussion in Chapter 11). In the primate somatic sensory cortex there appears to be a differentiation of submodalities in terms of areas 1, 2, and 3 (Welker, W. I., personal communication; see Chapter 11). Parcellations of the posterior association cortex of the primate in terms of lesion deficits on complex sensory and learning tasks (see Pribram, 1960) are suggestive in this context. It is possible that more detailed correspondences will be found to exist between histological characteristics of association cortex and behavioral functions.

Developmental aspects of cortical function have received considerable attention. Hebb (1949) stressed two types of seemingly complementary observations: First, large cortical lesions in adult humans have little effect on complex behavior such as IQ test performance, and second, visual deprivation during development produces severe deficits in the visual performance of adults following restoration of sight (see Riesen, 1947; Hebb, 1949). On the basis of these and other types of data he emphasized the importance of sensory stimulation during development in the formation of neural substrates subserving the more complex perceptual and learning aspects of performance. Studies comparing the effects of cortical lesions in infant and adult animals do not in general appear to support such an interpretation. Kennard (1938) showed that ablations of motor cortex in infant monkeys had much less damaging effects on subsequent adult performance than did lesions in adults. Similar data are available for somatic sensory and visual cortex (Benjamin and Thompson, 1959; Doty, 1961, see Chapter 11). Even the type of performance involved in delayed response shows comparable effects. Infant monkeys with prefrontal lesions in infancy show little subsequent deficit, whereas adult animals with such lesions are markedly impaired (Harlow, Akert, and Schiltz, 1964). It must, however, be emphasized that these experiments have not for the most part considered the more complex aspects of performance. Further, early and/or extensive sensory experience may be crucial in allowing recovery of function mediated by undamaged portions of the CNS.

Recent experiments by Hubel and Wiesel (1963 a, b, c) have raised serious questions concerning the role of sensory stimulation in the development of the neural substrates of "complex perception." We noted earlier that cells in the visual cortex of the cat respond to highly complex, organized aspects of the visual field such as form and movement. These would seem to be the types of relations that ought to develop through experience, if visual "perception" is indeed learned. Hubel and Wiesel found that neurons in the cortex of the newborn kitten respond to the same complex aspects of stimuli as in adults. Varying periods of light deprivation following birth caused *regressive* changes in the degree of organized responsiveness. The term "perception," incidentally, is difficult to define precisely to the mutual satisfaction of all psychologists. It usually refers to response (such terms can only be defined in terms of responses) to more complex or "learned" aspects of stimuli such as "straightness" or "roundness". The studies by Hubel and Wiesel clearly show that cells in the visual cortex already respond to complex or perceptual aspects of stimuli at birth, before visual experience can play any significant role. Visual deprivation after birth does not prevent the development of complex perception; instead it produces deteriorative and regressive changes in the pre-existing complex neural organization.

Comparison of electrophysiological data, particularly from recent micro-electrode studies, with various aspects of behavioral performance suggests a very tentative generalization; namely that the cerebral cortex may be the *final common path for behavioral response tendency*. This has been strikingly evident in psychophysical studies. Mountcastle and his colleagues (Mountcastle et al., 1963) have shown that response patterns of neurons in the cerebral cortex are related to stimuli by the same power function equation that Stevens (1961) found to relate stimulus intensity and behavioral response in psychophysical judgment. Jung (1961) demonstrated clear parallels between single cell responses in the visual cortex and a variety of visual psychophysical phenomena. Bartley (1939) showed the interrelations of brightness enhancement and the alpha rhythm. Hubel and Wiesel (1963) showed that neurons of the visual cortex respond to the same complex perceptual aspects of the stimulus as do organisms. Degree of behavioral stimulus generalization for tone frequency can be predicted accurately on the basis of patterns of response of single nerve cells in the auditory cortex (Thompson, 1965). Some of the more recent findings concerning association area functions, particularly of the frontal cortex, are not unrelated to such a view (see above and Pribram, 1964; Teuber, 1964). All of these data are consistent with the idea that the cerebral cortex may be the final common pathway determining response probability. To paraphrase Mountcastle et al. (1963): patterns of neural activity in the cerebral cortex are predictively related to behavioral response tendency in such a way that subsequent neural transformations from cortex to behavior may well occur along linear coordinates.

Suggested readings

Field, J. (Ed.) *Handbook of physiology. Section I: neurophysiology.* Vol. III, Washington, D.C.: American Physiological Society, 1960.

Morrell, F. Electrophysiological contributions to the neural basis of learning. *Physiol. Rev.,* **41**, 1961, 443–494.

Warren, J. M., and Akert, K. (Eds.) *The frontal granular cortex and behavior.* New York: McGraw-Hill, 1964.

CHAPTER 16

HYPOTHALAMUS AND LIMBIC SYSTEM: THE NEURAL SUBSTRATES OF EMOTION AND MOTIVATION

The emotional and motivational aspects of behavior have traditionally been emphasized in physiological psychology. Nonetheless it is surprisingly difficult to define the terms "emotion" and "motivation" in a scientifically acceptable manner. This is in marked contrast to their common usage in everyday language. Most of us feel convinced that we are conveying meaningful information when we say that a person is angry, afraid, happy, etc., or more generally that someone is acting in an emotional way. Actually, there are at least two quite different types of meanings, or levels of discourse, involved in such statements. On the one hand they refer to the subjective experience of emotion and on the other hand to behavioral responses. Because we cannot study subjective experience directly we must resort to measurement of verbal descriptions of emotional experience. Although a good deal of interesting work has been done at this level, the end result all too often reduces to collections of adjectives telling us little more than the fact that people can be moderately consistent in using such words.

A large variety of nonverbal behavioral measures of emotion have been used (obviously so in animal studies). These definitions generally include both skeletal-muscle and *autonomic*-effector responses. Either or both categories of response may of course be ambiguous. A rat may jump about wildly or " freeze " and remain motionless when given a strong shock. In both cases he will probably defecate, urinate, and show marked changes in heart rate, respiration, and other autonomic indices. On the other hand extreme facial pallor in man, an autonomic effect characteristic of fear, also occurs when a person stands up suddenly after bending down for a period of time. Injection of adrenalin will produce most of the peripheral autonomic responses characteristic of fear, but the skeletal muscular components will be absent (the subjective experience of fear, incidentally, will likely be absent as well under these conditions).

Elementary discussions of the so-called "theories" of emotion often fail to distinguish between description of the subjective experience and the behavioral syndrome. Many years ago William James and C. G. Lange proposed the theory that emotional *experience* resulted from sensations of the skeletal and autonomic responses that occur during emotional behavior. As James put it: when we meet a bear in the woods and run, we are afraid because we run; we do not run because we are afraid. An alternative point of view was developed by Cannon and his associates, who showed that cats would still exhibit emotional behavior such as hissing and spitting after all feedback from autonomic responses of the body was eliminated. They concluded that autonomic sensory feedback was not necessary for emotional behavior. These two theories are in no sense contradictory. One concerns emotional *experience* and the other emotional *behavior*. In recent years there has been a tendency away from attempts to characterize and study global emotional syndromes like fear and anger. Instead, a simplified bit of " emotional " behavior (such as change in heart rate, amount of defecation, amplitude of startle response, or amount of aggression) is operationally defined in relation to a particular stimulus or training situation and the relevant behavioral and/or physiological variables analyzed in some detail.

Motivation is in many ways an even more elusive concept than emotion. An eminent authority in the field recently characterized motivation as follows:

There is no question but that the idea of motivation or some similar notion appears in almost every systematic account of behavior. Contemporary psychological theorists as well as their more philosophically oriented predecessors have frequently relied upon some kind of moving, pushing, driving, or energizing force or agency. The ubiquity of the concept of motivation, in one guise or another, is nevertheless surprising when we consider that its meaning is often scandalously vague. . . . It will be sufficient to note that, depending upon the particular writer consulted, motivation can be conscious or unconscious; it can be the same as, or different from, drive; it may or may not guide behavior; and all motives can be either learned or instinctive. Moreover, arguments can be found to support the view that motivation is both crucial to behavior and a useless concept, that it is simply the energy that moves the body, or that it is identical with the neural discharges of specific central nervous-system structures. We thus find ourselves in the position of trying to deal with an allegedly vital factor in the face of violent disagreements as to its origins, its essential nature, and its particular roles as a behavior determinant. (Brown, 1961, p. 24.)

It seems clear that any very general definitions of motivation and emotion may overlap. Emotional behavior is eminently energized or driven. One very active current research area concerns a region of overlap between motivation and emotion, namely learned emotional behavior. Fear often seems to function as a general energizer, and its reduction following some particular stimulus and/or response can serve to reinforce the learning of the new response. In short, the emotional behavior of fear can serve as an acquired source of drive or motivation (Mowrer, 1939). This is often termed conditioned fear or conditioned emotional responses (CER). A classical experiment by Miller (1948) illustrates the point. Rats were trained to escape shock by running from a white compartment through an open door to a black compartment of a box. Subsequently they were placed in the white compartment with shock omitted, the door closed, and a wheel inserted which when turned would open the door. Even in the absence of shocks (other than in the initial door open training session) the animals learned to turn the wheel to escape from the white compartment. Thus the fear that was presumably conditioned to the white box during the initial escape training appeared to serve as a reinforcer for learning of the subsequent wheel turning response. Brown and Jacobs (1949) carried the experiment one step further and showed that if the animals were given strong shock (paired with tones and lights) in the locked white compartment and not allowed to escape, they would subsequently learn to escape from the white compartment when the light and tone were presented in the absence of shock.

In the experiments described above it was presumed that fear became conditioned and served as the motivation for subsequent learning. However, there were no measurements of fear per se. An ingeneous experiment by Brown, Kalish, and Farber (1951) used an independent measure of conditioned fear to demonstrate this point. Rats were given paired presentations of a CS (buzzer and light) and shock in a small compartment on a stabilimeter (device to measure degree of bodily movements). Test trials consisting of a sudden loud sound (with no shock) were interspersed, and the magnitude of the startle response measured. The experimental group received the test sound in place of shock at certain of the conditioning trials and controls received the test sound at times other than conditioning trials. Thus magnitude of the startle response to the loud test sound served as an independent behavioral measure of the degree to which fear was conditioned to the light-buzzer CS. The startle response increased markedly over trials for the experimental group but did not change for the control group. To the extent that fear is measured by the startle response, it would seem that conditioned fear did indeed develop.

There are at least two different theoretical positions concerning the role of reinforcement or drive reduction in fear conditioning. On the one hand, Hull (1952) regarded drive reduction as essential for the occurrence of emotional conditioning. For fear responses to be conditioned to a CS, for example, the responses must be followed by some type of reinforcing event. Mowrer (1947),

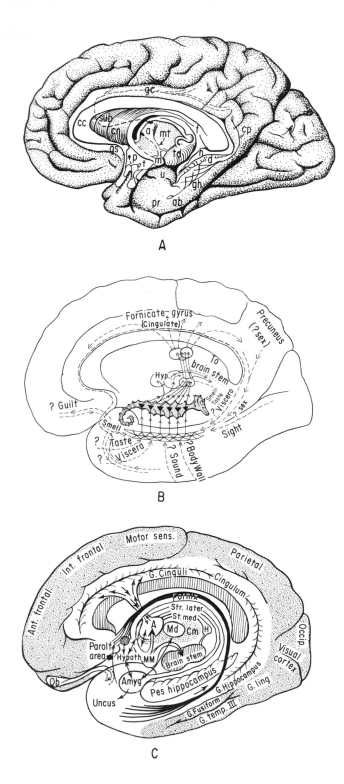

A

B

C

on the other hand, asserts that occurrence of the CS and the fear responses contiguously in time is the necessary and sufficient condition for the learning of emotional responses. As we will see later in the chapter, this issue of the importance of reinforcement in emotional conditioning has a direct bearing on experiments attempting to condition emotional responses elicited by brain stimulation.

It is hoped that this somewhat lengthy introduction provides a definitional and behavioral context of sorts for examining the neural structures believed to be most directly involved in the emotional and/or motivational aspects of behavior, namely the *hypothalamus* and the *limbic system*.

The nuclei of the hypothalamus, lying below the thalamus at the base of the forebrain, bear a closer resemblance to actual neural *control centers* than any other portion of the brain. In addition to many other functions they are concerned with the emotional aspects of behavior, exerting direct influences over the various autonomic control regions in the lower brain stem. Moreover, electrical stimulation of the hypothalamus can produce integrated emotional behavior patterns that include both autonomic and skeletal muscle components. Rage elicited by appropriate hypothalamic stimulation in the cat resembles normal rage in all respects, including a direct attack on the nearest likely offender (usually the experimenter, if he happens to be present).

The limbic system is a group of structures and regions in the forebrain anatomically closely interconnected with one another and with the hypothalamus. The major structures of the limbic system include the *amygdala*, a large nuclear mass embedded in the depth of the temporal lobe; the *hippocampus*, a long tubelike structure of cortical tissue embedded in the cerebrum; the *septum*, a nuclear region in the anterior medial depths of the forebrain; the *olfactory projection fields*, regions which receive direct anatomical projections from the olfactory bulb; and several areas defined as "old cortex" (more primitive in appearance than neocortex) that have been termed *juxta-allocortex* (Pribram and Kruger, 1954) which lie on the medial and basal portions of the cerebral hemispheres. Other terms that have been used to describe portions of the limbic system include "rhinencephalon" (nosebrain) and "visceral brain." At one time most of the limbic structures were believed to be part of the olfactory system, hence the term "rhinencephalon." However, it now seems clearly established that this is not the case. The general locations of these limbic structures are shown in Figure 16.1. The size of the limbic system in relation to the

Figure 16.1. Schematic presentation of the principal connections of the limbic system. A, the original proposal of Papez (1937). Key: a, anterior nucleus; ab, angular bundle; cc, corpus callosum; cn, caudate nucleus; cp, posterior cingulum; d, dentate gyrus; f, fornix; gc, cingulate gyrus; gh, hippocampal gyrus; gs, subcallosal gyrus; h, hippocampus nudus; m, mammillary body; mt, mammillothalamic tract; p, pars optica of the hypothalamus; pr, pyriform area; sub, subcallosal bundle; t, tuber cinereum; td, mammillotegmental tract; th, hypophyseal tract; u, uncus. B, modified version from MacLean (1949). C, version by Penfield and Jasper (1954). (From Russell, 1961)

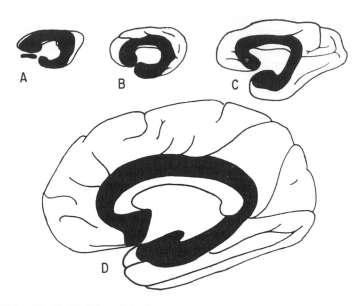

Figure 16.2.   The limbic lobe of the brain of the rabbit **A**; cat **B**; monkey **C**; and man **D**, shown in black. The lobe is seen as a "common denominator" of the medial cortex of the cerebrum. Approximately to scale. (From Russell, 1961, modified from MacLean, 1954)

rest of the brain is compared for several species in Figure 16.2. The limbic system exhibits just the opposite phyologenetic trend from the cerebral cortex—it is relatively smallest in the "highest" animals.

Perhaps the most widely used classification of limbic structures at present was developed by Pribram and Kruger (1954). They subdivided the limbic regions into three separate systems: the *rhinal* system, receiving direct connections from the olfactory bulb; the *Paleol* system, which includes a portion of the old cortex and the amygdala; and finally the *hippocampal cingulate* system, including the hippocampus and related regions of the old cortex. Perhaps the first person to propose that these diverse structures of the limbic system formed a functional unit was Papez, who published a theoretical paper on "A Proposed Mechanism of Emotion" in 1937. MacLean (1949) has further developed this view.

There is as yet no unanimity of opinion regarding the extent to which the hypothalamus and the various components of the limbic system interact with one another to form a unified functional system controlling emotional behavior. There is no doubt that all these structures are anatomically interconnected by fairly direct pathways. However, the behavioral roles of some of these structures, particularly portions of the limbic system like the hippocampus and the amygdala, are by no means clear and little is known about how they interact in emotional behavior. In this chapter we will first describe the organization and behavioral roles of the hypothalamus and the major components of the limbic system separately, and then examine the extent to which they act as a unified functional system in mediating the complex emotional and motivational aspects of behavior.

THE HYPOTHALAMUS

The hypothalamic nuclei lie at the base of the brain below the thalamus, in the general region of the optic chiasm (see Figure 16.3). The general location of the hypothalamus is intermediate between the higher regions of the brain and the brain system. It is in close juxtaposition to the pituitary gland, and closely adjacent to the structures of the limbic system. The major fiber bundles projecting directly to the hypothalamus come from several of the limbic structures, from the prefrontal region of the cerebral cortex, and from the diffuse thalamic system. Its major efferent projections are to the brainstem and spinal cord, to

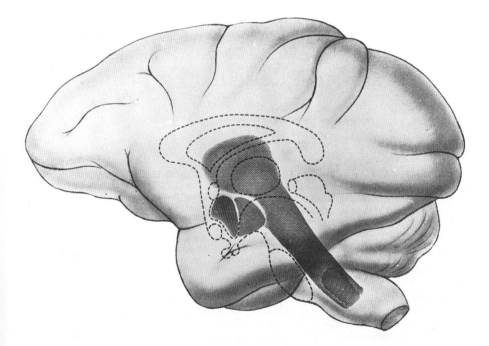

Figure 16.3. Schematic view of the monkey's brain showing the general location of the hypothalamus in relation to the reticular formation, both, of course, lying in the depths of the brain. The anterior and posterior portions of the hypothalamus are shown as two separate pie-shaped wedges (hatched) lying just below the rostral portion of the tube-shaped reticular formation (long vertical hatches). (From Livingston, 1955)

the anterior thalamus, and to the pituitary gland. These input-output relations can be summarized in an oversimplified fashion by saying that most input to the hypothalamus comes from higher regions of the brain that are neither sensory or motor in function, and most output goes to lower autonomic and glandular regulatory regions of the brain. In addition it is interrelated with the reticular formation and diffuse thalamic system.

A schematic diagram of the relative location of the nuclei and major fiber bundles comprising the hypothalamus is shown in Figure 16.4. The arrangement of the various hypothalamic nuclei is complex, and a detailed appreciation of their anatomical organization is not really of much help in terms of functional considerations. However several regions may be rather generally differentiated. The preoptic areas (1 and 2 in Figure 16.4) are anatomically considered to be a part of the forebrain separate from the hypothalamus, although they represent a forward extension of the gray matter of the hypothalamus in front of the optic chiasm. Stimulation of these regions yields peripheral responses of the type

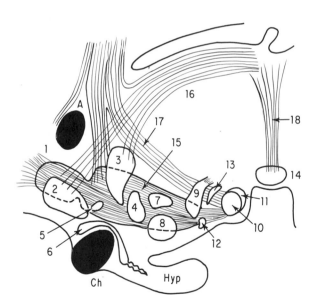

Figure 16.4.   Diagram showing the relative positions in a sagittal plane of the hypothalamic nuclei in a typical mammalian brain and their relation to the fornix (17), stria habenularis (16), and fasciculus retroflexus or habenulo-peduncular tract (18). A, anterior commissure: Ch, optic chiasma; Hyp, hypophysis; 1, lateral preoptic nucleus (permeated by the medial forebrain bundle); 2, medial preoptic nucleus; 3, paraventricular nucleus; 4, anterior hypothalamic area; 5, suprochiasmatic nucleus; 6, supraoptic nucleus; 7, dorsomedial hypothalamic mammillary nucleus; 11, lateral mammillary nucleus; 12, premammillary nucleus; 13, supramammillary nucleus; 14, interpeduncular nucleus (a mesencephalic element in which the habenulo-peduncular tract terminates); 15, lateral hypothalamic nucleus (permeated by the medial forebrain bundle). (From LeGros Clark, 1938)

produced by activity of the parasympathetic portion of the autonomic system (i.e. decreased blood pressure and contraction of the bladder; Ranson, 1937; Ranson and Magoun, 1939). Several of the nuclei that lie close to the pituitary gland (supraoptic nucleus, paraventricular nucleus, and nuclei of the tuberal region) send fibers to the "neurohypophyseal" portion of the pituitary gland and are intimately involved in neural control of the pituitary gland. Stimulation of the remainder of the hypothalamic nuclei yields various peripheral autonomic responses, such as are known to be mediated by the activity of the sympathetic portion of the autonomic nervous system (i.e. increased blood pressure, sweating, dilatation of the pupils, etc.). The lateral hypothalamic nucleus, which runs the entire length of the hypothalamus in a lateral position, is particularly capable of yielding autonomic responses upon stimulation. In some instances (e.g. temperature control) very small regions of hypothalamus may be critically involved, whereas in other cases a given autonomic response may be elicited from a variety of regions.

As suggested by the very brief anatomical description given above, the hypothalamus exerts its control on the autonomic aspects of behavior by two quite distinct mechanisms. On the one hand it influences the activity of other groups of neurons, both autonomic and somatic, in the brain stem and other regions of the CNS; on the other hand it acts as the major neural control center for the endocrine glands, both by exerting neural control over the pituitary gland and by directly releasing hormones itself. Although these neural and glandular control systems of the hypothalamus obviously work by quite different anatomical and physiological mechanisms, they function together in an integrated fashion. Thus stimulation of the "drinking center" of the hypothalamus produces drinking behavior *and* releases an antidiuretic hormone that acts to prevent the body from excreting water. To simplify our discussion we will treat the neural and glandular actions of the hypothalamus more or less separately. Remember, however, that in the intact organism they are two different but complementary aspects of hypothalamic action. Thus in experiments in which the behavioral effects of electrical stimulation of the hypothalamus are described, some components of the behavior are neurally controlled but others may be the results of endocrine gland actions.

The hypothalamus appears to have been designed in such a way as to frustrate experimental analysis of its physiological and behavioral functions. The hypothalamus of the rat, the favored experimental preparation, is about the size of a large pinhead. All of the many nuclei and fiber tracts described above lie within this tiny area. In contrast to the thalamus, in which a given nucleus defined in histological terms can often be related to a specific type of sensory or other projection system, there is usually little correlation between structurally defined nuclei and functional roles in the hypothalamus. Finally, attempts to determine the functions of the various hypothalamic nuclei by lesion and stimulation techniques are obfuscated by the fact that numerous fiber tracts, some of them unrelated to the hypothalamic nuclei per se, pass in, around, and through the hypothalamus. It is virtually impossible to determine whether a given lesion or stimulation effect is due to the nuclei in question or to adjacent fiber tracts.

The hypothalamus: emotional behavior

An intact hypothalamus is a prerequisite for integrated emotional behavior patterns. Bard (1928) demonstrated that fully developed rage, with both autonomic and skeletal muscular components, could be elicited in cats with all brain tissue above the level of the hypothalamus removed. However, if the hypothalamus was also removed, only fragmented components of the response could be elicited (see Bard and Macht, 1958). The rage exhibited by hypothalamic cats (i.e. cats with all neural tissue *above* the hypothalamus removed) includes spitting, snarling, biting, struggling, clawing, tail lashing, erection of the hair, rise in blood pressure, increased heart rate, sweating, and other autonomic components. Bard described the integrated rage pattern of the hypothalamic cat as *sham rage*. This phrase seems to have been interpreted by some to imply that the animal was not exhibiting "real" rage. Actually Bard used the phrase to emphasize that he was describing the behavioral aspects of rage rather than any subjective or experiential factors. The sham rage of the hypothalamic animal is the fully integrated behavior pattern typical of rage in the intact cat, with one important exception: the animal doesn't show directed attack against likely offenders because he is blind, the visual system having been removed.

In the same year that Bard described his lesion experiments, W. R. Hess (1928) reported that he could elicit a full-blown rage in intact cats by electrical stimulation of the hypothalamus. Hess, working in Zurich, was the pioneer in the study of the effects of electrical stimulation of the brain on behavior. The far reaching significance of his work was not fully appreciated at the time, possibly because it was available only in German until fairly recently (see Hess, 1954; 1957). Hess received the Nobel Prize for his work in 1949. Akert, a student and associate of Hess, has recently summarized Hess's contributions and placed them in an adequate historical perspective (1961).

Hess found that repetitive electrical stimulation of several regions of the hypothalamus would elicit rage behavior in the cat. As Akert has described it:

The observer first notes signs of arousal, the assumption of the defensive position, and angry vocalizations, climaxing in the retraction of the ears by the hissing, spitting animal. At this moment, a well directed attack follows the slightest provocation. The aggressive behavior, however, ceases immediately upon termination of the stimulation, but a lowered threshold for noxious stimuli usually persists for a short time.

The location of this area that Hess (1961, p. 291) termed the "affective defense region of the hypothalamus" is schematized in Figure 16.5, together with other types of stimulation effects obtained by Hess and his co-workers.

Perhaps the most important aspects of Hess's rage or affective defense reaction are that it is integrated and that it involves directed attack. This contrasts markedly with the findings of Masserman (1941), who reported he could

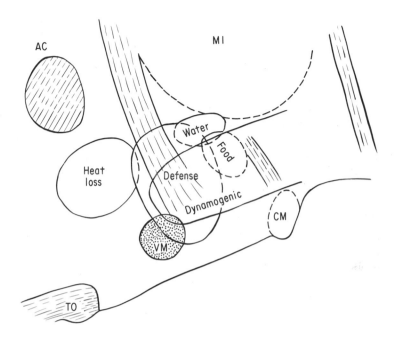

Figure 16.5. Localization and mutual relationships of hypothalamic threshold areas for affective defense, heat loss, water intake, food intake, and dynamogenic activity. The last mentioned response is situated more laterally than affective defense. None of these areas corresponds closely to a nucleus or nuclear complex. Abbreviations shown: AC, anterior commissure; CM, mammillary body; MI, massa intermedia; TO, optic tract; VM, ventromedial hypothalamic nucleus. (From Akert, 1961)

elicit only fragments of the rage response such as hissing or salivation, but no directed attack, as a result of hypothalamic stimulation. Masserman characterized this type of behavior as "sham rage" and implied that it was not "real" rage. Hess's observation of integrated and directed rage have been verified by other workers (Hunsperger, 1956; Ingram, 1952; Nakao and Maki, 1958). Masserman did not specify the location of his stimulating electrodes and it seems probable that he was stimulating a different region of the hypothalamus or brainstem. Subsequent localization studies (see Akert, 1961) indicate that the critical region for directed rage is in the prefornical portion of the hypothalamus surrounding the fornix (the latter, a fiber pathway from the hippocampus to the hypothalamus and other structures, is believed not to be involved). The region appears to continue caudally through the posterior hypothalamus into the central gray matter of the midbrain (Hunsperger, 1956).

Hess and his associates noted that flight rather than attack often resulted from stimulation of the "affective defense" region. Partly for this reason they termed the behavioral syndrome resulting from such hypothalamic stimulation "affective defense." Miller (1961) and Roberts (1958 a,b) have described three types of reactions to hypothalamic stimulation: alarm, flight, and rage. Their flight reaction closely resembles Hess's affective defense reaction and is elicited from the same region of the hypothalamus. Judges could reliably rate the animals' behavior as alarm, flight, or rage. Recently, Yasukochi (1960) reported that stimulation of the anterior hypothalamus produced fear behavior, stimulation of the middle sector produced rage, and stimulation of the posterior portion yielded "curiosity and alertness."

Miller and Roberts attempted to condition the flight reaction, using the brain stimulus as the UCS in a fear conditioning situation. When the animal was placed in a special compartment, the brain stimulus was turned on and the flight response was elicited. Numerous trials of this sort pairing being placed in the compartment and brain stimulation produced no signs of conditioning. This is directly contrary to the results obtained if painful peripheral shock is used rather than brain shock. As we noted earlier, a few pairings of test compartment and strong foot shock lead to a very strong conditioned fear reaction—the animal struggles to escape the compartment when placed in it and shows symptoms characteristic of fear. However, while conditioned fear was not established it was possible to use the brain stimulus as a negative reinforcement. Cats would learn the correct turn in a T-maze in order to turn the brain stimulus off. Thus the brain stimulus acted like a peripheral shock in that it could serve as a simple negative reinforcer, but unlike peripheral shock, the actual behavioral responses elicited by the brain stimulus could not themselves be conditioned.

Miller (1961) reports success in conditioning one cat that exhibited a clear rage reaction to brain stimulation. The brain stimulus was paired with presentations of a toy dog. The animal quickly learned to attack the toy dog ferociously, even in the absence of brain stimulation. However, it turned out that the stimulating electrode was below the base of the brain and was undoubtedly producing peripheral pain by stimulation of the tissues on the base of the skull. Masserman (1941) was totally unable to condition the fragmented components of "sham rage" under the conditions of his experiments. If a sound was paired with the hypothalamic stimulus, the latter evoking some aspect of rage such as a piloerection (hair raising) response, this response never became conditioned to the sound. However, it will be recalled that hypothalamic stimulation, as carried out by Masserman, never led to an integrated rage response with directed attack. It remains to be determined whether the directed rage in Hess's experiments can be conditioned to a neutral stimulus. Miller and Robert's negative results with the flight response suggest that it may not be possible to do so. Until this rather crucial experiment is done we must accept Masserman's conclusion that electrically evoked hypothalamic rage cannot be conditioned.

The issue of the conditionability of the rage (or fear) reaction evoked by electrical stimulation of the hypothalamus is of some importance in relation to the theoretical analysis of the basic factors underlying conditioned emotional responses discussed earlier in the chapter. At present the evidence indicates that emotional responses elicited by hypothalamic stimulation contiguous with a CS do not become conditioned to the CS. This would seem to be in opposition to Mowrer's theory of contiguity and tend to support Hull's view that drive reduction is necessary as well as contiguity.

The effects of hypothalamic lesions on emotional behavior have generally been complementary to the stimulation experiments. In both cats (Wheatley, 1944) and rats (Hetherington and Ranson, 1939) lesions in the ventromedial region of the hypothalamus produce ferocious and savage animals.

The hypothalamus: feeding and drinking behavior

In 1939 Hetherington and Ranson demonstrated that bilateral electrolytic lesions in the ventromedial hypothalamus of the rat caused *hyperphagia* (excessive feeding) which led to extreme obesity. This basic observation has been confirmed in numerous subsequent experiments (Anand et al., 1955; Brobeck et al., 1943; Teitelbaum, 1961; Wheatly, 1944). Because the lesioned animals are generally rather inactive, it was initially thought that they became fat due to decreased work output or change in metabolic functions. However, Brobeck et al. (1943) showed that obesity was simply the result of over-eating. Following ventromedial hypothalamic lesions the animals showed two quite distinct phases. During the first (dynamic) phase they eat up to three times their normal amount of food and rapidly gain in weight (see Figure 16.6). In the second (static) phase, food intake decreases to nearly normal, and the excess overweight is maintained. Detailed analysis of metabolic factors by Brobeck and his associates showed that there appear to be no metabolic disturbances in hypothalamic hyperphagia; hypothalamic lesioned animals become fat because they overeat.

The marked increase in eating behavior following medial hypothalamic lesions could be due to several factors. The animals could have a greater motivation to eat food (i.e. always act as though "hungry"). On the other hand alterations in weight regulation mechanisms, rather than food intake regulation, could produce hyperphagia (i.e., the animal might eat more to establish a higher baseline weight). Altered palatability of foods is still another possibility. They are, of course, not mutually exclusive and could interact or overlap. Teitelbaum analyzed these alternatives in a series of ingenious experiments (see Teitelbaum, 1955; Teitelbaum and Campbell, 1958; Williams and Teitelbaum, 1959; and the review by Teitelbaum, 1961). If the caloric content of food is diluted by cellulose (this adds bulk but has no nutritive value) normal animals will increase their food intake proportionally to maintain body weight. However, hypothalamically hyperphagic animals will *stop eating*. By the same token, normal rats will eat food that has been adulterated with small amounts of quinine (which gives it a bitter taste). Hypothalamically obese animals, on the other hand, will stop eating such food. If saccharin (which tastes sweet but has no caloric value) is added, normal rats will maintain normal body weight, but hypothalamically obese animals will eat much more than normal. All of these results show that hypothalamic hyperphagic rats are much more influenced by the taste of food than are normal rats.

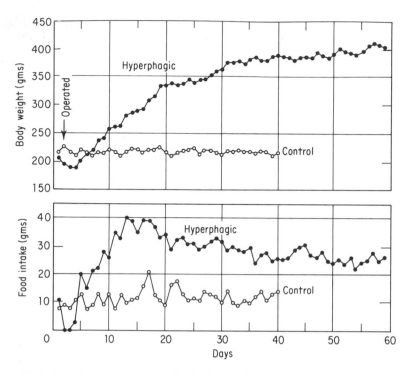

Figure 16.6. Development of hyperphagia in rats following lesions of the ventromedial hypothalamus. Note that food intake increases markedly at first and then levels off, but that body weight increases more slowly and for a longer period of time. (From Teitelbaum, 1961)

Teitelbaum (1961) has suggested that the increased effectiveness of the palatability of food in determining food intake in the lesioned animals indicates that the animals may in fact have a reduced motivation for food. This seemingly paradoxical conclusion was first proposed by Miller et al. (1950), who showed that hypothalamically hyperphagic rats will not work as hard to obtain food as will normal rats. Teitelbaum (1957) further showed that hyperphagic animals do not increase their random activity as much as do normal ones when they are deprived of food, and will not press a lever as much to obtain food as will normal animals. Even though hyperphagic rats overeat they are less hungry than normal rats. (However, Falk, 1961, has noted that obese animals may not work well simply because they are too heavy.) In interpreting these findings Teitelbaum suggests that the basic defect in hypothalamic hyperphagic rats is in their base weight regulation. He suggests that the crucial ventromedial region of the hypothalamus is a satiety center, which normally acts to inhibit feeding when adequate food intake has occurred. In the lesioned animal, feeding continues until a much higher base weight is established. The entire concept of a ventromedial satiety center, incidentally, has recently been rejected in an interesting paper by Reynolds (1965). We will examine Reynolds' criticisms after discussing the effects of lateral hypothalamic lesions on feeding and drinking behavior.

Electrolytic destruction of the lateral hypothalamus produces just the opposite effect from destruction of the ventromedial region: animals will not eat or drink, and if not force-fed will die (Anand and Brobeck, 1951; Anand et al., 1955). In a careful series of papers, Teitelbaum and Stellar (1954) and Teitelbaum and associates (see review by Teitelbaum and Epstein, 1962) demonstrated that both loss of eating (aphagia) and loss of drinking (adipsia) occurred following lateral lesions. Aphagia is always accompanied by adipsia. Interestingly enough, recovery of eating behavior seems to be the rule rather than the exception, if adequate postoperative care and forced feeding are provided. However, drinking behavior may never return. The recovery stages for animals that do eventually recover both eating and drinking following lateral hypothalamic lesions are shown in Figure 16.7.

The complementary effects of ventromedial and lateral hypothalamic lesions suggest a very neat schema for the hypothalamic control of eating and drinking: the lateral hypothalamus is a feeding center and the ventromedial hypothalamus is a satiety center. The two centers would then exert reciprocal control on one another, regulated in turn by sensory factors both of the internal environment (stomach contractions, blood sugar level, etc.) and of the chemical senses.

Drug injection experiments have provided very nice complementary data for the feeding-satiety centers hypothesis. Epstein (1960) found that injection of hypertonic saline (which presumably activates neural tissue) in the ventromedial

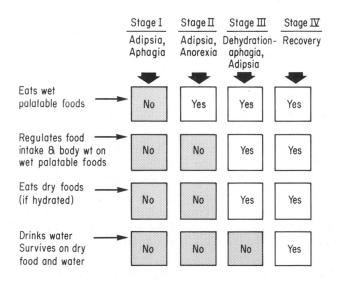

Figure 16.7.   Stages of recovery seen in the lateral hypothalamic syndrome. (From Teitelbaum and Epstein, 1962)

region of the hypothalamus depressed feeding. Injection of procaine (a local anesthetic that blocks nerve activity), on the other hand, induced eating in satiated animals. Injections of these drugs in the lateral hypothalamus produced just the opposite effects—saline led to increased food intake and procaine to cessation of eating. Grossman (1960) has obtained a similar increase in eating following injection of epinephrine in the lateral hypothalamus.

A contrary interpretation of the literature on hypothalamic control of eating has recently been proposed by Reynolds (1965). He asserts that there is no ventromedial satiety center. Reynolds notes that all experiments demonstrating hyperphagia following ventromedial lesions have been done using electrolysis (dc current destruction of tissue). He compared electrolytic and rf (radio frequency) lesions of this region of the hypothalamus and found that even with excessive tissue destruction in the ventromedial region, little or no hyperphagia developed following rf lesions (Reynolds, 1963). Additional evidence suggests that electrolytic lesions may induce scar tissue formation and electrode metal ion deposits in surrounding tissues, which in turn could induce abnormal activity. Consequently Reynolds suggests that the hyperphagia following electrolytic lesions of the ventromedial hypothalamus results from abnormally heightened activity in the lateral feeding center, due to abnormal tissue reactions bordering the more medially placed lesions. Rf lesions of the lateral hypothalamus, incidentally, produce the same aphagia and adipsia that result from electrolytic lesions. Reynolds concludes that there is only one hypothalamic center concerned with feeding, namely the lateral feeding center. Reynolds points out that the observation that hyperphagic animals work less for food has also recently been questioned. Hamilton and Brobeck (1964) reported that hyperphagic monkeys actually work harder for food for a wide range of fixed ratio reinforcement schedules. Reynolds' hypothesis, it should be noted, cannot explain Epstein's drug injection results, particularly the increased eating following procaine injections in the ventromedial region of the hypothalamus.

Reynolds' experiments are very extensive (55 rats with electrolytic lesions vs 40 rats with rf lesions) and carefully done, and cannot lightly be rejected. On the other hand, Hoebel (1965) reported that rf lesions destroying the ventromedial region of the hypothalamus in 16 rats produced the marked and typical hyperphagia seen following electrolytic lesions in all animals. It is rather discouraging for the student (and the textbook writer) to find that two carefully controlled and executed studies in which apparently identical procedures were carried out yielded exactly opposite results. A great deal more work is obviously needed before such discrepancies can be clarified. This direct contradiction of data, incidentally, is a good example of the kinds of limitations associated with the lesion technique that were discussed in relation to cortical lesions in Chapter 11. A depth lesion is even more subject to difficulties of interpretation than is a surface lesion. Depth lesions in a region like the hypothalamus, which is densely packed with a variety of nuclei and fiber tracts, cannot selectively destroy only one anatomical entity. It may well be that the discrepancies in studies on eating behavior will never be resolved solely by lesion experiments.

The results of experiments involving electrical stimulation of the hypothalamus, though not entirely consistent, do seem in general to be complementary to the lesion experiments insofar as eating and drinking behavior is concerned. Review articles commonly state rather dogmatically that all stimulation studies have found increased eating during stimulation of the lateral feeding center and cessation of feeding during stimulation of the ventromedial satiety center. Actually, the results are not quite this clear and consistent. Hess and his associates (see Akert, 1961; Brügger, 1943; Hess, 1954), and Andersson (1951), using Hess's techniques, demonstrated clearly that in both cat and goat electrical stimulation of the lateral hypothalamus produces a wide variety of eating responses—lapping, licking, chewing, sniffing, salivation, etc. Most of these responses were described as reflex-type feeding responses; they were fragmented responses rather than integrated "eating" behavior. Brügger (1943), working in Hess's laboratory, observed aggressive and integrated eating behavior following stimulation in a more dorsomedial portion of the hypothalamus overlapping Hess's affective defense region. Delgado and Anand (1953) produced marked and long lasting increased food intake from stimulation of the lateral hypothalamus. Food ingestion typically increased following cessation of the stimuli. Larsson (1954) stimulated the lateral hypothalamic region in goats and sheep and found increased food intake as a result of "reflex-type" eating behavior during stimulation when food was present and available. Smith (1961) using rats, demonstrated long lasting increases in eating following lateral hypothalamic stimulation, and decreases in eating following ventromedial stimulation. Wyrwicka and Dobrzecka (1960) have obtained similar results.

Insofar as cessation of eating following ventromedial stimulation is concerned, such stimulation may simply be serving as a strong aversive stimulus. Krasne (1962) has shown that ventromedial stimulation effective in stopping the animal from eating can also serve as a powerful negative reinforcer in producing escape learning. In this context it is of interest to note that electrical stimulation of the lateral hypothalamus is itself positively reinforcing. In Olds' well known experiments in which a rat can deliver an electrical shock to his own brain by pressing a lever (these experiments will be discussed later in this chapter), placement of the electrode in many locations, including the lateral hypothalamus, results in high rates of lever pressing. A close relationship seems to exist between eating behavior and self stimulation of the lateral hypothalamus. Self stimulation rates are higher when rats are hungry (Margules and Olds, 1962). If the ventromedial satiety center is destroyed, both eating and self stimulation increase (Hoebel and Teitelbaum, 1962; Hoebel, 1965).

To summarize, there seems to be general agreement that stimulation of the lateral hypothalamus increases eating behavior, but varying interpretations of why it occurs. Hess's data suggest that it may be a fortuitous result of reflex eating when food happens to be present. However, the majority of experiments have reported that eating continues long after stimulation has ceased, suggesting a more general integrative action. The self-stimulation data are consistent with this interpretation. Stimulation of the ventromedial hypothalamus, on the other hand, is consistently observed to be aversive, hence no conclusions can be drawn regarding any specific actions it may have on eating behavior. Finally, Brügger's eating syndrome seems to stand somewhat apart, being produced by stimulation of a region that appears to be neither the lateral feeding center nor the ventro-medial satiety center.

The hypothalamus: sexual behavior

The mechanisms controlling sexual behavior are extremely complex. All levels of the nervous system from the spinal cord to the cerebral cortex are concerned, as are a host of endocrine gland actions. Space limitations preclude any kind of adequate summary of even the neural aspects of sex here. The reader is urged to consult reviews by Beach (1958; 1964), Goy and Young (1957), Sawyer, (1960), and Young (1961) for overviews.

The hypothalamus plays a very fundamental role in the control of sexual behavior. Research on hypothalamic mechanisms is complicated by the fact that the hypothalamus exerts both neural control and endocrine control on sexual behavior. If a lesion is made in the hypothalamus, any defects that might appear in sexual behavior could be the result of damage to neural mechanisms, damage to hypothalamic-pituitary mechanisms, or more likely to both. We will limit our brief discussion here to those effects believed to be mediated by neural actions. Hypothalamic-pituitary relations will be considered below.

In an early experiment, Fisher, Magoun, and Ranson (1938) showed that female cats with lesions in the anterior hypothalamus in the general region of the supraoptic nuclei did not mate. Brookhart et al. (1940; 1941) demonstrated a comparable effect of anterior hypothalamic lesions in the female guinea pig. They were unable to restore normal function by treatment with estrogen (a hormone which is released from the ovary as a result of pituitary actions and which plays a crucial role in sex behavior). This finding suggested that the effect of the hypothalamic lesion was not due to pituitary malfunction. Maes (1940) was able to demonstrate that sexual behavior in female cats was essentially normal following removal of the entire pituitary gland, if the animals were treated with estrogen. Consequently, the deficit reported by Ranson et al., and Brookhart et al., appears to be due to interference with neural rather than endo-crine mechanisms. Sawyer and Robison (1956) were able to demonstrate two separate hypothalamic control mechanisms, one neural and one via the pituitary, in female cats and rabbits. Anterior lesions abolish sexual behavior even with estrogen treatment. On the other hand, ventromedial lesions lead to atrophy of the ovaries (due to lack of normal hypothalamic-pituitary endocrine actions on the ovaries). This effect is prevented by estrogen treatment. Lesions of the mam-millary region produce a comparable effect to the ventromedial lesions.

Similar dual neural and endocrine hypothalamic control systems have been found for male sexual behavior. Brookhart and Dey (1941) permanently eliminated sex behavior in male guinea pigs without damage to the testes (im-plying normal pituitary function) by lesions in the anterior hypothalamus. An extensive and careful investigation by Phoenix (1959) demonstrated the same permanent abolition of sexual behavior in male guinea pigs following hypothalamic lesions, even with treatment by testosterone propionate (a synthetic analogue of the androgen normally secreted by the testes). Beach has reported similar observations (1958). Rodgers (1954) on the other hand, showed that although lesions in the ventromedial region of the hypothalamus cause male rats to cease mating, their behavior was restored to normal by androgen injections. Soulairac and Soulairac (1956) reported elimination of male rat mating behavior (without gonadal atrophy) after destruction of the medial preoptic area and suprachiasmatic nuclei. More recently, Heimer and Larsson (1964, 1967) and Larsson and Heimer (1964) have shown rather conclusively that the crucial region lies in what they term the "preoptic-anterior hypothalamic continuum." Fairly large lesions in this area, but no other region of the hypothalamus, permanently eliminated mating behavior in all animals (male rats). Hormone treatment did not restore mating behavior in the large lesion animals but did in animals with smaller lesions.

Electrical and chemical stimulation experiments have provided evidence in accord with the lesion data. Electrical stimulation of the anterior hypothalamic "sex center" elicits pronounced sexual behavior in male monkeys (MacLean and Ploog, 1962) and in male rats (Vaughan and Fisher, 1962). Penile erection is continuous during stimulation; one animal in the Vaughan and Fisher study was reported to have 20 ejaculations in one hour of stimulation (!). Harris (1964) has shown that behavioral estrous can be induced in female cats by direct injection of estrogen in the hypothalamus in doses too small to have any effect on the uterus. Michael (1962) was able to establish estrous behavior lasting as long as two months by implanting a solid estrogen pellet in the hypothalamus of female cats. The effect was not obtained when the estrogen was implanted elsewhere in the brain. An even more dramatic and somewhat puzzling effect was reported a few years ago by Fisher (1956). He found that injection of testosterone in the anterior hypothalamic region produced female sexual behavior patterns in *male* rats.

Gross EEG activity of the hypothalamus appears to correlate well with behavioral signs of sexual activity. In the estrous cat, vaginal stimulation is followed by a vigorous behavioral afterreaction that may represent orgasm (see Sawyer, 1960). Concomitant with behavioral "orgasm," EEG activity of the anterior hypothalamus shows marked high amplitude slow waves (see Figure 16.8; Porter et al., 1957; Sawyer, 1960). Green (1954) reports similar heightened hypothalamic EEG activity during courtship and mating in the rabbit. Kawakami and Sawyer (1959) have observed an EEG "afterreaction" involving, first, several minutes of sleeplike EEG from the hypothalamus (and hippocampus as well), followed by extreme EEG arousal (by contrast with cortical EEG pathways, large slow waves are referred to as arousal activity when they occur in the hypothalamus and hippocampus; see discussion of hippocampal theta below, p. 562). This same sequence of EEG activity can be induced by direct electrical stimulation of the hypothalamus.

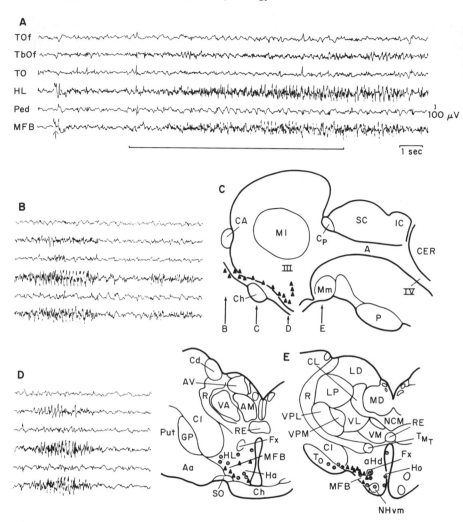

Figure 16.8. Selected EEG tracings during vaginal stimulation (**A**) and "after-reaction" (**B, D**) which lasted 3.3 min in an estrous cat. Dramatic changes are seen in lateral hypothalamic (HL) and medial forebrain bundle (MFB) channels. **C** and **E** are, respectively, a sagittal reconstruction and two cross sections of the cat brainstem showing areas from which altered electrical activity was recorded (solid triangles) and areas failing to show these changes (stippled circles). (Adapted from Porter et al., 1957; Sawyer, 1960)

In summary, all lines of evidence agree in demonstrating a crucial role for the hypothalamus in the neural control of sexual behavior. In female cats with brain transections, the characteristic integrated estrous behavior pattern is seen only if the hypothalamus and lower brain structures are intact (Bard, 1940). As far as the male is concerned, reflex genital erection and ejaculation can be induced after complete transection of the spinal cord in the lumbar region. Nonetheless, the hypothalamic regions are essential for normal sexual activity in the otherwise intact male.

The hypothalamus: homeostasis

The hypothalamus plays a crucial role in the control of several vital regulatory mechanisms. A good example is *temperature regulation*. If the body temperature goes up, the hypothalamus induces sweating, panting, and cutaneous vasodilatation and if the body temperature goes down, it induces shivering and cutaneous vasoconstriction. The efficiency and sensitivity of the hypothalamic thermostat and the peripheral mechanisms it utilizes are quite remarkable. The human body maintains a constant temperature within about 1° F of 98.6° F in the face of environmental temperatures ranging from −20° to +130° F. There appear to be two separate centers in the hypothalamus for temperature control, a " heat center " in the anterior hypothalamus that acts to cool the body, and a "cold center" in the posterior hypothalamus that acts to warm the body. Ranson and Magoun (1939) demonstrated that these two centers can act independently. A very tiny lesion placed just above and in front of the optic chiasm eliminates the ability of an otherwise intact animal to prevent overheating. Alternatively, a somewhat larger posterior lesion in the region of the mammillary bodies eliminates the ability of the animal to prevent overcooling.

Electrical brain stimulation experiments have given results consistent with the lesion data. Hess and associates have obtained panting and salivation by stimulation of the anterior "heat center" in the hypothalamus of the cat, and Andersson et al. (1956) produced panting and cutaneous vasodilatation by electrical stimulation of the same region in the goat. Panting, incidentally, is a highly integrated response combining both somatic and autonomic efferent systems. The animal must adopt a particular posture and jaw position (somatic responses) as well as increase his output of saliva (autonomic response).

A very sensitive receptor system must exist to allow the fine degree of temperature control exerted by the hypothalamus. Peripheral temperature receptors (see Chapter 10) provide temperature information for the hypothalamus. In addition, there appear to be thermoreceptors in the hypothalamus itself. Heating of the blood as it enters the brain (by warming the carotid arteries) induces sweating, panting, and vasodilatation, even though the skin temperature is not altered. Conversely, cooling of the carotid blood induces vasoconstriction and shivering. It seems likely that the temperature receptors of the brain are contained in the hypothalamus. Direct local heating of the rostral hypothalamus itself, using a very small diathermy probe, can induce sweating, panting, and vasodilatation, even when the body temperature itself is maintained below normal (Magoun et al., 1938; Folkow et al., 1949). If specific heat receptors in fact exist in the hypothalamus, it should be possible to record receptor potentials from them. Von Euler (1950) has reported what he terms to be receptor potentials of the heat receptors from the medial preoptic "heat center." He warmed the blood as it entered the brain via the carotid arteries, and measured both the local temperature and the slow electrical potentials of the hypothalamic heat center. He obtains slow potential changes that developed in parallel with increases in hypothalamic temperature.

Regulation of *water balance* is another vital function of the hypothalamus. Electrical stimulation of a restricted region that overlaps Hess's affective defense area and the eating area defined by Brügger (see Figure 16.5) produces forceful and compulsive drinking. Andersson (1952, 1953) elicited excessive drinking in goats by microinjections of hypertonic salt solution in the drinking center. Control injections of normal or hypotonic saline did not produce this effect. Since all nerve cells are sensitive to salt concentration, this alone does not prove the existence of specific osmoreceptors. In addition, injection of hypo- or hypertonic saline in the carotid arteries can predictably alter hypothalamic action. These effects are abolished if the local blood supply to the hypothalamus is clamped off (Verney, 1947). Cross and Green (1959) studied single nerve cell activity in the hypothalamic osmoreceptor region in response to direct local injections of hypertonic saline. They found cells in the supraoptic region that increased their firing rates in response to saline, and cells in the paraventricular region that tended to stop firing as a result of saline injection (see Figure 16.9). Thus it seems likely that specific osmoreceptors exist in the hypothalamus.

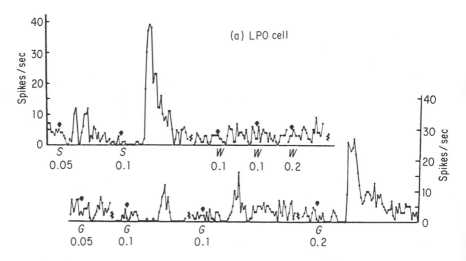

Figure 16.9.   Response to hypertonic injections in a lateral preoptic neuron. Delayed acceleration produced by injection of 0.05–0.1 ml of 9 percent NaCl (*S*) and by 0.05–0.2 ml of 50 percent glucose (*G*, amounts given in ml): hypertonic glucose was only half as effective as hypertonic NaCl in equal osmolar concentration, and injections of water (*W*) had no effect. (Cross and Green, 1959)

Stimulation of the drinking center also causes the release of a specific pituitary hormone, the antidiuretic hormone (ADH), also called vasopressin, that causes the body to retain fluids. It acts at the renal tubules of the kidney to promote reabsorption of water, thus preventing fluid loss in the urine. We will discuss hypothalamic-pituitary relations further below. The parallel elicitation of drinking behavior and release of ADH is just one of many instances in which activation of the hypothalamus produces both neural and endocrine effects.

Hypothalamic-pituitary relations

The interrelations of the hypothalamus and pituitary gland (also called the hypophysis) are of fundamental importance. The pituitary is something of a "master gland" in the endocrine system, controlling activity of other endocrine glands by releasing into the blood stream substances capable of stimulating them. The hypothalamus in turn exerts considerable control on the pituitary gland. Finally, there is evidence suggesting that the pituitary gland and even the hypothalamus itself are directly influenced by hormones produced by the various endocrine glands, thus providing for a regulatory feedback mechanism.

A schematic diagram illustrating the anatomical and neurosecretory relations of the hypothalamus and the pituitary gland is given in Figure 16.10. Two separate systems are shown, the neuronal pathway from the supraoptic and peraventricular nuclei to the *neurohypophysis* (the posterior portion of the pituitary gland deriving embryologically from neural tissue), and the more recently studied vascular relationships between the infundibular and tuberal areas of the hypothalamus and the *adenohypophysis* (the anterior portion of the pituitary gland derived embryologically from gland tissue). Excellent reviews of hypothalamic-pituitary relations may be found in Harris (1955 a,b); Fields et al. (1956); Reichlin (1963) and Harris (1960).

It now seems generally agreed that two hormones, oxytocin and vasopressin, are manufactured in the cell bodies of the supraoptic and paraventricular nuclei in the hypothalamus and pass down the nerve fibers by axonal flow to storage locations in the neural lobe of the pituitary gland (Ortmann, 1960). With appropriate stimulation these hormones are released into the blood stream. Oxytocin causes contractions of the uterus and ejection of milk from the mammary glands. Vasopressin (the antidiuretic, ADH) controls the uptake and excretion of water by body tissues, particularly the kidney, and also causes some increase in blood pressure. Damage to the regions of the hypothalamus producing vasopressin causes the condition known as *diabetes insipidus*, in which vast quantities of water are consumed and subsequently excreted as extremely dilute urine. The exact molecular structures of oxytocin and vasopressin have been established by DuVigneaud and his associates (see DuVigneaud, 1954).

The evidence favoring the neurosecretory function of the nerve cells in the supraoptic and paraventricular nuclei of the hypothalamus has been very carefully reviewed by Ortmann (1960). First, a neurosecretory substance has been

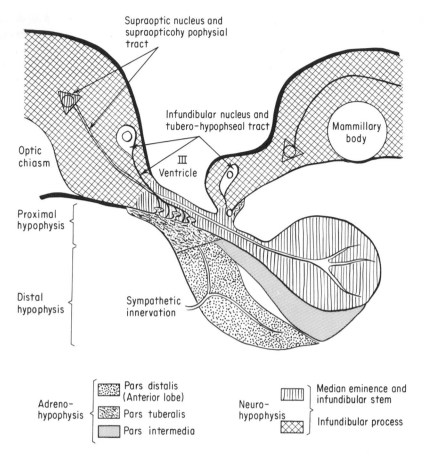

Figure 16.10. Interrelationships of hypothalamus and pituitary gland (see text). (From Reichlin, 1963)

identified in the hypothalamic neurons by histological staining techniques. It closely resembles, and may be identical with, oxytocin and vasopressin. Both the neural secretory substances, or the hormones themselves, are present in the nerve axon and in their region of termination in the neurohypophysis. Second, activation of the neurons depletes these substances from the neurons and from the neurohypophysis. There is a close correlation between the depletion of the hormones from the neurons and their appearance peripherally. Third, when the neural stalk containing these axons that connect the hypothalamic nuclei with the neurohypophysis is cut, the neurosecretory substance and the hormones disappear from the neurohypophysis and the portion of the axons distal to the cut, and accumulate in the portion of the axons proximal to the cut. In sum, either the hormones or their immediate precursors, the neurosecretory substances, appear to be manufactured in the nerve cell bodies of the supraoptic and paraventricular nuclei. They are then transported down these nerve cell axons to be stored and released in the neurohypophysis. The neural portion of the pituitary gland, then, is primarily simply a region where the terminations of axons from the hypothalamus lie in close proximity to the blood vessels and release hormones into the blood.

The anterior or glandular portion of the pituitary gland (adenohypophysis, see Figure 16.10) itself secretes six hormones whose structure and functions are well understood. These include ACTH (the "stress" hormone which controls activity of the adrenal glands), a thyrotrophic hormone controlling activity of the thyroid gland, which in turn regulates cellular metabolism, several gonadotrophic substances regulating activities of the ovaries and testes, and a somatotrophic substance that directly regulates tissue growth. Evidence is beginning to accumulate in favor of the hypothesis that release of several of these substances from the pituitary is under control of nerve cells from the infundibular and tuberal regions of the hypothalamus. Control is believed to be indirect in that neurons from these regions secrete substances into blood vessels that immediately supply the anterior portion of the pituitary. Hence control would be by local circulation from hypothalamus to pituitary gland.

Harris (1960) and Reichlin (1963) have carefully reviewed the evidence favoring this local circulation hypothesis. It has been shown that if the blood vessels going directly from the hypothalamus to the pituitary are cut, and a plate inserted to prevent them from regenerating, the loss in anterior pituitary function is marked and constant. The possibility that this is simply due to atrophy of the anterior pituitary resulting from loss of a portion of its blood supply is countered by the fact that if the vessels are simply cut and allowed to regenerate, exactly the same degree of atrophy results as occurs if regeneration is prevented by plate insertion. However with cutting but no plate insertion the anterior pituitary functions return to normal (i.e. when the local blood supply from the hypothalamus is established). Harris (1950) showed that there is a very close correlation between the degree of vascular regeneration and behavioral measures of endocrine function, such as reproductive capacity, following section of these blood vessels. Finally, if the adenohypophysis is transplanted to a region remote from the hypothalamus its functional activity is virtually abolished (Benoit, 1962 and Assenmacher, 1955; Greer et al., 1953). This is in marked contrast to the nearly normal functions of transplanted thyroid, adrenal, and gonads (ovaries and testes). In other words the peripheral endocrine glands can function anywhere so long as they have access to pituitary substances of the general blood circulation that control their activity. However, the anterior pituitary gland itself must have a direct blood flow from the hypothalamus to maintain normal functions.

The regions of the hypothalamus that seem to be crucially involved in control of anterior pituitary activity are indicated in Figure 16.11. The stippled areas in the figure indicate regions in which electrical stimulation and lesions have produced systematic changes in pituitary secretion.

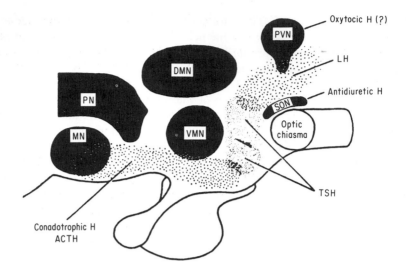

Figure 16.11. Diagram of a midline sagittal section through the hypothalamus and pituitary gland. Various hypothalamic nuclei (DMN), dorsomedial nucleus; MN, mammillary nuclei; PN, posterior nucleus; PVN, paraventricular nucleus; SON, supraoptic nucleus; VMN ventromedial nucleus) are indicated in black. The stippled areas indicate the sites where electrical stimulation or lesions have resulted in changes of pituitary secretion. (See text.) (From Harris, 1955)

The interrelations of the nervous system, particularly the hypothalamus, the anterior pituitary gland, and the peripheral target endocrine glands are well illustrated in the diagram of Figure 16.12, taken from Harris (1960). An interesting aspect of this regulatory system is the feedback actions of hormones secreted by the target organs on the activity of the hypothalamus and pituitary. For example, a rise in the blood concentrations of ovarian hormones exerts an effect on the CNS (probably the hypothalamus) which results in a decreased secretion of gonadotrophic hormone from the anterior pituitary. This in turn decreases the output of ovarian hormones from the ovaries.

A dramatic example of this type of feedback control by peripheral endocrine glands on CNS function is the recent observation that pre- and perinatal gonadal hormones exert an influence on the differentiation of neural tissues destined to mediate sexual behavior (Phoenix et al., 1959; Young, Goy, and Phoenix, 1964; Grady, Phoenix, and Young, 1965). Thus in the experiment by Grady et al., male rats were castrated at varying ages from 1 day to 90 days after birth, and females at 90 days, and their mating behavior as adults compared when given various hormones. The day 1 castrates displayed more female behavior than those castrated after day 5. In sum, their results indicated that feminization occurs in genotypic females or in either sex when gonads are absent. Masculinization occurs when androgen is present regardless of genotypic sex. It would seem that neural control mechanisms, likely involving the hypothalamus, are altered in the course of postnatal development by the presence or absence of various gonadal hormones in the rat. These data further suggest that development of adult male and female sexual morphology and behavior depends upon the presence of appropriate hormones during a *critical stage* of maturation. A striking example of this was provided by Whalen and Nadler (1963); they showed that a *single* injection of estrogen into the female rat on the fourth day after birth prevents the development of spontaneous sexual receptivity.

Another example of the feedback relations between the hypothalamus-pituitary system concerns response to stress. Some years ago Selye (1950) demonstrated that the pituitary releases ACTH in response to physiological stress. This in turn stimulates the release of adrenal cortical steroids. High blood levels of steroids in turn clamp down the pituitary release of ACTH. Accumulating evidence suggests a close relationship between this hypothalamic-pituitary function and conditioned avoidance learning. An example is shown in Figure 16.13, taken from a study by Brush and Levine (1966). The upper graph (solid line) illustrates performance of separate groups of rats on a second training session following an initial shock avoidance conditioning session. There is a marked inversion for the one hour group, the mean performance being considerably lower than for shorter

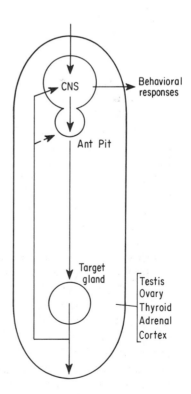

Figure 16.12.   To illustrate the reciprocal relationship between the central nervous system and endocrine system. The central nervous system mediates the effects of environmental changes, and exerts a regulatory influence over the anterior pituitary gland, which in turn controls the ovary, testis, thyroid, and adrenal cortex. The hormones from the latter glands in turn " feed back " to the central nervous system and pituitary gland to influence (1.) the behavior of the animal and (2.) the activity of the anterior pituitary. (From Harris, 1960)

or longer intersession intervals. The lower graph (solid line) of Figure 16.13 shows mean blood levels of corticosterone in other groups of animals at comparable times after an identical initial training session. The correspondence of the two curves is suggestive. Furthermore, injection of ACTH immediately after training (points labeled *A* in both groups; *P* and *S* refer to placebo and saline control injection groups) produces a marked elevation in both shock avoidance performance and, of course, blood sterone levels, for the one hour interval condition. In short, there is a direct correlation between blood levels of corticosterones and conditioned avoidance performance, both when the corticosterone level is the result of previous experience and when it is the result of ACTH injection.

We indicated earlier that the hypothalamus is perhaps the closest thing in the brain to a "center" (or collection of centers). The concept of centers is an

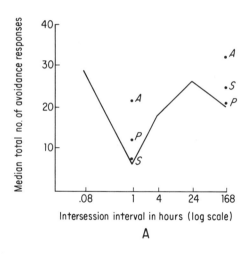

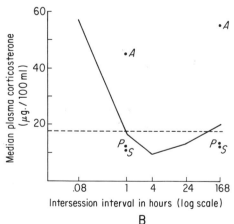

Figure 16.13. **A,** solid line represents mean number of avoidance responses by groups of rats in a second training session at various intersession intervals after an initial training session. Dots refer to groups given ACTH (*A*), placebo (*P*), or saline (*S*) injections one hour before the second training session. **B,** solid line represents median plasma levels of corticosterone in groups of rats measured at the same time intervals following an initial training session as those in the behavioral data given above. Dots refer to corticosterone levels one hour after injection of the same substances indicated above. (From Brush and Levine, 1966)

old one in the history of brain function, dating back at least to the days of phrenology. When thinking of brain function in terms of centers it is easy to be misled into "anthropomorphic" concepts, i.e. there is a small man inside the center who controls activity of the center. The brain is simply a series of interconnections from input to output, and no matter how complicated the wiring diagrams and interactions may be, every structure in the brain is part of some network, and has input and output connections. Electrical stimulation of the hypothalamus in the waking animal can produce a "rage" or a "fear" response. These behavior patterns are *integrated*, in that a wide variety of autonomic responses occur together in the same manner that they do in natural rage or fear. All the various components of these responses can also be elicited separately by stimulation of various brain stem regions concerned with autonomic reflexes. In addition some of the autonomic responses can be elicited by stimulation of higher regions such as the cerebral cortex, particularly from those regions that form portions of the limbic system such as the prefrontal and cingulate areas. However the hypothalamus is one of the few places *inside* the CNS in which electrical stimulation will yield an integrated pattern of emotional behavior.

Bard (1956) lists several generalizations which summarize current views of hypothalamic function rather concisely:

There is no reason to suppose that the hypothalamus is a center essential to various sympathetic reflexes . . .; these are managed by bulbospinal mechanisms. The sympathetic discharges obtained from the hypothalamus by punctate stimulation are to be attributed to activation of its own intrinsic mechanism. . . . The hypothalamic representation of the sympathetic is merely a part of the neural mechanisms which elaborate the patterned modes of behavior seen in strong emotional excitement and during exposure to cold. Furthermore, since these patterned responses are made up of the integrated actions of somatic and viseral effectors, it is a mistake to regard the hypothalamus as exclusively an autonomic center.

THE AMYGDALA

The attention of psychologists was first focused upon the amygdaloid region by the results of now classic experiments of Klüver and Bucy (1937). These workers reported a variety of striking behavioral alterations following bilateral removal of the temporal lobes in monkeys. Although their lesions included hippocampus, temporal neocortex and other structures as well as the anygdala, many of their findings have been replicated in experiments using more restricted lesions removing little more than the amygdala (see the recent review by Goddard, 1964). The behavioral syndrome following such lesions (the Klüver-Bucy syndrome) includes compulsive oral responses (putting all objects in the mouth), loss of fear and aggressiveness, hyper-sexuality, and increased activity.

The amygdala (or amygdaloid nucleus or anygdaloid complex), is a portion of the limbic system lying deep in the base of the temporal lobe (see Figure 16.14). In spite of very considerable research efforts, the functions of this large nuclear mass in the cerebrum remain enigmatic. Histological studies have subdivided the amygdala into a number of nuclei; however on the basis of such evidence as we possess concerning its functions and connections it is more convenient to divide it into two portions, a centromedial region receiving direct input from the olfactory bulb, and a basolateral portion which does not have olfactory connections (see Gloor, 1960). That the centromedial region plays a role in olfaction is not certain however, because the amygdala is well developed in the porpoise,

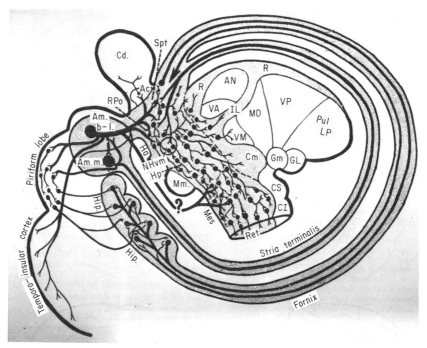

Figure 16.14.   Schematic representation of the neuronal organization of the amygdaloid projection system as revealed by electrophysiological studies. The stippled area indicates subcortical integrative structures regulating "global" somato-autonomic responses, diffuse projection mechanisms, and limbic structures projecting into this subcortical system. Key: Ac, anterior commissure; Am. b-1, basolateral subdivision of the amygdala; Am. m, corticomedial subdivision of the amygdala; AN, anterior thalamic nuclei; Cd, caudate nucleus; CI, inferior colliculus; Cm, center median thalamic nucleus; CS, superior colliculus; GL, lateral geniculate body; Gm, medial geniculate body; Ha, anterior hypothalamus; Hip, hippocampus; Hp, posterior hypothalamus; IL, intralaminar thalamic nuclei; LP, lateral posterior thalamic nucleus; MD, medial dorsal thalamic nucleus; Mes, mesencephalon; Mm, mammillary body; NHvm, ventromedial hypothalamic nucleus; Pul, pulvinar; R, reticular thalamic nucleus; Ret, reticular formation; Rpo, preoptic area; Spt, septal region; VA, ventral anterior thalamic nucleus; VM, ventral medial thalamic nucleus; VP, ventral posterior thalamic nucleus. (From Gloor, 1955)

in which there is complete absence of the primary olfactory system. The other major anatomical input to the amygdala is from the basal temporal cortex. It also apparently receives relatively direct connections from the reticular formation (Machne and Segundo, 1956). Major direct outputs from the amygdala go to the septal area, the hypothalamus, the caudate nucleus, and limbic portions of the cerebral cortex.

Considerable interest has centered on Klüver and Bucy's report that loss of fear and aggressiveness follows amygdalectomy. Goddard (1964) recently completed a careful survey of literature concerned with the behavioral effects of amygdalectomy. Taming and placidity, even of such ferocious animals as the wild Norway rat and the lynx, were obtained in a total of 43 studies. On the other hand, there are approximately ten experiments in which marked rage has developed following amygdalectomy. To take specific examples, Bard and Mountcastle at Johns Hopkins University (1947) found that amygdalectomy resulted in rage and hyposexuality. An equally careful experiment by Schreiner and Kling (1953), at Walter Reed, indicated that taming and hypersexuality followed amygdalectomy. Pribram (1962) has contrasted the behavior of Baltimore cats and Washington cats, and suggests that Hollywood cats have provided the answer. In an experiment by Green, Clemente, and De Groot (1957) at U.C.L.A., either rage or taming were produced by amygdalectomy. Pribram has proposed that territorial behavior may hold the key—the behavior of amygdalectomized cats is that of normal cats in home territory (i.e. cats may be most sexually aggressive and least fearful on home territory). After surgery cats can no longer make the distinction between home and foreign territories. On the other hand, Goddard (1964) notes that all animals in the Green et al. experiment that showed rage also had damage to the hippocampus and developed periodic epileptic seizures. Clearly the issue remains to be resolved.

A number of experiments suggest that amygdalectomy may interfere with avoidance learning. Thus amygdalectomy has retarded rate of acquisition of a conditioned avoidance response in rats (Robinson, 1963) and cats (Brady et al., 1954). Amygdalectomized monkeys rapidly extinguish preoperatively learned avoidance responses and are slow to acquire new avoidance responses. After learning, stronger levels of shock are necessary to maintain performance (Weiskrantz, 1956; Pribram and Weiskrantz, 1957; Weiskrantz and Wilson, 1955; 1958).

The amygdala also seems to play a role in social dominance. Rosvold et al. (1964) reported a drop in social dominance following the lesion if the animals are kept in group situations, but an increased aggressiveness if the animals are kept in individual cages. Pribram (1962) has noted that the effects of amygdalectomy on social behavior are as much a consequence of the immediate preoperative dominance situation as they are the consequence of the lesion itself. Pribram's graphic illustration of this is shown in Figure 16.15.

The amygdala has been implicated as a crucial structure in the development of psychomotor epilepsy (Jackson, 1889; Gibbs et al., 1937; Gloor, 1960). In man such seizures are relatively brief periods of confusion with subsequent lack of

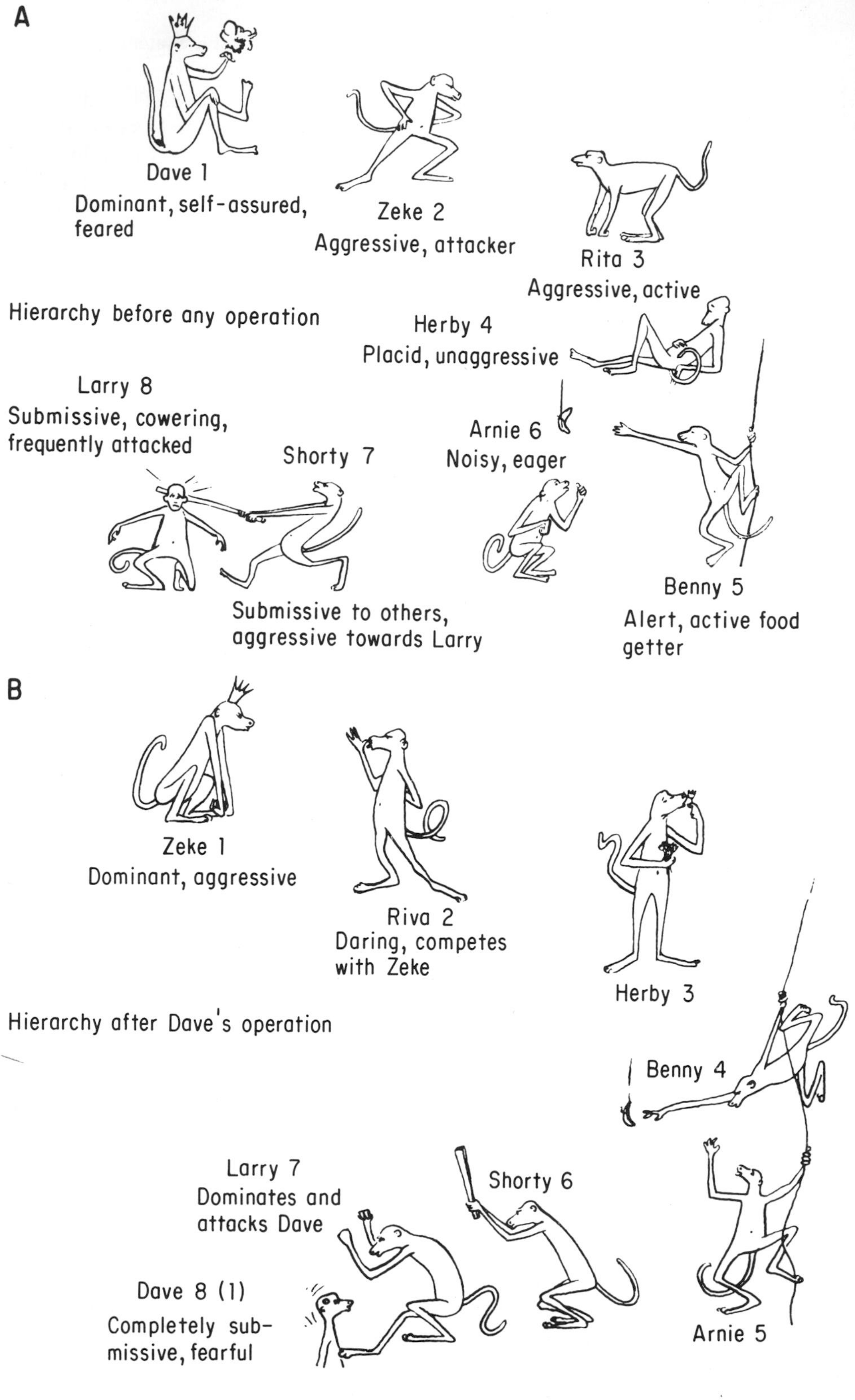

A

Dave 1
Dominant, self-assured, feared

Zeke 2
Aggressive, attacker

Rita 3
Aggressive, active

Hierarchy before any operation

Herby 4
Placid, unaggressive

Larry 8
Submissive, cowering, frequently attacked

Shorty 7

Arnie 6
Noisy, eager

Submissive to others, aggressive towards Larry

Benny 5
Alert, active food getter

B

Zeke 1
Dominant, aggressive

Riva 2
Daring, competes with Zeke

Herby 3

Hierarchy after Dave's operation

Benny 4

Larry 7
Dominates and attacks Dave

Shorty 6

Dave 8 (1)
Completely sub-missive, fearful

Arnie 5

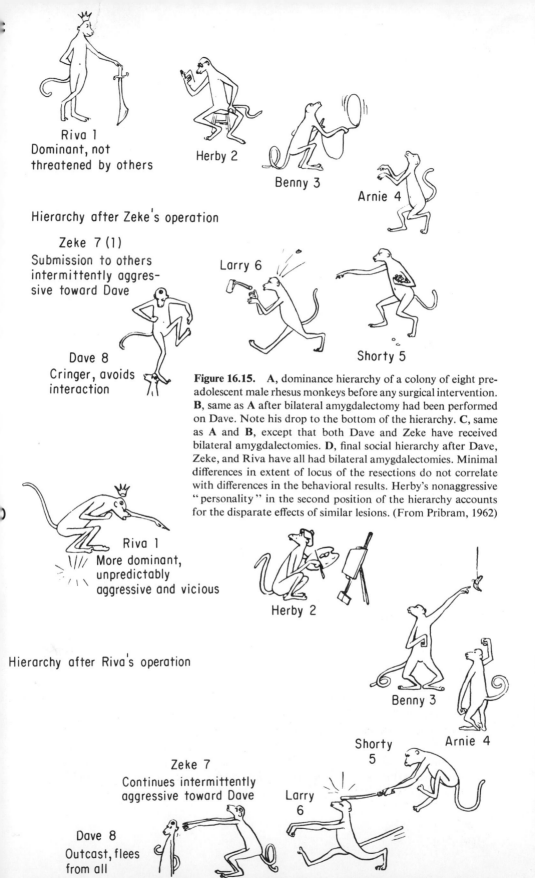

Riva 1
Dominant, not
threatened by others

Herby 2

Benny 3

Arnie 4

Hierarchy after Zeke's operation

Zeke 7 (1)
Submission to others
intermittently aggres-
sive toward Dave

Larry 6

Shorty 5

Dave 8
Cringer, avoids
interaction

Figure 16.15. A, dominance hierarchy of a colony of eight preadolescent male rhesus monkeys before any surgical intervention.
B, same as A after bilateral amygdalectomy had been performed
on Dave. Note his drop to the bottom of the hierarchy. C, same
as A and B, except that both Dave and Zeke have received
bilateral amygdalectomies. D, final social hierarchy after Dave,
Zeke, and Riva have all had bilateral amygdalectomies. Minimal
differences in extent of locus of the resections do not correlate
with differences in the behavioral results. Herby's nonaggressive
"personality" in the second position of the hierarchy accounts
for the disparate effects of similar lesions. (From Pribram, 1962)

Riva 1
More dominant,
unpredictably
aggressive and vicious

Herby 2

Hierarchy after Riva's operation

Benny 3

Shorty
5

Arnie 4

Zeke 7
Continues intermittently
aggressive toward Dave

Larry
6

Dave 8
Outcast, flees
from all

memory for the period of seizure. During the seizure however the patient may carry on a variety of organized behavior sequences, and if interrupted becomes aggressive. The behavioral expression of psychomotor epilepsy has been to some degree reproduced in animals by irritative lesions (produced by application of alumina cream) of the amygdala (Gastaut et al., 1953).

A vast array of autonomic reactions have been elicited by electrical stimulation of the amygdala, including respiratory changes, cardiovascular changes, gastrointestinal activity, uterine contractions, pupillary changes, salivation, piloerection, etc. (see Gloor, 1960). The most common "integrated" patterns of behavior following amygdaloid stimulation include feeding behavior, attention, fear and rage (Goddard, 1964). In a careful summary, Gloor (1960) finds no consistent areal localization of any of the reported responses to stimulation of the amygdala; almost any type of response can be elicited by stimulation of almost any region of the amygdala.

As should be clear from our discussion, it is impossible to make any general statement regarding the functions of the amygdala. It appears to be involved in a variety of emotional and motivational aspects of behavior, but does not seem to be essential for any type of behavior.

Hippocampus

The hippocampus is a rather large nuclear mass lying in the depths of the cerebrum, shaped grossly like a long curved tube (i.e. seahorse) bordering the floor of the lateral ventricle (see Figure 16.16). Like the amygdala it is a large nuclear structure, forming a portion of the limbic system, whose functions are unknown. Application of the classical experimental maneuvers of stimulation and lesion have produced no clear results when applied to the hippocampus. It was previously thought to be part of the olfactory system but the evidence to the contrary is now rather convincing. The porpoise, for example, has no peripheral olfactory system at all, but does have a large hippocampus. Moreover, this structure has its greatest elaboration in "microsomatic" (i.e. small smell) animals like man and other primates, where the primary olfactory system is very much underdeveloped. In primitive vertebrates, the earliest form of hippocampus is actually the prototype or initial portion of cerebral cortex to develop in the subsequent evolution of the brain. In other words, the first cerebral cortex to appear is hippocampus. As the true neocortex develops, the hippocampus becomes enfolded in the temporal lobe. The hippocampus receives direct connections from several regions of the limbic cortex (the entorhinal area, the presubiculum, and septal area) and sends all its efferent fibers out the fornix to the mammillary bodies of the hypothalamus, the diffuse thalamic system, and the brain stem.

The gross electrical activity recorded from the hippocampus in infraprimate mammals exhibits a characteristic slow (4 to 7 per second) "theta" rhythm

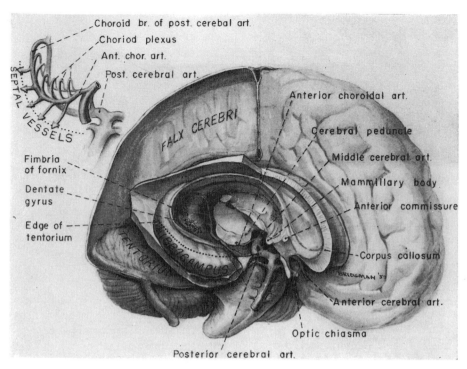

Choroid br. of post. cerebal art.

Choriod plexus

Ant. chor. art.

Post. cerebral art.

SEPTAL VESSELS

Anterior choroidal art.

FALX CEREBRI

Cerebral peduncle

Middle cerebral art.

Fimbria of fornix

Mammillary body

Dentate gyrus

Anterior commissure

Edge of tentorium

TENTORIUM

HIPPOCAMPUS

Corpus callosum

BRIDGMAN '57

Anterior cerebral art.

Optic chiasma

Posterior cerebral art.

Figure 16.16.   Drawing of a dissected human hippocampus. The hemisphere has been partially removed, the midbrain is cut across and the third ventricle exposed. The dotted line represents the edge of the tentorium which, as shown in the diagrammatic insert, crosses at right angles to the vessels which supply the hippocampus. In cases of temporal herniation they may be occluded. (From Green, 1960)

under certain conditions (see Figure 16.17). In particular, stimuli of any sensory modality which produce EEG arousal in the cerebral cortex will elicit a hippocampal theta rhythm (Jung and Kornmuller, 1938; Green and Arduini, 1954). In general when the neocortical EEG shows arousal the hippocampus shows theta activity, and when the cortical EEG is synchronized, the hippocampal activity is desynchronized. Thus the theta rhythm of the hippocampus is often referred to as the hippocampal arousal response. It is perhaps of interest that it is almost impossible to record the theta rhythm in the hippocampus of the monkey, except under conditions "likely to produce extreme emotional reactions" (Green, 1960). The rhythm can also be evoked by electrical stimulation of the midbrain reticular formation, the septal area, and the hypothalamus, but not by direct stimulation of the hippocampus itself (Green, 1960). Microelectrode studies of single hippocampal nerve cells have shown that bursts of cellular activity tend to occur in synchrony with the grossly recorded theta rhythm and can be evoked by essentially all types of sensory stimulation (Green and Machne, 1955).

Auditory

Figure 16.17. Examples of hippocampal theta activity in response to a sudden click stimulus; curarized rabbit with local anesthetics. L. hip, left hippocampus; R. hip, right hippocampus. (From Green and Arduini, 1954)

The histological organization of the hippocampus makes it a structure ideally suited for analyses of neuronal synaptic mechanisms in cortical tissue (Renshaw et al., 1940). In contrast to the six-layered structure of the cerebral cortex, it has only one densely packed layer of cells, the hippocampal pyramidal cells. These can be activated both monosynaptically (by electrical stimulation of input fiber systems) and antidromically (via electrical stimulation of the fornix). There have been several intracellular analyses of the mechanisms of synaptic activation in hippocampal pyramids (von Euler et al., 1958; Kandel, Spencer, and Brinley, 1961; Kandel and Spencer, 1961; Spencer and Kandel, 1961; Andersen, Eccles, and Løyning, 1963). Of particular interest are the long lasting IPSPs from recurrent inhibitory neurons which may control the frequency of the theta rhythm (Spencer and Kandel, 1962). The grossly recorded theta wave may itself represent primarily the summed IPSPs generated in the pyramidal cells; this same type of mechanism, you may recall, has been suggested for control of rhythmicity in the thalamus (see Chapter 15).

There has been considerable speculation about possible hippocampal function but there is a lack of solid evidence. The hippocampus has been implicated in emotion, visceral activity, immediate memory, and as a part of a behavioral suppressor system. For example, after the hippocampus has been removed in humans, a deficit in immediate memory is often observed (Milner and Penfield, 1955). Such a patient can remember quite well events that happened weeks or months ago but cannot recall what he had for breakfast. On the other hand, some of the emotional alterations seen in the Klüver-Bucy syndrome (see above) have been interpreted as being related to hippocampal damage (when the temporal lobe is removed, most of the hippocampus is also removed).

Kimble (1963) completed an extensive investigation of the behavioral deficits following bilateral hippocampectomy in rats. Both normals and cortical control lesion groups were used (the hippocampus was removed by suction, which necessitates removal of overlying cortex). He used a variety of tests, including open field exploratory behavior, visual discriminations, and maze learning. The hippocampal animals exhibited repetitive running behavior, being much more active in the open field situation, performed more poorly on the successive brightness discrimination, and made more errors in maze learning than did either control group. Both the hippocampal and cortical control lesion groups showed less than normal "passive avoidance" (animals are trained to approach a goal box for food, shocked in the goal box, and the degree of subsequent avoidance of the goal box measured). There were no indications of any changes in the emotionality of the hippocampal animals. The animals with hippocampal lesions also showed normal learning of a simultaneous brightness discrimination. Kimble summarizes his interpretation of these findings as follows: "at the present stage of our knowledge of brain function in general and hippocampal function in particular, any monolithic interpretation of the behavior of hippo-campectomized animals is likely to be an oversimplification. Although the present experiments do not fully clarify the role of the hippocampus in behavior, they do indicate that neither a motivational-emotional hypothesis nor a short term memory concept is able to account for the behavior of the hippocampals." On the other hand, Thomas and Otis (1958) found that lesions including portions of the hippocampus and the cingulate cortex caused a marked impairment in maze learning ability. It may be that it is necessary to damage both the hippocampus and certain portions of the cortical limbic system to produce learning deficits. Such joint damage effects are very likely to occur in humans with brain damage. Isaacson and Wickelgren (1962) have reported deficits on passive avoidance following hippocampal lesions, as occurs in cortical limbic and septal lesions (see p. 568).

Adey et al. (1960) has studied EEG activity of the hippocampus in cats during learning of a simple visual discrimination task. A rather complicated analysis of the data indicated that the phase relations (a measure of the "timing" of the waves) between wave patterns recorded from the deeper and the more superficial portions of the hippocampal cortex change as a function of learning. Early in learning the activity recorded from the deeper layers of the hippocampal cortex precedes that from the more superficial layers; later, when performance has improved, the reverse is the case. In this connection it is of interest that input to the deeper layers is from other deep structures of the brain, whereas input to the more superficial layers is from the adjacent entorhinal and cingulate cortex.

Green (1960) has pointed out that hypotheses relating the hippocampus to immediate memory, emotional behavior, etc., are based primarily on lesion and stimulation experiments, and must be viewed with considerable caution. The hippocampus has perhaps the lowest electrical seizure discharge threshold of any structure in the CNS (Jung, 1950). Stimulation and lesion techniques can easily induce seizure activity which becomes generalized, thus interfering with whatever ongoing behavioral responses the animal is making. The behavioral manifestations of hippocampal seizure activity have been described as analogous to those of psychomotor epilepsy in humans (see above). The fact that section of the fornix, which contains all output fibers connecting the hippocampus to the rest of the brain, has few behavioral effects supports the notion that the dramatic results of some hippocampal lesion and stimulation studies are an indirect result of seizure activity (Green, 1960).

LIMBIC PORTIONS OF THE CEREBRAL CORTEX

The cortical components of the limbic system are found mostly on the medial wall of the hemisphere, the base and tip of the temporal lobe, and the frontal pole (see Figure 16.18). These areas have been characterized as "juxtallocortex"

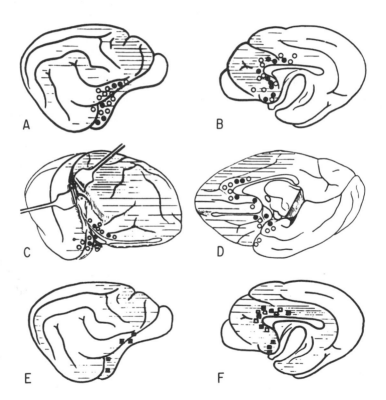

Figure 16.18.   Electrographic effects evoked upon electrical stimulation of the limbic region. Lateral and medial views of the cat's brain (**A–B** and **E–F**) and the monkey's brain (**C–D**). Sections **A** to **D**: Points from which generalized activation of the ECG was obtained upon electrical stimulation indicated by ●. Activation of the ECG mainly in the shaded areas, usually on both hemispheres, obtained upon stimulation of points indicated by ○. Sections **E–F**: Points from which generalized depression of the ECG was obtained upon electrical stimulation indicated by ■. Electrical after discharges in the shaded areas were occasionally produced by stimulation of points in the anterior limbic region indicated by □. At other times depression of the ECG was obtained in the same shaded areas as a result of anterior limbic stimulation. (From Kaada, 1951)

(Pribram and Kruger, 1954) separating neocortex from old structures such as the hippocampus and amygdala. Electrical stimulation of these medial regions of the cerebral cortex have elicited a wide variety of responses, particularly autonomic responses. These include respiratory changes, alterations in muscular tone, vocalization, eating movements, cardiovascular changes, alterations in gastric motility, pupillary changes, piloerection, GSR activity, etc., and changes in cortical EEG activity (see the reviews by Kaada, 1951; 1960).

In view of the richness and complexity of autonomic activity elicitable by stimulation of the cingulate and other regions of the limbic cortex, the almost universally negative findings of ablation studies are somewhat surprising. In general, there have been no changes in motor performance, no changes in muscular reflex activity, no disturbances of respiration, cardiovascular reflexes, gastrointestinal functions, pupillary activity and so on. The more general behavioral changes seem to be diminution of fear and rage, but these changes appear to be short lived, disappearing within a few weeks or months (Ward, 1948). Both Pribram and Fulton (1954) and Mirsky et al. (1957) have reported that virtually total ablation of the limbic cortex, including anterior cingulate gyrus, pre- and sub-callosal, and medial frontal areas does not lead to any prolonged alterations in the social behavior of monkeys. Bilateral removal of the cingulate cortex in cats does not appear to alter the threshold of rage behavior (Bard, 1950). Some experiments suggest that lesions of the anterior cingulate gyrus may somewhat impair conditioned avoidance learning. Thus, Peretz (1960) found that rats with bilateral lesions in the area of the anterior cingulate gyrus took significantly longer to learn a conditioned avoidance response. Control procedures indicated that the results could not be accounted for in terms of lessened responsiveness to electric shock per se. You may recall from Chapter 11 that portions of the Klüver-Bucy syndrome could be reproduced by ablations limited to cerebral cortex of the temporal lobe (Meyer, 1958). Pribram and Bagshaw (1953) have been able to reproduce much of the Klüver-Bucy syndrome with bilateral lesions restricted to the anterior ventral portion of the temporal lobes. One interesting deficit that has been reported in animals with cingulate lesions is a change in ability to control body temperature. Thus Showers and Crosby (1958) have recorded a transitory drop in bodily temperature in monkeys with lesions in either the anterior or posterior cingulate cortex. In addition, sweating activity increased following the operations. Resistance to anoxia also appears to be impaired by damage to a portion of the limbic cortex. Davis (1951) observed that monkeys with bilateral lesions quickly collapsed when exposed to an altitude equivalent to 10,000 feet although normal animals are able to maintain normal activity at this altitude for considerable periods of time. These two effects, skin temperature control and resistance to anoxia, are consistent with the autonomic activity elicitable by stimulation of the limbic portions of the cerebral cortex.

The *septal* area includes a portion of limbic cortex and also some underlying nuclei. Lesions of the septal area in rats have been reported to produce an exaggerated startle response and a much increased aggressiveness and irritability

(Brady and Nauta, 1953). These same authors report that septal lesions weakened conditioned emotional responses but had no effect on the acquisition of new emotional responses. Tracy and Harrison (1956) showed that septal lesions may abolish lever pressing to escape an aversive noise stimulus, but do not interfere with aquisition or retention of lever pressing for food reward using the same noise as the discriminative stimulus. In other words septal lesions may selectively impair avoidance behavior without impairing approach behavior. An extensive study by Thomas et al. (1959) examined the effects of septal lesions upon maze performance in rats. The results were quite clear-cut. Septal lesions produced marked increases in exploratory behavior and in some animals changes in emotionality as well. Those animals showing increased emotionality made significantly more errors in maze learning than did control animals or the less severely emotional lesion animals. Thomas et al., suggest that the increased error scores of the septal lesion animals that were emotional were attributable more to excessive and persistent exploratory behavior rather than to any basic impairment in learning ability.

Many studies showing impairments in avoidance conditioning have been interpreted in terms of an "emotional" deficit in animals with limbic cortex lesions. McCleary (1961) has effectively shown that such a unifactor explanation is unlikely. Using cats with cingulate or septal lesions and two different shock-motivated avoidance tasks, he found a double dissociation between the lesions and the tasks. Cingulate lesions produced a deficit on "active" avoidance (animal required to perform a response) but not "passive" avoidance (animal required to inhibit a response); septal lesions interfered with passive but not active avoidance. Clearly, a change in emotionality cannot account for both results. More recent data have complicated this interpretation as well. Zucker (1965) has shown that cats with septal lesions that are impaired on the passive avoidance task used by McCleary show an inability to inhibit responding on some tasks but not on others. A further complication in evaluating the results of limbic system lesions comes from studies by Harvey et al. (1965a; 1965b). Many septal lesion studies showing failure to establish a conditioned emotional response in rats used water reinforcement for bar pressing. Harvey has shown that septal rats are actually thirstier than normals. Either a stomach "preload" of water to the lesioned rats or an increase in time of water deprivation of the normal group makes the performance of both groups identical on the establishment of a CER with water reinforcement. These careful studies emphasize the preliminary nature of our knowledge regarding limbic system functions in the mediation of emotional behavior.

Structural and functional interrelations
of limbic structures

Figure 16.19 illustrates some of the better known anatomical interconnections among limbic structures (see Kappers et al., 1963; Nauta, 1958, 1962; Papez,

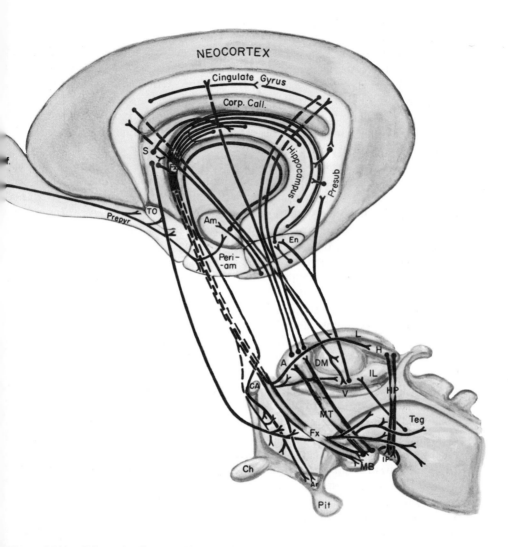

Figure 16.19. Schematic diagram of the principal anatomical relationships between the allocortex, the juxta-allocortex, and the several subcortical structures considered in the present treatment of the limbic system. The brain-stem portions of the system have been schematically displaced from the hilus of the hemisphere and represented in the lower half of the illustration in order to facilitate visualization of the numerous anatomical interconnections involving these structures. Abbreviations: A, anterior nucleus of the thalamus; Am, amygdaloid complex; Ar, arcuate nucleus; B.Olf, olfactory bulb; CA, anterior commissure; Ch, optic chiasm; Corp. Call, corpus callosum; DM, medial dorsal nucleus of the thalamus; En, entorhinal area; Fx, fornix; H, habenular comples; HP, habenulo-interpeduncular tract; IL, intralaminar thalamic nuclei; IP, interpeduncular nucleus; L, lateral thalamic nucleus; MB, mammillary body; MT, mammillothalamic tract; Periam, periamygdaloid cortex; Pit, pituitary; Pepyr, prepyriform cortex; Presub, presubiculum; S, septal region; Teg, midbrain tegmentum; TO, olfactory tubercle; V, ventral nucleus of the thalamus. (From Brady, 1961)

1937; Pribram and Kruger, 1954; Brady, 1961, 1962). The olfactory bulb projects directly to the olfactory tubercle, prepyriform cortex, periamygdaloid cortex, and a portion of the amygdaloid nucleus. The olfactory tubercle in turn projects to the *septal area*. The prepyriform and periamygdaloid cortical areas (lying on the base of the cerebral hemisphere) also receive projections from the *diffuse thalamic system*. The *entorhinal area*, lying just posterior to the periamygdaloid region, receives connections from the diffuse thalamic system and temporal neocortex, and projects to the *hippocampus*. This latter structure, embedded in the temporal lobe, also receives fibers from the presubiculum and from the septal area. All of its output is carried by a fiber bundle called the fornix. This projects to the *septal area*, several regions of the *hypothalamus*, the diffuse thalamic system, and the central gray of the midbrain. The *presubiculum*, all of whose output goes to the hippocampus, receives input from the cingulate gyrus and from the diffuse thalamic system. The *cingulate* gyrus in turn receives projections from the anterior thalamic nuclei and diffuse thalamic system. It projects to the presubiculum, several thalamic regions, the hypothalamus and several regions of the midbrain. The *amygdala*, lying near the base of the cerebrum, receives input from the olfactory bulb and the basal temporal neocortex, and sends fibers to the septal area and the hypothalamus. The septal area receives fibers from the hippocampus and amygdala, and connects to the thalamus, the hypothalamus, hippocampus, and brain stem. The reticular formation, finally, projects to the diffuse thalamic system, the hypothalamus, and the cerebral cortex, and receives projections from a variety of systems.

Perhaps the most significant generalizations to be made about all these structures are: one, they are all relatively directly interconnected with one another, and two, they all seem to be involved in one way or another with emotional aspects of behavior (some authorities feel that the hippocampus is an exception to this rule). Electrical stimulation of many limbic structures will elicit various types of autonomic responses. However, the hypothalamus appears to be the only structure where stimulation frequently evokes integrated emotional behavior patterns. Stimulation of other limbic structures will more commonly elicit only fragments of autonomic activity. Furthermore, integrated emotional behavior can occur in animals with all the neural tissue above the level of the hypothalamus removed. We will briefly examine two patterns of behavior; rage and electrical self-stimulation of the brain, which illustrate both the interrelations of the limbic structures and the difficulty of assigning specific roles to the various portions of the limbic system.

Emotional behavior

The classical studies by Bard and his colleagues provided the bulk of our information about the neural structures mediating rage. Bard (1928) showed that fully developed rage, with both autonomic and skeletal muscular components, could be elicited in decorticate cats only if the hypothalamus was intact. Section below the hypothalamus results in the animal showing only fragmented components of the response. As noted above, electrical stimulation of the hypothalamus can elicit directed rage behavior.

Many years ago Fulton and Ingram (1929) showed that cats with essentially total decerebration had low rage thresholds, exhibiting rage to mild and normally ineffective electrical stimulation of the skin. Bard and Mountcastle (1947) showed that if all neocortex is removed, but other areas of the cortex (i.e. limbic cortex) left intact, cats become extremely placid. If the limbic cortex of the medial wall is now removed, the animals become more subject to rage. If the amygdala is also bilaterally removed the animals become extremely ferocious. Bilateral removal of the amygdala alone may produce a ferocious cat or a placid cat. In general terms these results seem to suggest that the limbic cortex, and possibly the amygdala as well, serve to inhibit hypothalamic expression of rage, and the neocortex acts to lower rage reaction threshold. In addition, auditory and visual stimulation do not elicit rage in a totally decorticate cat but may do so in amygdalectomized animals. These findings are further complicated by the fact that removal of the amygdala in a ferocious animal such as the wild lynx produces a very docile and placid animal. Savage animals that have been made tame by amygdalectomy again become savage after lesions of the ventromedial nucleus of the thalamus, and animals made savage by septal lesions are then made placid by removal of the amygdala (Schreiner and Kling, 1953; Kling and Hutt, 1958).

To summarize (see Table 16.1), the hypothalamus is essential for integrative behavioral rage. The neocortex is important both in mediating and processing rage eliciting stimuli, and in permitting the animal to use sensory (e.g. visual) cues in making a directed rage attack. The role of the amygdala is ambiguous.

TABLE 16.1.   EFFECTS OF REMOVING VARIOUS CNS STRUCTURES ON INTEGRATED RAGE BEHAVIOR.*

Structure	Effect of removal on integrated rage behavior	Structure	Effect of removal on integrated rage behavior
Neocortex	↓	Amygdala +	
Limbic cortex	O	limbic cortex	↑
Neo + limbic cortex	↑	Amygdala + ventromedial nucleus (thalamus)	↑
Amygdala	↑ or ↓		
Septal area	↑	Hypothalamus	↓
Amygdala + septal area	↓	All tissue above hypothalamus	↑

* ↑ means increase in rage, and ↓ means decrease in rage.

Limbic cortex appears to play a similar but less important role than the amygdala. There is no one center for rage. The hypothalamus is the final common path for integrated expression of rage, but other components of the limbic system interact in a complex fashion in controlling emotional behavior.

Electrical self-stimulation of the brain

In 1954 Olds and Milner made the intriguing observation that rats would repeatedly deliver weak electric shocks to their own brains at high rates if the on-off switch was connected to a lever they could depress (see Figure 16.20). In terms of the volume of research that has been generated, this has been perhaps the most influential recent discovery in physiological psychology. Although the significance of the phenomenon remains somewhat obscure, it has seemed to many to provide an opening wedge to an understanding of the neural control of reward and reinforcement.

By far the most critical region of the brain for self-stimulation is the lateral

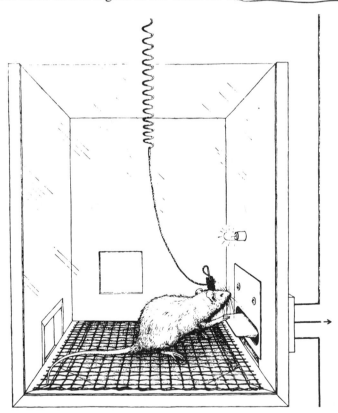

Figure 16.20.   Experimental arrangement for intracranial self-stimulation. When the rat presses the lever it triggers an electrical stimulus to its brain and simultaneously records action via wire at left. (From Olds, 1956)

hypothalamus, particularly that portion bordering the medial forebrain bundle. Most structures of the limbic system, including parts of the septal area, the amygdala, pyriform cortex, cingulate gyrus, hippocampus, and diffuse thalamic system yield moderate to very mild rates of self-stimulation (Olds, 1962). The septal area, initially thought to be the critical locus, now appears to be for the most part neutral or to give contradictory results (Olds, 1962). Interestingly, fairly high rates of self-stimulation can also be obtained if the electrodes are placed in the olfactory bulb (Phillips, 1964, personal communication). Electrical self-stimulation has been obtained in a variety of other species including cat, goldfish, pigeon, monkey, porpoise, and man. In the latter, verbal reports of stimulation have been vague but include such terms as "feeling of well being" and "extreme euphoria" (Heath and Mickle, 1960; Sem-Jacobsen and Torkildson, 1960). As might be expected, a number of regions of the brain produce avoidance behavior when stimulated (see Delgado, 1955; Roberts, 1958). Such negatively reinforcing areas include the medial lemniscus, spinothalamic tracts, central gray, ventrobasal complex of the thalamus, fornix, hippocampus, and other structures.

The relation of electrical self-stimulation to more ordinary forms of reward or reinforcement such as hunger, thirst, or sex drive reduction is unclear (Olds, 1958; Hodos and Valenstein, 1960). There are interrelationships, for example, between degree of hunger and self-stimulation rate for lateral hypothalamic stimulation (Hoebel and Teitelbaum, 1962). Self-stimulation can also serve to establish learned responses. However, complications have been introduced by studies showing that stimulation of a given region with a given stimulus may be either reinforcing or inhibiting depending upon training procedures, stimulus duration, and testing environment (Roberts, 1958; Bower and Miller, 1958; Brown and Cohen, 1959). Furthermore, when the electrical stimulus is turned off, extinction of the lever pressing response is generally very rapid, and under some conditions may appear to have an intrinsic decay time whether or not extinction responses are actually made (Deutsch and Howarth, 1963). Thus under conditions of continuous reinforcement the number of extinction lever presses an animal will make is a direct function of the length of time he has been held away from the lever. However, electrical self-stimulation can be established on intermittent reinforcement schedules where the stimulus is given very infrequently with considerable opportunity for extinction.

Concomitant recording of electrical activity during self-stimulation has suggested one possible explanation for the behavioral control exerted by such stimulation (Porter, Conrad, and Brady, 1959). Epileptic-like seizure discharges in the septal area, hypothalamus, and hippocampus seem to accompany self-stimulation. In other words rapid self-stimulation may in part be under the control of neural seizure rather than serving as a simple reward substrate. These observations are consistent with the low seizure thresholds of several components of the limbic system (see above), and possibly with the intrinsic decay time of lever pressing extinction.

The study of neural mechanisms and behavioral concomitants of electrical self-stimulation continues to be an area of considerable research activity in physiological psychology. In some interesting observations, Olds (1962) reported operant conditioning, via electrical brain stimulation, of single nerve cell discharges. The procedure involves first obtaining a single nerve cell response (extracellularly) and then delivering an electrical stimulus to the critical medial forebrain bundle area each time the unit fires spontaneously. Olds reports that unit firing can be increased (conditioned?) by such pairing for units in the cingulate gyrus, pyriform cortex and hippocampus, but not for neocortical cells.

CONCLUDING REMARKS

It is necessary to exhibit considerable caution in making global conclusions regarding the functions of the limbic system in emotional behavior. Autonomic responses in an integrated emotional pattern can also be elicited by strong shocks to the skin. Is the skin therefore part of the limbic system? Furthermore, the skeletal musculature is necessarily involved in the expression of emotional behavior, yet by definition it is not autonomic. The point of these strictures is simply to reemphasize the fact that the nervous system is a network of *interconnections*. Essentially all neural structures are involved in most integrated ongoing behavior patterns. The hypothalamus does have a special significance for emotional behavior. Stellar has characterized it as the generalized "final common path" for emotional expression. Other structures of the limbic system such as the hippocampus and the amygdala may in some instances generate autonomic activity only indirectly as a result of seizure initiation.

In this chapter we discussed a variety of specific behaviors such as hunger, emotional expression, and sex, but have avoided the more inclusive problems relating neural functions to general aspects of drive and motivation. As we noted at the beginning of the chapter, the term "motivation" is used to indicate that organisms engage in activity and "drive" commonly refers to the "energizing" aspects of motivation. Hull (1943) was perhaps the first to elaborate a molar behavioral analysis of generalized drive. Brown (1961) further developed the idea that drive is a nondirective energizing aspect of behavior and that learning provides direction for drive. Whatever the specific force of a drive, either hunger, thirst, etc., the net result is a change in general drive level. Stellar (1954) has presented a comprehensive summary diagram of many of the physiological factors contributing to the control of motivated behavior (see Figure 16.21). In his scheme the hypothalamus is considered to be the final common path for controlling behavioral motivation. Lindsley (1951), Hebb (1955) and others have suggested that the reticular formation might well be implicated in motivation and in fact serve as the neural substrate of Hull's general drive. However, some evidence indicates that electrical stimulation of the reticular formation may actually serve to decrease rather than increase drive level (Vierck, 1965). Brown

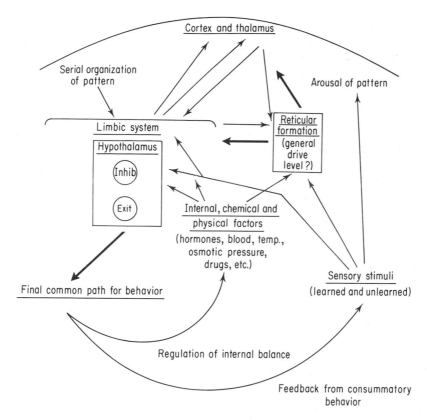

Figure 16.21. Schematic summary of some of the factors and structures that may be involved in the control of motivated behavior. (Modified from Stellar, 1954)

et al. (1967) have proposed a "graduated" drive theory, substituting a degree of specificity for drive in terms of stimulus conditions, that may well be more consistent with current data regarding the organization of the reticular formation. Alternatively, it has been argued that "drive" and "motivation" have no meaning in a generalized sense; instead the specific behavior patterns of animals can be analyzed and predicted in terms of specific situational and physiological determinants (see discussion by Zeigler, 1964).

Suggested readings

Field, J. (Ed.) *Handbook of physiology. Section I: neurophysiology.* Vol. II. Washington, D.C.: American Physiological Society, 1960.

McCleary, R. A., and Moore, R. Y. *Subcortical mechanisms of behavior.* New York: Basic Books, 1965.

Sheer, D. E. (Ed.) *Electrical stimulation of the brain.* Austin: University of Texas Press, 1961.

17

THE NEURONAL BASIS OF LEARNING

Т
he fundamental problem in physiological psychology is considered by many to be the nature of the physical-chemical changes underlying learning. Learning, broadly conceived as response modification resulting from experience, is undoubtedly the most widespread and important behavioral characteristic of higher animals. Because all behavior is a reflection of the actions of the nervous system, any normal changes in behavior such as learning must be the result of changes in the behavior of the nervous system. Because the nervous system is nothing more than a physical-chemical system, albeit a highly complicated one, any changes in the behavior of the nervous system must in turn reflect physical-chemical changes of one type or another.

The above reasoning is perhaps just an involved way of saying that learning involves the formation of physical "engrams" in the brain. The term "engram" has come into disrepute in recent years, perhaps because it has often been used to mean *localized* memory traces established in particular places in the brain. In the middle twenties Lashley (1929) set out to find the "engrams" formed in the cortex of the rat during maze learning. The results of his experiments, which indicated that the amount of cortex removed was the crucial factor and not the region from which it was removed, forced him and most other psychologists to abandon the whole concept of localized engrams for particular learned behaviors. This in no way negates the fact that physical changes in the brain must underlie learning. However, the nature of these physical changes remains completely obscure.

Three general strategies are being used today in the search for the physical basis of learning and memory. These approaches might be termed the *electrical correlates* of learning, the *biochemical correlates* of learning, and the analysis of *model systems* exhibiting "learning." We considered studies of the electrical correlates in our discussion of EEG and evoked response changes associated with learning in Chapter 15. One of the problems inherent in this approach is our inability at present to specify the kinds of activity in individual nerve cells which yield the electrical events recorded. This is particularly true for gross EEG and evoked response measures. Even assuming that consistent correlations between changes in the gross indices of brain activity and behavioral modifications will someday be established, we may still be unable to specify the kinds of alterations in synaptic interactions among neurons underlying such changes.

Studies of the biochemical correlates of learning are somewhat comparable to electrical studies in that intact organisms are normally trained in some type of learning situation, and chemicals are then extracted from the nerve tissue and analyzed. Although much of this work has been done at a gross tissue level, Hydén and his associates have perfected an exceedingly delicate dissection technique permitting analysis of substances removed from identified single nerve cells.

The difficulty of the search for electrical and chemical correlates of learning in the intact organism is compounded by the immense organizational complexity of the intact mammalian nervous system. The analysis of "learning" in the model neural system approaches the problem from the other end of the scale. A simplified neural system is chosen, in which some degree of analysis of the neuronal (i.e. synaptic) mechanisms underlying the behavior of the system is feasible, and learning or other types of response modifications are induced in the system. In this chapter we will take a brief look at the general nature of learning, at the biochemical and model systems approaches to learning, and conclude with a short survey of current views on the physical basis of learning and memory. The reader may wish to consult the review by Sharpless (1964) for a comprehensive discussion of the general problem of reorganization of function in the nervous system. Deutsch (1962) has carefully reviewed developments in the physiological bases of learning. The symposium on the "anatomy of memory" (Kimble, 1965) contains a wealth of material.

GENERAL CONSIDERATIONS OF LEARNING

The properties of any physical substrate or model of learning must be consistent with the known behavioral characteristics of learning. This point cannot be too strongly emphasized. It is obvious that a neural model must be in 'accord with the known facts of neural function. The necessary consistency with behavioral phenomena has often seemed less evident, perhaps because it is somewhat more removed. A neural model is at a more molecular level of discourse than behavioral observations. As Hebb (1958) has emphasized, if a neural model of learning is to be useful, the behavioral characteristics of learning must be deducible in a consistent fashion from the model. As an example, suppose a model asserts that extinction of a conditioned response is due to a simple dropping out of synaptic connections resulting from the passage of time. If this is the case, spontaneous recovery of the conditioned response, which almost invariably occurs after extinction, cannot possibly be predicted from the model. Consequently the *model* must be changed; the behavioral observation cannot be wished out of existence (see Hebb's 1958 discussion).

A nice illustration of this same general point has been noted by McGaugh (1965, pp. 240–241):

Some old work by Liddel will, I think, serve to illustrate the problem. Liddel first conditioned a sheep to flex its leg at the sound of a bell in order to avoid an electrical shock which was delivered to an electrode under its foot. After this conditioned response was well established, the sheep was picked up, turned over, and placed on its back so that its head was resting on the electrode. The bell was then rung and, instead of flexing its leg, the sheep stretched all four legs and lifted its head up from the platform. In attempting to define memory, I would emphasize a storage process which would allow for this change in response with changes in stimulus conditions.

General definitions of learning or conditioning all emphasize that it is a change in behavior under conditions of practice. However the term "learning" really implies much more than this. Habituation, fatigue, adaptation, sensitization, pseudoconditioning, imprinting, narcotics addiction, and many other phenomena could all be included in such a nonspecific descriptive category. William James (1890), and more recently Konorski (1948), have proposed that a more inclusive term, *behavioral plasticity*, be used to refer to all aspects of relatively long lasting response modification. Each particular phenomenon is then defined in terms of its own characteristics. Thus conditioning requires presentation of a conditioned stimulus (CS) followed by an unconditioned stimulus (UCS). If the UCS is given before the CS (backward conditioning) no conditioning develops. *Sensitization*, on the other hand, can occur without conditioning. If the UCS is given alone, a "sensitized" response may be elicited by subsequent presentation of the CS, even without previous CS-UCS pairing (see Hilgard and Marquis, 1940). To take examples of response decrement, *habituation* usually means a decrease in behavioral response resulting from repeated presentations of the UCS. However, it is commonly distinguished from *receptor adaptation*, in which the decrement can be attributed to decreased responsiveness in sensory receptors to the stimulus, as in adaptation of the pacinian corpuscle to a constant pressure (see Harris, 1943). Although the physical basis of learning may well be the most significant question for physiological psychology, it should be emphasized that all aspects of behavioral plasticity pose important problems for the physiological analysis of behavior.

We noted in Chapter 15 that many examples of "conditioned" changes in EEG activity or evoked responses may instead be examples of sensitization or pseudoconditioning. To determine what aspect of behavioral plasticity is most closely related to a given alteration in neural function, a number of controls are required. The *parametric* characteristics of the behavioral and neural changes must be defined. "Parametric" here simply refers to the types of changes in response that occur when different values of a stimulus or training variable are used. One of the characteristic parameters of conditioning is the time relations of the CS and UCS: the occurrence and magnitude of the conditioned response is a function of this time relation. Changes in an evoked response must correlate with this and other parameteric characteristics of behavioral conditioning before they can be considered to reflect neural processes underlying conditioning. Thus any physical substrate of learning must be consistent with the known parametric features of learning.

In the following discussion we will use classical and instrumental conditioning to illustrate the learning process (in the physiological literature classical conditioning is often termed "type I" and instrumental conditioning termed "type II"). The basic difference between the two is simply that in instrumental conditioning the response of the animal is instrumental in determining whether or not the UCS or "reinforcing stimulus" will occur. In classical conditioning, the responses of the animal are irrelevant to the occurrence of the UCS. If leg flexion produced by a shock UCS is conditioned to a tone, instrumental conditioning procedures are such that when the leg flexes to the tone, the shock is avoided. In classical conditioning, the shock will be delivered to the leg whether or not the conditioned leg flexion occurs to tone. When an "unpleasant" UCS such as shock is used, instrumental escape or avoidance conditioning is usually more effective (Brogden et al., 1938). However, in situations in which a "non-noxious" stimulus such as food reward is used, classical and instrumental procedures are both very effective (Pavlov, 1927; Skinner, 1938). For our purposes these differences are relatively unimportant. Both classical and instrumental conditioning exhibit many similar parametric characteristics (see Hilgard and Marquis, 1940; Brogden, 1951; Kimble, 1961):

1. Up to a point, the stronger the UCS, the more rapid is the conditioning.
2. The most effective time relations for conditioning appear to be when the CS begins about 1/2 second prior to the UCS. As the time between CS and UCS increases, the efficiency of conditioning decreases. Backward conditioning does not occur.
3. The greater the time between trials, the fewer the trials required for conditioning.
4. If the CS is repeatedly given without the UCS after conditioning has occurred, the conditioned response will extinguish.

5. Following extinction, the conditioned response to the CS will exhibit spontaneous recovery in the absence of UCS presentations.
6. If reinforcement is given on only part of the trials, conditioning occurs more slowly but is more resistant to extinction.
7. If a response is conditioned to one stimulus it will generalize to other stimuli. The greater the dissimilarity between stimuli, the less generalization will occur.
8. If an additional neutral stimulus is paired with the CS after conditioning, it will subsequently elicit conditioned responses.
9. If conditioning and extinction series are repeated, both processes will occur progressively more rapidly.

A satisfactory neurophysiological model of learning should be able to predict all these and a number of other more specialized characteristics of conditioning.

Although there are several analyses of hypothetical brain processes in learning (Hilgard and Marquis, 1940; Hull, 1943; Konorski, 1948; Hebb, 1949), to date there have been no systematic attempts to deduce the phenomena of learning from neural models stated in terms of specific neural processes. We seem to know a good deal more today about what the neural basis of learning is *not* than about what it is. For example, a common view of learning holds that conditioning involves increases in synaptic efficacy resulting from use. In other words, the more often the conditioned stimulus and the conditioned response occur together, the greater is learning. Actually just the opposite is the case. Repeated presentations of the CS *without the UCS* leads to extinction of the conditioned response, not to increased responding. As Sharpless (1964) points out, use alone is perhaps a necessary but certainly not a sufficient condition for learning. We noted earlier that extinction cannot be simply a fading away of synaptic connections due to disuse, because spontaneous recovery of the extinguished response occurs.

In evaluating the experiments and theories concerned with the physical basis of behavioral plasticity discussed below, it is well to keep in mind the constraints imposed on physical models by the characteristics of the behavioral phenomena.

BIOCHEMICAL STUDIES OF LEARNING

Acetylcholine

Perhaps the most ambitious studies of the biochemical correlates of learning have come from the Berkeley group (see reviews by Rosenzweig, Krech, and Bennett, 1960; Bennett, Diamond, Krech, and Rosenzweig, 1964). You will recall that acetylcholine (ACh) is known to act as a synaptic transmitter at the neuromuscular junction and in one type of spinal cord synapse. It is widely distributed in the brain and appears a likely candidate for a possible excitatory synaptic transmitter substance. On the basis of such evidence Rosenzweig, Krech, Bennett, and their co-workers at the University of California adopted the reasonable hypothesis that correlations might exist between measures of acetylcholine levels in various regions of the brain and measures of behavior. Unfortunately, reliable assay techniques for ACh were not available at that time so they used methods measuring amount of acetylcholine esterase (AChE) activity. AChE, remember, is the enzyme that inactivates ACh when the latter is released at neuromuscular junctions or other sites. Because the main function of AChE is to inactivate ACh, it initially seemed a reasonable assumption that AChE levels would reflect concentrations of ACh. In contrast to ACh, reliable techniques for assaying concentrations of AChE were available.

The behavioral test they employed to measure what they termed "adaptive behavior" was an unsolvable maze (see Figure 17.1). At each choice point the

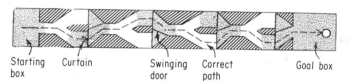

Starting box	Curtain	Swinging door	Correct path	Goal box

Figure 17.1.   Floor plan of the unsolvable maze used in studies relating brain ACh and adaptive behavior. (From Krech, 1932)

animal faced a lighted alley and a dark alley. The lighted alley was correct half the time and the dark alley half the time. By the same token the right alley was correct half the time and the left alley was correct half the time. Thus any given cue is associated with the correct choice only half the time, and regardless of the animal's selection of cues, his performance in terms of correct choices will always be at a chance level. In this type of impossible maze, rats typically tend to adopt either a visual "hypothesis," i.e. go always to the light side or always to the dark side; or a spatial "hypothesis," i.e. always left or always right. Cortical AChE content was assayed on small blocks of tissue taken from the somatic sensory, visual or other areas after the brain had been frozen (see Figure 17.2).

Their initial experimental hypothesis was:

The rats' spatial or visual preferences in attempting to solve a spatial-visual problem are a function of the relatively greater AChE activity in the somatic sensory or visual area, respectively, of the cerebral cortex.

Unfortunately the hypothesis was not confirmed. Rats showing a strong spatial "hypothesis" had significantly greater AChE in the somatic sensory cortex, the visual cortex, the motor cortex, and in fact in all cortical areas.

The next hypothesis was phrased in more general terms:

Over-all levels of cortical AChE activity are positively related to efficiency of synaptic transmission and are therefore positively correlated with problem-solving ability.

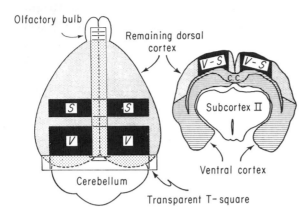

Figure 17.2. To the left, dorsal aspect of the rat brain, showing how samples of the visual cortex (*V*) and of the somesthetic cortex (*S*) are dissected, guided by a small transparent T-square. To the right, a transverse section of the rat brain. Total cortex is made up of four samples: the *V* and *S* sections—telescoped together in this diagram—plus the remaining dorsal cortex, plus the ventral cortex. The rest of the brain, labeled Subcortex II here, includes the olfactory bulbs and the cerebellum. (From Bennett, Diamond, Krech, and Rosenzweig, 1964)

Before considering their experimental findings, it may perhaps be instructive to analyze the assumption involved in this hypothesis. The first assumption is, of course, that levels of AChE accurately reflect levels of ACh. Second, the inferred levels of ACh are assumed to reflect concentrations at neural synapses. Third, ACh is assumed to be the major synaptic transmitter, and is assumed to be excitatory, i.e. the transmitter substance at excitatory synapses. Finally, it is assumed that the concentrations of this supposed excitatory transmitter substance are positively correlated with problem solving ability.

Tower (1958) has pointed out that the first assumption must be in error. AChE is present in the CNS in much greater concentrations than necessary to inactivate ACh. Furthermore it is present in two forms: "true" AChE found in association with nerve cells, and "pseudo" or serum AChE, present in the blood and all body tissues including glial cells in the brain (see Chapter 5). The assay technique used by the Berkeley group did not distinguish between the two types and hence did not necessarily reflect amount of AChE associated with nerve cells, let alone the amount of ACh. As far as ACh acting as the one and only transmitter is concerned (second and third assumptions), it appears unlikely that ACh is the transmitter substance at many central excitatory synapses (e.g. monosynaptic excitation in the spinal cord). Furthermore, inhibitory synaptic actions are fully as important as excitatory synaptic actions in neural functions; hence any theory that excludes inhibitory actions from consideration must be incomplete. Finally, there would seem to be questionable justification for assuming that amount of an hypothetical excitatory transmitter substance would correlate with problem-solving ability. If any one neural factor has a general correlation with behavioral complexity it is the increase in the complexity of anatomical and physiological organization of the CNS. The wiring diagram may well be much more important than how much "juice" is available at the synapses. However, in spite of these problems, the hypothesis yielded much valuable research.

Rosenzweig, Krech, Bennett, and several of their associates completed a number of experimental tests of this second hypothesis, using a variety of learning tasks such as maze learning. Results tended not to support the hypothesis. There was a general tendency for correlations between number of errors in maze learning and AChE concentrations to be positive. Correlations were quite low but nonetheless significant. If hypothesis 2 were correct, the correlation should be negative and large—animals with greater cortical AChE should make fewer errors in maze learning.

Despite the negative results regarding the hypothesis, many interesting observations came out of these studies. Genetic background was found to be a factor of importance. Descendants of the Tryon Maze Bright strain of rats (bred for maze learning ability) had significantly greater AChE than did descendants of the Tryon Maze Dull strain. Further studies of genetic influence indicated that level of AChE was positively related to learning ability in some strains but negatively related in others. The relation of cortical and subcortical AChE is a further complication. Subcortical AChE was related to brain weight but cortical AChE was not. However, the ratio of cortical and subcortical AChE did seem, under some conditions, to have reliable relationships with behavior.

As a result of their experiments the Berkeley group have concurred that there is no necessary relationship between ACh levels and measured AChE levels. Their final hypothesis relating brain activity and learning (in 1960) read:

Learning capacity is related to the levels of both ACh and AChE, such that, within limits, the greater the amount of ACh functioning at the synapse, the greater the efficiency of transmission, and consequently the greater the learning ability.

This hypothesis obviates the problems involved in inferring ACh from measured AChE, but leaves open some of the other issues noted above.

Bennett, Diamond, Krech, and Rosenzweig (1964) reviewed recent experiments indicating that the early environmental experience of rats has a marked influence on the concentrations of adult brain AChE, and even on the weight and thickness of the cerebral cortex. In typical experiments, two groups of rats were used: an experimental group raised in a "rich" early environment (see Figure 17.3); and a control group, litter mates of the experimental group comparable in every possible way, raised in an impoverished environment. The net results indicated that the "rich" group had a significantly thicker and heavier cerebral cortex, and a significantly greater amount of AChE in the cortex. Actually the AChE content was less in the "rich" group on a weight basis, but the total amount was much greater because of the increased size of the cerebral cortex. Additional control experiments seemed to rule out differential handling of the animals, and negative effects of isolation in the control group, as possible contaminating variables.

These experiments are an excellent example of how research develops following a seemingly clear-cut discovery. Initially it appeared that ACh levels might be related to behavior in a simple way, i.e. a positive relationship between learning ability and cortical ACh content. However, the measure of AChE,

Figure 17.3. The "rich" early environment of experimental animals in the study by Bennett, Diamond, Krech, and Rosenzweig (1964)

which was thought to assay ACh, appears to vary independently. AChE activity in turn is related to a variety of other variables such as genetic background, brain weight, and region of brain. The nature of early experience was shown to have a marked effect not only on brain chemistry but on the thickness of cortex as well. These findings are all clearly of importance and will have much influence on subsequent research in neurochemistry and behavior.

Ribose nucleic acids

Considerable research is currently being devoted to the possible role of ribose nucleic acids (RNA) in learning. You may recall from Chapter 5 that RNA content of nerve cells varies with their activity, is intimately involved in the manufacture of cellular protein, and becomes depleted in the absence of neural activity. Halstead (1951) was perhaps the first to suggest that memory engrams might be stored in "template" protein molecules in nerve cells. More recently Hydén has postulated that RNA may form the molecular basis of learning.

Hydén and his associates have published a number of experiments in which animals trained in various learning situations were found to have altered nerve cell RNA content and structure. We will examine some of the experimental findings before considering the possible mechanisms whereby RNA might serve as a memory coding system.

An experiment by Hydén and Egyhazi (1962) is perhaps one of the more carefully controlled to date, and has been widely quoted. Young rats were required to learn to balance on a "tight wire" to reach a platform containing food. They could only obtain food in this manner. Performance improved rapidly until, after several days of training, they could cross the tight wire easily. At this point the animals were sacrificed and the Deiters cells (large neurons in the vestibular nuclei of the brainstem that are 2nd order sensory neurons receiving input from the vestibular portion of the 8th cranial nerve) were removed and analyzed for RNA content. Two control groups were used, one group of normal animals that had no treatment and another group spun daily in a small "rat centrifuge." The latter group served as a control for activation of the vestibular system, per se. The average RNA content of cells in the experimental groups was 751 micromilligrams, for the spun control group was 722 micromilligrams, and for the untreated control group was 683 micromilligrams. It was concluded that the numerically higher mean concentration in the experimental group cells resulted from their learning to walk the tight wire. They also reported changes in the relative composition of RNA for the groups. Thus the percentage adenine in RNA was 24.1 percent for the experimental group, 21.3 percent for the spun control group, and 21.4 percent for the untreated control. The percentage uracil was decreased from 20.5 to 18.2, producing a shift in the adenine to uracil ratio. Hydén argues in later works (1965) that it is this change in base ratio which is specific to the learning process; quantitative changes occur as a result of activity per se, but he reports qualitative alterations only in the experimental group. Hydén and Egyhazi (1963) reported that the RNA content of glial cells in Deiters nucleus was found to have a similar relative composition. Hydén and associates have done a variety of other experiments similar to the one just described (see Gaito, 1966).

There are serious problems of interpretation in evaluating these intriguing findings. Perhaps the most important difficulty concerns the functional equivalence of the neural activation for the spun controls and the tight-wire experimentals. Clearly quite different situations obtained: the spun animals are passively spun and the experimentals must walk a tight wire. The animals, and the vestibular nuclei, are doing quite different things in the two situations, irrespective of possible "learning" effects. Because RNA is known to vary with degree of neural activity, irrespective of learning (Chapter 5), it is necessary to control amount of neural activity in order to determine the extent to which any change in RNA content or structure is related to the learning aspect of the situation. Unfortunately there have been no experiments to date using control groups adequate to demonstrate a change in RNA as a result of *learning* rather than merely as a result of different levels of neural activity.

Quite different types of evidence have also been obtained purporting to show that RNA plays a significant role in memory. Intact animals have been fed RNA and their performance in learning situations measured. Thus Cameron and Solyom (1961) reported that administration of RNA to aged individuals brought about memory improvement. In an extensive study by Cook et al. (1963) rats were injected with doses of RNA. The rats were trained to jump on a pole from a shock grid floor to avoid shock when a buzzer was turned on (i.e. conditioned avoidance response). The RNA treated animals learned significantly better than the controls and were slower to extinguish the conditioned response. Unfortunately, these experiments do not control for possible nutritive and other "side" effects of RNA. (It is possible that animals and humans performed better in these learning situations because of more adequate health resulting from RNA administration.) In any event, such experiments cannot be said to provide direct evidence for the function of RNA in learning.

An alternative type of experiment concerns injection of substances that inactivate RNA metabolic functions. Thus, Dingman and Sporn (1961) injected 8-azaGuanine (an RNA inhibitor) in rats. In one experiment the treated animals had a significantly greater mean number of errors in maze learning than did control animals. However in other experiments run by Dingman and Sporn there were no significant differences between groups. Flexner et al. (1963) injected an antibiotic substance, puromycine. This substance markedly inhibits protein synthesis in cells. They found that subcutaneous injection of the substance had no effect, but direct injection in the ventricles of the brain, or in the hippocampus, did cause significant impairment of learning. If given during the course of learning a particular task, the treatment abolished learning of that task, but did not impair previous learning nor prevent subsequent learning from taking place. Experiments such as these, in which RNA or protein synthesis inhibitors are administered to animals, must be interpreted with considerable caution. Clearly these substances impair virtually all metabolic activities of cells relative to protein manufacture, hence virtually all functions of cells are abnormal. Any impairment of learning or other types of performance might be on the basis of general interference with metabolic functions. However, the Flexner study showed the effect to be a specific impairment of current learning; performance (as measured on previously learned tasks) was not altered. The implications of this finding for the RNA hypothesis, although indirect, are certainly suggestive.

There is thus no *direct* evidence demonstrating that RNA plays a significant role in learning. Furthermore, there are several rather serious conceptual problems to be solved if such hypotheses are to be elaborated. The actual *mechanisms* whereby a "memory trace" (whatever this may be) is stored in RNA are completely unknown. Hydén (1961) has suggested that a train of impulses in a nerve cell changes the stability of certain proteins of the RNA molecules in the nerve cell. Which changes occur are said to be a function of the frequency of nerve discharge. The changed RNA is said to manufacture altered proteins, which would exert a different effect on the production and release of transmitter substances at synapses a given cell makes with other nerve cells. Briggs and Kitto (1962) have objected that there is no known mechanism by which RNA may be changed in the cell other than by mutation of either itself or its template, DNA. They suggest that enzyme changes involving RNA may underly learning. Recently, Gaito (1963) has proposed an analogous but alternative biochemical memory storage theory to that of Hydén implicating DNA rather than RNA.

The basic problem in RNA theories of learning is the manner in which the alterations in neuronal activity get coded and decoded by RNA. Because learning involves altered output to constant input it is self-evident that the patterns of interaction among nerve cells must change during learning. How are these changes mediated by RNA? Deutsch (1962) has pointed out that the mechanisms for altering the RNA molecule and retrieving information from it are obscure, particularly in view of the extreme rapidity of information retrieval in the brain. Eccles (1964), referring to Hydén's work, raises an even more difficult issue: "Unfortunately, this hypothesis ignores the immense organizational specificity of the nervous system and instead assumes that the specificity attaches to the frequency pattern of the nerve impulse, and not to the lines of communication of the nerve fibers. This hypothesis is therefore unacceptable on neurological grounds; nevertheless Hydén's experiments are of great value in relation to the orthodox growth theory of learning."

In sum, there is as yet no good evidence that RNA plays any special role in *learning*. A rather subtle point is involved in evaluating experiments on this relationship. Because RNA content is related to neuron activity, and there must be alterations in neuron activity corresponding to the altered behavior of the organism in learning, it follows that there must of necessity be some alterations in RNA content during learning. However, these RNA alterations might have nothing whatever to do with learning itself, but rather be due to on-going neural activity concomitant with behavior. Changes in patterns of neural activity are the results of altered synaptic activation. Until a great deal more is known about the patterns of change in synaptic activation that accompany learning, it will probably not be possible to differentiate between RNA changes due simply to amount of neural activity and RNA changes that may be involved in specific storing of memory.

The problems encountered in research on acetylcholine and RNA are illustrative of the difficulties facing investigators of neurochemistry and behavior. Nevertheless, it is highly probable that phenomena such as learning must have chemical substrates. Synaptic transmission is chemically mediated; hence interactions of all neurons in the brain can be expressed in chemical terms The very ingenious work by Hydén and his associates has shown that altered behavioral conditions appear to alter the content and structure of neural and glial RNA. Future research will undoubtedly emphasize the inter-relations of chemistry and behavior to an increasing degree.

Glial cells

You may recall from Chapter 5 that glial cells far outnumber nerve cells in the mammalian brain. The morphological relations between neurons and glia are very complex. The thin, folded membranes of the glia appear to cover every sort of the neuronal surface not covered by synaptic knobs (DeRobertis et al., 1961). Traditionally, glia have been supposed to play primarily supportive and nutritive roles for neurons. Recent experiments indicate a close inverse relationship for enzymatic changes in neurons and glia during increased function and hypoxia (Hydén and Lange, 1962; Hamberger and Hydén, 1963).

In view of the close physical and biochemical interrelations of neurons and glial cells, it would not be too surprising if glial cells influenced the physiological activity of nerve cells. Galambos (1961) has gone one step further and suggested that glia may play a special role in learning; that the essential product of glial action is innate and acquired behavioral responses, in which neurons merely execute the instructions given to them by the glia. As yet there is little evidence concerning this hypothesis. Perhaps the most suggestive data has come from an experiment by Egyhazi and Hydén (1962). Using the "rat on a tightwire" procedure described above, they reported that while RNA in Deiters cells (neurons of a vestibular nucleus) increased there was a corresponding decrease in RNA content of associated glial cells. However, there was a parallel increase in the base ratio of adenine/uracil for RNA of both neurons and glia.

A general type of glial influence on nerve cell activity has been suggested by Desmedt and LaGrutta (1957). They compared the effects of substances that inhibit "true" cholinesterase or "pseudo" cholineasterase on EEG arousal in the brain-stem sectioned cat. (As noted above and in Chapter 5, most "true" ChE in the brain is in nerve cells and most "pseudo" ChE is in glial cells.) The "true" ChE inhibitor was ineffective but the "pseudo" ChE produced EEG arousal.

Because the lines of communication in the CNS are neural, if glia are to influence behavior they must do so by influencing the behavior of neurons. Consequently, if glial theories of behavioral control or modification are valid, it must be shown that glial cells can control and alter the electrophysiological activity of neurons. To date the evidence for this proposition is largely negative. Tasaki and Chang (1958) reported intracellular recordings from cells they supposed to be glial in the cortex of the cat. The resting membrane potentials (-50 to -70 mV) showed sudden small reductions followed by gradual repolarization. After extremely strong (10–30 ma) electrical stimulation similar effects were reported for isolated glial cells in tissue culture (Hild and Tasaki, 1962; Hild, 1964). Kuffler and Potter (1964) in a very careful study dissected out a glial-neural system from the leech and compared neural and glial membrane changes to electrical stimulation. They found no interactive effects between neurons and glia, either during widespread neural activity or when large dc currents were passed through neural or glial cells. Thus while glial cells may exhibit changes in membrane potential during electrical stimulation, they do not appear to influence the electrophysiological activity of nerve cells. Until neural-glial interactions can be demonstrated at this level, the role of glial cells in learning and other behavioral phenomena will probably remain a matter of speculation.

LEARNING IN MODEL SYSTEMS: INVERTEBRATES

There are basically two different types of preparations used to analyze learning in simplified neural systems. On the one hand, learning has been studied in primitive invertebrates whose nervous systems are relatively simple. (Not all invertebrates, incidentally, have simple nervous systems. The octopus is capable of very complex visual discrimination learning and has a highly complicated CNS, see Young, 1961.) Preparations that have been utilized include the abdominal ganglion of Aplysia (a sea slug), Planaria (a flatworm), and the prothoracic ganglion of the cockroach and locust. The alternative approach has been to study behavioral plasticity in simplified preparations of the mammalian CNS, in which some degree of neuronal analysis is possible.

Learning and sensitization in the sea slug

The sea slug, *Aplysia,* is a favored preparation of neurophysiologists. The abdominal ganglion of this mollusk has relatively few cells, many of very large size. A variety of synaptic processes occur, including both chemical excitatory and inhibitory transmission and electrical synaptic transmission. Some of the neural arrangements in the Aplysia abdominal ganglion are rather remarkable. Tauc and Gershenfeld (1962) obtained considerable evidence indicating that ACh acts as a transmitter substance causing either excitation (i.e. depolarization) or inhibition (i.e. hyperpolarization) in the large ganglion cells. A given ganglion cell is either excited or inhibited: both effects do not occur in the same cell.

In a recent series of papers, Kandel, Tauc, and associates have demonstrated some intriguing analogues of behavioral plasticity in the responses of abdominal ganglion cells of Aplysia (Kandel and Tauc, 1964; 1965a and b; Kandel, Waziri and Frazier, 1965). Two types of conditioning paradigms were used, one analogous to classical conditioning and one analogous to instrumental or operant procedures. In the classical conditioning experiments, an intracellularly recorded EPSP was produced by a *test* stimulus (a shock to one input nerve of the ganglion). This served as the CS. The UCS (or, as the authors termed it, a "priming" stimulus) was shock to another input nerve. Typically, when the test and priming stimuli were paired a few times the EPSP to the test stimulus alone was markedly increased. The authors termed this phenomenon *heterosynaptic facilitation.*

To determine the extent to which heterosynaptic facilitation resembles classical conditioning, it is necessary to run control conditions where the test and

A

B

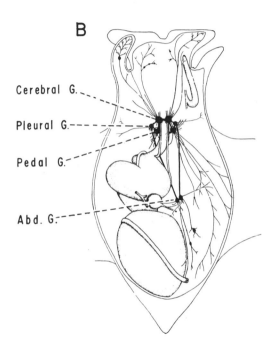

Cerebral G.

Pleural G.

Pedal G.

Abd. G.

Figure 17.4. A, the sea slug *Aplysia*. **B,** sketch of the neural ganglia of *Aplysia*. (Kandel, personal communication). **C,** response to an Aplysia cell that follows the classical conditioning paradigm. Paired test and priming stimuli yield an increase in test EPSP that considerably outlast the period of pairing. Separate presentations of the test and priming stimuli yield no increase. **D,** response of an Aplysia cell illustrating sensitization. The test EPSP response increases equally following paired test and priming stimuli and following stimulus alone. (From ◀ Kandel and Tauc, 1965a) ▶

priming stimuli are both given but not paired. The investigators were very careful to make this distinction and use the appropriate control procedures. Examples of their findings are shown in Figure 17.4. In general, they were able to distinguish two classes of cells. Identifiable giant cells of the ganglion, and some unidentified cells, exhibited an increase in EPSP response to the test (CS) stimulus following both paired and unpaired presentations of the priming (USC) stimulus (see Figure 17.4D). This increase in responsiveness not dependent on pairing is a clear analogue of behavioral sensitization. The excitability of the giant nerve cell membrane does not change during the period of sensitized response, suggesting that the sensitization effect may not be due to any alteration in the giant cell membrane itself. Curare, which blocks the ACh inhibition of the cell, does not abolish the sensitization effect. Kandel and Tauc suggested that

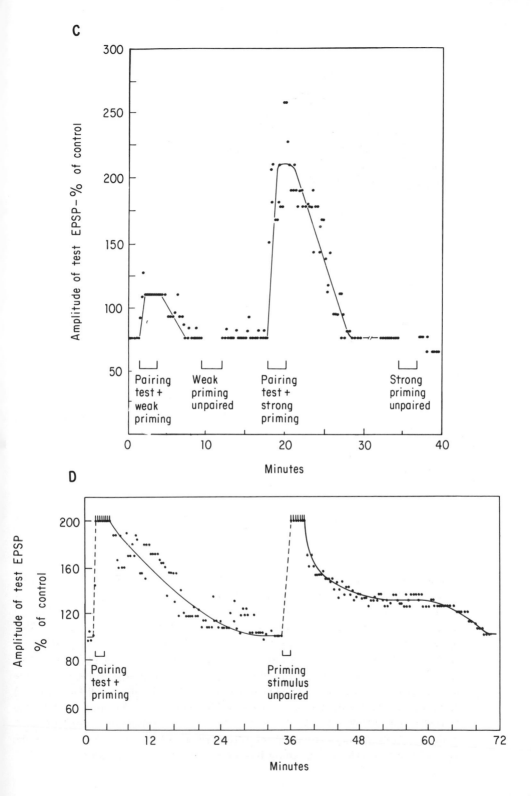

the response facilitation or sensitization is the result of a presynaptic mechanism of some type.

In addition some unidentified cells of the ganglion (6 out of 15 studied) exhibited an increased EPSP that was *specific to pairing*. Figure 17.4C illustrates a cell whose test EPSP increased markedly following paired test and priming stimuli but did not increase following comparable presentation of the priming stimuli alone. These observations are one of the closest analogues to classical conditioning demonstrated to date in a simplified invertebrate preparation.

Kandel et al. (1965) have also obtained a most interesting type of operant conditioning of Aplysia ganglion cells. If stimuli are delivered at times contingent upon the level of spontaneous activity of the cell, the discharge frequency of the cell can be predictively altered. Finally, these investigators have obtained a clear example of habituation of cell responses to repeated stimuli (see discussion below of habituation). They present evidence suggesting that two quite different mechanisms may be responsible for the habituatory response decrement, one a diminution in response of an evoked excitatory synaptic potential, and the other a recruitment of spontaneously occurring inhibitory synaptic potentials. As they note, the existence of two quite different analogues for habituation emphasizes the possibility that a variety of different cellular mechanisms may be able to produce the same types of plastic changes in behavior.

Learning in the headless cockroach and locust

In 1962 Horridge published an intriguing demonstration of what appears to be learning in the thoracic ganglion of the cockroach. As was noted briefly in Chapter 5, insects typically have a series of segmental ganglia; in the cockroach a given set of legs are directly controlled by the ganglia at that level of the body. The largest and most complex ganglion, the head ganglion or " brain," was first removed in Horridge's experiment by decapitating the roaches (headless cockroaches can live for ten days or more). The experimental arrangement used by Horridge is shown in Figure 17.5. The animals are beheaded and all but one prothoracic leg removed. During the training trials (Figure 17.5A) the experimental animal (P = positional) is placed such that if the leg drops down enough to touch the water, the foot receives a shock. The UCR to shock is a leg flexion that withdraws the leg from the water. Horridge used a very clever "yoked control" design: a control animal (R = random in Figure 17.5A) was connected via the P leg such that whenever P received a shock, R also received a shock. The basic difference between the two preparations is that P only receives shocks when the leg is down in the water, but R receives shocks randomly in relation to leg position. After training, test trials were run with both preparations arranged independently such that each received shocks only when the foot touched the water (Figure 17.5B). Horridge reported that in the test trials the "conditioned" P limbs received shocks (touched the water) relatively few times but the R limbs required many additional training trials to "learn" to avoid shock.

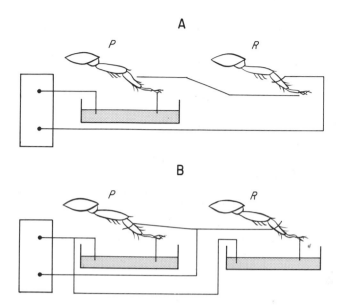

Figure 17.5. Experimental arrangement for the study of "conditioning" in the cockroach prothoracic ganglion. **A**, training phase. The *P* leg is shocked whenever it touches the water and the *R* leg is shocked whenever the *P* leg is shocked. **B**, testing phase. Each leg is now shocked when it touches the water independently of the other. (From Horridge, 1962)

This experiment illustrates a most ingenious control for sensitization. Both limbs receive the same number of shocks in the same temporal pattern during the training phase, the only difference being that in the *P* animals shock is always associated with proprioceptive cues of limb extention, whereas in the *R* leg there is no relation between shock and limb position. In the testing phase, each preparation was trained separately.

Horridge's experiment has been replicated by Eisenstein and Cohen (1965). They used the same "yoked control" procedure and also employed decapitated cockroaches. In addition they severed the posterior connectives of the pro-thoracic ganglion. This procedure isolates the prothoracic ganglion from the rest of the CNS and leaves the sensory and motor nerves to the prothoracic legs intact. Results of their experiments, averaged for 12 experimentals and 12 controls are shown in Figure 17.6. The ordinate is simply the number of shocks received per minute by the two different types of preparations. During training the number of leg extensions (hence number of shocks, see Figure 17.5A) de-creased in a fairly regular fashion. During testing, in which both legs are in-dependently shocked for extension (see Figure 17.5B) the previously trained *P* legs received very few shocks but the control *R* legs required a considerable number of training trials before they learned to avoid shock. The crucial point in these experiments is of course the difference in behavior of the experimental

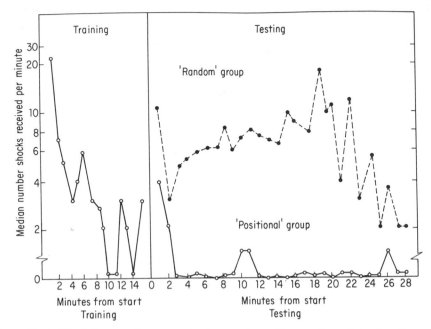

Figure 17.6. The left curve illustrates the decrease in median number of shocks taken per minute by the *P* animals during training, and the right curves show the difference in median number of shocks taken by *P* and *R* animals during testing. (From Eisenstein and Cohen, 1965)

and control groups. Both receive the same series of shocks in training; hence shock "sensitization" effects alone cannot explain the differences seen during testing.

In an additional control experiment Eisenstein and Cohen removed the prothoracic ganglion as well, so that the preparation being tested consisted solely of the leg, with peripheral portions of the nerves and the muscles. No neural synapses remained. These isolated legs were run through the same procedures. The results shown in Figure 17.7 indicate that there are now no differences between the behavior of the experimental *P* and control *R* legs. Interestingly enough, both appear to "learn" in that there is a progressive decrease in the number of shocks received (i.e. number of leg extensions). This effect must be due to the direct action of the shock on the peripheral neuromusculature, because all other neural tissue has been removed.

The fact that the isolated legs "learn" the shock avoidance response as well as the ganglionic preparations raises some rather serious problems of interpretation. Both the *P* and *R* legs perform well during the testing phase. The performance of both groups is similar to the testing performance of the *P* group of ganglion animals. The only difference between the ganglion groups and the isolated leg groups is the absence of learned leg withdrawal during training of the *R* ganglion group. (It would almost seem as though the ganglion functions to prevent learning.) Actually, the fact that the isolated leg ceases to extend as well as does the ganglionic leg is strong presumptive evidence that the modified reponse may not be entirely due to ganglionic learning, but rather in part to an altered neuromuscular state resulting from applications of the electric shock. The fact that only the *P* ganglion animals "learn" does however indicate that there is interaction of ganglionic actions and neuromuscular actions. One other problem is suggested by Horridge's observation that the headless cockroach makes intermittent "searching" movements with the legs when they are not in contact with an object, and that these searching movements gradually cease. Thus it is conceivable that unshocked animals might also "learn" to keep their legs raised. This might then suggest that shock in the *R* ganglion group served to prevent habituation of the leg searching response. These possibilities must await experimental determination.

Although many insect neurons are small and notoriously difficult to study electrophysiologically, there are relatively few neurons in the prothoracic ganglion of the cockroach. The differential "learning" or response modification shown by the *P* and *R* ganglion animals in Horridge's and Eisenstein and Cohen's

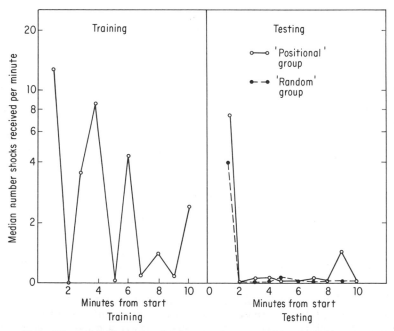

Figure 17.7.   The curve illustrates the decrease in the median number of shocks taken per minute by the *P* ganglionless animals during training. The right curves show the median number of shocks taken by the ganglionless *P* and *R* groups during testing. Note lack of difference between *P* and *R* groups during testing. (From Eisenstein and Cohen, 1965)

experiments suggests that this preparation may have considerable value as a model neural system for the study of learning.

Hoyle (1965) has noted that a variety of muscle responses can produce the gross movements studied by Horridge and by Cohen and Eisenstein, thus complicating possible neural analyses. He has completed an extensive study of behavioral plasticity in the headless locust (*Schistocerca gregaria*), utilizing intracellular recordings of muscle junction potentials from an identified leg muscle.

Perhaps the most intriguing observations concern instrumental or operant conditioning of the discharge frequency of muscle junction potentials in response to contiguous or noncontiguous shock to afferent nerves. Examples are shown in Figure 17.8. In the upper graphs the shock was given (arrowhead marks) whenever

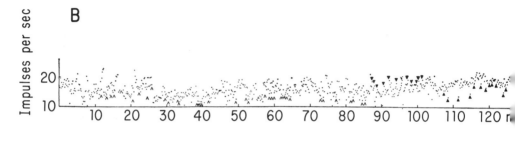

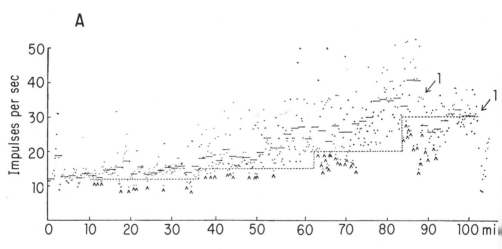

Figure 17.8. Operant conditioning of the spontaneous discharge frequency of a muscle junction potential recorded from the leg of a headless locust. **A**, afferent stimulation given each time the response frequency decreased (open arrows) produced a marked increase in frequency. **B**, control animal in which a comparable pattern of shocks was given but without any relation to response frequency (open arrowheads). There is no increase in response frequency Subsequent attempts to condition this unit by contiguous shocks (closed arrowheads) was not successful. (From Hoyle, 1965)

the discharge frequency fell below a given arbitrary level. As indicated, this produced a gradual but considerable rise in the discharge frequency. The necessary control procedure to show that the increase is not due merely to shock presentations irrespective of their contingency to response frequency is illustrated in the lower portion of Figure 17.8. Here, the same timing of shock (open arrowheads) was used as in a contingency preparation that showed an increase. For this preparation they were of course not contingent, i.e. the occurrence of the shock had no relation to discharge frequency. Under these conditions discharge frequency did not increase. Interpretation of this control example is complicated by the fact that subsequent contingent shocks (solid arrowheads at right) failed to produce an increase in frequency.

Hoyle's procedure is in many ways analogous to the experiments of Horridge and Cohen and Eisenstein. In the latter the leg was shocked each time it touched the water. Its elevation gradually increased. The afferent nerve in Hoyle's experiment was shocked each time the muscle junction potential firing frequency decreased. The frequency gradually increased. Both cases could be described in general terms as "learning to avoid the shock." The extent to which Hoyle's most interesting observations are a genuine analogue of operant conditioning in the intact mammal remains, of course, to be determined. However this line of investigation would seem to hold considerable promise for future research.

Learning in planaria?

There has been a great deal of recent interest in the possibility that a primitive invertebrate, the flatworm, *planaria*, can learn. In 1955 Thompson and McConnell published a report of simple conditioning in planaria. When shocked, planaria typically exhibit increased bodily movements and turning. Thompson and McConnell conditioned this response to presentations of a light. They used a total of four groups: an experimental group (E) given paired 2-sec light-shock trials, and control groups given light only (LC), shock only (SC), or neither light nor shock (RC). Results of their experiment are shown in Figure 17.9. This figure clearly demonstrates that the conditioned group becomes much more responsive to light than do the light only and no stimuli groups. However, the shock only control group (SC) begins at a higher level of performance than the experimental group, and the two groups do not differ greatly. A further problem in Thompson and McConnell's experiment lies in the fact that no backward control group was run where both light and shock were given unpaired. Jensen (1965), in evaluating this experiment, concluded that "the major effect in the experiment is the difference between groups which are shocked, and those which are not. Shock, not association of light and shock, would appear to be the important variable. Precise comparisons between the two groups receiving shocks would not seem justified, because only one of the two groups received test trials and because total number of light presentations is confounded with different training procedure."

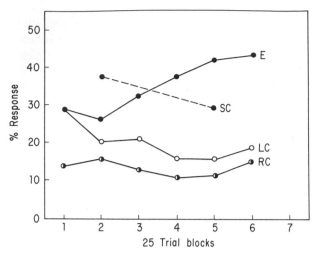

Figure 17.9. Percent responses shown during training by experimental and control groups of Planaria. E, light-shock conditioning group; LC, light alone control; RC, no stimuli control; SC, shock control. (Based on the data of Thompson and McConnell, 1955)

There have been a number of subsequent experiments on planaria learning, many of which have omitted necessary control groups on the basis of Thompson and McConnell's initial paper. Jensen (1965) has carefully reviewed all studies of planaria learning through 1964. In all experiments in which learning was reported, serious methodological and control problems exist. The most carefully controlled experiments generally have found negative results, in the sense that increased activity occurs whether or not the shock and light are paired. A careful study by vanDeventer and Ratner (1964) showed that all so called "learning" behavior shown by planaria in their experiments were explainable in terms of such variables as temperature, shape of trough, size of planaria, etc. Brown, Dustman, and Beck (1966a; 1966b), in careful and extensive experiments, have shown that such variables as worm length and illuminance of CS light have a marked effect on frequency of the unconditioned response to light. Furthermore sensitized responses to light resulting from alternating series of unpaired lights and shocks were as frequent as the "conditioned" responses in other studies. Finally, Calvin, a Nobel laureate biochemist at Berkeley, has devoted a considerable proportion of his laboratories' efforts (a total of 12 "man-years") to the search for learning in planaria. His conclusions are entirely negative (Bennett and Calvin, 1964, p. 23): "Unsuccessful efforts to demonstrate learning in planarias by classical conditioning, light habituation, maze learning, operant conditioning, and food reward methods are described. Until more adequate and more useful methods and descriptions of methods to train planarians are available, this animal appears to have little utility for proposed studies of the possible biochemical bases of learning." The reader is urged to consult Jensen's 1965 paper for a complete review of the Planaria learning literature.

Interest in planaria learning is due in part to the RNA hypothesis of the memory trace. McConnell, Jacobson, and Kimble (1959) reported that after cutting in half planaria that had "learned," the regenerated head and tail ends both "retained" the conditioned response to light. Corning and John (1961) repeated this experiment but raised the regenerating halves in a solution of RNA-ase (an enzyme that destroys RNA). The regenerated head end "retained" the response but the tail end did not. Gaito and Zavala (1964) have carefully analyzed these experiments and pointed out the many problems of control and interpretation involved. An even more dramatic example of "RNA coding of memory" is the cannibalism studies of the McConnell group (Selman et al., 1962). Planaria that had "learned" the response were ground up and fed to naïve planaria. These were reported to perform the "learned" task. On the basis of such reports, it was immediately suggested that in the universities of the future, old professors will be ground up and fed to the students. Unfortunately, Hartry et al. (1964) have subsequently shown that sensitization rather than learning seems to be involved in such experiments.

Although the alterations induced in planaria behavior by shock and light may not resemble learning as it is defined for mammals, they are of considerable interest in their own right. They are clearly examples of response alteration resulting from experience, possibly analogous to sensitization in mammals, and merit study. Jensen (1965) has emphasized that such experiments are perhaps more properly concerned with planaria behavior than with learning in mammals. The point raised by Jensen underlines the difficulty of generalizing from invertebrate neural tissue to the mammalian CNS. Even if a simplified invertebrate system can be shown to exhibit behavior similar to mammalian response modifiability (Aplysia and Planaria seem good candidates for sensitization and Aplysia and the cockroach and locust prothoracic ganglia appear to be good candidates for learning), how likely is it that the underlying neural mechanisms will be similar? Neurophysiological analyses of invertebrate systems are plagued by the fact that relatively less is known about the synaptic organization of these simple nervous systems than is now known about the mammalian CNS, particularly the spinal cord. Furthermore many lower species have rather specialized neural structures such as giant cells and electrically excitable synapses not found in mammals. The extent to which invertebrate models of behavioral plasticity will serve to elucidate the neural substrates of learning in higher organisms remains to be determined.

LEARNING IN MODEL SYSTEMS: THE MAMMALIAN CNS

It has proved extremely difficult to demonstrate clear-cut examples of conditioning in simplified preparations of the mammalian nervous system. Consequently, many investigators have adopted the opposite tactic of studying types of behavioral plasticity that do occur in simplified neuronal systems, in which some degree of analysis of the neural mechanism involved is possible.

An interesting example of a model system approach to response modification is a series of experiments by Morrell (1961a, b, and c) utilizing the cerebral cortex as the model system. He produced changes in the neuronal activity of cells in a region of one hemisphere of the cortex of cat, and studied the induced changes in the homologous region of the opposite hemisphere. A portion of the suprasylvian gyrus was sprayed with ethyl chloride. This induced a permanent epileptogenic focus of activity. Nerve cells in the sprayed region periodically exhibited spiking discharges characteristic of epileptic seizure activity. Analogous tissue of the opposite hemisphere also showed such epileptic activity, presumably mediated via the connecting fibers of the corpus callosum going from one hemisphere to the other. After a time, the tissue in the hemisphere not treated began to show epilepticlike electrical activity spontaneously and independently of that occurring on the treated hemisphere. It continued to do so after section of the corpus callosum. This could be viewed as a permanent modification in the neuronal behavior induced via neuronal transmission. RNA content was found to have changed, even in cells of the untreated hemisphere, after they began to show spontaneous epilepticlike activity.

A possible analogue of short term memory has been reported to occur following dc polarization of the cerebral cortex (Rusinov, 1953; Morrell, 1961). Rusinov observed that a 2–10 microampere direct current anodal polarization applied to the motor cortex in conjunction with sensory stimuli produced an effect much like short-term memory or learning. He found that the dc polarization of the motor area did not produce movement of the corresponding limbs under the polarizing electrode. A sensory stimulus applied by itself likewise did not produce motor responses. However, when the sensory stimulus was superimposed upon the dc polarization a movement was elicited, and the stimulus continued to elicit the movement for about one half hour after the dc polarization was removed. Morrell (1961a, b, and c) repeated Rusinov's work with comparable results. He noted further that the post dc response (the response occurring after removal of the dc polarization) occurred only to stimuli that had been associated with the dc polarization, other stimuli of the same magnitude and mode would not elicit the response. The implication is that the past history of a stimuli may be crucial in the determination of response probability in this situation.

Kupfermann (1965), using rats as subjects, was unable to replicate many of these results. Different groups of animals received cathodal or anodal polarization in visual or somatomotor cortex throughout training, but none of the animals showed impairment on brightness or pattern discrimination. The only deficit appeared to be on the reversal of the pattern discrimination, and then only in rats receiving cathodal polarization in visual cortex.

Morrell (1961c) also studied the effects of dc polarization on single cell discharges in the visual cortex. One neuron, for example, responded with a burst envelope when a flash of light was presented to the eye of the animal and followed a stimulus train of three flashes per second by giving three burst envelopes per second. An anodal dc polarization was then paired with the flash train for several minutes, the polarization being applied to the cortex overlying the unit being studied. In the postpolarization period a single flash produced a unit response of three burst envelopes per second. These effects are extremely interesting examples of short term plasticity exhibited by the behavior of neurons in the cerebral cortex.

Use and Disuse

Perhaps the most common simplified mammalian CNS preparation for the study of behavioral plasticity has been the neurally isolated spinal cord (usually the caudal third) of the cat. We saw in earlier chapters how much progress has been made in understanding synaptic mechanisms in the mammalian spinal cord. Thanks to the elegant studies by Eccles, Lloyd, and many others it is now possible to specify the synaptic events underlying certain aspects of the behavior exhibited by the spinal animal.

One of the most direct ways to alter the extent to which a given neural system is used is to increase or decrease the amount of input to the system. If degree of use produces the kinds of changes that underlie learning and other aspects of behavioral plasticity, then the study of altered use may provide basic information regarding these physical changes. One of the simplest ways to change the extent to which a given neural system is used is to damage a portion of the system. Contrary to earlier belief, extensive regeneration can occur in the brain following destruction of neural tissue. Such regeneration does not, in general, repair the original damage (as is often the case in peripheral nerve injury) but compensating growth processes do occur. A clear example in the spinal cord is *sprouting* (McCouch et al., 1958). If dorsal root fibers are sectioned there is a sprouting of collateral fibers in the spinal cord that grow out from adjacent intact afferent nerve fibers. Thus there is an actual growth of new nerve processes within the central nervous system following removal of a portion of the input. The effect of this growth is to increase innervation of adjacent neurons whose normal innervation was removed by the dorsal root section (see Figure 17.10). Rose et al. (1961) have shown that extensive " sprouting " of collateral fibers also occurs in the cerebral cortex if lesions are limited to one or a few layers.

Because extensive growth processes occur in the CNS following damage, we may ask whether such processes are related to neural changes accompanying normal aspects of behavior plasticity. Eccles (1961) has proposed the straightforward generalization that use strengthens neural transmission and disuse weakens it. An experiment by Eccles and McIntyre (1953) illustrates the point. They sectioned the afferent nerve fibers on one side of the spinal cord peripheral to the dorsal root ganglion. This preserves the central pathways of these fibers so that they can subsequently be stimulated and reflex activities of the spinal cord tested. Some weeks following afferent input nerve section there was a marked depression of monosynaptic reflexes on the sectioned side. Control monosynaptic reflex responses from the intact opposite side of the cord were not significantly altered. In this experiment, unlike the sprouting experiment described above, the section was done peripheral to the dorsal root ganglia

Figure 17.10.   An example of sprouting in the spinal cord of the monkey following section of some afferent input. Photomicrographs illustrate dorsal horn region of cord. The left picture is the control and the right shows the marked increase in the number of afferent fibers following lesion. (From McCouch, Austin, Liu, and Liu, 1958)

containing the cell bodies of the afferent fibers, so that the fibers themselves do not degenerate. The major alteration here is that all *normal* afferent input activity has been abolished by the section. There are some structural changes resulting but these are minor compared to the extensive changes when section is made central to the dorsal root ganglia, with subsequent total degeneration of the fibers. More recently, Eccles et al. (1959) have obtained comparable results using intracellular recording of excitatory postsynaptic potentials induced mono-synaptically in motor neurons of the spinal cord. Disuse was produced by sever-ing the nerve to one muscle, other nerves serving as controls. After two to four weeks, the monosynaptic excitatory action of the disused path on the same motor neuron is reduced by about 50 percent relative to the control input path not having reduction. This experiment is illustrated in Figure 17.11. One of the problems in these experiments is that there are small changes in the dorsal root fibers following section distal to the dorsal root ganglia. There is some degree of shrinkage of the dorsal root fibers themselves. Eccles points out that it is conceivable that this shrinkage may extend directly to the synaptic terminals and account in part for the depressed synaptic efficacy.

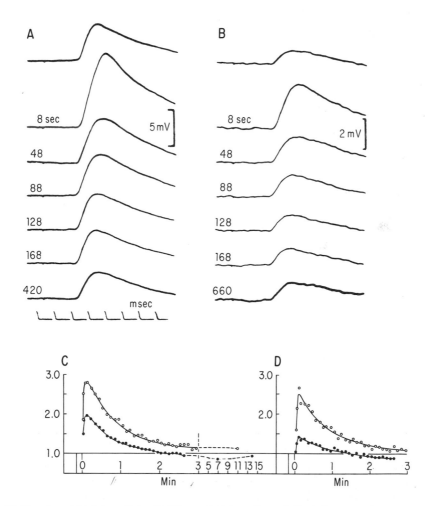

Figure 17.11. **A** and **B**, intracellular EPSPs evoked in a flexor *hallucis longus* motoneurone by maximum Group 1a volleys in flexor *hallucis longus* nerve (**A**), and in flexor *digitorum longus* nerve (**B**) which had been severed 15 days previously. Top records in **A** and **B** were taken before the conditioning tetanus 400 c/s for 10 seconds, and the subsequent records at the indicated intervals after the tetanus. Same time scale throughout, but different voltage scales for the two series as indicated. **C** and **D**, plots of the time courses of post-tetanic potentiations of EPSPs produced by a conditioning tetanus of 10 seconds at 400 c/s as indicated by the hatched columns. Specimen records are shown in **A** and **B**. In **C** the heights of the EPSPs are plotted relative to the control height. Open circles are for the operatively severed pathway (FDL) and filled circles for the control pathway (FHL). **D** as for **C**, but for maximum slopes of the rising phases of the EPSPs. Note that in **C** the time scale is greatly shortened after 3 minutes. (From Eccles, Krnjevic and Miledi, 1959)

An alternative method of producing disuse of the monosynaptic pathway has been to impose disuse on the muscle by cutting the tendons that attach the muscles to bone. Following this procedure (called tenotomy) the muscles are not stretched to anything like their normal extent during behavior. Remember that the monosynaptic connections on motor neurons of the spinal cord are afferent input from the muscles stretch receptors; hence reduction in degree of muscle stretch by tenotomy should reduce markedly the degree of monosynaptic activation of the motor neurons. Interestingly enough, experiments by Baranek and Hník (1959), and Kozak and Westerman (1961), demonstrated that some weeks following tenotomy volleys in the nerves of the tenotomized muscles had a more powerful synaptic action than did control nerves on the other side. In other words just the opposite effect occurred than would have been predicted. The changes themselves, although they might have been initiated by supraspinal influences, took place within the spinal cord because they were not altered by transecting the spinal cord in the final experimental tests. These experimental results are illustrated in Figure 17.12. However, Kozak and Westerman (1961) report that in chronic spinal animals there is no increase in monosynaptic reflexes from tenotomized muscles. They suggest that in the previous experiments

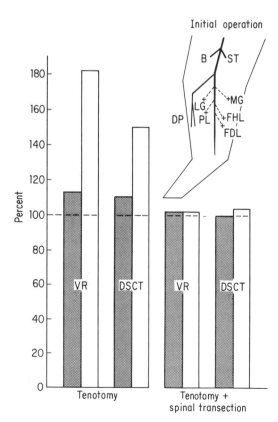

Figure 17.12. Inset is a diagram of the initial operative procedure showing the nerves to tenotomized ($+$ $---$) and normal ($\underline{\quad\quad}$) muscles. Monosynaptic responses recorded from ventral roots (VR) and dorsal spinocerebellar tract response DSCT from ipsilateral half-cord. The results depicted in the histogram are averages of pooled reflex responses from 21 animals in the first group and 5 in the second group. The ordinate indicates the mean percentage ratio of corresponding reflexes from tenotomized side/normal side for the groups of nerves to normal (filled columns) and tenotomized (open columns) muscles. Thus 100 percent indicates bilateral symmetry and a ratio of 1.00. The mean enhancement of VR and DSCT responses from tenotomized muscle is statistically significant, $P<0.01$, and is prevented by spinal transection with tenotomy. (From Kozak and Westerman, 1961)

the fact that the spinal cord was not sectioned until the final test permitted supraspinal actions on the motor neuron to induce the changes. Thus, it may be that in tenotomized muscles there is an increase in supraspinal activation of gamma motor neurons, resulting from altered afferent input, with a consequent increase in gamma motor neuron activation and hence alpha motor neuron activation. If muscle is tenotomized and the spinal cord is immediately sectioned, there is no subsequent alteration in the monosynaptic reflex response; however, if the spinal cord is not cut, there is a marked increase in the amplitude of the monosynaptic reflex response. As Eccles (1964) points out, "these tenotomy experiments are important in displaying the plastic properties of monosynaptic reflexes, but they cannot yet be regarded as establishing that increased use raises the potency of synapses."

In a very intriguing experiment, R. M. Eccles, Kozak, and Westerman (1962) attempted to utilize forced use and disuse in altering synaptic efficacy. Synergistic groups of ankle and toe extensor muscles were used. All but one of the synergist group of muscles were denervated. It was hoped that under these conditions the remaining innervated muscle would be under greater mechanical stress than control muscles on the other side, which in turn would lead to an increased afferent monosynaptic bombardment of motor neurons, thus leading to an increased activation of the synapses. The experimental arrangement is illustrated in Figure 17.13. As indicated, the remaining intact afferent nerve input is used as the experimental test input and the same afferent nerve on the opposite side of the cord is used as the control input. Animals were then given forced walking exercise for one half hour every day. This should result in much greater activation of the experimental test input than of the control input, in which all muscle afferent nerves were intact. Following a series of such forced exercise sessions acute spinal experiments were performed in which the monosynaptic reflex response to the comparable inputs on both sides were measured. It was found that, as predicted, the input from the reduced experimental afferent side was markedly enhanced relative to response from the control side. At this point it could be concluded that the forced exercise produced greater use, and greater synaptic activation, and hence permanent alterations in synaptic efficacy. However, Eccles, Kozak, and Westerman went on to try the necessary control experiment of immobilizing the animals and maintaining them immobile for a comparable period of time following section of the nerves on the experimental side. Unfortunately, exactly the same asymmetry of monosynaptic reflexes was observed in these animals as in the previous animals given forced exercise. Thus the alterations in synaptic efficacy that did occur appear to have been the indirect result of section rather than the result of exercise. Whether there was increased exercise or no exercise made no difference in the degree of change in the monosynaptic reflex from the reduced input side.

The examples discussed above show that the effects of use and disuse in monosynaptic reflexes are somewhat contradictory. It is perhaps significant that the kinds of maneuvers producing clear increases in monosynaptic reflexes with excessive use and decreases with disuse are artificial. Cutting nerves or inactivating

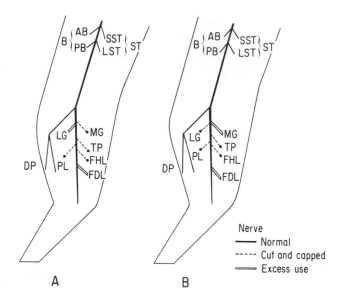

Figure 17.13.   Two alternative procedures used in an experiment on forced use and disuse. In A, LG and FDL intact, MG, TP, FHL and PL denervated; in B, MG, FDL, intact, LG, TP, FHL, and PL cut and capped. Letters stand for nerves innervating various muscles. (From Eccles, Kozak, and Westerman, 1962)

muscles are somewhat removed from the realm of normal behavior. The experiments by R. M. Eccles, Kozak, and Westerman could not demonstrate any effect by using forced exercise with normal movements. It may be that the monosynaptic reflex connections of the spinal cord are sufficiently specialized for particular kinds of responses that they cannot be made to yield plastic alterations through normal behavioral channels.

Gerard and colleagues (Chamberlain, Halick, and Gerard, 1963) have studied an interesting plastic change in the spinal reflexes of rats following cerebellar damage (first described by DiGiorgio, 1929). It is an example of a use-disuse effect with a relatively short time constant; approximately one hour. Lesions were made in one hemisphere of the cerebellum. The lesion immediately produces a postural asymmetry: one hind leg is extended and the other tends to be flexed, as illustrated in Figure 17.14. If the spinal cord is transected within 45 minutes of the cerebellar lesion, the asymmetry vanishes. However, if more than 45 minutes elapse between the cerebellar lesion and the spinal transection, the asymmetry remains permanent (see Figure 17.14). In other words the cerebellar lesion causes a change in the reflex actions of the cord which become permanently "laid-down" within the spinal cord after 45 minutes or so. The neural mechanisms involved in this interesting example of plasticity would seem potentially amenable to analysis.

CONTROL

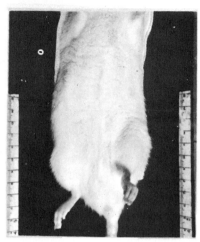
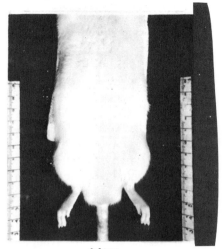

Before   After

Figure 17.14.   Above, pictures taken before and after spinal transection. Interval between development of asymmetry (by unilateral cerebellar lesion) and cord transection was 30 minutes. Below, same as above except time between cerebellar and cord lesions was 60 minutes. Same asymmetry now remains *after* the cord transection. (From Chamberlain, Halick, and Gerard, 1964)

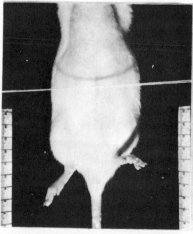
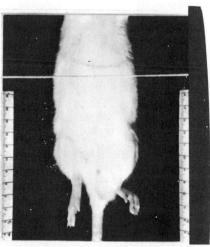

Before   After

Habituation and sensitization of spinal reflexes

Phenomena resembling behavioral habituation and sensitization have been known for many years to occur in reflexes of the transected spinal cord (Sherrington, 1906). As noted earlier, behavioral habituation is simply response decrement as a result of repeated stimulation. For example, if a moderate electric shock is delivered to the foot of a normal but restrained animal for the first time, the animal will show marked struggling and leg flexion movements. However, if the stimulus is repeated a few times, the responses will decrease considerably and may even disappear. Habituation is commonly differentiated from response decrements due to trauma, growth, aging, etc. In the foot shock example above, if the shock is withheld for a period of time after habituation and then given again, the response will reappear with normal strength. This spontaneous recovery is a common control used to show the habituation is a *reversible* response decrement. Habituation is usually distinguished from receptor adaptation and muscle fatigue (Harris, 1943). Response decrements due to altered sensitivity of receptors are often termed receptor adaptation and response decrements due to decremental effects occurring at the neuromuscular junctions or muscles are often termed muscular fatigue. Habituation has been characterized as being due to central rather than peripheral processes (Harris, 1943). Virtually all responses of the intact organism initially elicited by a given stimulus, ranging in complexity from leg flexion to exploratory and play behavior (Welker, 1961), show habituation with repeated stimulation.

Response sensitization may be defined simply as an increased response strength to a given stimulus as a result of some other, usually strong, stimulus. The galvanic skin reflex (GSR) is a good case in point. Suppose we were measuring the GSR activity of sweat glands in the palm of the hand in response to a sound of moderate intensity. The response would probably be of relatively low amplitude and somewhat irregular in occurrence. If a strong shock is delivered to the skin, the sound alone will now evoke a much larger GSR response; the response has been sensitized. The response increase due to sensitization is of course distinguished from conditioning in that no pairing of shock and sound is necessary to produce the effect. Sensitization effects themselves typically habituate; after a number of shock presentations the response to the sound will decrease to the initial weak level.

To summarize, habituation and sensitization refer to reversible decreases or increases in response strength due to "experience" (i.e. to presentations of stimuli). They are related in this general sense to conditioning or learning, and are often considered as aspects of learning, but are distinguished from conditioning by the absence of stimulus pairing.

Sherrington (1906) was perhaps the first to study systematically these types of changes in spinal reflexes. He did not term response decrements habituation, but rather referred to them as fatigue. However he was careful to define fatigue only as a response decrement due to repeated stimulation. The general experimental arrangement for the study of spinal flexion reflex habituation and sensitization is illustrated in Figure 17.15. If hind limb reflexes are employed, the spinal cord is usually cut in the mid-thoracic region. Various hind limb muscles and nerves may be dissected out for particular types of stimulation and response measures. The basic procedure involves electrical shock to skin and cutaneous nerves and measurement of the flexion reflex response strength (*Rm*) or motor nerve response (*Rn* or *R*α). If a cutaneous stimulus (*a*) is given every few seconds, the flexion reflex response typically decreases in strength (habituation). If a

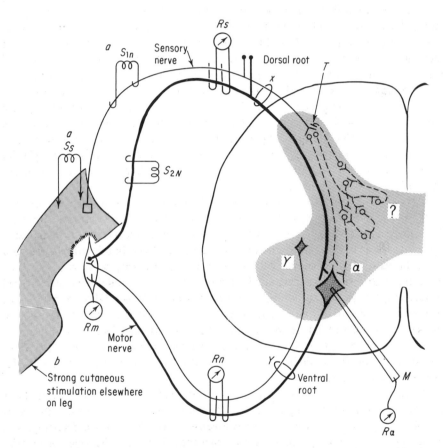

Figure 17.15. Experimental arrangements used to study habituation and/or sensitization of the hindlimb flexion reflex in the acute spinal cat. Electrical stimuli can be delivered to skin (*a*, *S*ₛ; *b*) or to afferent nerves (*S*₁ₙ, cutaneous nerve; *S*₂ₙ , muscle nerve; *x*, dorsal root). Responses can be recorded from the muscle (*Rm*), the motor nerve (*Rn*), the motor neurons (*R*α with microelectrode *M*), or from ventral root (*y*).

strong shock is given to some other portion of the skin or to another afferent nerve (*b*), responses to the original test stimulus (*a*) will increase in strength for a period of time (sensitization).

Prosser and Hunter (1936) completed a careful study of flexion reflex habituation in the chronic spinal rat. The animals were suspended in a hammock, skin or nerves of the hind limb shocked, and the hind limb flexion reflex recorded. They gave brief trains of shocks every ten seconds and found that the flexion reflex showed marked habituation within a period of ten minutes or so. If the shock was withheld, the response returned to normal strength in a period of minutes. They ruled out the possibility that the response decrement was due to receptor adaptation; the same habituation and recovery occurred when they stimulated afferent nerves rather than skin. Hence the habituation effect must be central to the afferent nerve at the point simulated, and could not be due to receptor adaptation. Muscle fatigue appeared to be unlikely because electric shocks to the nerves that innervated the muscles produced a muscle response that did not decrease when the reflex response was habituated.

The extent to which spinal flexion reflex habituation resembles habituation of responses in the intact organism is determined by the extent to which both phenomena follow the same set of laws. Thompson and Spencer (1966) surveyed the behavioral literature on response habituation and identified some nine parametric characteristics of response habituation in intact animals. They found that spinal flexion reflex habituation exhibited the same nine parametric features. An example of habituation and spontaneous recovery of the spinal flexion reflex is shown in Figure 17.16A. Brief trains of shocks were given every 10 seconds to skin of the hind leg during habituation training, and once every 3 minutes during recovery. Individual responses are shown to illustrate response variability. Note that the response habituation has an approximately exponential form, and the spontaneous recovery has a long and variable time course.

Examples of four of the parametric features of flexion reflex habituation that parallel response habituation of the intact animal are shown in Figure 17.16. The effects of repeated habituation and spontaneous recovery series on habituation are shown in Figure 17.16B. After the first habituation series, the response was allowed to recover to control level and then rehabituated. In the second habituation series the response exhibits greater habituation. The same holds true for most behavioral responses of the intact animal. In Figure 17.16C the effect of stimulus frequencies is shown. Habituation is more rapid when the stimulus is given more frequently. The effect of stimulus strength is illustrated in Figure 17.16D. In general, the weaker the stimulus the greater the degree of habituation. Finally, Figure 17.16E illustrates stimulus generalization of habituation. An habituating stimulus is given once per second to an afferent nerve and a test stimulus interposed once per minute to another afferent nerve. As the response to the habituating (1/sec) stimulus develops, a small but significant degree of habituation develops for the response to the 1/min test nerve (i.e. habituation generalizes to the test channel). These examples illustrate that the parametric

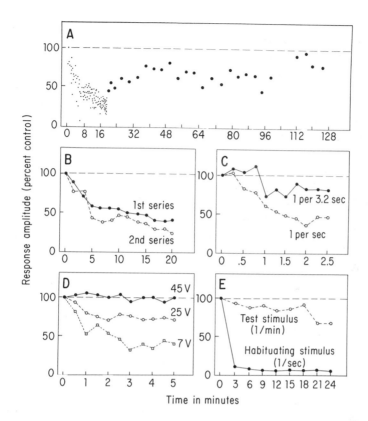

Figure 17.16. **A,** habituation (zero min to arrow) and spontaneous recovery (arrow to 128 min) of the hind limb flexion reflex of the spinal cat in response to repeated skin shocks. Stimuli were brief trains of shocks (5 in 50 msec) delivered every 10 sec during habituation and every 3 min during spontaneous recovery (except for a 12 min period of no stimuli at about 100 min). In this and all subsequent figures the response measured is tension developed by contraction of the tibialis anterior muscle, expressed as percent mean initial control response amplitude. **B,** effect of repeated habituation and spontaneous recovery series on degree of habituation. Response recovered to control level following first habituation series and was then rehabituated (second series). Conditions as in **A.** Data are averages of 10 trial blocks. **C,** effect of stimulus frequency on habituation. Single shocks given 1/3.2 sec in one habituation series and 1/sec in the other to the saphenous nerve. Data are averages over 16-sec periods of time. **D,** effect of stimulus intensity on habituation. Brief trains of shocks (as in **A**) were delivered every 10 sec to the saphenous nerve with spontaneous recovery allowed after each series. Voltages refer to output of stimulator and were attenuated, but in the same ratios, when delivered to the nerve. Data averaged over 3 trial blocks. **E,** stimulus generalization of habituation. Single shocks to two separate branches of the saphenous nerve. The habituating stimulus to one branch was given 1/sec and the test stimulus to the other branch was given 1/min. Data are averages over 3 trial blocks for response to the test stimulus, and averages over the same periods of time for response to the habituating stimulus. (From Thompson and Spencer, 1966)

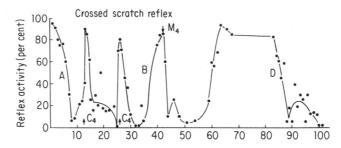

Figure 17.17. Contralateral scratch reflex activity elicited by 10-min daily stimulation of the left flank (mean of 3 cats). The response declined over 8 days, but was increased by chlorpromazine (C) 4 mgm/kgm intramuscularly on two occasions. Activity returned on cessation of stimulation and was reduced for 18 days by a single dose of meprobamate (M) 4 mgm/kgm by mouth. The second training at day 83 habituated the scratch response more rapidly. (From Kozak, MacFarlane, and Westerman, 1962)

features of repeated habituation, stimulus frequency, stimulus strength, and stimulus generalization of the spinal flexion reflex parallel comparable habituation effects of the intact animal.

The spinal reflex habituation illustrated in Figure 17.16 typically requires a period of many minutes to recover. However some types of response habituation in normal organisms may last for much longer periods of time; days or weeks. Nesmeianova (1957) illustrated that habituation of the scratch reflex in chronic spinal dogs could last for a period of days. In an interesting paper, Kozak, MacFarlane, and Westerman (1962) were able to demonstrate long lasting reversible habituation in chronic spinal kittens. The animals were subjected to thoracic spinal section during the first week of life and the experiment conducted after three months. These preparations show markedly exaggerated reflex responses. A variety of reflexes were studied, including a crossed scratch reflex to rubbing of the flank, leg flexion to hot and cold stimuli applied to the paw, toe fanning to rubbing of the toe, etc. These reflexes all exhibited long-term habituation. An example of habituation of the crossed scratch reflex is shown in Figure 17.17 (averaged for three animals). The flank was rubbed gently for ten minutes each day (when dots are shown). The percent scratch reflex activity decreased over a ten-day period (A). The response was restored by the administration of chlorpromazine (C_4) twice, and then allowed to recover spontaneously over an 8-day period of no stimulation (B). It was then subsequently depressed by administration of meprobamate (M_4). Note that in the second habituation series in the absence of drug (D in Figure 17.17) habituation occurs more rapidly than in the first series, as was noted above for the flexion reflex in the acute spinal cat. The fact that the centrally acting drugs used had such a marked effect on the strength of the response was taken as presumptive evidence that the long-lasting reflex habituation effects were due to central mechanisms. Thus, it is possible to establish very long-lasting but reversible habituatory changes in the reflex responses of chronic spinal animals. Habituation of the flexion and "scratch" (Abwisch) reactions has also been reported for the chronic spinal frog (Afelt, 1963).

Unit discharges of single ventral root fibers (Y in Figure 17.15) to repeated cutaneous stimulation in cat have been investigated extensively by Buchwald, Halas, and Schramm (1965). They stimulated skin of the hind paw with a 0.5 second 60-cps shock train given at rates ranging from 1/5 sec to 1/45 sec and recorded (extracellularly) discharge patterns of two types of single ventral root fibers: those showing only phasic response to the stimulus, and those showing ongoing tonic activity. The phasic units probably represent alpha motor neurons and the tonic units were either tonic alpha motor neurons or gamma motor neurons. An example of habituation of a phasic unit is shown in Figure 17.18. As the stimulus is repeated the discharge frequency of the unit decreases markedly. Habituation of a tonic unit is shown in Figure 17.19 (small spikes).

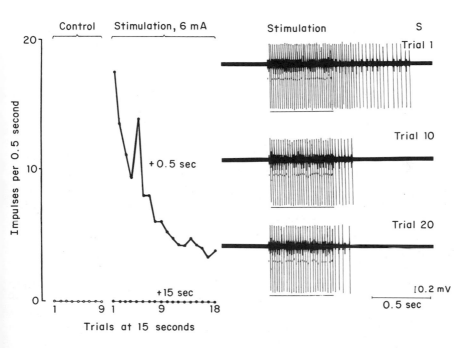

Figure 17.18. Decreasing responses of phasic efferent unit to repeated stimulation. Graph represents discharges per 0.5 sec during all control and stimulation trials; $+0.5$ sec indicates the discharge rate 0.5 sec after onset of stimulus, and $+15$ sec indicates discharge rate 15 sec after stimulus onset. Each point graphed represents the running average of three trials. Traces at right are samples of the graphed efferent unit responses for the trials indicated. Duration of the 0.5-sec stimulus is indicated by the bar under each trace. Cutaneous stimulation of 6 mA repeated at intervals of 15 sec. (From Buchwald, Halas, and Schramm, 1965)

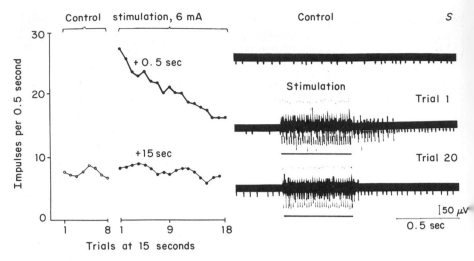

Figure 17.19. Decreasing responses of tonically discharging efferent unit to 6-mA cutaneous stimulation repeated at 15-sec intervals. During early trials the tonic unit is markedly accelerated and a second, slightly larger unit discharges in the $+0.5$-sec poststimulus period. These responses progressively diminish with repeated stimulation even though the tonic discharge rate returns to control levels after each stimulation. (From Buchwald, Halas, and Schramm, 1965)

In a smaller percentage of cases they also observed increased frequency of firing during the habituation training. Most of the units showing increased firing rates were of the tonic type.

The possible synaptic mechanisms underlying flexion reflex habituation in the acute spinal cat have been studied in a recent series of experiments (Spencer, Thompson, and Neilson, 1966 a,b,c; Thompson and Spencer, 1966) The basic neuronal system is illustrated in the schematic drawing in Figure 17.15, showing a cross section of the spinal cord with associated peripheral nerves, receptors, and flexor muscles. Amplitude of a flexor muscle response (R_m), or a motor nerve or ventral root response (R_n), or intracellularly recorded single alpha motor neuron responses (R_α), is measured to weak skin (S_s), cutaneous nerve (S_{1n}) or muscle nerve (S_{2N}) shocks repeated every few seconds. The gamma afferent fibers coming from the muscle can be stimulated at S_{2N} to produce monosynaptic activation of the alpha motor neurons. The flexion reflex is a polysynaptic reflex having unknown central connections through interneurons (indicated by "?" in Figure 17.15) to the alpha motor neurons.

In initial experiments the flexion reflex of the muscle was habituated to repeated skin shock, as in the studies by Sherrington, Prosser, and Hunter, and others described above. An example of habituation and spontaneous recovery of the flexion reflex was shown in Figure 17.16A. In agreement with previous studies it was found that stimulation of the skin afferent nerve (S_{1n}) produced the same habituation as did stimulation of the skin itself. Furthermore, the afferent nerve response monitored at R_s demonstrated no decrease in the afferent nerve volley during repeated stimulation, thus showing that the muscle response habituation cannot be due to any decrease in the incoming nerve activity.

The possibility that flexion reflex habituation was due to muscle fatigue or changes at neuromuscular junctions was ruled out by recording efferent nerve responses, either of the peripheral nerves or of the ventral roots (R_n). The same response habituation occurs when the motor nerve response is measured. These findings suggest that the processes responsible for response decrement are central rather than peripheral. However there is one other possible peripheral mechanism that could play an important role, the gamma motor neuron system. Repeated activation of the muscle and the gamma motor neuron (γ in Figure 17.15) might result in altered activity in the spindle organs and gamma afferent fibers, which could act back to alter the activity of the alpha motor neurons (α in Figure 17.15) controlling the muscle. This possibility was evaluated by sectioning all dorsal and ventral roots, stimulating the central stumps of the dorsal roots, and recording the motor nerve output from the central stumps of the ventral roots (i.e. stimulating at point X and recording at point Y in Figure 17.15). The habituatory response decrement occurred here just as in the more intact preparation. Furthermore, adminsitration of flaxedil (which abolishes spindle afferent activity) did not alter the habituation process. Consequently crucial participation of the gamma motor neuron system in habituation was ruled out. Spinal reflex habituation must be due to processes occurring within the spinal cord.

One possible mechanism that could produce habituation would be decreased activity of the terminals of the stimulated cutaneous afferent nerve fibers in the spinal cord as a direct result of stimulation (synaptic terminals marked T in Figure 17.15). The stimulus generalization experiment of Figure 17.16E rules this out as the exclusive cause of habituation. If one cutaneous nerve is stimulated repeatedly to produce habituation, and habituation were due solely to decreased activity of these nerve terminals because of previous activity, there would be no stimulus generalization of habituation to other nerves. Because there was stimulus generalization of habituation (Figure 17.16E), this possibility is unlikely.

Perhaps the most interesting data came from intracellular recordings (M in Figure 17.15) from motor neurons participating in the flexion reflex being habituated. This permits evaluation of the possibility that response habituation is due to a decreased excitability of the motor neurons themselves. In particular, the excitability of the motor neurons can be measured independently of the cutaneous nerve habituating stimuli by stimulation of the gamma afferent fibers (S_{2N}) (i.e. the large group I sensory fibers) that have direct monosynaptic connections on the alpha motor neurons. If the monosynaptic response of the motor neurons does not change during the course of habituation, then it is likely that the tonic excitability of the motor neurons is unchanged.

This experiment is illustrated in Figure 17.20. The upper line shows the polysynaptic intracellular response of the motor neuron to the cutaneous nerve habituating stimulus during the control period (A), after habituation (B), and

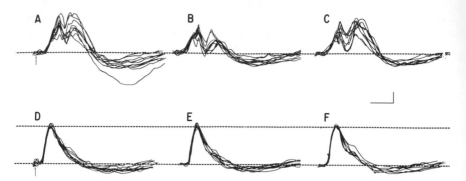

Figure 17.20. Upper line: polysynaptic PSPs recorded intracellularly from a motor neuron (by M in Figure 17.15) during: **A**, control period; **B**, habituation; **C**, after spontaneous recovery. Lower line: monosynaptic PSPs recorded from same motor neuron (by stimulation of S_{2N} in Figure 17.15) interpolated every 30 sec during: **D**, control; **E**, habituation, and **F**, recovery. Note that there is *no change* in the monosynaptic PSP. (From Spencer and Thompson, unpublished observations)

after spontaneous recovery (C). The membrane response has a large initial depolarization (due to polysynaptic EPSPs) and a smaller after-hypolarization. Note that after habituation (B) the depolarization is markedly reduced, but that it recovers in C. Thus the membrane response of the motor neuron exhibits the same habituatory response decrement as do the muscle and gross nerve responses. The lower line of responses in Figure 17.20 are monosynaptic responses to a 1/min stimulus of the monosynaptic pathway (S_{2N} in Figure 17.15) interpolated during the control period (D), habituation (E), and recovery (F). There is no change in the excitability of the motor neuron, as measured by the monosynaptic response. Several other lines of evidence were also consistent with this conclusion.

The possibility that postsynaptic inhibition acts on the motor neuron at the time of each habituating stimulus also appears to be unlikely. Note in Figure 17.20 that the hyperpolarizing component of the polysynaptic postsynaptic potential (reflecting IPSP activity) also decreases during habituation (i.e. from A to B). Several other lines of evidence also argued against this possibility. Finally, the possibility that pre- and postsynaptic inhibitory processes were occurring elsewhere in the system (in the interneurons between input fibers and motor neurons indicated by "?" in Figure 17.15) were tested with drugs. Strychnine abolishes most known instances of postsynaptic inhibition in the spinal cord and picrotoxin markedly reduces presynaptic inhibition (see Chapters 7 and 8 and Eccles, 1964). Administration of these drugs, separately and in combination, had no significant effects on habituation. Consequently, it may be suggested that presynaptic and postsynaptic inhibition are not crucially responsible for the response decrements seen during habituation.

These experimental results suggest that spinal flexion reflex habituation is not due to peripheral receptor or muscular changes, to gamma motor neuron activity, to changes in the afferent terminals of the cutaneous input nerve, to changes in the excitability of the motor neurons, or to postsynaptic inhibition acting on the motor neurons. Clearly the processes responsible for the response decrement are likely to occur within the interneurons (? in Figure 17.15) interposed between the input afferent fibers and the motor neurons. The investigators suggested that these processes may be a polysynaptic analogue of the low frequency depression reported for monosynaptic reflexes. Alternatively, pre- and postsynaptic inhibitory processes acting on interneurons could be responsible. Sharpless (1964) has suggested that a process of "membrane desensitization," due to repeated applications of transmitter substance, may be responsible for long-lasting habituation effects.

Sensitization of the flexion reflex is relatively easy to obtain in the spinal animal. In the experimental arrangement shown in Figure 17.15, the relatively weak skin test stimulus (*a*) is given infrequently (e.g. 1/min) so that no habituation occurs. If another strong skin stimulus is given, the flexion response to the test stimulus will increase for a period of many minutes (see Figure 17.21A). Possible neuronal mechanisms involved in this reflex sensitization were also investigated in the experiments described above (Spencer, Thompson, and

Figure 17.21. A, effect of a strong sensitizing stimulus on a control reflex response. Test stimulus was a brief train of shocks to skin once every two minutes and the sensitizing stimulus (solid bar) was a strong shock train delivered elsewhere on the limb for 15 seconds. **B,** independence of habituation and dishabituation. Habituation stimulus (arrow to bar) was brief skin shock train given 1/sec and test stimulus given 1/min. Following the strong (pinch) dishabituatory stimulus (bar) the habituating stimulus was discontinued and a test stimulus delivered 1/min. Note that the response dishabituates, *then* "*rehabituates*" and spontaneously recovers, even though there is no further habituation training. (From Thompson and Spencer, 1966)

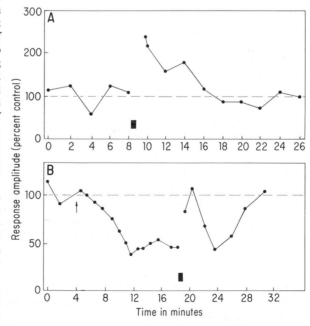

Neilsen, 1966a, b, c, Thompson and Spencer, 1966). It was found that the gamma system may play a role, in that the time course of sensitization is generally shorter when the gamma system is cut than when it is intact. Furthermore, there are generally increases in the excitability of the motor neurons during sensitization; both polysynaptic and monosynaptic motor neuron postsynaptic potentials increase during sensitization. Sensitization, like habituation, can still be obtained after administration of strychnine and picrotoxin, suggesting that pre- and postsynaptic inhibition may not be crucially involved.

The fact that increased excitability of the motor neurons generally occurs during sensitization, while there is no change in motor neuron excitability during habituation, suggests that rather different neuronal processes may be involved in the two phenomena. The phenomenon of post-tetanic potentiation (PTP) resembles sensitization in that it is a long-lasting increase in response strength following a brief increase in the stimulus frequency (see Chapter 12). It has been suggested that a type of interneuron "afterdischarge" effect may be responsible for spinal flexion reflex sensitization (Spencer, Thompson, and Neilsen, 1966c; Thompson and Spencer, 1966). Examples of habituation and "dishabituation" or sensitization of polysynaptic PSPs recorded from a motor neuron are shown in Figure 17.22.

Sensitization, incidentally, has often been studied within the context of response habituation. If the strong extra stimulus is given after the reflex response has been habituated, the response will recover. This has been termed "dishabituation" or "disinhibition" (Prosser and Hunter, 1936; Lehner, 1941).

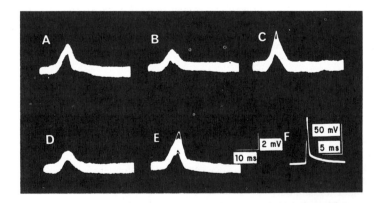

Figure 17.22. Polysynaptic PSPs from a deep peroneal motor neuron (identified by antidromic activation as shown in F). **A**, control period: stimulation 1/30 sec. **B**, after habituation training: stimulation 1/sec. **C**, sensitization: response increase after a strong tetanus (100/sec for 4 sec) to another cutaneous nerve. **D**, response decrement after continued habituation training (1/sec). **E**, after spontaneous recovery with stimulation 1/30 sec as in **A**. Note that the sensitized response in **C** is larger than the initial control level (**A**). (From Spencer, Thompson, and Neilson, 1966a)

Recent evidence indicates that dishabituation of an habituated spinal final flexion reflex may instead be the result of superimposing the independent sensitization effect on the habituated response. A behavioral demonstration of the independence of the two processes of habituation and sensitization is illustrated in Figure 17.21B. The flexion reflex was first habituated, and then dishabituated, and the habituating stimulus turned off and given only infrequently to test response strength. Note that the response then "rehabituates," even though it is no longer being habituated. Finally, the response spontaneously recovers to normal levels. If the dishabituation effect of the strong stimulus simply acted to "break up" habituation, the response would not return to habituated level after "dishabituation," but would remain at the control level. Because it does return to the habituated level, in the *absence of habituation training*, it would seem clear that sensitization is a separate process from habituation and does not simply "break up" habituation. This behavioral demonstration of the independence of habituation and sensitization is consistent with the neurophysiological data given above indicating that different processes may be involved in the two phenomena.

These findings are perhaps instructive in the sense that they illustrate both the strengths *and* the weaknesses of the model neural systems approach to the neural basis of behavioral plasticity. A number of specific hypotheses could be tested and to some extent disproved. However, the analysis was a great deal more successful in demonstrating what the neuronal bases of flexion reflex habituation and sensitization are *not*, than what they are. These model neural systems permit the use of "strong inference" where hypotheses can be disproved, but the current lack of knowledge of interneuron organization and actions is still a limiting factor in ascertaining the fundamental synaptic processes responsible for habituation and sensitization. As we noted above in our discussion of planaria learning, an even greater problem in the model neural system approach concerns the extent to which synaptic mechanisms of the model system (i.e. spinal cord) will parallel those of the intact nervous system. This problem of inference can only be settled by future research.

Spinal conditioning

The occurrence of spinal conditioning is still a subject of debate. In view of our greatly increased recent understanding of synaptic mechanisms involved in spinal reflexes, we would have a much better chance of analyzing the synaptic basis of learning if conditioning could be demonstrated to occur in the acute neurally isolated spinal cord. An important series of papers by Shurrager, Culler, and colleagues (Shurrager and Culler, 1940; Shurrager and Shurrager, 1941, 1946) reported classical conditioning of the hind limb flexion reflex in the acute spinal dog. Subsequent experiments by another group (Kellogg, 1947; Kellogg et al., 1946; Kellogg et al., 1947; Deese and Kellogg, 1949) reported entirely negative results. More recently, Dykman and Shurrager reported spinal conditioning in the chronic spinal kitten (1956). Nesmeianova (1957) has reported conditioning of the scratch reflex in the chronic spinal dog. The negative findings of Kellogg and colleagues have tended to receive greater weight. This is perhaps unfortunate in view of the extreme importance of spinal conditioning as a model system. Kellogg's experiments did not reproduce the procedures of Shurrager. In fact they seem designed in such a way as to load the dice against the possible development of conditioning. To date there have been no published accounts of attempts to reproduce Shurrager's procedure.

In Shurrager's experiments the response measured was a twitch of the semitendinosus muscle, a hindlimb flexor. The CS was a shock or tap to the tail and the UCS a strong shock to the footpad. Contrary to general opinion, Shurrager and Culler (1940) ran all the necessary controls to demonstrate conditioning, including presentation of the CS alone, the UCS alone, and alternating series of CS and UCS not paired. None of the control procedures produced conditioning. They were also able to demonstrate one of the parametric relations characteristic of conditioning, namely successively more rapid conditioning and extinction series. However, their response measure, visual observation of muscle twitches, may not have been reliable.

Kellogg's experiments used chronic spinal dogs and measured gross flexion of the entire leg. The UCS was shock to the hindpaw and the CS was shock to the *opposite* hindpaw. Using these procedures, conditioning could not be demonstrated. It is important to note that the unconditioned response to the CS would be flexion of that limb and extension of the opposite limb (crossed extension reflex). Thus the CS would tend to evoke reflex extension of the same limb whose flexion response was being conditioned. This would appear to reduce the chances that conditioning could develop. There would seem to be urgent need of further studies exploring the possibilities of acute spinal conditioning. Spinal conditioning, per se, is probably of no importance in the normal behavior of the intact mammal. Its significance lies in the fact that the spinal cord can serve as a simplified model system where some degree of analysis of the basic neural processes underlying learning could be achieved.

CURRENT VIEWS OF THE PHYSICAL BASIS OF LEARNING

A variety of evidence suggests that there may be two different types of neural processes involved in learning, a short term "consolidation" of recent experience, and a long-term permanent storage of the "memory trace." This *consolidation hypothesis* (Müller and Pilzecker, 1900; Hebb, 1949; and others) is based on experiments showing that drastic alterations in the state of brain activity interfere selectively with recently learned responses. The classical experiment is that by Duncan (1949). He trained rats to avoid shock to the feet in a shuttle box situation. A light, presented 10 seconds before shock, served as the CS; the animals received one trial per day for 18 days. A total of nine groups of animals were used in the experiment. Rats in 8 of the groups received an electroconvulsive

(ECS) shock after each day's trial, the trial-ECS interval ranging from 20 seconds to 14 hours. In the ninth group the clips were placed on the animal's ear for delivery of the ECS, but the ECS was not actually delivered. The results of this experiment are illustrated in Figure 17.23, in which performance is plotted as a function of time between learning trial and ECS each day. As seen, the closer the ECS is to the learning trial the more deleterious effect it has on performance. If the two are separated by more than an hour there appears to be no effect of the ECS on learning. In a variety of subsequent experiments and observations, ECS, epileptic convulsions, hypoxia, depressant drugs, and anesthetics have been reported to have similar effects (Russell and Nathan, 1946; Thompson and Pryer, 1956; Thompson, 1957; Thompson and Pennington, 1957; Deutsch, 1962; Pearlman et al., 1961, Chorover and Schiller, 1965). All of these procedures produced marked transient changes in the state of brain activity. It has been hypothesized that relatively short-term electrical activity, perhaps some sort of reverberating circuits in which activity cycles in closed loops around chains of

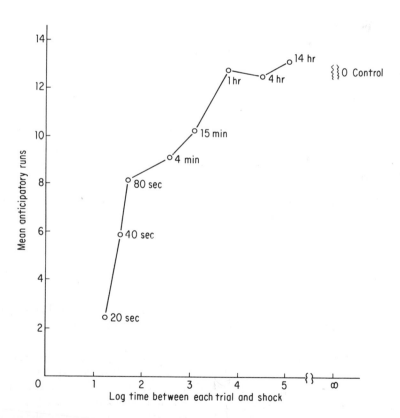

Figure 17.23. Effect of electroconvulsive shock (ECS) on performance in a simple shock avoidance learning task in rats. Anticipatory runs are "correct" (i.e. shock is avoided). Parameter is time after trial (1 trial per day) that ECS is given. (From Duncan, 1949)

neurons, represents the initial storage of the "memory trace." During the half hour or so of reverberation more permanent memory traces would then be laid down. Procedures that interfere with electrical activity should have a progressively greater effect on learning as they are applied closer in time to the learning trials.

It has been suggested that the supposed interference effects of ECS on recent learning may be nothing other than conditioned fear (Coons and Miller, 1960). Thus the ECS could simply act as a strong negative reinforcer. Actually Duncan ran the necessary control for this possibility in his original experiment: control animals were given the ECS through the feet instead of across the head (when given through the feet it does not produce convulsions or coma). Results tended not to support the conditioned fear hypothesis but were somewhat ambiguous. Other investigations have attempted to separate conditioned fear and memory loss effects (Brady, 1951; Brady and Hunt, 1952; Hudspeth, McGaugh, and Thomson, 1964). To oversimplify an extensive and complex literature: it does appear that ECS impairs short-term learning (over a range of several minutes) in addition to producing conditioned fear effects.

It can be argued that if some sort of electrical reverberation is involved in short-term memory storage, substances which increase electrical activity ought to improve learning. Early experiments by Hull and Lashley showed that caffeine and strychnine did improve maze learning performance in rats. McGaugh and his colleagues have completed an extensive series of experiments showing comparable effects of strychninelike substances and of picrotoxin. In the initial experiments (e.g. McGaugh and Petrinovich, 1959) the drugs were given prior to learning trials. The direct effects of these drugs on performance in maze running may be confounded with possible effects on consolidation. Consequently in subsequent experiments the drugs were given immediately *after* each learning trial (Breen and McGaugh, 1961; McGaugh, Westbrook, and Thompson, 1962; McGaugh et al., 1962; Stratton and Petrinovich, 1963). Significant facilitation of learning was still obtained. However, it could be argued that improvement with post-trial injections is due to a rewarding effect of the drugs rather than any direct effect on memory storage.

Westbrook and McGaugh (1963) attempted to circumvent this possibility in an ingenious adaptation of the *latent learning* paradigm. In brief, four groups of rats were trained in a maze learning situation (one trial/day). Two groups were given immediate post-trial injection of a strychninelike drug and the other two groups given saline injections. One drug group and one saline group were given no food reward in the alley goal box during the first 5 days (trials). The other groups were rewarded throughout. The results are shown in Figure 17.24. Scores of the food rewarded drug group (RRE) and the food rewarded saline group (RRC) improved over the first five days, but the drug-no food group (NRE) and saline-no food group (NRC) did not. However, when reward was given to all groups on trials 5 to 10 the drug effect clearly separated the groups: both drug groups doing significantly better than the saline groups. The essential point here is that if the drug injections were rewarding, the drug group given no

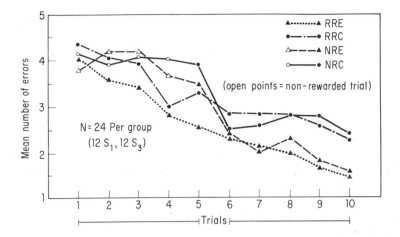

Figure 17.24. Consolidation effect of strychninelike drug in a latent learning situation. Two groups were given food reward during the first five days and two were not. All groups were given food thereafter. One of the food and one of the no food groups were given the drug after each daily trials and the other groups were given saline. (Food-drug = RRE; food-saline = RRC; no food-drug = NRE; no food-saline = NRC). (From Westbrook and McGaugh, 1963)

food reward during the first 5 days should exhibit improved performance (i.e. the drug would reward performance). Because no such result occurred, it would seem that drug effects on maze performance cannot be attributed solely to possible reward value of drug injection.

The consolidation hypothesis makes no attempt to analyze the synaptic mechanisms involved in consolidation. In this connection it is perhaps significant that strychnine and picrotoxin, which both have excitant effects on performance, act by quite different synaptic mechanisms, at least in the spinal cord. Strychnine impairs postsynaptic inhibition and picrotoxin impairs presynaptic inhibition. It seems somewhat puzzling that substances acting on synaptic function in such diverse ways would have identical effects on the complex alterations in synaptic organization that must occur during learning. Experimental investigation of the consolidation hypothesis is currently an area of very considerable activity (see McGaugh, 1966).

Also related to the consolidation problem are certain studies involving re-organization of function following brain lesion. In several of these studies the role of experience in the recovery process following lesion has been examined. Harlow (1939) showed that recovery of pattern vision after unilateral lesions of the striate cortex in monkeys did not occur if animals were kept in the dark postoperatively, but did if they were kept in a lighted room. Meyer (1958) investigated this problem extensively using rats trained to respond to a light. First, bilateral lesions of visual cortex abolished the discrimination, but it was subsequently relearned. If the lesion was made on one side, the animals kept in the dark for 12 days, and the other visual area removed, the animals were like the bilateral lesion group—they had to relearn the discrimination. However, another group given the same sequence of two lesions but kept in the normally lighted home cage between lesions showed considerable retention of the discrimination (see Figure 17.25). It is important to note that interlesion training on the discrimination was not necessary to maintain the discrimination, only exposure to a normally lighted environment. Although neural processes involved

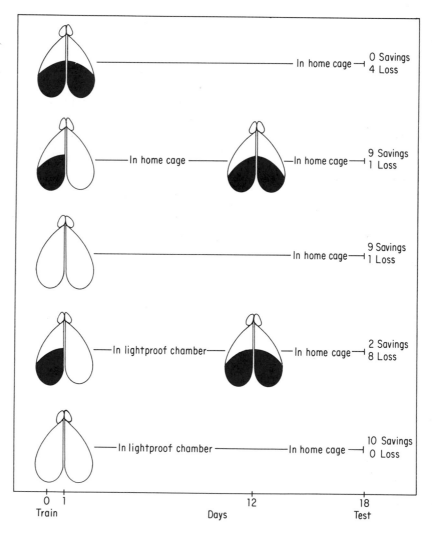

Figure 17.25. Crucial importance of the interlesion experience in determining recovery of function after a bilateral cortical lesion done in two stages. (From Meyer, 1958)

in this phenomenon are not known at present, it represents an intriguing example of "consolidation" following simple stimulation.

Experiments investigating the "consolidation" effect uniformly find that well-learned responses seem impervious to assault. It would appear necessary to postulate some type of relatively permanent structural changes forming a physical basis of the memory trace. Hebb (1949), Eccles (1957, 1964) and others have postulated swelling of presynaptic terminal knobs, growth of new presynaptic terminals and other comparable processes. The views represented by hypotheses concerning RNA and glia cells contrast somewhat with the synaptic growth hypothesis. We have described the experiments by Hydén and colleagues showing increased RNA synthesis in active neurons. Hydén assumes that frequency modulation of impulses is the basic form of coding and that this is related to the sequence or ordering of bases in the RNA molecule. Galambos (1961) has suggested that glia may play a special role in learning. There is as yet no direct evidence implicating alterations in synaptic terminals, RNA coding, glia participation, or any other specific mechanisms that might form the immediate neural substrates of permanent alterations in synaptic efficacy during learning.

Learning involves altered responses to stimuli. Because the nervous system is composed of elements interconnecting through synapses, it would seem fairly clear that learning results in altered patterns of interaction among the myriad nerve cells from input stimuli to behavioral output. The mechanisms and character of altered synaptic organization must be specified for an understanding of the neural basis of learning. At present RNA and glia hypotheses can offer no help in solving this more general problem. However, it is likely that changes in synaptic efficacy during learning involve increased or decreased activity in excitatory and inhibitory neurons, with associated changes in RNA content. A cell would presumably need to step up RNA production if it were to grow more efferent terminals. Because synaptic transmission is chemically mediated in the mammal, a variety of chemical as well as structural alterations are likely to participate in neural changes during learning. The study of the chemical and structural bases of learning in the nervous system has only begun.

SUGGESTED READINGS

Fessard, A., Gerard, R. W., & Konorski, J. (Eds.) *Brain mechanisms and learning.* Springfield, Ill.: Thomas, 1961.

Kimble, D. P. (Ed.) *The anatomy of memory.* Palo Alto, Calif.: Science and Behavior Books, 1965.

Reiss, R. F. (Ed.) *Neural theory and modeling.* Stanford: Stanford Univ. Press, 1964.

BIBLIOGRAPHY

Aceves, J., & Machne, X. The action of calcium and of local anesthetics on nerve cells and their interaction during excitation. *J. Pharmacol.*, 1963, **140**, 138–148.

Acheson, G. H. Physiology of neuro-muscular junctions: chemical aspects. *Fed. Proc.*, 1948, **7**, 447–457.

Adametz, J. H. Rate of recovery of functioning in cats with rostral reticular lesions. *J. Nerosurg.*, 1959, **16**, 85–98.

Ades, H. W. Central auditory mechanisms. Pp. 585–613 in Field, J., Magoun, H. W., & Hall, V. E. (Eds.) *Handbook of physiology*, *Neurophysiology*, vol. I, Washington, D.C.: American Physiological Society, 1959.

Adey, W. R. The sense of smell. Pp. 535–548 in Field, J., Magoun, H. W., & Hall, V. E. (Eds.) *Handbook of physiology*, *Neurophysiology*, vol. I, Washington, D.C.: American Physiological Society, 1959.

Adey, W. R., Dunlop, C. W., & Hendrik, C. E. Hippocampal slow waves: distribution and phase relationships in the course of approach learning. *Arch. Neurol.*, 1960, **3**, 74–90.

Adrian, E. D. *The basis of sensation, the action of sense organs.* London: Christophers Ltd., 1928.

Adrian, E. D. Discharge frequencies in cerebral and cerebellar cortex. *J. Physiol.*, 1935, **83**, 32–33.

Adrian, E. D. The spread of activity in the cerebral cortex. *J. Physiol.*, 1936, **88**, 127–161.

Adrian, E. D. Double representation of the feet in the sensory cortex of the cat. *J. Physiol.*, 1940, **98**, 16.

Adrian, E. D. Afferent areas in the cerebellum connected with the limbs. *Brain*, 1943, **66**, 289–315.

Adrian, E. D. Brain rhythms. *Nature*, 1944, **153**, 360–362.

Adrian, E. D. The electrical activity of the mammalian olfactory bulb. *Electroencephalog. clin. Neurophysiol.*, 1950, **2**, 377–388.

Adrian, E. D. Sensory messages and sensation. The response of the olfactory organ to different smells. *Acta physiol. Scand.*, 1953, **29**, 5–14.

Adrian, E. D. The basis of sensation: some recent studies of olfaction. *Brit. med. J.*, 1954, **1**, 287–290.

Adrian, E. D., & Bronk, D. The discharge of impulses in motor nerve fibers, Part II: The frequency of discharge in reflex and voluntary contractions. *J. Physiol.*, 1929, **67**, 119–151.

Adrian, E. D., & Matthews, R. The action of light on the eye. *J. Physiol:* I, 1927, **63**, 378–414; II, 1927, **64**, 279–301; III, 1928, **65**, 273–298.

Adrian, E. D., & Matthews, B. H. C. The interpretation of potential waves in the cortex. *J. Physiol.*, 1934a, **81**, 440–471.

Adrian, E. D., & Matthews, B. H. C. Berger rhythm: potential changes from occipital lobes in man. *Brain*, 1934b, **57**, 355–385.

Adrian, E. D., & Moruzzi, G. Impulses in the pyramidal tract. *J. Physiol.*, 1939, **97**, 153–199.

Adrian, E. D., & Yamagiwa, K. The origin of the Berger rhythm. *Brain*, 1935, **58**, 323–351.

Afelt, Z. Variability of reflexes in chronic spinal frogs. Pp. 37–41 in Gutmann, E., & Huik, P. (Eds.) *Proceedings of the conference on central and peripheral mechanisms of motor functions.* Prague, Czechoslovakia: Czechoslovak Acad. of Science, 1963.

Affanni, J., Mancia, M., & Marchiafava, P. L. Role of the pupil in changes in evoked responses along the visual pathways. *Arch. Ital. Biol.*, 1962, **100**, 287–296.

Akert, K. Diencephalon. Pp. 288–310 in Sheer, D. E. (Ed.) *Electrical stimulation of the brain*, Austin, Texas: Univ. of Texas Press, 1961.

Akert, K. Comparative anatomy of frontal cortex and thalamofrontal connections. Pp. 372–396 in Warren, J. M., & Akert, K. (Eds.) *The frontal granular cortex and behavior.* New York: McGraw-Hill, 1964.

Akert, K., & Andersson, B. Experimenteller Beitrag zur Physiologie des Nucleus Caudatus. *Acta physiol. Scand.*, 1951, **22**, 281–298.

Akert, K., Koella, W. P., & Hess, R., Jr. Sleep produced by electrical stimulation of the thalamus. *Am. J. Physiol.*, 1952, **168**, 260–267.

Akert, K., & Welker, W. I. Problems and methods of anatomical localization. Pp. 251–260 in Sheer, D. E. (Ed.) *Electrical stimulation of the brain.* Austin, Texas: Univ. of Texas Press, 1961.

Akert, K. Frontispiece in Warren, J. M., & Akert, K. (Eds.) *The frontal granular cortex and behavior.* New York: McGraw-Hill, 1964.

Akimoto, H., Yamogushi, N., Okabe, K., Nakagawa, T., Nakamura, I., Abe, K., Torii, H., & Masahashi, K. On the sleep induced through stimulation on the dog thalamus. *Folia psychiat. neurol. Jap.*, 1956, **10**, 117–146.

Albe-Fessard, D., Mallart, A., & Aleonard, P. Réponses cérébrales évoquées enregistries chez le chat éveille libre et comportement attentif. *J. Physiol. (Paris)*, 1960, **52**, 7.

Albe-Fessard, D., Rocha-Miranida, D., & Oswaldo-Cruz, E. Activités d'origine somesthétique évoquées au niveau du cortex non-spécifique et du centre médian du thalamus chez le singe anesthésié au chloralose. *Electroencephalog. clin. Neurophysiol.*, 1959, **11**, 777–787.

Albe-Fessard, D., & Rougeul, A. Activités bilaterales tardines evoquées sur le cortex du chat sous chloralose par stimulation d'une voic somesthésique. *J. Physiol. (Paris)*, 1955, **47**, 69–72.

Albino, R., & Burnand, G. Conditioning of the alpha rhythm in man. *J. exp. Psychol.*, 1964, **67**, 539–544.

Alekseyeva, T. T. Correlation of nervous and humoral factors in the development of sleep in non-disjointed twins. *Zh. vysshei nerv. Deiat.*, 1958, **8**, 835–844.

Allen, W. F. Formatis reticularis and reticulo spinal tracts, their visceral functions and possible relationships to tonicity and clonic contractions. *J. Wash. Acad. Sci.*, 1932, **22**, 490–495.

Allen, W. F. Effect of destroying three localized cerebral cortical areas for sound on correct conditioned differential responses of the dog's foreleg. *Am. J. Physiol.*, 1945, **144**, 415–428.

Allen, W. F. Effect of partial and complete destruction of the tactile cerebral cortex on correct conditioned differential foreleg responses from cutaneous stimulation. *Am. J. Physiol.*, 1947, **151**, 325–337.

Allison, A. C. The morphology of the olfactory system in the vertebrates. *Biol. Rev.*, 1953, **28**, 195–244.

Amassian, V. E. Studies on organization of a somesthetic association area, including a single unit analysis. *J. Neurophysiol.*, 1954, **17**, 39–58.

Amassian, V. E., Patton, N. E., Woodbury, J. W., Towe, A., & Schlag, J. E. An interpretation of the surface response in somatosensory cortex to peripheral and interareal afferent stimulation. *Electroencephalog. clin. Neurophysiol.*, 1955, **7**, 480–483.

Amassian, V. E., & Berlin, L. Early cortical projection of Group I afferents in the forelimb muscle nerves of cat. *J. Physiol.*, 1958, **143**, p. 61.

Amassian, V. E., & Walter, H. J. Spatiotemporal patterns of activity in individual reticular neurons. Pp. 69–110 in Jasper, H. H., (Ed.), *Reticular formation of the brain*, Boston: Little, Brown, 1958.

Amoore, J. E. The stereochemical theory of olfaction. I. Identification of the seven primary odors. *Proc. Sci. Sect. Toilet Goods Assoc.*, 1962a, Suppl. to **37**, 1–12.

Amoore, J. E. The stereochemical theory of olfaction. II. Elucidation of the stereochemical properties of the olfactory receptor sites. *Proc. Sci. Sect. Toilet Goods Assoc.*, 1962b, Suppl. to **37**, 13–47.

Amoore, J. E. Current status of the steric theory of odor. *Ann. N.Y. Acad. Sci.*, 1964, **116**, 457–476.

Amoore, J. E., Johnston, J. W., Jr., & Rubin, M. The stereochemical theory of odor. *scient. Am.*, 1964, **210**, 42–49.

Anand, B. K., & Brobeck, J. R. Hypothalamic control of food intake in rats and cats. *Yale J. biol. Med.*, 1951, **24**, 123–140.

Anand, B. K., Dua, S., & Schoenberg, K. Hypothalamic control of food intake in cats and monkeys. *J. Physiol.*, 1955, **127**, 143–152.

Andersen, P., Eccles, J. C., & Sears, T. A. Presynaptic inhibitory action of cerebral cortex on the spinal cord. *Nature*, 1962, **194**, 740–741.

Andersen, P., Eccles, J. C., & Løyning, Y. Recurrent inhibition in the hippocampus with identification of the inhibitory cell and its synapses. *Nature*, 1963, **198**, 540–542.

Andersen, P., Eccles, J. C., & Sears, T. A. Cortically evoked depolarization of primary afferent fibers in the spinal cord. *J. Neurophysiol.*, 1964, **27**, 63–77.

Andersson, B. The effect and localization of electrical stimulation of certain parts of the brain stem in sheep and goats. *Acta physiol. Scand.*, 1951, **23**, 8–24.

Andersson, B. Polydipsia caused by intrahypothalamic injections of hypertonic NaCl solutions. *Experientia*, 1952, **8**, 157–158.

Andersson, B. The effect of injections of hypertonic NaCl solutions into different parts of the hypothalamus of goats. *Acta physiol. Scand.*, 1953, **28**, 188–201.

Andersson, B., Grant, R., & Larsson, S. Central control of heat loss mechanisms in the goat. *Acta physiol. Scand.*, 1956, **37**, 261–280.

Andersson, S. A. Projection of different spinal pathways to the second somatic sensory area in cat. *Acta physiol. Scand.*, 1962, **56**, Suppl. 194.

Andersson, S., & Gernandt, B. E. Cortical projection of vestibular nerve in cat. *Acta otolaryng.*, 1954, Suppl. 116, 10–18.

Andersson, S., & Gernandt, B. E. Ventral root discharge in response to vestibular and proprioceptive stimulation. *J. Neurophysiol.*, 1956, **19**, 524–543.

Applebaum, J., Silva, E. E., & Frick, O. Frequency discrimination and "arousal" reaction. *Proc. XXI Intern. Physiol. Congr., Buenos Aires*, 1959, p. 18.

Araki, T., & Terzuolo, C. A. Membrane currents in spinal mononeurons associated with the action potential and synaptic activity. *J. Neurophysiol.*, 1962, **25**, 772–789.

Arduini, A., & Hirao, T. On the mechanism of the EEG sleep patterns elicited by acute deafferentation. *Arch. Ital. Biol.*, 1959, **97**, 140–155.

Armstrong, M. D., & Tyler, F. H. Studies on phenylketonuria. I. Restricted phenylalanine intake in phenylketonuria. *J. clin. Invest.*, 1955, **34**, 565–580.

Artemyev, V. V., & Bozladnova, N. I. Electrical reaction of the auditory area of the cortex of the cerebral hemisphere during the formation of a conditioned defense reflex. *Trudy Pavlov Inst. Fiziol.*, 1952, **I**, 228–236.

Asahina, K., & Yamanaka, M. The relationship between steady potential and other electrical activities of cerebral cortex. *Jap. J. Physiol.*, 1960, **10**, 258–266.

Aserinsky, E., & Kleitman, N. A motility cycle in sleeping infants as manifested by ocular and gross bodily activity. *J. appl. Physiol.*, 1955, **8**, 11–18.

Axelrod, S., & Diamond, I. T. Effects of auditory cortex ablation on ability to discriminate between stimuli presented to the two ears. *J. comp. physiol. Psychol.*, 1965, **59**, 79–98.

Ayer, A. J. Pp. 70–74 in Laslett, P. (Ed.) *The physical basis of mind*, New York: Macmillan, 1950.

Bagshaw, M. H., & Pribram, K. H. Cortical organization in gustation (Macaca mulatta). *J. Neurophysiol.*, 1953, **16**, 499–508.

Bain, W. A. A method of demonstrating the humoral transmission of the effects of cardiac vagus stimulation in the frog. *Quart. J. exp. Physiol.*, 1932, **22**, 269–274.

Baker, P. F., Hodgkin, A. L., & Shaw, T. I. Replacement of the protoplasm of a giant nerve fibre with artificial solutions. *Nature*, 1961, **190**, 885–887.

Baránek, R., & Hník, P. Long-term effects of tenotomy on spinal monosynaptic responses in the cat. *Science*, 1959, **130**, 981–982.

Barber, T. X. Toward a theory of pain: Relief of chronic pain by prefrontal leucotomy, opiates, placebos, and hypnosis. *Psychol. Bull.*, 1959, **56**, 430–460.

Bard, P. A diencephalic mechanism for the expression of rage with special reference to the sympathetic nervous system. *Am. J. Physiol.*, 1928, **84**, 490–515.

Bard, P. Studies on the cortical representation of somatic sensibility. Harvey Lecture, Feb. 1938. *Bull. N.Y. Acad. Med.*, 1938, **14**, 585–607.

Bard, P. The hypothalamus and sexual behavior. *Ass. res. nerv. dis. Proc.*, 1940, **20**, 551–579.

Bard, P. Central nervous mechanisms for the expression of anger in animals. Pp. 211–237 in Reynolds, M. L. (Ed.) *Feelings and emotions: The Moosehart symposium*. New York: McGraw-Hill, 1950.

Bard, P. *Medical physiology*. St. Louis: Mosby, 1956.

Bard, P., & Macht, M. B. The behavior of chronically decerebrate cats. Pp. 55–71 in *Ciba Foundation Symposium, Neurological basis of behavior*, London: Churchill, 1958.

Bard, P., & Mountcastle, V. B. Some forebrain mechanisms involved in expression of angry behavior. *Ass. res. nerv. dis. Proc.*, 1947, **27**, 362–404.

Barker, D. The innervation of the muscle spindle. *Quart. J. micr. Sci.*, 1948, **89**, 143–186.

Barker, D. The structure and distribution of muscle receptors. Pp. 227–240 in Barker, D. (Ed.) *Symposium on muscle receptors*, Hong Kong: Hong Kong Univ. Press, 1962.

Barlow, H. B. Summation and inhibition in the frog's retina. *J. Physiol.*, 1953, **119**, 69–88.

Barron, D. H., & Matthews, B. H. C. The interpretation of potential changes in the spinal cord. *J. Physiol.*, 1938, **92**, 276–321.

Bartley, S. H. Subjective brightness in relation to flash rate and the light-dark ratio. *J. exp. Psychol.*, 1938, **23**, 313–319.

Bartley, S. H. Some factors in brightness discrimination. *Psychol. Rev.*, 1939, **46**, 337–358.

Bartley, S. H. *Vision*, New York: Van Nostrand, 1941.

Batini, C., Moruzzi, G., Palestini, M., Rossi, G. F., & Zanchetti, A. Effects of complete pontine transections on the sleep-wakefulness rhythm: The midpontine pretrigeminal preparation. *Arch. Ital. Biol.*, 1959, **97**, 1–12.

Batini, C., Palestini, M., Rossi, G. F., & Zanchetti, A. EEG activation patterns in the mid-pontine pretrigeminal cat following sensory deafferentation. *Arch. Ital. Biol.*, 1959, **97**, 26–32.

Battig, K., Rosvold, H. E., & Mishkin, M. Comparison of the effects of frontal caudate lesions on discrimination learning in monkeys. *J. comp. physiol. Psychol.*, 1962, **55**, 458–463.

Bazzet, C., & Penfield, W. A study of the Sherrington decerebrate animal in the chronic as well as the acute condition. *Brain*, 1922, **45**, 185–264.

Beach, F. A. Neural and chemical regulation of behavior. Pp. 263–284 in Harlow, H. F., & Woolsey, C. N. (Eds.) *Biological and biochemical bases of behavior*. Madison.: Univ. of Wisconsin Press, 1958.

Beach, F. A. Biological bases for reproductive behavior. In Etkin, Wm. (Ed.) *Evolution of social behavior*. Chicago: Univ. of Chicago Press, 1964.

Beck, E. C., Doty, R. W., & Kooi, K. A. Electrocortical reactions associated with conditioned flexion reflexes. *Electroencephalog. clin. Neurophysiol.*, 1958, **10**, 279–289.

Beck, L. H., & Miles, W. R. Some theoretical and experimental relationships between infrared absorption and olfaction. *Science*, 1947, **106**, 511.

Beidler, L. M. Properties of chemoreceptors of tongue of rat. *J. Neurophysiol.*, 1953, **16**, 595–607.

Beidler, L. M. Techniques and methods for research in flavors. Pp. 7–43 in Mitchell, J. H., Leinen, N. J., Mrak, E. M., & Bailey, S. D. (Eds.) *Chemistry of natural food flavors*. Chicago: Quartermaster Research and Engineering Command, 1957.

Beidler, L. M. Comparison of gustatory receptors, olfactory receptors, and free-nerve endings. Pp. 191–200 in *Sensory receptors*. Cold Spring Harbor, N.Y.: Cold Spring Harbor Lab. of Quant. Biology, 1965.

Beidler, L. M., Nejad, M. S., Smallman, R. L., & Tateda, H. Rat taste cell proliferation. *Fed. Proc.*, 1960, **19**, 303–304.

Benjamin, R. M. Some thalamic and cortical mechanisms of taste, Pp. 309–330 in Zotterman, Y. (Ed) *Olfaction and Taste*. New York: Macmillan, 1963.

Benjamin, R. M., & Pfaffmann, C. Cortical localization of taste in albino rat. *J. Neurophysiol.*, 1955, **18**, 56–64.

Benjamin, R. M., & Thompson, R. F. Differential effects of cortical lesions in infant and adult cats on roughness discrimination. *Exper. Neurol.*, 1959, **1**, 305–321.

Benjamin, R. M., & Welker, W. I. Somatic receiving areas of cerebral cortex of squirrel monkey (*Saimiri sciureus*). *J. Neurophysiol.*, 1957, **20**, 286–299.

Bennett, E. L., & Calvin, M. Failure to train planarians reliably. *Neurosci. res. program Bull.*, 1964, **2**, No. 4, 3–12.

Bennett, E. L., Diamond, M. C., Krech, D., & Rosenzweig, M. R. Chemical and anatomical plasticity of brain. *Science*, 1964, **146**, 610–619.

Benoit, J. Hypothalamic-hypophyseal control of the sexual activity in birds. *Gen. comp. Endocr.* 1962, Suppl. 1, 254–274.

Benoit, J., & Assenmacher, I. Le contrôle hypothalamique de l'activité préhypophysaire gonadotrope, *J. Physiol. (Paris)*, 1955, **74**, 427–567.

Bental, E., & Bihari, B. Evoked activity of single neurons in sensory association cortex of the cat. *J. Neurophysiol.*, 1963, **26**, 207–214.

Berger, H. Über das elektrenkephalogramm des menschen. *Arch. Psychiat. Nervenkr.*, 1929, **87**, 527–570.

Berman, A. L. Overlap of somatic and auditory cortical response fields in anterior ectosylvian gyrus of cat. *J. Neurophysiol.*, 1961, **24**, 595–607. (a)

Berman, A. L. Interaction of cortical responses to somatic and auditory stimuli in anterior ectosylvian gyrus of cat. *J. Neurophysiol.*, 1961, **24**, 608–620. (b)

Bernard, J. W., & Woolsey, C. N. A study of localization in the cortico-spinal tracts of monkey and rat. *J. comp. Neurol.*, 1956, **105**, 25–50.

Bernhard, C. G. Analysis of the spinal cord potentials in leads from the cord dorsum. Pp. 43–62 in Malcolm, J. L., & Grey, J. A. B. (Eds.) *The spinal cord*, Boston: Little, Brown, 1953.

Bernstein, J. Untersuchunger zur Thermodynamik der bioelektrischen Ströme. Erster Teil. *Pflügers Arch. ges. Physiol.*, 1902, **92**, 521–562.

Bessou, P., Emonet-Denand, F., & Laporte, Y. Increase of primary ending's dynamic sensitivity by slow α fibers innervating muscle spindles. *Life Sci.*, 1963, **1**, 948–952.

Bickford, R. G., Galbraith, R. F., & Jacobson, J. L. The nature of averaged evoked potentials recorded from the human scalp. *Electroencephalog. clin. Neurophysiol.*, 1963, **15**, 720.

Bierbrodt, E. Der Larvenkopf von *Panorpa communis* L. und seine Verwandlung, mit besonderer Berucksichtigung des Gehirns und der Augen. *Zool. Jb. (Anat.)* 1942, **68**, 49–136.

Bindman, L. J., Lippold, O. C. J., & Redfearn, J. W. T. The prolonged after-action of polarizing currents on the sensory cerebral cortex. *J. Physiol.*, 1962, **162**, 45–46.

Bishop, G., & O'Leary, J. The effect of polarizing currents on cell potentials and their significance in the interpretation of central nervous activity. *Electroencephalog. clin. Neurophysiol.*, 1950, **2**, 401–416.

Bizzi, E., & Spencer, A. Enhancement of EEG synchrony in the acute *cerveau isolé*. *Arch. Ital. Biol.*, 1962, **100**, 234–247.

Bloom, G., & Evastrom, H. The structure of the epithelial surface in the olfactory region. *Exp. cell. Res.*, 1952, **3**, 699–701.

Blum, J. S., Chow, K. L., & Pribram, K. H. A behavioral analysis of organization of parieto-temporo-preoccipital cortex. *J. comp. Neurol.*, 1950, **93**, 53–100.

Blum, R. A. The effect of bilateral removal of the prefrontal granular cortex on delayed response performance and emotionality in chimpanzee. *Amer. Psychologist*, 1948, **3**, 237–238.

Bok, S. T. *Histonomy of the cerebral cortex*. Amsterdam: Elsevier, 1959.

Bonvallet, M., & Allen, M. E. Prolonged spontaneous and evoked reticular activation following discrete bulbar lesions. *Electroencephalog. clin. Neurophysiol.*, 1963, **15**, 969–988.

Bonvallet, M., Dell, P. & Heibel, G. Tonus sympathique et activité électrique corticale. *Electroencephalog. clin. Neurophysiol.*, 1954, **6**, 119–144.

Bonvallet, M., Hugelin, A., & Dell, P. Sensibilité comparée du système reticulé activateur ascendant et du centre respiratoire au gaz du sang et à l'adrénaline. *J. Physiol. (Paris)*, 1955, **47**, 651–654.

Bonvallet, M., Hugelin, A., & Dell, P. Milieu intérieur et activité automatique des cellules réticulaires mésencéphaliques. *J. Physiol. (Paris)*, 1956, **48**, 403–406.

Boring, E. G. *Sensation and perception in the history of experimental psychology*. New York: Appleton-Century-Crofts, 1942.

Boring, E. G. *A History of experimental psychology*. New York: Appleton-Century-Crofts, 1950.

Bower, G. H., & Miller, N. E. Rewarding and punishing effects from stimulating the same place in the rats brain. *J. comp. physiol. Psychol.*, 1958, **51**, 669–674.

Boyd, I. A. The structure and innervation of the nuclear leg muscle fibre system and the nuclear chain muscle fibre system in mammalian muscle spindles. *Phil. Trans. roy. soc. series B*, 1962, **245**, 81–136.

Bradley, P. B. The central action of certain drugs in relation to the reticular formation of the brain. Pp. 123–149 in Jasper, H. H. (Ed.) *Reticular formation of the brain*. Boston: Little, Brown, 1958.

Bradley, P. B. Intermediation between administered drugs and behavioral effects: The electro-physiological approach. Pp. 338–344 in de Reuck, A. V. S., & Knight, J. (Eds.) *Ciba Foundation Symposium, Animal behavior and drug action*. Boston: Little, Brown, 1964.

Brady, F. V. The effect of electro-convulsive shock on a conditioned emotional response: the permanence of the effect. *J. comp. physiol. Psychol.*, 1951, **44**, 507–511.

Brady, J. V. Motivational-emotional self-stimulation. Pp. 413–430 in Sheer, D. E. (Ed.) *Electrical stimulation of the brain*. Austin, Texas: Univ. of Texas Press, 1961.

Brady, J. V. Psychophysiology of emotional behavior. Pp. 343–385 in Bachrach, A. J. (Ed.) *Experimental foundations of clinical psychology*. New York: Basic Books, 1962.

Brady, J. V., & Hunt, H. F. The effect of electro-convulsive shock on a conditioned emotional response: a control for impaired hearing. *J. comp. physiol. Psychol.*, 1952, **45**, 180–182.

Brady, J. V., & Nauta, W. J. H. Subcortical mechanisms in emotional behavior: affective changes following septal forebrain lesions in the albino rat. *J. comp. physiol. Psychol.*, 1953, **46**, 339–346.

Brady, J. V., Schreiner, L., Geller, I., & Kling, A. Subcortical mechanisms in emotional behavior: the effect of rhinencephalic injury upon the acquisition and retention of a conditioned avoidance response in cats. *J. comp. physiol. Psychol.*, 1954, **47**, 179–186.

Brazier, M. A. B. Studies of evoked responses by flash in man and cat. Pp. 151–168 in Jasper, H. H. (Ed.) *Reticular formation of the brain*. Boston: Little, Brown, 1958.

Brazier, M. A. B. The historical development of neurophysiology. Pp. 1–58 in Field, J. Magoun, H. W., and Hall, V. E. (Eds.) *Handbook of physiology, Neurophysiology*, I. Washington, D.C.: American Physiological Society, 1959.

Brazier, M. A. B. *The electrical activity of the nervous system*. New York: Macmillan, 1960.

Brazier, M. A. B. The analysis of brain waves. *Sci. Am.*, 1962, **206**, 142–153.

Breen, R. A., & McGaugh, J. L. Facilitation of maze learning with post-trail injections of picrotoxin. *J. comp. physiol. Psychol.*, 1961, **54**, 498–501.

Bremer, F. *Bull. de l'Acad. Roy de Med. de Belgique*, 1937, **2**, 6e série, 68–86.

Bremer, F. *Cerveau isolé* et physiologie du sommeil. *Comp. Rend. Soc. biol.*, 1935, **118**, 1235–1241.

Bremer, F. *Some problems in neurophysiology*. London: Athlone Press, 1953.

Bremer, F., & Terzuolo, C. Contribution a l'étude des méchanismes physiologiques du maintien de l'activité vigile du *cerveau*. Interaction de la formation réticulée et de l'écorce cérébrale dans le processus du réveil. *Arch. int. Physiol.*, 1954, **62**, 157–178.

Briggs, M. H., & Kitto, G. B. The molecular basis of memory and learning. *Psychol. Rev.*, 1962, **69**, 537–541.

Brobeck, J. R., Tepperman, J., & Long, C. N. H. Experimental hypothalamic hyperphagia in the albino rat. *Yale J. biol. Med.*, 1943, **15**, 831–853.

Brodal, A. *The reticular formation of the brain stem, anatomical aspects and functional correlations*. London: Oliver and Boyd, 1957.

Brodie, B. B., & Shore, P. A. A concept for a role of serotonin and norepinephrine as chemical mediators in the brain. *Ann. N. Y. Acad. Sci.*, 1957, **66**, 631–642.

Brody, E. B., & Rosvold, H. E. Influence of prefrontal lobotomy on social interaction in a monkey group. *Psychosom. Med.*, 1952, **14**, 406–415.

Brogden, W. J. Sensory preconditioning. *J. exp. Psychol.*, 1939, **25**, 323–332.

Brogden, W. J. Animal studies of learning. Pp. 568–612 in Stevens, S. S. (Ed.) *Handbook of experimental psychology*. New York: Wiley, 1951.

Brogden, W. J., & Culler, E. A. Device for motor conditioning of small animals. *Science*, 1936, **83**, 269.

Brogden, W. J., & Gantt, W. H. Intraneural conditioning: cerebellar conditioned reflexes. *Arch. neurol. Psychiat.*, 1942, **48**, 437–455.

Brogden, W. J., Lipman, E. A., & Culler, E. The role of incentive in conditioning and extinction. *Amer. J. Psychol.*, 1938, **51**, 109–117.

Bromiley, R. B. Conditioned responses in a dog after removal of neocortex. *J. comp. physiol. Psychol.*, 1948, **41**, 102–110.

Brookhart, J. M. A study of cortico-spinal activation of motor neurons. *Ass. Res. nerv. Dis. Proc.*, 1952, **30**, 157–173.

Brookhart, J. M. The cerebellum. Pp. 1245–1280 in Field, J., Magoun, H. W., & Hall, V. E. (Eds.) *Handbook of physiology, Neurophysiology*, II. Washington, D.C.: American Physiological Society, 1960.

Brookhart, J. M., & Dey, F. L. Reduction of sexual behavior in male guinea pigs by hypothalamic lesions. *Amer. J. Physiol.*, 1941, **133**, 551–554.

Brookhart, J. M., Dey, F. L., & Ranson, S. W. Failure of ovarian hormones to cause mating reactions in spayed guinea pigs with hypothalamic lesions. *Proc. Soc. exp. Biol.*, 1940, **44**, 61–64.

Brookhart, J. M., Dey, F. L., & Ranson, S. W. The abolition of mating behavior by hypothalamic lesions in guinea pigs. *Endocrinology*, 1941, **28**, 561–565.

Brookhart, J. M., Moruzzi, G., & Snider, R. S. Spike discharges of single units in the cerebellar cortex. *J. Neurophysiol.*, 1950, **13**, 465–486.

Brookhart, J. M., Moruzzi, G., & Snider, R. S. Origin of cerebellar waves. *J. Neurophysiol.*, 1951, **14**, 181–190.

Brookhart, J. M., & Zanchetti, A. The relation between electro-cortical waves and responsiveness of the cortico-spinal system. *Electroencephalog. clin. Neurophysiol.*, 1956, **8**, 427–444.

Brouwer, B., & Zeeman, W. P. C. The projection of the retina in the primary optic neuron in monkeys. *Brain*, 1926, **49**, 1–35.

Brown, G. W., & Cohen, B. D. Avoidance and approach learning motivated by stimulation of identical hypothalamic loci. *Amer. J. Physiol.*, 1959, **197**, 153–157.

Brown, H. M., Dustman, R. E., & Beck, E. C. Experimental procedures contributing to "learning" in regenerated planaria. *Physiol. and Behav.*, 1966a, **1**, 245–249.

Brown, H. M., Dustman, R. E., & Beck, E. C. Sensitization in planaria. *Physiol. and Behav.*, 1966b, in press.

Brown, J. S. *The motivation of behavior*. New York: McGraw-Hill, 1961.

Brown, J. S., Anderson, D. C., & Brown, C. S. Conflict as a function of food-deprivation time during approach training, avoidance training and conflict tests. *J. exp. Psychol.*, 1967, in press.

Brown, J. S., & Jacobs, A. The role of fear in the motivation and acquisition of responses. *J. exp. Psychol.*, 1949, **39**, 747–759.

Brown, J. S., Kalish, H. I., & Farber, I. E. Conditioned fear as revealed by magnitude of startle response to an auditory stimulus. *J. exp. Psychol.*, 1951, **41**, 317–328.

Brown, K. T., & Wiesel, T. N. Intraretinal recording in the unopened cat eye. *Am. J. Ophthal.*, 1958, **46**, 91–96.

Brown, K. T., & Wiesel, T. N. Intraretinal recording with micropipette electrodes in the intact cat eye. *J. Physiol.*, 1959, **149**, 537–562.

Brugger, M. Fresstreib als hypothalamisches symptom. *Helvet. physiol. pharmacol. Acta*, 1943, **I**, 183–198.

Brush, F. R., & Levine, S. Adrenocortical activity and avoidance learning as a function of time after avoidance training. *Physiol. Behav.*, 1967 (in press).

Brutkowski, S. Prefrontal cortex and drive inhibition. Pp. 242–270 in Warren, J. M., & Akert, K. (Eds.) *The frontal granular cortex and behavior*. New York: McGraw-Hill, 1964.

Buckner, D. N., & McGrath, J. J. (Eds.) *Vigilance: A symposium*. New York: McGraw-Hill, 1963.

Buchthal, F., & Kaiser, E. The rheology of the cross-striated muscle fiber, with particular reference to isotonic conditions. *Dan. Biol. Med.*, 1951, **21**, 1–318.

Buchwald, J. S., Halas, E. S., & Schramm, S. Progressive changes in efferent unit responses to repeated cutaneous stimulation in spinal cats. *J. Neurophysiol.* 1965, **28**, 200–215.

Buchwald, J. S., Halas, E. S., & Schramm, S. Changes in cortical and subcortical unit activity during behavioral conditioning. *Physiol. Behav.*, 1966, **1**, 11–22.

Bullock, T. H., & Horridge, G. A. *Structure and function in the nervous system of invertebrates*. San Francisco: W. H. Freeman, 1961.

Bureš, J., & Buresova, O. Cortical spreading depression as a memory disturbing factor. *J. comp. physiol. Psychol.*, 1963, **56**, 268–272.

Bureš, J., Petran, M., & Zachar, J., *Electrophysiological methods in biological research* (2nd ed.). New York: Academic Press, 1962.

Burns, B. D. *The mammalian cerebral cortex*. London: Edward Arnold Publ., 1958.

Buser, P., & Borenstein, P. Suppression selective des réponses "associatives" par stimulation réticulaire chez le chat sous anesthésie profonde au chloralose. *J. Physiol. (Paris)*, 1957, **49**, 86–89.

Buser, P., & Borenstein, P. Réponses somésthesique, visuelles et auditives, recueillés au niveau du cortex "associatif" suprasylvien chez le chat curarisé non anesthésie. *Electroencephalog. clin. Neurophysiol.*, 1959, **11**, 285–304.

Buser, P., Borenstein, P., & Bruner, J. Étude des systèmes "associatifs" visuels et auditifs chez le chat anesthésie au chloralose. *Electroencephalog. clin. Neurophysiol.*, 1959, **11**, 305–324.

Buser, P., & Imbert, M. Sensory projections to the motor cortex in cats: a microelectrode study. Pp. 607–626 in Rosenblith, W. A., *Sensory communication*. New York: Wiley, 1961.

Butler, R. A., Diamond, I. T., & Neff, W. D. Role of auditory cortex in discrimination of changes in frequency. *J. Neurophysiol.*, 1957, **20**, 108–120.

Butter, C. M., Mishkin, M., & Rosvold, H. E. Stimulus generalization in monkeys with inferotemporal lesions and lateral occipital lesions. Pp. 119–133 in Mostofsky, D. I. (Ed.) *Stimulus generalization*. Stanford, Calif.: Stanford Univ. Press, 1965.

Caldwell, P. C., Hodgkin, A. L., Keynes, R. D., & Shaw, T. I. The effects of injecting "energy rich" phosphate compounds on the active transport of ions in the giant axon of *loligo*. *J. Physiol.*, 1960, **152**, 561–590.

Caldwell, P. C., & Keynes, R. D. The utilization of phosphate bond energy for sodium extrusion from giant axons. *J. Physiol.*, 1957, **137**, 12–13.

Cameron, D. E., & Solyom, L. Effects of ribonucleic acid on memory. *Geriatrics*, 1961, **16**, 74–81.

Cannon, W. B., & Rosenblueth, A. *Autonomic neuro-effector systems*. New York: Macmillan, 1937.

Cannon, W. B., & Uridil, J. E. Some effects on the denervated heart of stimulating the nerves of the liver. *Amer. J. Physiol.*, 1921, **58**, 353–364.

Carpenter, D., Lundberg, A., & Norrsell, U. Effects from the pyramidal tract on primary afferents and on spinal reflex actions to primary afferents. *Experientia*, 1962, **18**, 337–338.

Carpenter, D., Lundberg, A., & Norrsell, U. Primary afferent depolarization evoked from the sensorimotor cortex. *Acta physiol. Scand.*, 1963, **59**, 126–142.

Carreras, M., & Andersson, S. A. Response properties of neurons of the anterior ectosylvian gyrus of the cat. *J. Neurophysiol.*, 1963, **26**, 100–126.

Carreras, M., & Levitt, M. Microelectrode analysis of the second sematosensory cortical area in the cat. *Fed. Proc.*, 1959, **18**, 24.

Caspersson, T. O. *Cell growth and cell functions*. New York: Norton, 1950.

Caton, R. The electric current of the brain. *Brit. med. J.*, 1875, **2**, 278–296.

Cerletti, A., & Rothlin, E. Role of 5-hydroxytryptamine in mental diseases and its antagonism to lysergic acid derivatives. *Nature*, 1955, **176**, 785–786.

Chamberlain, T. J., Halick, P., & Gerard, R. W. Fixation of experience in the rat spinal cord. *J. Neurophysiol.*, 1963, **26**, 662–673.

Chambers, W., & Lui, J. Microscopic anatomy of the spinal cord. Pp. 187–202 in Austin, G. (Ed.) *The spinal cord, basic aspects and surgical considerations*. Springfield, Ill.: Charles C. Thomas, 1961.

Chambers, W. W., & Sprague, J. W. Functional localization in the cerebellun. I. Organization in the longitudinal cortico-nuclear zones and their contribution to the control of posture, both extrapyramidal and pyramidal. *J. comp. Neurol.*, 1955, **103**, 105–129.

Chang, H. T. Dendritic potential of the cortical neurons produced by direct electrical stimulation of the cerebral cortex. *J. Neurophysiol.*, 1951, **14**, 1–23.

Chang, H. T. The evoked potentials. Pp. 299–313 in Field, W., Magoun, H. W., & Hall, V. E. (Eds.) *Handbook of physiology, Neurophysiology*, I. Washington, D.C.: American Physiological Society, 1959.

Chang, H. T., Ruch, T. C., & Ward, A. A., Jr. Topographical representation of muscles in motor cortex of monkeys. *J. Neurophysiol.*, 1947, **10**, 39–56.

Chang, J. J., & Hild, W. Contractile responses to electrical stimulation of glial cells from the mammalian central nervous system cultivated in vitro. *J. cell. comp. Physiol.*, 1959, **53**, 139–144.

Chorover, S. L., & Schiller, P. H. Short-term retrograde amnesia in rats. *J. comp. physiol. Psychol.*, 1965, **59**, 73–78.

Chow, K. L. Effects of partial extirpations of the posterior association cortex on visually mediated behavior in monkeys. *Comp. Phychol. Mongr.*, 1951, **20**, 187–217.

Chow, K. L. Conditions influencing the recovery of visual discriminative habits in monkeys following temporal neocortical ablations. *J. comp. physiol. Psychol.*, 1952a, **45**, 430–437.

Chow, K. L. Further studies on selective ablation of associative cortex in relation to visually mediated behavior. *J. comp. physiol. Psychol.*, 1952b, **45**, 109–118.

Chow, K. L. Effects of temporal neocortical ablation on visual discrimination learning sets in monkeys. *J. comp. physiol. Psychol.*, 1954, **47**, 194–198.

Chow, K. L. Effect of local electrographic after-discharge on visual learning and retention in monkey. *J. Neurophysiol.*, 1961a, **24**, 391–400.

Chow, K. L. Anatomical and electrographical analysis of temporal neocortex in relation to visual discrimination learning in monkey. Pp. 507–525 in Delafresnaye, J. F. (Ed.) *Brain mechanisms and learning.* Oxford: Blackwell, 1961b.

Chow, K. L., Blum, J. S., & Blum, R. A. Cell ratios in the thalamo-cortical visual system of *Macaca mulatta. J. comp. Neurol.*, 1950, **92**, 227–239.

Chow, K. L., Dement, W. C., & John, E. R. Conditioned electrocorticographic potentials and behavioral avoidance response in cat. *J. Neurophysiol.*, 1957, **20**, 482–493.

Chow, K. L., & Hutt, P. J. The "association cortex" of *Macaca mulatta*: a review of recent contributions to its anatomy and functions. *Brain*, 1953, **76**, 625–677.

Clare, M. H., & Bishop, G. H. Responses from an association area secondarily activated from optic cortex. *J. Neurophysiol.*, 1954, **17**, 271–277.

Clark, W. E. L. *The hypothalamus.* London: Oliver and Boyd, 1938.

Clark, W. E. L., & Meyer, M. The terminal connexions of the olfactory tract in the rabbit. *Brain*, 1947, **70**, 304–328.

Clark, W. E. L., & Penman, G. G. The projection of the retina in the lateral geniculate body. *Proc. roy. Soc. Series B*, 1934, **114**, 291–313.

Cole, K. S., & Curtis, H. J. Electric impedance of squid giant axon during activity. *J. gen. Physiol.*, 1939, **22**, 649–670.

Cole, K. S., & Hodgkin, A. L. Membrane and protoplasm resistance in the squid giant axon. *J. gen. Physiol.*, 1939, **22**, 671–687.

Cook, L., Davison, A. B., Davis, D. J., Green, H., & Fellows, E. J. Ribonucleic acid: effect on conditioned behavior in rats. *Science*, 1963, **141**, 268–269.

Cooke, P. M., & Snider, R. S. The electrocerebellogram as modified by afferent impulses. *Electroencephalog. clin. Neurophysiol.*, 1954, **6**, 415–423.

Coombs, J. S., Curtis, D. R., & Eccles, J. C. The generation of impulses in motoneurons. *J. Physiol.*, 1957, **139**, 232–249.

Coombs, J. S., Eccles, J. C., & Fatt, P. Excitatory synaptic actions in motor neurons. *J. Physiol.*, 1955a, **130**, 374–395.

Coombs, J. S., Eccles, J. C., & Fatt, P. The inhibitory suppression of reflex discharges from motoneurons. *J. Physiol.*, 1955b, **130**, 396–413.

Coons, E. E., & Miller, N. E. Conflict *vs.* consolidation of memory traces to explain "retrograde amnesia" produced by ECS. *J. comp. physiol. Psychol.*, 1960, **53**, 524–531.

Corning, W. C., & John, E. R. Effect of ribonuclease on retention of conditioned response in regenerated planarians. *Science*, 1961, **134**, 1363–1365.

Cowey, A. Projection of the retina on to striate and prestriate cortex in the squirrel monkey, *Saimiri sciureus. J. Neurophysiol.*, 1964, **27**, 366–393.

Crepox, P., & Fadiga, E. La stimolazione chimica della corteccia cerebellare. *Arch. Sci. Biol.*, 1956, **40**, 66–80.

Creutzfeldt, O., & Jung, R. Neuronal discharge in the cat's motor cortex during sleep and arousal. Pp. 131–170 in Wolstenholme, G. E. W., & O'Connor, M. (Eds.) *Ciba Foundation Symposium, The nature of sleep.* Boston: Little, Brown, 1961.

Cross, B. A., & Green, J. D. Activity of single neurons in the hypothalamus: effect of osmotic and other stimuli. *J. Physiol.*, 1959, **148**, 554–569.

Crossland, J. The problem of non-cholinergic transmission in the central nervous system. *Proc. int. neurochem. Sympos.*, 1957, **2**, 523–541.

Cruikshank, R. M. Human occipital brain potentials as affected by intensity-duration variables of visual stimulation. *J. exp. Psychol.*, 1937, **21**, 625–641.

Curtis, D. R. The pharmacology of central and peripheral inhibition. *Pharmacol. Rev.*, 1963, **15**, 333–363.

Curtis, D. R., & Eccles, J. C. The time courses of excitatory and inhibitory synaptic actions. *J. Physiol.*, 1959, **145**, 529–546.

Curtis, D. R., & Eccles, J. C. Synaptic action during and after repetitive stimulation. *J. Physiol.*, 1960, **150**, 374–398.

Curtis, D. R., & Phillis, J. W. The action of procaine and atropine on spinal neurones. *J. Physiol.*, 1960, **153**, 17–34.

Curtis, D. R., Phillis, J. W., & Watkins, J. C. Actions of amino-acids on the isolated hemisected spinal cord of the toad. *Brit. J. Pharmacol.*, 1961, **16**, 262–283.

Curtis, D. R., & Watkins, J. C. Analogues of glutamic and γ-amino-μ-butyric acids having potent actions on mammalian neurones. *Nature*, 1961, **191**, 1010–1011.

Curtis, H. J., & Cole, K. S. Membrane resting and action potentials from the squid giant axon. *J. cell. comp. Physiol.*, 1942, **19**, 135–144.

Dale, H. H. The action of certain esters and ethers of choline, and their relation to muscarine. *J. Pharmacol. exp. Ther.*, 1941, **6**, 147–190.

Davies, P. W. Chamber for microelectrode studies in the cerebral cortex. *Science*, 1956, **124**, 179–180.

Davis, G. D. Thesis. New Haven; Yale Univ., 1951. Cited pp. 74–75 in Fulton, J. F. *Frontal lobotomy and affective behavior*. London: Chapman, 1951.

Davis, H. Psychophysiology of hearing and deafness. Pp. 1116–1142 in Stevens, S. S. (Ed.) *Handbook of experimental psychology*. New York: Wiley, 1951.

Davis, H. Biophysics and physiology of the inner ear. *Physiol. Rev.*, 1957, **37**, 1–49.

Davis, H. Excitation of auditory receptors. Pp. 565–585 in Field, J., Magoun, H. W., & Hall, B. E. (Eds.) *Handbook of physiology, Neurophysiology*, **I**. Washington, D.C.: American Physiological Society, 1959.

Davis, H. Some principles of sensory receptor action. *Physiol. Rev.*, 1961, **41**, 391–416.

Davis, H. Enhancement of evoked cortical potentials in humans related to a task requiring a decision. *Science*, 1964, **145**, 182–183.

Davis, H., Benson, R. W., Covell, W. P., Fernández, C., Goldstein, R., Katsuki, Y., Legouix, J. P., McAuliffe, D. R., & Tasaki, I. Acoustic trauma in the guinea pig. *J. Acoust. Soc. Amer.*, 1953, **25**, 1180–1189.

Davis, H., Deatherage, B. H., Rosenblut, B., Fernandez, C., Kimura, R., & Smith, C. A. Modification of cochlear potentials produced by streptomycin poisoning and by extensive venous obstruction. *Laryngoscope*, 1958, **68**, 596–627.

de Groot, J. *The rat forebrain in stereotaxic coordinates*. Amsterdam: North-Holland Pub. Co., 1959.

De Lorenzo, A. J. Studies on the ultrastructure and histophysiology of cell membranes, nerve fibers and synaptic junctions in chemoreceptors. Pp. 5–18 in Zotterman, Y. (Ed.) *Olfaction and taste*. New York: Macmillan, 1963.

De Valois, R. L. Analysis and coding of color vision in the primate visual system. Pp. 567–580 in *Sensory Receptors*, Cold Spring Harbor, N.Y.: Cold Spring Harbor Lab. of Quant. Biology, 1965.

De Valois, R. L. Color vision mechanisms in the monkey. *J. gen. Physiol.*, 1960, **43**, Part 2, 115–128.

De Valois, R. L., & Jones, A. E. Single cell analysis of the organization of the primate color-vision system. Pp. 178–191 in Jung, R., & Kornhuber, H. (Eds.) *The visual system: Neurophysiology and psychophysics*. Berlin: Springer-Verlag, 1961.

De Valois, R. L., Smith, C. J., Karoly, A. J., & Kitai, S. T. Electrical responses of primate visual system. I: Different layers of macaque lateral geniculate nucleus. *J. comp. physiol. Psychol.*, 1958a, **51**, 662–668.

De Valois, R. L., Smith, C. J., Kitai, S. T., & Karoly, A. J. Responses of single cells in monkey lateral geniculate nucleus to monochromatic light. *Science*, 1958b, **127**, 238–239.

Dean, R. B. Theories of electrolyte equilibrium in muscle. *Biol. Symp.*, 1941, **3**, 331–348.

Deese, J., & Kellogg, W. N. Some new data on the nature of "spinal conditioning." *J. comp. physiol. Psychol.*, 1949, **42**, 157–160.

Del Castillo, J., & Katz, B. Quantal components of the end-plate potential. *J. Physiol.*, 1954, 560–573.

Del Castillo, J., & Katz, B. A comparison of acetylcholine and stable depolarizing agents. *Proc. roy. Soc. Series B*, 1957, **146**, 362–368.

Delafresnaye, J. F. (Ed.) *Brain mechanisms and learning.* Springfield, Ill.: Charles C. Thomas, 1961.

Delgado, J. M. R. Study of some cerebral structures related to transmission and elaboration of noxious stimulation. *J. Neurophysiol.*, 1955, **18**, 261–275.

Delgado, J. M. R., & Anand, B. K. Increased food intake induced by electrical stimulation of the lateral hypothalamus. *Am. J. Physiol.*, 1953, **172**, 162–168.

Delgado, J. M. R., Roberts, W. W., & Miller, N. E. Learning motivated by electrical stimulation of the brain. *Am. J. Physiol.*, 1954, **179**, 587–593.

Dell, P., Bonvallet, M., & Hugelin, A. Tonus sympathique, adrenaline et controle reticulaire de la motricite spinale. *Electroencephalog. clin. Neurophysiol.*, 1954, **6**, 599–618.

Dement, W. The occurrence of low voltage, fast electroencephalogram patterns during behavioral sleep in the cat. *Electroencephalog. clin. Neurophysiol.*, 1958, **10**, 291–296.

Dement, W., & Kleitman, N. Cyclic variations in EEG during sleep and their relations to eye movements, body motility, and dreaming. *Electroencephalog. clin. Neurophysiol.*, 1957, **9**, 673–690.

Dempsey, E. W., & Morison, R. S. The production of rhythmically recurrent cortical potentials after localized thalamic stimulation. *Amer. J. Physiol.*, 1942a, **135**, 293–300.

Dempsey, E. W., & Morison, R. S. The interaction of certain spontaneous and induced cortical potentials. *Amer. J. Physiol.*, 1942b, **135**, 301–308.

Dempsey, E. W., & Morison, R. S. The electrical activity of a thalamocortical relay system. *Amer. J. Physiol.*, 1943, **138**, 283–396.

Denney, D., & Brookhart, J. M. The effects of applied polarization on evoked electro-cortical waves in the cat. *Electroencephalog. clin. Neurophysiol.*, 1962, **14**, 885–897.

DeRobertis, E. D. P. Submicroscopic morphology of the synapse. *Int. Rev. Cytol.*, 1959, **8**, 61–96.

DeRobertis, E., & Gerschenfeld, M. M. Submicroscopic morphology and function of glial cells. *Int. Rev. Neurobiol.*, 1961, **3**, 1–65.

Desmedt, J. E. Neurophysiological mechanisms controlling acoustic input. Pp. 152–164 in Rasmussen, G. L., & Windle, W. F. (Eds.) *Neural mechanisms of the auditory and vestibular systems.* Springfield, Ill.: Charles C. Thomas, 1960.

Desmedt, J. E., & La Grutta, G. The effect of selective inhibition of pseudocholinesterase on spontaneous and evoked activity of the cat's cerebral cortex. *J. Physiol.*, 1957, **136**, 20–40.

Desmedt, J. E., & Mechelse, K. Suppression of acoustic input by thalamic stimulation. *Proc. Soc.. exp. Biol.*, 1958, **99**, 772–775.

Deutsch, J. A. Higher nervous function: The physiological bases of memory. *Ann. Rev. Physiol.*, 1962, **24**, 259–286.

Deutsch, J. A. Learning and electrical self-stimulation of the brain. *J. theoret. Biol.*, 1963, **4**, 193–214.

Deutsch, J. A., & Deutsch, D. Attention: Some theoretical considerations. *Psychol. Rev.*, 1963, **70**, 51–61.

Deutsch, J. A., & Howarth, C. I. Some tests of a theory of intracranial self-stimulation. *Psychol. Rev.*, 1963, **70**, 444–460.

Diamond, I. T., & Chow, K. L. Biological psychology. Pp. 158–241 in Koch, S. (Ed.) *Psychology: A study of a science.* 4. New York: McGraw-Hill, 1962.

Diamond, I. T., & Neff, W. D. Ablation of temporal cortex and discrimination of auditory patterns. *J. Neurophysiol.*, 1957, **20**, 300–315.

Di Giorgio, A. M. Persistenza nell'animale spinale, di asimmetric posturali e motorie di origine cerebellare. Nota I–III. *Arch. Fisiol.*, 1929, **27**, 518–580.

Dingman, W., & Sporn, M. B. The incorporation of 8-azaguanine into rat brain RNA and its effect on maze learning by the rat: An inquiry into the biochemical basis. *J. psychiat. Res.*, 1961, **1**, 1–11.

Dodt, E. Centrifugal impulses in rabbit's retina. *J. Neurophysiol.*, 1956, **19**, 301–307.

Doty, R. W. Potentials evoked in cat cerebral cortex by diffuse and punctiform photic stimuli. *J. Neurophysiol.*, 1958, **21**, 437–464.

Doty, R. W. Functional significance of the topographical aspects of retino-cortical projection. Pp. 228–247 in Jung, J., & Kornhuber, H. (Eds.) *The visual system: Neurophysiology and psychophysics*. Berlin: Springer-Verlag, 1961a.

Doty, R. W. Conditioned reflexes formed and evoked by brain stimulation. Pp. 397–412 in Sheer, D. E. (Ed.) *Electrical stimulation of the brain*. Austin, Texas: Univ. of Texas Press, 1961b.

Doty, R. W. Conditioned reflexes elicited by electrical stimulation of the brain in macaques. *J. Neurophysiol.*, 1965, **28**, 623–640.

Doty, R. W. Ability of *macaques* to discriminate locus of electrical stimuli applied to neocortex. *XXIII Int. Congr. physiol. Sci.*, Abstract, 1965a.

Doty, R. W., Beck, E. C., & Kooi, K. A. Effect of brain-stem lesions on conditioned responses of cats. *Exp. Neurol.*, 1959, **1**, 360–385.

Doty, R. W., & Giurgea, C. Conditioned reflexes established by coupling visual and motor cortex stimulation. *Physiologist*, 1958, **1**, 17.

Doty, R. W., & Giurgea, C. Conditioned reflexes established by coupling electrical excitations of two cortical areas. Pp. 133–151 in Delafresnaye, J. F. (Ed.) *Brain mechanisms and learning*. Oxford: Blackwell, 1961.

Doty, R. W., Rutledge, L. T., Jr., & Larsen, R. M. Conditioned reflexes established to electrical stimulation of cat cerebral cortex. *J. Neurophysiol.*, 1956, **19**, 401–415.

Doty, R. W., & Rutledge, L. T. Generalization between cortically and peripherally applied stimuli eliciting conditioned reflexes. *J. Neurophysiol.*, 1959, **22**, 428–435.

Dow, R. S. The electrical activity of the cerebellum and its functional significance. *J. Physiol.*, 1938, **94**, 67–86.

Dow, R. S., & Moruzzi, G. *The physiology and pathology of the cerebellum*. Minneapolis: Univ. of Minnesota Press, 1958.

Downman, C. B. B., & Woolsey, C. N. Inter-relations within the auditory cortex. *J. Physiol.*, 1954, **123**, 43–44.

Dubner, R., & Rutledge, L. T. Recording and analysis of converging input upon neurons in cat association area cortex. *J. Neurophysiol.*, 1964, **27**, 620–634.

Duffy, E. *Activation and behavior*. New York: Wiley, 1962.

Durup, G., & Fessard, A. L'électroencéphalogramme de l'homme. *Année psychol.*, 1935, **36**, 1–32.

Duncan, C. P. The retroactive effect of electroshock on learning. *J. comp. physiol. Psychol.*, 1949, **42**, 34–44.

Dusser de Barenne, J. G., & McCulloch, W. S. Suppression of motor response obtained from area 4 by stimulation of area 4s. *J. Neurophysiol.*, 1941, **3**, 311–323.

DuVigneaud, V. Hormones of the posterior pituitary gland: oxytocin and vasopresin. Pp. 1–26 in *The Harvey Lectures*. New York: Academic Press, 1954–1955.

Dykman, R. A., & Shurrager, P. S. Successive and maintained conditioning in spinal carnivores. *J. comp. physiol. Psychol.*, 1956, **49**, 27–35.

Eccles, J. C. An electrical hypothesis of synaptic and neuro-muscular transmission. *Ann. N. Y. Acad. Sci.*, 1946, **47**, 429–455.

Eccles, J. C. *The neurophysiological basis of mind*. Oxford: The Clarendon Press, 1952.

Eccles, J. C. *The physiology of nerve cells*. Baltimore: Johns Hopkins Press, 1957.

Eccles, J. C. The behavior of nerve cells. Pp. 28–47 in Wolstenholme, G. E. W., & O'Connor, C. M. (Eds.) *Ciba Foundation Symposium, Neurological basis of behavior*. London: Churchill, 1958.

Eccles, J. C. The nature of central inhibition. *Proc. roy. Soc. Series B*, 1961, **153**, 445–476.

Eccles, J. C. Spinal neurones: synaptic connections in relation to chemical transmitters and pharmacological responses. In Uvnös, B. (Ed.) *Proc. 1st. int. pharmacol. Meeting*, 1962, **8**, 157–182.

Eccles, J. C. Presynaptic and Postsynaptic inhibitory actions in the spinal cord. In Moruzzi, G., Fessard, A., & Jasper, H. H. (Eds.) *Progress in brain research, brain mechanisms*. Amsterdam: Elsevier Publishing Co., 1963.

Eccles, J. C. *The physiology of synapses*. New York: Academic Press, 1964.

Eccles, J. C., Eccles, R. M., & Fatt, P. The action potentials of the alpha motoneurones supplying fast and slow muscles. *J. Physiol.*, 1958, **142**, 275–291.

Eccles, J. C., Eccles, R. M., & Lundberg, A. Synaptic actions on motoneurons in relation to two components of the Group I muscle afferent volley. *J. Physiol.*, 1957, **136**, 527–546.

Eccles, J. C., Eccles, R. M., & Lundberg, A. The convergence of monosynaptic excitatory afferents on to many different species of alpha motoneurons. *J. Physiol.*, 1957, **137**, 22–50.

Eccles, J. C., Eccles, R. M., & Lundberg, A. Synaptic actions on moroneurons caused by impulses in golgi tendon organ afferents. *J. Physiol.*, 1957, **138**, 227–252.

Eccles, J. C., Eccles, R. M., & Magni, F. Central inhibitory action attributable to presynaptic depolarization produced by muscle afferent volleys. *J. Physiol.*, 1961, **159**, 147–166.

Eccles, J. C., Kastyuk, P. G., & Schmidt, R. F. The effect of electric polarization of the spinal cord on central afferent fibres and on their excitatory synaptic action. *J. Physiol.*, 1962, **162**, 138–150.

Eccles, J. C., & Krnjević, K. Potential changes recorded inside primary afferent fibres within the spinal cord. *J. Physiol.*, 1959, **149**, 250–273.

Eccles, J. C., Krnjević, K., & Miledi, R. Delayed effects of peripheral severance of afferent nerve fibres on the efficacy of their central synapses. *J. Physiol.*, 1959, **145**, 204–220.

Eccles, J. C., Magni, F., & Willis, W. D. Depolarization of central terminals of Group I afferent fibres from muscle. *J. Physiol.*, 1962, **160**, 62–93.

Eccles, J. C., & McIntyre, A. K. The effects of disuse and of activity on mammalian spinal reflexes. *J. Physiol.*, 1953, **121**, 492–516.

Eccles, R. M., Kozak, W., & Westerman, R. A. Enhancement of spinal monosynaptic reflex responses after denervation of synergic hind-limb muscles. *Exp. Neurol.*, 1962, **6**, 451–464.

Eccles, R. M., & Libet, B. Origin and blockade of the synaptic responses of curarized sympathetic ganglia. *J. Physiol.*, 1961, **157**, 484–503.

Eccles, R. M., & Lundberg, A. Integrative pattern of Ia synaptic actions on motoneurons of hip and knee muscles. *J. Physiol.*, 1958, **144**, 271–298.

Egyhazi, E., & Hyden, H. Experimentally induced changes in the base composition of the ribonucleic acids of isolated nerve cells and their oligodendroglial cells. *J. biophys. biochem. Cytol.*, 1961, **10**, 403–410.

Eisenstein, E. M., & Cohen, M. J. Learning in an isolated prothoracic insect ganglion. *Animal Behav.*, 1965, **13**, 104–108.

Eldred, E., & Hagbarth, K. E. Facilitation and inhibition of gamma efferents by stimulation of certain skin areas. *J. Neurophysiol.*, 1954, **17**, 59–65.

Elliott, T. R. On the action of adrenalin. *J. Physiol.*, 1904, **31**, xx–xxi.

Emmers, R., & Akert, K. *A stereotaxic atlas of the brain of the squirrel monkey (Saimiri Sciureus)*. Madison: Univ. of Wisconsin Press, 1963.

Engberg, I., Lundberg, A., & Ryall, R. W. Reticulospinal inhibition of transmission through interneurons of spinal reflex pathways. *Experientia*, 1965, **21**, 612.

Englehardt, V. A., & Ljubimova, M. N. Myosine and adenosinetriphosphatase. *Nature*, 1939, **144**, 668–669.

Epstein, A. N. Reciprocal changes in feeding behavior produced by intra-hypothalamic chemical injections. *Amer. J. Physiol.*, 1960, **199**, 969–974.

Erlanger, J., & Gasser, H. S. *Electrical signs of nervous activity*. Philadelphia: Univ. of Pennsylvania Press, 1937.

Erlich, P. *Das Sauerstoffbedürfnis des Organismus. Eine farbenanalytische Studie*. Berlin: 1885.

Estes, W. K., & Atkinson, R. C. Stimulus sampling theory. Pp. 121–268 in Luce, R. D., Bush, R. R., & Galanter, E. (Eds.) *Handbook of mathematical psychology*, **II**. New York: Wiley, 1963.

Evarts, E. V. Effect of ablation of prestriate cortex on auditory-visual association in monkey. *J. Neurophysiol.*, 1952, **15**, 191–200.

Evarts, E. V. Effects of sleep and waking on activity of single units in the unrestrained cat. In Wolstenholme, G. E. W., & O'Connor, M. (Eds.) *Ciba Foundation Symposium, The nature of sleep*. London: Churchill, 1961, 171–187.

Evarts, E. V. Photically evoked responses in visual cortex units during sleep and waking. *J. Neurophysiol.*, 1963, **26**, 229–248.

Falk, J. L. The behavioral regulation of water-electrolyte balance. Pp. 1–37 in Jones, M. R. (Ed.) *Nebraska symposium on motivation*. Lincoln, Nebraska: Univ. of Nebraska Press, 1961.

Fatt, P. Biophysics of junctional transmission. *Physiol. Rev.*, 1954, **34**, 674–710.

Fatt, P., & Katz, B. An analysis of the end-plate potential recorded with an intra-cellular electrode. *J. Physiol.*, 1951, **115**, 320–370.

Fatt, P., & Katz, B. Spontaneous threshold activity at motor nerve endings. *J. Physiol.*, 1952, **117**, 109–128.

Feldberg, W. S. Intermediation between administered drugs and behavioral effects: The neurophysiological approach. Pp. 360–373 in de Reuck, A. V. S., & Knight, J. (Eds.) *Ciba Foundation Symposium, Animal behavior and drug action*. Boston: Little, Brown, 1964.

Feldman, S. M., & Waller, H. J. Dissociation of electrocortical activation and behavioral arousal. *Nature*, 1962, **196**, 1320–1322.

Ferrier, D. *Functions of the brain* (2nd Ed.). London: Smith and Elder, 1886.

Field, J., Magoun, H. W., & Hall, V. E. (Eds.) *Handbook of physiology, Neurophysiology*, **I**. Washington D.C.: American Physiological Society, 1959.

Field, J., Magoun, H. W., & Hall, V. E. (Eds.) *Handbook of physiology, Neurophysiology*, **II**. Washington, D.C.: American Physiological Society, 1960a.

Field, J., Magoun, H. W., & Hall, V. E. (Eds.) *Handbook of physiology, Neurophysiology*, **III**. Washington, D.C.: American Physiological Society, 1960b.

Fields, W. S., Guillemin, R., & Corton, C. A. (Eds.) *Hypothalamic-hypophysial interrelationships*. Springfield, Illinois: Charles C. Thomas, 1956.

Findlay, M., Rossiter, R. J., & Strickland, K. P. Factors affecting the incorporation of radioactive phosphate into the pentose nucleic acids of brain slices. *Biochem. J.*, 1954, **58**, 236–243.

Fischman, M. W., & Meikle, T. H. Visual intensity discrimination in cats after serial tectal and cortical lesions. *J. comp. physiol. Psychol.*, 1965, **59**, 193–201.

Fisher, A. E. Maternal and sexual behavior induced by intracranial chemical stimulation. *Science*, 1956, **124**, 228–229.

Fisher, C., Magoun, H. W., & Ranson, S. W. Dystocia in diabetes insipidus. *Amer. J. Obstet. Gynec.*, 1938, **36**, 1–9.

Flexner, J. B., Flexner, L. B., & Stellar, E. Memory in mice as affected by intracebral puromycin. *Science*, 1963, **141**, 57–59.

Florey, E., & McLennan, H. Effects of an inhibitory factor (Factor I) from brain on central synaptic transmission. *J. Physiol.*, 1955, **130**, 446–455.

Folkow, B., Ström, G., & Uvnäs, B. Cutaneous vasodilation elicited by local heating of the anterior hypothalamus in cats and dogs. *Acta physiol. Scand.*, 1949, **17**, 317–326.

Forbes, A., & Morison, B. R. Cortical response to sensory stimulation under deep barbiturate narcosis. *J. Neurophysiol.*, 1939, **2**, 112–128.

Fox, C. A. Amygdalo-thalamic connections in Macaca mulatta. *Anat. Rec.*, 1949, **103**, 537–538.

Fox, C. A., McKinley, W. A., & Magoun, H. W. An oscillographic study of olfactory system of cats. *J. Neurophysiol.*, 1944, **1**, 1–16.

Fox, C. A., & Schmitz, J. T. A Marchi study of the distribution of the anterior commissure in the cat. *J. comp. Neurol.*, 1943, **79**, 297–314.

Fox, S. S., & O'Brian, J. H. Duplication of evoked potential waveform by curve of probability of firing of a single cell. *Science*, 1965, **147**, 888–890.

Frank, K. Basic mechanisms of synaptic transmission in the central nervous system. *I.R.E. Trans. Med. Electron.*, 1959, **M.E. 6**, 85–88.

Frank, K., & Fuortes, M. G. F. Presynaptic and postsynaptic inhibition of monosynaptic reflexes. *Fed. Proc.*, 1957, **16**, 39–40.

Franz, S. I. On the functions of the cerebrum: the frontal lobes in relation to the production and retention of simple sensory-motor habits. *Amer. J. Physiol.*, 1902, **8**, 1–22.

French, G. M. Locomotor effects of regional ablation of frontal cortex in rhesus monkeys. *J. comp. physiol. Psychol.*, 1959, **52**, 18–24.

French, G. M. Spatial discontiguity in monkeys with lesions of the frontal cortex. *Science*, 1962, **135**, 728–729.

French, G. M. The frontal lobes and association. Pp. 56–73 in Watten, J. M., & Akert, K. (Eds.) *The frontal granular cortex and behavior*. New York: McGraw-Hill, 1964.

French, G. M., & Harlow, H. F. Variability of delayed-reaction performance in normal and brain-damaged rhesus monkeys. *J. Neurophysiol.*, 1962, **25**, 585–599.

French, J. D., Hernandez-Peón, R., & Livingston, R. B. Projections from cortex to cephalic brain stem (reticular formation) in monkey. *J. Neurophysiol.*, 1955, **18**, 44–55 and 74–95.

French, J. D., & Magoun, H. W. Effects of chronic lesions in central cephalic brain stem of monkeys. *Arch. neurol. Psychiat.*, 1952, **68**, 591–604.

French, J. D., Van Amerongen, F. K., & Magoun, H. W. An activating system in the brain stem of the monkey. *Arch. neurol. Psychiat.*, 1952, **68**, 577–590.

French, J. D., Verzeano, J., & Magoun, H. W. An extralemniscal sensory system in the brain. *Arch. neurol. Psychiat.*, 1953, **69**, 505–518.

Fritsch, G., & Hitzig, E. Ueber die elektrische Erregbarkeit des Grosshirns. *Arch. anat. Physiol. wiss. Med.*, 1870, **37**, 300–332.

Frommer, G. P. Gustatory afferent responses in the thalamus. Pp. 50–59 in Kare, M. R., & Halpern, B. P. (Eds.) *The physiological and behavioral aspects of taste*. Chicago: Univ. of Chicago, 1961.

Fulton, J. F. *Functional localization in the frontal lobes and cerebellum*. Oxford: Clarendon Press, 1949a, b.

Fulton, J. F. *Physiology of the nervous system* (3rd ed.). New York: Oxford Univ. Press, 1949a, b.

Fulton, J. F., & Ingram, F. D. Emotional disturbances following experimental lesions of the base of the brain. *J. Physiol.*, 1929, **67**, xxvii–xxviii.

Furshpan, E. J., & Potter, D. D. Slow postsynaptic potentials recorded from the giant motor fibre of the crayfish. *J. Physiol.*, 1959, **145**, 326–335.

Furshpan, E. J., & Potter, D. D. Transmission at the giant synapses of the crayfish. *J. Physiol.*, 1959, **145**, 289–325.

Furukawa, T., & Furshpan, E. J. Two inhibitory mechanisms in the Mouthner neurons of goldfish. *J. Neurophysiol.*, 1963, **26**, 140–176.

Fuster, J. M. Effects of stimulation of brain stem on tachistoscopic perception. *Science*, 1958, **127**, 150.

Gaito, J. DNA and RNA as memory molecules. *Psychol. Rev.*, 1963, **70**, 471–480.

Gaito, J. Macromolecules and brain. Pp. 89–102 in Gaito, J. (Ed.) *Macromolecules and behavior*. New York: Meredith, 1966.

Gaito, J., & Zavata, A. Neurochemistry and learning. *Psychol. Bull.*, 1964, **61**, 45–62.

Galambos, R. Suppression of auditory nerve activity by stimulation of efferent fibres to cochlea. *J. Neurophysiol.*, 1956, **19**, 424–437.

Galambos, R. Electrical correlates of conditioned learning. Pp. 375–415 in Brazier, M. A. B.

(Ed.) *The central nervous system and behavior.* Trans. 1st Conf. Josiah Macy, Jr. Found., New York, 1958.

Galambos, R. Studies of the auditory system with implanted electrodes. Pp. 137–151 in Rasmussen, G. L., & Windle, W. F. (Eds.) *Neural mechanisms of the auditory and vestibular systems.* Springfield: Charles C Thomas, 1960a.

Galambos, R. Some neural correlates of conditioning and learning. Pp. 120–132 in Ramey, E. R., & O'Doherty, D. S. (Eds.) *Electrical studies on the unanesthetized brain.* New York: Hoeber, 1960b.

Galambos, R. A glia-neural theory of brain function. *Proc. nat. acad. Sci.,* 1961, **47**, 129–136.

Galambos, R., & Davis, H. The response of single auditory-nerve fibers to acoustic stimulation. *J. Neurophysiol.,* 1943, **6**, 39–58.

Galambos, R., & Morgan, C. T. The neural basis of learning. Pp. 1471–1499 in Field, J., Magoun, H. W., & Hall, V. E. (Eds.) *Handbook of physiology, Neurophysiology,* 3. Washington, D.C.: American Physiological Society, 1960.

Galambos, R., Myers, R. E., & Sheatz, G. Extralemniscal activation of auditory cortex in cats. *Amer. J. Physiol.,* 1961, **200**, 23–28.

Galambos, R., Schwartzkopff, J., & Rupert, A. Microelectrode study of superior olivary nuclei. *Amer. J. Physiol.,* 1959, **197**, 527–536.

Galambos, R., Sheatz, G., & Vernier, V. G. Electrophysiological correlates of a conditioned response in cats. *Science,* 1956, **123**, 376–377.

Gamble, J. E., & Patton, H. D. Pulmonary edema and hemorrhage from preoptic lesions in rats. *Amer. J. Physiol.,* 1953, **172**, 623–631.

Garcia, J., Buchwald, N. A., Bach-y-Rita, G., Feder, B. H., & Koelting, R. A. Electroencephalographic responses to ionizing radiation. *Science,* 1963, **140**, 289–290.

Gardner, E. *Fundamentals of neurology.* Philadelphia: W. B. Saunders, 1963 (4th ed.).

Gasser, H. S. The control of excitation in the nervous system. *Harvey Lectures,* 1937, **32**, 169–193.

Gastaut, H. Etat actuel des connaissances sur l'électroencéphalographie du conditionnement. Marseille Colloquium, 1955. *Electroencephalog. clin. Neurophysiol.,* 1957, Suppl. 6, 133–160.

Gastaut, H., Naquet, R., & Vigouroux, R. Un cas d'épilepsie amygdalienne experimentale chez le chat. *Electroencephalog. clin. Neurophysiol.,* 1953, **5**, 291–294.

Gastaut, H., Régis, H., Dongier, S., & Roger, A. Conditionnement électroencéphalographique des décharges épileptiques et notion d'épilepsie reflexo-conditionnée. *Rev. Neurol.,* 1956, **94**, 829–835.

Gatenby, J. B., & Beams, H. W. (Eds.) *The microtomists' vade-mecum.* Philadelphia: Blakiston, 1950.

Gauthier, C., Mallica, A., & Moruzzi, G. Physiological evidence of localized cerebellar projections to bulbar reticular formation. *J. Neurophysiol.,* 1956, **19**, 468–483.

Geldard, F. A. *The human senses.* New York: J. Wiley, 1953.

Gerken, G. M., & Neff, W. D. Experimental procedures affecting evoked responses recorded from auditory cortex. *Electroencephalog. clin. Neurophysiol.,* 1963, **15**, 947–957.

Gernandt, B. E. Vestibular mechanisms. Pp. 549–564 in Field, J., Magoun, H. W., & Hall, V. E. (Eds.) *Handbook of physiology, Nuerophysiology,* I. Washington, D.C.: American Physiological Society, 1959.

Gernandt, B. E., & Thulin, C. A. Vestibular connections of the brain stem. *Amer. J. Physiol.,* 1952, **171**, 121–127.

Gernandt, B. E., & Thulin, C. A. Vestibular mechanisms of facilitation and inhibition of cord reflexes. *Amer. J. Physiol.,* 1953, **172**, 653–660.

Gernandt, B. E., & Thulin, C. A. Reciprocal effects upon spinal motoneurons from stimulation of bulbar reticular formation. *J. Neurophysiol.,* 1955, **18**, 113–129.

Gershuni, G. V., Kozhevnikov, V. A., Maruseva, A. M., Avakyan, R. V., Radionova, E. A., Altman, J. A., & Soroko, V. I. Modifications in electrical responses of the auditory system in different states of higher nervous activity. Pp. 115–124 in Jasper, H. H., & Smirnov, G. D. (Eds.) *The Moscow colloquium on electroencephalography of higher nervous activity. Electro-encephalog. clin. Neurophysiol.*, Suppl. 13, 1960.

Gesteland, R. C., Lettvin, J. Y., Pitts, W. H., & Rojas, A. Odor specificities of the frog's olfactory receptors. Pp. 19–34 in Zotterman, Y. (Ed.) *Olfaction and taste*. New York: Macmillan, 1963.

Giacobini, E. Metabolic relations between glia and neurons studied in single cells. Pp. 15–38 in Cohen, M. M., & Snider, R. S. (Eds.) *Morphological and biochemical correlates of neural activity*. New York: Hoeber, 1964.

Gibbs, F. A., Gibbs, E. L., & Lennox, W. G. Epilepsy: a paroxysmal cerebral dysrhythmia. *Brain*, 1937, **60**, 377–388.

Glaser, G. H. The normal electroencephalogram and its reactivity. Pp. 3–26 in Glaser, G. H. (Ed.) *Electroencephalography and behavior*. New York: Basic Books, 1963.

Glickman, S. E. Effects of peripheral blindness on exploratory behavior in the hooded rat. *Canad. J. Psychol.*, 1958, **12**, 45–51.

Glickman, S. E., & Feldman, S. M. Habituation of the arousal response to direct stimulation of the brain stem. *Electroencephalog. clin. Neurophysiol.*, 1961, **13**, 703–709.

Glickstein, M., & Sperry, R. W. Intermanual somesthetic transfer in split brain monkeys. *J. comp. physiol. Psychol.*, 1960, **53**, 322–327.

Gloor, P. Amygdala. Pp. 1395–1420 in Field, J., Magoun, H. W., & Hall, V. E. (Eds.) *Handbook of physiology, Neurophysiology*, **II**. Washington, D.C.: American Physiological Society, 1960.

Goddard, G. V. Functions of the amygdala. *Psychol. Bull.*, 1964, **62**, 89–109.

Goldberg, J. M., & Neff, W. D. Frequency discrimination after bilateral ablation of cortical auditory areas. *J. Neurophysiol.*, 1961, **24**, 119–128.

Goldring, S., & O'Leary, J. L. Experimentally derived correlates between ECG and steady cortical potential. *J. Neurophysiol.*, 1951, **14**, 275–288.

Goodman, L. S., & Gilman, A. *The pharmacological basis of therapeutics* (3rd Ed.). New York: Macmillan, 1965.

Goy, R. W., & Young, W. C. Somatic basis of sexual behavior patterns in guinea pigs: factors involved in the determination of the character of the soma in the female. *Psychosom. Med.*, 1957, **19**, 144–151.

Grady, K. L., Phoenix, C. H., & Young, W. C. Role of the developing rat testes in differentiation of the neural tissue mediating mating behavior. *J. comp. physiol. Psychol.*, 1965, **59**, 176–182.

Granit, R. A physiological theory of colour perception. *Nature*, 1943, **151**, 11–14.

Granit, R. *Sensory mechanisms of the retina*. London: Oxford Univ. Press, 1947.

Granit, R. *Receptors and sensory perception*. New Haven, Conn.: Yale Univ. Press, 1955.

Granit, R. Neural activity in the retina. Pp. 693–712 in Field, J., Magoun, H. W., & Hall, V. E. (Eds.) *Handbook of physiology, Neurophysiology*, **I**. Washington, D.C.: American Physiological Society, 1959.

Granit, R. Neurophysiology of the retina. Pp. 575–692 in Davson, H. (Ed.) *The eye*, **2**. New York: Academic Press, 1962.

Granit, R., & Helme, T. Changes in retinal excitability due to polarization and some observations on the relation between the processes in retina and nerve. *J. Neurophysiol.*, 1939, **2**, 556–565.

Granit, R., Job, C., & Kaada, B. R. Activation of muscle spindles in pinna reflex. *Acta physiol. Scand.*, 1952, **27**, 161–168.

Granit, R., & Kaada, B. R. Influence of stimulation of central nervous structures on muscle spindles in cat. *Acta physiol. Scand.*, 1952, **27**, 130–160.

Granit, R., Kellerth, J. O., & Williams, T. D. "Adjacent" and "remote" post-synaptic inhibition in motoneurons stimulated by muscle stretch. *J. Physiol.*, 1964, **174**, 453–472.

Grastýan, E., Lissák, K., Madarász, I., & Donhoffer, H. Hippocampal electrical activity during the development of conditioned reflexes. *Electroencephalog. clin. Neurophysiol.*, 1959, **11**, 409–430.

Gray, E. G. A morphological basis for presynaptic inhibition? *Nature*, 1962, **193**, 82–83.

Gray, E. G. Electron microscopy of presynaptic organelles of the spinal cord. *J. Anat.*, 1963, **97**, 101–106.

Gray, J. A. B. Initiation of impulses at receptors. Pp. 123–146 in Field, J., Magoun, H. W., & Hall, V. E. (Eds.) *Handbook of physiology, Neurophysiology*, I. Washington, D.C.: American Physiological Society, 1959.

Gray, J. A. B., & Malcolm, J. L. The initiation of nerve impulses by mesenteric Pacinian corpuscles. *Proc. roy. Soc. Series B*, 1950, **137**, 96–114.

Gray, J. A. B., & Sato, M. Properties of the receptor potential in Pacinian corpuscles. *J. Physiol.*, 1953, **122**, 610–636.

Green, J. D. Electrical activity of the hippocampus of conscious rabbits. *Anat. Rec.*, 1954, **118**, 304.

Green, J. D. The hippocampus. Pp. 1373–1389 in Field, J., Magoun, H. W., & Hall, V. E. (Eds.) *Handbook of physiology, Neurophysiology*, II. Washington, D.C.: American Physiological Society, 1960.

Green, J. D., & Arduini, A. Hippocampal electrical activity in arousal. *J. Neurophysiol.*, 1954, **17**, 532–557.

Green, J. D., Clemente, C. D., & de Groot, J. Rhinencephalic lesions and behavior in cats. *J. comp. Neurol.*, 1957, **108**, 505–545.

Green, J. D., & Machne, X. Unit activity of rabbit hippocampus. *Amer. J. Physiol.*, 1955, **181**, 219–224.

Greer, M. A., Scow, R. O., & Grobstein, C. Thyroid function in hypophysectomized mice bearing intraocular pituitary implants. *Proc. Soc. exp. Biol.*, 1953, **82**, 28–30.

Grillner, S., Hongo, T., & Lund, S. Monosynaptic excitation of spinal gamma-motoneurons from the brain stem. *Experientia*, 1967 (in press).

Gross, C. G. Locomotor activity under various stimulus conditions following partial lateral frontal cortical lesions in monkeys. *J. comp. physiol. Psychol.*, 1963, **56**, 232–236.

Grosser, G. S., & Harrison, J. M. Comments on behavioral interaction between stimulated cortical points. *J. comp. physiol. Psychol.*, 1960, **53**, 229–233.

Grossman, S. P. Eating or drinking elicited by direct adrenergic or cholinergic stimulation of hypothalamus. *Science*, 1960, **132**, 301–302.

Grundfest, H. Ionic mechanisms in electrogenesis. *Ann. N.Y. Acad. Sci.*, 1961, **94**, 405–457.

Guzman-Flores, C., Alcaraz, M., & Harmony, T. Role of the intrinsic ear muscles in the process of acoustic habituation. *Bol. Inst. Estud. Med. Biol.*, 1960, **18(3)**, 135–140.

Hagbarth, K.-E., & Kerr, D. I. B. Central influences on spinal afferent conduction. *J. Neurophysiol.*, 1954, **17**, 295–307.

Haggar, R. A., & Barr, M. L. Quantitative data on the size of synaptic end bulbs in the cat's spinal cord. *J. comp. Neurol.*, 1950, **93**, 17–35.

Haider, M., Spong, R., & Lindsley, D. B. Attention, vigilance, and cortical evoked potentials in humans. *Science*, 1964, **145**, 180–182.

Halstead, W. C. *Cerebral mechanisms for behavior.* New York: Wiley, 1951.

Hamberger, A., & Hyden, H. Inverse enzymatic changes in neurons and glia during increased function and hypoxia. *J. cell Biol.*, 1963, **16**, 521–525.

Hamilton, C. L., & Brobeck, J. R. Hypothalamic hyperphagia in the monkey. *J. comp. physiol. Psychol.*, 1964, **57**, 271–278.

Hamlyn, L. H. The fine structure of the mossy fiber endings in the hippocampus of the rabbit. *J. Anat.*, 1962, **96**, 112–120.

Hampson, J. L., Harrison, C. R., & Woolsey, C. N. Cerebro-cerebellar projections and the somatotopic localization of motor function in the cerebellum. *Ass. Res. nerv. Dis. Proc.*, 1952, **30**, 299–316.

Hanbery, J., & Jasper, H. H. Independence of diffuse thalamocortical projection system shown by specific nuclear destruction. *J. Neurophysiol.*, 1953, **16**, 252–271.

Hara, K. Visual defects resulting from prestriate cortical lesions in cats. *J. comp. physiol. Psychol.*, 1962, **55**, 293–298.

Harlow, H. F. Recovery of pattern discrimination in monkeys following unilateral occipital lobectomy. *J. comp. Psychol.*, 1939, **27**, 467–489.

Harlow, H. F. The formation of learning sets. *Psychol. Rev.*, 1949, **56**, 51–65.

Harlow, H. F. Behavioral contributions to interdisciplinary research. Pp. 3–23 in Harlow, H. F., & Woolsey, C. N. (Eds.) *Biological and biochemical bases of behavior.* Madison, Wis.: Univ. of Wisconsin Press, 1958.

Harlow, H. F. The development of learning in the rhesus monkey. *Amer. Scientist*, 1959, **47**, 459–479.

Harlow, H. F., Akert, K., & Schiltz, K. A. The effects of bilateral prefrontal lesions on learned behavior of neonatal, infant, and preadolescent monkeys. Pp. 126–148 in Warren, J. M., & Akert, K. (Eds.) *The frontal granular cortex and behavior.* New York: McGraw-Hill, 1964.

Harris, G. W. Oestrous rhythm, pseudopregnancy, and the pituitary stalk in rats. *J. Physiol.*, 1950, **111**, 347–360.

Harris, G. W. The function of the pituitary stalk. *Bull. Johns Hopkins Hosp.*, 1955a, **97**, 358–375.

Harris, G. W. *Neural control of the pituitary gland.* London: Arnold, 1955b.

Harris, G. W. Central control of pituitary secretion. Pp. 1007–1038 in Field, J., Magoun, H. W., & Hall, V. E. (Eds.) *Handbook of physiology, Neurophysiology,* **II**. Washington, D.C.: American Physiological Society, 1960.

Harris, G. W. Sex hormones, brain development and brain function. *Endocrinology*, 1964, **75**, 627–648.

Harris, J. D. Habituatory response decrement in the intact organism. *Psychol. Bull.*, 1943, **40**, 385–422.

Hartline, H. K. The response of single optic nerve fibers of the vertebrate eye to illumination of the retina. *Amer. J. Physiol.*, 1938, **121**, 400–415.

Hartline, H. K. The receptive field of the optic nerve fibers. *Amer. J. Physiol.*, 1940, **130**, 690–699.

Hartline, H. K., & Ratliff, F. Inhibitory interaction of receptor units in the eye of limulus. *J. gen. Physiol.*, 1957, **40**, 357–376.

Hartline, H. K., & Ratliff, F. Spatial summation of inhibitory influences in the eye of limulus, and the mutual interaction of receptor units. *J. gen. Physiol.*, 1958, **41**, 1049–1066.

Hartline, H. K., Ratliff, F., & Miller, W. H. Inhibitory interaction in the retina and its significance in vision. In Florey, E. (Ed.) *Nervous inhibition.* New York: Pergamon, 1961, Pp. 241–284.

Hartry, A. L., Keith-Lee, P., & Morton, W. D. Planaria: memory transfer through cannibalism reexamined. *Science*, 1964, **146**, 274–275.

Harvey, J. A., & Hunt, H. F. Effect of septal lesions on thirst in the rat as indicated by water consumption and operant responding for water reward. *J. comp. physiol. Psychol.*, 1965, **59**, 49–56.

Harvey, J. A., Lints, C. E., Jacobsen, L. E., & Hunt, H. F. Effects of lesions in the septal area on conditioned fear and discriminated instrumental punishment in the albino rat. *J. comp. physiol. Psychol.*, 1964, **59**, 37–48.

Hassler, R. Die extrapyramidalen Rindensysteme und die zentrale Regelung der Motorik. *Deutsch. Z. Nervenheilk.*, 1956, **175**, 233–258.

Head, H. *Studies in neurology.* London: Oxford, 1920.

Hearst, E., Beer, B., Sheatz, G., & Galambos, R. Some electrophysiological correlates of conditioning in the monkey. *Electroencephalog. clin. Neurophysiol.*, 1960, **12**, 137–152.

Heath, R. G., & Mickle, W. A. Evaluation of seven years' experience with depth electrode studies in human patients. Pp. 214–242 in Ramey, E. R., & O'Doherty, D. S. (Eds.) *Electrical studies on the unanesthetized brain.* New York: Hoeber, 1960.

Hebb, D. O. *The organization of behavior*. New York: Wiley, 1949.

Hebb, D. O. Drives and the c.n.s. (conceptual nervous system). *Psychol. Rev.*, 1955, **62**, 243–254.

Hebb, D. O. *A textbook of psychology*. Philadelphia: Saunders, 1958.

Hecht, S., Schlaer, S., & Pirenne, M. R. Energy, quanta and vision. *J. gen. Physiol.*, 1942, **25**, 819–840.

Heimer, L., & Larsson, K. Impairment of mating behavior in male rats following lesions in the preoptic-anterior hypothalamic continuum. *Exp. Brain Res.*, 1967 (in press).

Henning, H. *Der Geruch* (2nd Ed.). Leipzig: Barth, 1924.

Hern, J. E. C., Landgren, S., Phillips, C. G., & Porter, R. Selective excitation of corticofugal neurons by surface-anodal stimulation of the baboon's motor cortex. *J. Physiol.*, 1962, **161**, 73–90.

Hernández-Peón, R. Central mechanisms controlling conduction along central sensory pathways. *Acta neurol. Lat.-Amer.*, 1955, **1**, 256–264.

Hernández-Peón, R. Neurophysiological correlates of habituation and other manifestations of plastic inhibition (internal inhibition). Pp. 101–114 in Jasper, H. H., & Smirnov, G. D. (Eds.) *The Moscow colloquium on electroencephalography of higher nervous activity. Electroencephalog. clin. Neurophysiol.*, Suppl. 13, 1960.

Hernández-Peón, R., Guzman-Flores, C., Alcaraz, M., & Fernandez-Guardiola, M. Habituation in the visual pathway. *Acta neurol. Lat. Amer.*, 1958, **4**, 121–129.

Hernández-Peón, R., & Hagbarth, K.-E. Interaction between afferent and cortically induced reticular responses. *J. Neurophysiol.*, 1955, **18**, 44–55.

Hernández-Peón, R., Jouvet, M., & Scherrer, H. Auditory potentials at cochlear nucleus during acoustic habituation. *Acta neurol. Lat.-Amer.*, 1957, **3**, 144–156.

Hernández-Peón, R., Scherrer, H., & Jouvet, M. Modification of electrical activity in cochlear nucleus during "attention" in unanesthetized cats. *Science*, 1956, **123**, 331–332.

Hernández-Peón, R., Scherrer, H., & Velasco, M. Central influences on afferent conduction in the somatic and visual pathways. *Acta neurol. Lat.-Amer.*, 1956, **2**, 8–22.

Hess, E. H. Altitude and pupil size. *Scient. Amer.*, 1965, **212** (4), 46–54.

Hess, W. R. Stammgarglien-reizversuche. (Verh. Deutsch. physiol. Ges., Sept., 1927), *Ber. ges. Physiol.*, 1928, **42**, 554.

Hess, W. R. *Vegetative Funktionen und Zwischenhirn*. Basel: Benno Schwabe, 1948.

Hess, W. R. *Diencephalon: autonomic and extrapyramidal functions*. New York: Grune & Stratton, 1954.

Hess, W. R. *The functional organization of the diencephalon*. New York: Grune & Stratton, 1957.

Hetherington, A. N., & Ranson, S. W. The spontaneous activity and food intake of rats with hypothalamic lesions. *Amer. J. Physiol.*, 1942, **136**, 609–617.

Hild, W. Electrophysiological phenomena observed in single neurons and neuro-glial cells in cultures of central nervous tissue. In Brazier, M. A. B. (Ed.) *UCLA Forum in Medical Sciences*, No. 2, *Brain function*, II. Berkeley: Univ. of California Press, 1964.

Hild, W., & Tasaki, I. Morphological and physiological properties of neurons and glial cells in tissue culture. *J. Neurophysiol.*, 1962, **25**, 277–304.

Hilgard, E. R., & Marquis, D. G. *Conditioning and learning*. New York: Appleton-Century-Crofts, 1940.

Hill, A. V. The onset of contraction. *Proc. roy. Soc. Series B*, 1949, **136**, 242–254.

Hind, J. E. An electrophysiological determination of tonotopic organization in auditory cortex of cat. *J. Neurophysiol.*, 1953, **16**, 475–489.

Hind, J. E., Goldberg, J. M., Greenwood, D. D., & Rose, J. E. Some discharge characteristics of single neurons in the inferior colliculus of the cat. II. Timing of the discharges and observations on binaural stimulation. *J. Neurophysiol.*, 1963, **26**, 321–341.

Hind, J. E., Rose, J. E., Davies, P. W., Woolsey, C. N., Benjamin, R. M., Welker, W. S., & Thompson, R. F. Unit activity in the auditory cortex. Pp. 201–210 in Rasmussen, G. L., &

Windle, W. F. (Eds.) *Neural mechanisms of the auditory and vestibular systems.* Springfield: Charles C Thomas, 1961a.

Ho, T., Wang, Y. R., Lin, T. A., & Cheng, Y. F. Predominance of electrocortical sleep patterns in the *encèphale isolé* cat and new evidence for a sleep center. *Physiol. bohemoslov.*, 1960, 9, 85–92.

Hodgkin, A. L. Ionic movements and electrical activity in giant nerve fibres. *Proc. roy. Soc. Series B*, 1958, 148, 1–37.

Hodgkin, A. L. The ionic basis of nervous conduction. *Science*, 1964, 145, 1148–1154.

Hodgkin, A. L., & Huxley, A. F. Action potentials recorded from inside nerve fiber. *Nature*, 1939, 144, 710–711.

Hodgkin, A. L., & Huxley, A. F. Currents carried by sodium and potassium ions through the membrane of the giant axon of *Loligo. J. Physiol.*, 1952a, 116, 449–472.

Hodgkin, A. L., & Huxley, A. F. The components of membrane conductance in the giant axon of *Loligo. J. Physiol.*, 1952b, 116, 473–496.

Hodgkin, A. L., & Huxley, A. F. A quantitative description of membrane current and its application to conduction and excitation in nerve, *J. Physiol.*, 1952c, 117, 500–544.

Hodgkin, A. L., Huxley, A. F., & Katz, B. Ionic currents underlying the activity in the giant axon of the squid. *Arch. Sci. physiol.*, 1949, 3, 129–150.

Hodgkin, A. L., Huxley, A. F., & Katz, B. Measurements of current-voltage relations in the membrane of the giant axon of *Loligo. J. Physiol.*, 1952, 116, 424–448.

Hodgkin, A. L., & Katz, B. The effect of sodium ions on the electrical activity of the giant axon of the squid. *J. Physiol.*, 1949, 108, 37–77.

Hodgkin, A. L., & Keynes, R. D. The mobility and diffusion coefficient of potassium in giant axons from *Sepia. J. Physiol.*, 1953, 119, 513–528.

Hodgkin, A. L., & Keynes, R. D. Experiments on the injection of substances into squid giant axons by means of a microsyringe. *J. Physiol.*, 1956, 131, 592–616.

Hodos, W., & Valenstein, E. S. Motivational variables affecting the rate of behavior maintained by intracranial stimulation. *J. comp. physiol. Psychol.*, 1960, 53, 502–508.

Hoebel, B. Hypothalamic lesions by electrocauterization: disinhibition of feeding and self-stimulation. *Science*, 1965, 149, 452–453.

Hoebel, B., & Teitelbaum, P. Hypothalamic control of feeding and self-stimulation. *Science*, 1962, 135, 375–376.

Hoff, E. C., & Hoff, H. E. Spinal terminations of the projection fibers from the motor cortex of primates. *Brain*, 1934, 57, 454–474.

Hongo, T., & Jankowska, E. Effects from the sensorimotor cortex on the spinal cord after section of the medullary pyramids in cats. *Exp. Brain Res.*, 1967 (in press).

Hongo, T., Jankowska, E., & Lundberg, A. Effects evoked from the rubrospinal tract in cats. *Experientia*, 1965, 21, 525–526.

Horn, G. Electrical activity of the cerebral cortex of the unanesthetized cat during attentive behavior. *Brain*, 1960, 83, 57–76.

Horridge, G. A. Learning leg position by the ventral nerve cord in headless insects. *Proc. roy. Soc., Series B*, 1962, 157, 33–52.

Horsley, V., & Clarke, R. H. The structure and functions of the cerebellum examined by a new method. *Brain*, 1908, 31, 45–124.

Hoyle, G. Neurophysiological studies on "learning" in headless insects. Pp. 203–232 in Treherne, J. E., & Beament, J. W. L. (Eds.) *The physiology of the insect central nervous system.* New York: Academic Press, 1965.

Hubbard, R., & Wald, G. Cis-trans isomers of vitamin A and retinene in the rhodopsin system. *J. gen. Physiol.*, 1952–53, 36, 269–315.

Hubel, D. H. Single unit activity in lateral geniculate body and optic tract of unrestrained cats. *J. Physiol.*, 1960a, 150, 91–104.

Hubel, D. H. Electrocorticograms in cats during natural sleep. *Arch. Ital. Biol.*, 1960b, 98, 171–181.

Hubel, D. H., Henson, C. D., Rupert, A., & Galambos, R. Attention units in the auditory cortex. *Science*, 1959, 129, 1279–1280.

Hubel, D. H., & Wiesel, T. N. Receptive fields of single neurones in the cat's striate cortex. *J. Physiol.*, 1959, **148**, 574–591.

Hubel, D. H., & Wiesel, T. N. Integrative action in the cat's lateral geniculate body. *J. Physiol.*, 1961, **155**, 385–398.

Hubel, D. H., & Wiesel, T. N. Receptive fields, binocular interaction and functional architecture in the cat's visual center. *J. Physiol.*, 1962, **160**, 106–154.

Hubel, D. H., & Wiesel, T. N. Shape and arrangement of columns in cat's striate cortex. *J. Physiol.*, 1963a, **165**, 559–568.

Hubel, D. H., & Wiesel, T. N. Receptive fields of cells in striate cortex of very young, visually inexperienced kittens. *J. Neurophysiol.*, 1963b, **26**, 994–1002.

Hubel, D. H., & Wiesel, T. N. Single-cell responses in striate cortex of kittens deprived of vision in one eye. *J. Neurophysiol.*, 1963c, **26**, 1003–1017.

Hubel, D. H., & Wiesel, T. N. Receptive fields and functional architecture in two nonstriate visual areas (18 and 19) of the cat. *J. Neurophysiol.*, 1965, **28**, 229–289.

Hudspeth, W. T., McGaugh, T. L., & Thomson, C. W. Aversive and amnesic effects of electroconvulsive shock. *J. comp. physiol. Psychol.*, 1964, **57**, 61–64.

Hughes, J. R. Post-tetanic potentiation. *Physiol. Rev.*, 1958, **38**, 91–113.

Hull, C. L. *Principles of behavior.* New York: Appleton-Century-Crofts, 1943.

Hull, C. L. *A behavior system: an introduction to behavior theory concerning the individual organism.* New Haven: Yale Univ. Press, 1952.

Hunsperger, R. W. Affektreaktionen auf elektrische reizung in hirnstamm der katze. *Helvet. physiol. pharmacol. Acta*, 1956, **14**, 70–92.

Hunt, C. C. The reflex activity of mammalian small-nerve fibres. *J. Physiol.*, 1951, **115**, 456–469.

Hunt, C. C., & Kuno, M. Background discharge and evoked responses of spinal interneurons. *J. Physiol.*, 1959, **147**, 364–384.

Hunter, W. S. The delayed reaction in animals and children. *Behav. Monogr.*, 1913, **2**, 1–86.

Huttenlocher, P. R. Evoked and spontaneous activity in single units of medial brain stem during natural sleep and waking. *J. Neurophysiol.*, 1961, **24**, 451–468.

Huxley, A. *Point counterpoint.* New York: Doubleday, 1928.

Huxley, A. F. Muscle-structure and theories of contraction. *Progr. Biophys.*, 1957, **7**, 255–318.

Huxley, A. F. Excitation and conduction in nerve: quantitative analysis. *Science*, 1964, **145**, 1154–1159.

Hydén, H. Nucleic acids and proteins. Pp. 204–233 in Elliott, K. A. C., Page, I. H., & Quastel, J. H. (Eds.) *Neurochemistry: the chemical dynamics of brain and nerve.* Springfield: Charles C. Thomas, 1955.

Hydén, H. Biochemical changes in glial cells and nerve cells at varying activity. Pp. 64–89 in Hoffmann-Ostenhof, O. (Ed.) *Proc. Fourth Int. Congr. Biochem.*, 3. London: Pergamon Press, 1959.

Hydén, H. Satellite cells in the nervous system. *Scient. Am.*, 1961, **205**, 62–83.

Hydén, H. Activation of nuclear RNA in neurons and glia in learning. Pp. 178–240 in Kimble, D. P. (Ed.) *The anatomy of memory.* Palo Alto: Science and Behavior Books, 1965.

Hydén, H., & Egyhazi, H. Nuclear RNA changes of nerve cells during a learning experiment in rats. *Proc. nat. Acad. Sci.*, 1962, **48**, 1366–1375.

Hydén, H., & Egyhazi, H. Glial RNA changes during a learning experiment in rats. *Proc. nat. Acad. Sci.*, 1963, **49**, 618–624.

Hydén, H., & Lange, P. A kinetic study of the neuron-glia relationships. *J. cell Biol.*, 1962, **13**, 233–237.

Hydén, H., & Pigon, A. A cytophysiological study of the functional relationship between oligodendroglial cells and nerve cells of Dieters' nucleus. *J. Neurochem.*, 1960, **6**, 57–72.

Ingram, W. R. Brain stem mechanisms in behavior. *Electroencephalog. clin. Neurophysiol.*, 1952, **4**, 397–406.

Ingvar, D. H. Extraneuronal influences upon the electrical activity of isolated cortex following stimulation of the recticular activating, system. *Acta physiol. Scand.*, 1955, **33**, 169–193.

Ingvar, D. H. Cortical state of excitability and cortical circulation. Pp. 381–408 in Jasper, H. H. (Ed.) *Reticular formation of the brain.* Boston: Little, Brown, 1958.

Ingvar, D. H., Krakau, T., & Söderberg, U. The cerebral blood flow during different EEG responses elicited by brain stem stimulation. *Electroencephalog. clin. Neurophysiol.,* 1957, **9**, 371.

Isaac, W., & DeVito, J. L. Effect of sensory stimulation on the activity of normal and prefrontal lobectomized monkeys. *J. comp. physiol. Psychol.,* 1958, **51**, 172–174.

Isaacson, R. L., & Wickelgren, W. O. Hippocampal ablation and passive avoidance. *Science,* 1962, **138**, 1104–1106.

Ivy, A. C., & Schnedorf, J. G. On the hypnotoxin theory of sleep. *Amer. J. Physiol.,* 1937, **119**, 342.

Jackson, J. H. On a particular variety of epilepsy ("intellectual aura"): one case with symptoms of organic brain disease. *Brain,* 1889, **11**, 207.

Jacobsen, C. F. Functions of the frontal association area in primates. *Arch. neurol. Psychiat.,* 1935, **33**, 558–569.

James, W. *The principles of psychology.* New York: Henry Holt, 1890.

Jansen, J., & Brodal, A. Experimental studies on the intrinsic fibers of the cerebellum. II. The cortico-nuclear projection. *J. comp. Neurol.,* 1940, **73**, 267–321.

Jansen, J., & Brodal, A. *Aspects of cerebellar anatomy.* Oslo: Johan Grundt Tanum, 1954.

Jansen, J. K. S., & Matthews, P. B. C. The dynamic responses to slow stretch of muscle spindles in the decerebrate cat. *J. Physiol.,* 1961, **159**, 20–22.

Jansen, J. K. S., & Matthews, P. B. C. The effects of fusimotor activity on the static responsiveness of primary and sensory endings of muscle spindles in the decerebrate cat. *Acta physiol. Scand.,* 1962, **55**, 376–386.

Jasper, H. H. Recent advances in our understanding of ascending activities of the reticular system. Pp. 319–331 in Jasper, H. H. (Ed.) *Reticular formation of the brain.* Boston: Little, Brown, 1958.

Jasper, H. H. Unspecific thalamocortical relations. Pp. 1307–1322 in Field, J., Magoun, H. W., & Hall, V. E. (Eds.) *Handbook of physiology, Neurophysiology,* **II.** Washington, D.C.: American Physiological Society, 1960.

Jasper, H. H., & Ajmone-Marsan, C. *A stereotaxic atlas of the diencephalon of the cat.* Ottawa: National Research Council of Canada, 1954.

Jasper, H. H., & Cruikshank, R. M. Electroencephalography. II. Visual stimulation and the after image as affecting the occipital alpha rhythm. *J. gen. Psychol.,* 1937, **17**, 29–48.

Jasper, H. H., Ricci, G. F., & Doane, B. Patterns of cortical neuronal discharge during conditioned responses in monkeys. Pp. 277–290 in Wolstenholme, G. E. W., & O'Connor, G. M. (Eds.), *Ciba Foundation Symposium, Neurological Basis of Behavior.* London: Churchill, 1958.

Jasper, H. H., Ricci, G., & Doane, B. Microelectrode analysis of cortical cell discharge during avoidance conditioning in the monkey. Pp. 137–155 in Jasper, H. H., & Smirnov, G. D. (Eds.) *The Moscow colloquium on electroencephalography of higher nervous activity. Electroencephalog. clin. Neurophysiol.,* 1960, Suppl. 13.

Jasper, H. H., & Shagass, C. Conditioning the occipital alpha rhythm in man. *J. exp. Psychol.,* 1941, **28**, 373–388.

Jefferson, A. A., & Schlapp, W. Some effects of repetitive stimulation of afferents on reflex conduction. Pp. 99–119 in Malcolm, J. L., & Gray, J. A. B. (Eds.) *Ciba Foundation Symposium, The spinal cord.* London: Churchill, 1953.

Jensen, D. D. Paramecia, planaria, and pseudo-learning. *Learning and associated phenomena in invertebrates: Animal Behaviour Supplement,* 1965, Number 1, 9–20.

Jimenez-Castellanos, J. Thalamus of the cat in Horsley-Clarke coordinates. *J. comp. Neurol.,* 1949, **91**, 307–339.

John, E. R., & Killam, K. F. Electrophysiological correlates of avoidance conditioning in the cat. *J. pharmacol. exp. Therap.,* 1959, **125**, 252–274.

Johnston, J. W., & Sandoval, A. Organoleptic quality and the stereochemical theory of olfaction. *Proc. sci. sect. toilet goods Assn.*, 1960, **33**, 3–18.

Jouvet, M. Telencephalic and rhombencephalic sleep in the cat. Pp. 188–208 in Wolstenholme, G. E. W., & O'Connor, M. (Eds.) *CIBA Foundation Symposium, The nature of sleep.* London: Churchill, 1961.

Jouvet, M. Recherches sur les structures nerveuses et les mecanismes reponsibles des différentes phases du sommeil physiologique. *Arch. Ital. Biol.*, 1962, **100**, 125–206.

Jouvet, M., & Hernàndez-Péon, R. Mecanismes neurophysiologiques concernant l'habituation, l'attention et le conditionnement. Pp. 39–49 in Fischgold, H., & Gastaut, H. (Eds.) *Conditionnement et reactivite en electroencephalographie. Electroencephalog. clin. Neurophysiol.*, 1957, Suppl. 6.

Jouvet, M., & Michel, F. Corrélations électromyographiques du sommeil chez le chat décortiqué et mésencéphalique chronique. *Compt. Rend. Soc. Biol.*, 1959, **153**, 422–425.

Jung, R. Über die Beteiligung des thalamus, der stammganglion und des ammonshorns am elektrokrampf. *Arch. Psychiat. Nervenkr.*, 1950, **184**, 261–265.

Jung, R. Coordination of specific and nonspecific afferent impulses at single neurons of the visual cortex. Pp. 423–434 in Jasper, H. H. (Ed.) *Reticular formation of the brain.* Boston: Little, Brown, 1958.

Jung, R. Neuronal integration in the visual cortex and its significance for visual information. Pp. 627–674 in Rosenblith, W. A. (Ed.) *Sensory communication.* New York: Wiley, 1961.

Jung, R., & Hassler, R. Extrapyramidal motor system. Pp. 863–927 in Field, J., Magoun, H. W., & Hall, V. E. (Eds.) *Handbook of physiology, Neurophysiology*, **II**. Washington, D.C.: American Physiological Society, 1960.

Jung, R., & Kornmüller, A. E. Eine Methodik der Ableitung lokalisierte potential Schwankungen aus subcorticalen Hirngebieten. *Arch. Psychiat. Nervenkr.*, 1938, **109**, 1–30.

Jung, R., & Kornhuber, H. (Eds.) *The visual system: neurophysiology and psychophysics.* Berlin: Springer-Verlag, 1961.

Jus, A., & Jus, C. Studies on photic driving conditioning in man. *Electroencephalog. clin. Neurophysiol.*, 1959, **11**, 178.

Kaada, B. R. Somato-motor, autonomic and electrocorticographic responses to electrical stimulation of "rhinencephalic" and other structures in primates, cat and dog; study of responses from limbic, sub-callosal, orbito-insular, piriform and temporal cortex, hippocampus-fornix and amygdala. *Acta physiol. Scand.*, 1951, Suppl. 83, **24**, 1–285.

Kaada, B. R. Cingulate, posterior orbital, anterior insular and temporal pole cortex. Pp. 1345–1372 in Fields, J., Magoun, H. W., & Hall, V. E. (Eds.) *Handbook of physiology, Neurophysiology*, **II**. Washington, D.C.: American Physiological Society, 1960.

Kamiya, J. Behavioral, subjective and physiological aspects of drowsiness and sleep. Pp. 145–174 in Fiske, D. W., & Maddi, S. R. (Eds.) *Functions of varied experience.* Homewood, Ill.: Dorsey, 1961.

Kandel, E. R., & Spencer, W. A. Electrophysiology of hippocampal neurons. II. Afterpotentials and repetitive firing. *J. Neurophysiol.*, 1961, **24**, 243–259.

Kandel, E. R., & Spencer, W. A. Excitation and inhibition of single pyramidal cells during hippocampal seizure. *Exp. Neurol.*, 1961, **4**, 162–179.

Kandel, E. R., Spencer, W. A., & Brinley, F. J. Electrophysiology of hippocampal neurons. I. Sequential invasion and synaptic organization. *J. Neurophysiol.*, 1961, **24**, 225–242.

Kandel, E. R., & Tauc, L. Mechanisms of prolonged heterosynaptic facilitation. *Nature*, 1964, **202**, 145–147.

Kandel, E. R., & Tauc, L. Heterosynaptic facilitation in neurones of the abdominal ganglion of *aplesia depilans. J. Physiol.*, 1965a, **181**, 1–27.

Kandel, E. R., & Tauc, L. Mechanisms of heterosynaptic facilitation in the giant cell of the abdominal ganglion of *Aplepia depilans. J. Physiol.*, 1965b, **181**, 28–47.

Kandel, E. R., Waziri, R., & Frazier, W. T. Conditioning paradigms and cellular neurophysiological analogues of learning in an isolated invertebrate ganglion. Paper presented at the Eastern Psychological Association Meetings, 1965.

Kappers, C. U. A., Huber, G. C., & Crosby, E. C. *The comparative anatomy of the nervous system of vertebrates.* New York: Macmillan, 1963.

Katsuki, Y. Neural mechanisms of auditory sensation in cats. Pp. 561–583 in Rosenblith, W. A. (Ed.) *Sensory communication.* New York: Wiley, 1961.

Katsuki, Y., Sumi, T., Uchiyama, H., & Watanabe, T. Electrical responses of auditory neurons in cat to sound stimulation. *J. Neurophysiol.,* 1958, **21**, 569–588.

Katz, B. The transmission of impulses from nerve to muscle and the sub-cellular unit of synaptic action. *Proc. roy. Soc. Series B,* 1962, **155**, 455–479.

Kellogg, W. N. Is "spinal conditioning" conditioning? A reply to "a comment." *J. exp. Psychol.,* 1947, **37**, 263–265.

Kellogg, W. N., Deese, J., & Pronko, N. H. On the behavior of the lumbospinal dog. *J. exp. Psychol.,* 1946, **36**, 503–511.

Kellogg, W. N., Deese, J., Pronko, N. H., & Feinberg, M. An attempt to condition the chronic spinal dog. *J. exp. Psychol.,* 1947, **37**, 99–117.

Kempinsky, W. H. Cortical projection of vestibular and facial nerves in cat. *J. Neurophysiol.,* 1951, **14**, 203–210.

Kennard, M. A. Reorganization of motor function in the cerebral cortex of monkeys deprived of motor and premotor areas in infancy. *J. Neurophysiol.,* 1938, **1**, 477–496.

Kennard, M. A., & McCulloch, W. S. Motor response to stimulation of cerebral cortex in absence of areas 4 and 6 (*Macaca mulatta*). *J. Neurophysiol.,* 1943, **6**, 181–189.

Kennedy, T., Kiang, N., & Sutton, S. Auditory projection areas of the center in monkey (*Macaca mulatta*). *Amer. J. Physiol.,* 1955, **183**, 634.

Kerr, D. I. B., & Hagbarth, K. E. An investigation of olfactory centrifugal fiber system. *J. Neurophysiol.,* 1955, **18**, 362–374.

Kety, S. S. Blood flow and metabolism of the human brain in health and disease. Pp. 440–457 in Elliot, K. A. C., Page, I. H., & Quastel, J. H. (Eds.) *Neurochemistry: The chemical dynamics of brain and nerve.* Springfield: Charles C. Thomas, 1955.

Key, B. J., & Bradley, P. B. The effect of drugs on conditioned arousal responses. *Electroencephalog. clin. Neurophysiol.,* 1959, **11**, 841.

Keynes, R. D. The leakage of radioactive potassium from stimulated nerve. *J. Physiol.,* 1951a, **113**, 99–114.

Keynes, R. D. The ionic movements during nervous activity. *J. Physiol.,* 1951b, **114**, 119–150.

Keynes, R. D., & Lewis, P. R. The sodium and potassium content of cephalopod nerve fibers. *J. Physiol.,* 1951, **114**, 151–182.

Kimble, D. P. The effects of bilateral hippocampal lesions in rats. *J. comp. physiol. Psychol.,* 1963, **56**, 273–283.

Kimble, D. P. (Ed.) *Anatomy of memory.* Palo Alto, Calif.: Science and Behavior Books, 1965.

Kimble, G. A. *Hilgard and Marquis' conditioning and learning.* (rev. ed.), New York: Appleton-Century-Crofts, 1961.

Kimura, D., & Beidler, L. M. Microelectrode study of taste bud of rat. *Amer. J. Physiol.,* 1956, **187**, 610.

Kleitman, N. Sleep. *Physiol. Rev.,* 1929, **9**, 624–665.

Kleitman, N. *Sleep and wakefulness.* Chicago: Univ. of Chicago Press, 1939.

Kling, A., & Hutt, P. J. Effect of hypothalamic lesions on the amygdala syndrome in the cat. *Arch. neurol. Psychiat.,* 1958, **79**, 511–517.

Klüver, H. An analysis of the effects of the removal of the occipital lobes in monkeys. *J. Psychol.,* 1936, **2**, 49–61.

Klüver, H. Certain effects of lesions of the occipital lobes in macaques. *J. Psychol.,* 1937, **4**, 383–401.

Klüver, H. Functional significance of the geniculo-striate system. *Biol. Symposia,* 1942, **7**, 253–299.

Klüver, H., & Bucy, P. C. "Psychic blindness" and other symptoms following bilateral temporal lobectomy in rhesus monkeys. *Amer. J. Physiol.,* 1937, **119**, 352–353.

Knott, J. R. Reduced latent time of blocking of the Berger rhythm to light stimuli. *Proc. soc. exp. Biol.*, 1938, **38**, 216–217.

Knott, J. R. Electroencephalography and physiological psychology: Evaluation and statement of problem. *Psychol. Bull.*, 1941, **38**, 944–875.

Knott, J. R., & Henry, C. E. The conditioning of the blocking of the alpha rhythm of the human encephalogram. *J. exp. Psychol.*, 1941, **28**, 134–144.

Koelle, G. B. A proposed dual humoral role of acetylcholine: its functions at the pre- and postsynaptic sites. *Nature*, 1961, **190**, 208–211.

Koelle, G. B. A new general concept of the neurohumoral functions of acetylcholine and acetylcholinesterase. *J. pharm. Pharmacol.*, 1962, **14**, 65–90.

Köhler, W., & Held, R. The cortical correlate of pattern vision. *Science*, 1949, **110**, 414–419.

Köhler, W., Neff, W. D., & Wegener, J. Currents of the auditory cortex in the cat. *J. cell. comp. Physiol.*, 1955, **45**, Suppl., 1–24.

Köhler, W., & O'Connell, D. N. Currents of the visual cortex in the cat. *J. cell. comp. Physiol.*, 1957, **49**, Suppl., 1–43.

Köhler, W., & Wegener, J. Currents of the human auditory cortex. *J. cell. comp. Physiol.*, 1955, **45**, Suppl., 25–54.

Konishi, J., & Zotterman, Y. Taste functions in fish. Pp. 177–192 in Zotterman, Y. (Ed.) *Olfaction and taste.* New York: Macmillan, 1963.

Konorski, J. *Conditioned reflexes and neuron organization.* London: Cambridge Univ. Press, 1948.

Konorski, J. A new method of physiological investigation of recent memory in animals. *Bull. Acad. pol. Sci.*, 1959, **7**, 115–117.

Konorski, J. The physiological approach to the problem of recent memory. Pp. 115–132 in Delafresnaye, J. F. (Ed.) *Brain mechanisms and learning.* Oxford: Blackwell, 1961.

Konorski, J., & Lawicka, W. Analysis of errors by prefrontal animals on the delayed response test. Pp. 271–294 in Warren, J. M., & Akert, K. (Eds.) *The frontal granular cortex and behavior.* New York: McGraw-Hill, 1964.

Kozak, W., MacFarlane, W. V., & Westerman, R. Long-lasting reversible changes in the reflex responses of chronic spinal cats to touch, heat and cold. *Nature*, 1962, **193**, 171–173.

Kozak, W., & Westerman, R. A. Plastic changes of spinal monosynaptic responses from tenotomized muscle in cats. *Nature*, 1961, **189**, 753–755.

Krasne, F. B. General disruption resulting from electrical stimulus of ventro-medial hypothalamus. *Science*, 1962, **138**, 822–823.

Krauthamer, G., & Albe-Fessard, D. Inhibition of nonspecific sensory activities following striopallidal and capsular stimulation. *J. Neurophysiol.*, 1965, **28**, 100–124.

Krech, D. The genesis of "hypothesis" in rats. *Univ. Calif. Publ. Psychol.*, 1932, **6**, 45–64.

Kreindler, A., Unghar, I. U., & Volanskii, D. Effect of a circumscribed lesion of the reticular formation in the brain stem on the higher nervous activity of dogs. *Fiziol. zhur. (Mosk.)*, 1959, **45**, 247–256.

Krieg, W. J. S. *Functional neuroanatomy.* New York: McGraw-Hill, 1953.

Kruger, L., & Porter, P. A behavioral study of the functions of the rolandic cortex in the monkey. *J. comp. Neurol.*, 1958, **109**, 439–467.

Kryter, K. D., & Ades, H. W. Studies on the function of the higher acoustic nervous centers in the cat. *Amer. J. Psychol.*, 1943, **56**, 501–536.

Kuffler, S. W. Discharge patterns and functional organization of mammalian retina. *J. Neurophysiol.*, 1953, **16**, 37–68.

Kuffler, S. W., & Edwards, C. Mechanism of gamma-aminobutyric acid (GABA) action and its relation to synaptic inhibition. *J. Neurophysiol.*, 1958, **21**, 589–610.

Kuffler, S. W., & Potter, D. D. Glia in the leech central nervous system: Physiological properties and neuron-glia relationship. *J. Neurophysiol.*, 1964, **27**, 290–320.

Kuntz, A. *A textbook of neuroanatomy.* Philadelphia: Lea & Febiger, 1942.

Kupfermann, I. Effects of cortical polarization on visual discriminations. *Exp. Neurol.*, 1965, **12**, 179–189.

Lacey, J. I. The evaluation of autonomic responses: Toward a general solution. *Ann. N.Y. Acad. Sci.*, 1956, **67**, 123–164.

Lacey, J. I. & Lacey, B. C. The law of initial value in longitudinal study of autonomic responses and response patterns over a four year interval. *Ann. N.Y. Acad. Sci.*, 1962, **98**, 1257–1290; 1322–1326.

Landau, W., Clare, M. H., & Bishop, G. H. Effects of polarizing currents on certain evoked potentials in cerebral cortex. Pp. 72–75 in Yahr, M. D. (Ed.) *Trans. Amer. neurol. Assoc.* New York: Springer, 1962.

Landgren, S., Phillips, C. G., & Porter, R. Minimal synaptic actions of pyramidal impulses on some alpha motoneurons of the baboon's hand and forearm. *J. Physiol.*, 1962, **161**, 91–111. (a)

Landgren, S., Phillips, C. G., & Porter, R. Cortical fields of origin of the monosynaptic pyramidal pathways to some alpha motoneurons of the baboon's hand and forearm. *J. Physiol.*, 1962, **161**, 112–125. (b)

Landgren, S., & Wolsk, D. A new cortical area receiving input from Group I muscle afferents. *Life Sciences*, 1966, **5**, 75–79.

Lansing, R., Schwartz, E., & Lindsley, D. B. Presented in Lindsley, D. B. The reticular system and perceptual discrimination. Pp. 513–534 in Jasper, H. H. (Ed.) *Reticular formation of the brain.* Boston: Little, Brown, 1958.

Lansing, R. W., Schwartz, E., & Lindsley, D. B. Reaction time and EEG activation under alerted and non-alerted conditions. *J. exp. Psychol.*, 1959, **58**, 1–7.

Larsell, O. *Anatomy of the nervous system* (2nd ed.). New York: Appleton-Century-Crofts, 1951.

Larsson, K., & Heimer, L. Mating behavior of male rats after lesions in the preoptic area. *Nature*, 1964, **202**, 413–414.

Larsson, S. On the hypothalamic organization of the nervous mechanism regulating food intake. *Acta physiol. Scand.*, 1954, Suppl. 115, **32**, 1–63.

Lashley, K. S. Studies of cerebral function in learning. V. The retention of motor habits after destruction of the so-called motor areas in primates. *Arch. neurol. Psychiat.*, 1924, **12**, 249–276.

Lashley, K. S. *Brain mechanisms and intelligence.* Chicago: Univ. of Chicago Press, 1929.

Lashley, K. S. Mass action in cerebral function. *Science*, 1931, **73**, 245–254.

Lashley, K. S. The mechanism of vision. XII. Nervous structures concerned in the acquisition and retention of habits based on reactions to light. *Comp. Psychol. Monogr.*, 1935, **11**, 43–79.

Lashley, K. S. The mechanism of vision. XVII. The functioning of small remnants of the visual cortex. *J. comp. Neurol.*, 1939, **70**, 45–67.

Lashley, K. S. The mechanism of vision. XVII. Autonomy of the visual cortex. *J. genet. Psychol.*, 1942, **60**, 197–221.

Lashley, K. S. The mechanism of vision. XVIII. Effects of destroying visual "associative areas" of the monkey. *Genet. Psychol. Monogr.*, 1948, **37**, 107–166.

Lashley, K. S. In search of the engram. Pp. 454–482 in *Symp. Soc. exp. Biol.*, No. 4. New York: Cambridge Univ. Press, 1950.

Lashley, K. S., Chow, K. L., & Semmes, J. An examination of the electrical field theory of cerebral integration. *Psychol. Rev.*, 1951, **58**, 123–136.

Lashley, K. S., & Clark, G. The cytoarchitecture of the cerebral cortex of Ateles: a critical examination of architectonic studies. *J. comp. Neurol.*, 1946, **85**, 223–306.

Lassek, A. M. *The pyramidal tract. Its status in medicine.* Springfield: Charles C. Thomas, 1954.

Laursen, A. M. Corpus striatum. *Acta physiol. Scand.*, 1963, Suppl. 211, **59**, 1–106.

Lawicka, W., & Konorski, J. The physiological mechanism of delayed reactions. III. The effects of prefrontal ablations on delayed reactions in dogs. *Acta biol. Exp.*, 1959, **19**, 221–231.

Leão, A. A. P. Further observations on the spreading depression of activity in the cerebral cortex. *J. Neurophysiol.*, 1947, **10**, 409–414.

Leary, R. W., Harlow, H. F., Greenwood, D. D., & Settlage, P. H. Performance on double alternation problems by normal and brain-injured monkeys. *J. comp. physiol. Psychol.*, 1952, **45**, 576–584.

Lebedinskaia, S. I., & Rosenthal, J. S. Reactions of a dog after removal of the cerebral hemisphere. *Brain*, 1935, **58**, 412–419.

Legendre, R., & Pieron, H. Le problème des facteurs du sommeil. Resultats d'injections vasculaires et intracérébrales de liquides insomniques. *Compt. Rend. Soc. Biol.*, 1910, **68**, 1077–1079.

Lehner, F. Az eredményes gondolkodás menetének vizsgálata (The course of successful thinking). *Psychol. stud. Univ. Bp.*, 1939, **3**, 138–157.

Leksell, L. The action potential and excitatory effects of the small ventral root fibres to skeletal muscle. *Acta physiol. Scand.*, 1945, Suppl. 31, 1–84.

Lele, P. P., & Weddell, G. The relationship between neurohistology and corneal sensibility. *Brain*, 1956, **79**, 119–154.

Lennox, M. A., & Madsen, A. Cortical and retinal responses to colored light flash in anesthetized cat. *J. Neurophysiol.*, 1955, **18**, 412–424.

Lennox-Buchthal, M. A. Single units in monkey, *cercocebus torquatus atys*, cortex with narrow spectral responsiveness. *Vision Res.*, 1962, **2**, 1–15.

Lettvin, J. Y., Maturana, H. R., McCullock, W. S., & Pitts, W. H. What the frog's eye tells the frog's brain. *Proc. inst. Radio Engr.*, 1959, **47**, 1940–1951.

Levin, P. M., & Bradford, F. K. The exact origin of the cortico-spinal tract in the monkey. *J. comp. Neurol.*, 1938, **68**, 411–422.

Lewis, R., & Brindley, G. S. The extrapyramidal cortical motor map. *Brain*, 1965, **88**, 397–406.

Li, C.-L., Cullen, C., & Jasper, H. H. Laminar microelectrode studies of specific somatosensory cortical potentials. *J. Neurophysiol.*, 1965a, **19**, 111–130.

Li, C.-L., Cullen, C., & Jasper, H. H. Laminar microelectrode analysis of cortical unspecific recruiting responses and spontaneous rhythms. *J. Neurophysiol.*, 1956b, **19**, 131–143.

Li, C.-L., & Jasper, H. H. Microelectrode studies of the electrical activity of the cerebral cortex in the cat. *J. Physiol.*, 1953, **121**, 117–140.

Licklider, J. C. R. Basic correlates of the auditory stimulus. Pp. 985–1039 in Stevens, S. S. (Ed.) *Handbook of experimental psychology*. New York: Wiley, 1951.

Lilly, J. C. Correlations between neurophysiological activity in the cortex and short-term behavior in the monkey. Pp. 83–100 in Harlow, H. F., & Woolsey, C. N. (Eds.) *Biological and biochemical bases of behavior*. Madison: Wisconsin Press, 1958a.

Lilly, J. C. Discussion, p. 370 and pp. 241–303 in Brazier, M. A. B. (Ed.) The central nervous system and behavior. *Trans. 1st Conf. Josiah Macy Jr. Found.* New York, 1958b.

Lilly, J. C. The balanced pulse-pair waveform. Pp. 60–64 in Sheer, D. E. (Ed.) *Electrical stimulation of the brain*. Austin, Texas: Univ. of Texas Press, 1961.

Lindsley, D. B. Emotion. Pp. 473–516 in Stevens, S. S. (Ed.) *Handbook of experimental psychology*. New York: Wiley, 1951.

Lindsley, D. B. The reticular system and perceptual discrimination. Pp. 513–534 in Jasper, H. H. (Ed.) *Reticular formation of the brain*. Boston,: Little, Brown, 1958.

Lindsley, D. B. Attention, consciousness, sleep and wakefulness. Pp. 1553–1593 in Field, J., Magoun, H. W., & Hall, V. E. (Eds.) *Handbook of physiology, Neurophysiology*, **III**. Washington, D. C.: American Physiological Society, 1960.

Lindsley, D. B., Bowden, J., & Magoun, H. W. Effect upon EEG of acute injury to the brain stem activating system. *Electroencephalog. clin. Neurophysiol.*, 1949, **1**, 475–486.

Lindsley, D. B., Schreiner, L. H., Knowles, W. B., & Magoun, H. W. Behavioral and EEG changes following chronic brain stem lesions in the cat. *Electroencephalog. clin. Neurophysiol.*, 1950, **2**, 483–498.

Lindsley, D. B., Schreiner, L. H., & Magoun, H. W. An electromyographic study of spasticity. *J. Neurophysiol.*, 1949, **12**, 197–216.

Ling, G., & Gerard, R. W. The normal membrane potential of frog sartorius fibers. *J. cell. comp. Physiol.*, 1949, **34**, 383–396.

Livanov, M. N., & Poliakov, K. L. The electrical reactions of the cerebral cortex of a rabbit during the formation of a conditioned defense reflex by means of rhythmic stimulation. *Bull. Acad. sci. U.S.S.R. biol. Ser.*, 1945, **3**, 286–298.

Livingston, R. B. Some brain stem mechanisms relating to psychosomatic functions. *Psychosom. med.*, 1955, **17**, 347–354.

Livingston, R. B. Central control of receptors and sensory transmission systems. Pp. 741–760 in Field, J., Magoun, H. W., & Hall, V. E. (Eds.) *Handbook of physiology, Neurophysiology*, I. Washington, D.C.: American Physiological Society, 1959.

Llinas, R. Mechanisms of supraspinal actions upon spinal cord activities. Pharmacological studies on reticular inhibition of alpha extensor motoneurons. *J. Neurophysiol.*, 1964, **27**, 1127–1137.

Llinas, R., & Terzuolo, C. A. Mechanism of supraspinal actions upon spinal cord activities. Reticular inhibitory mechanisms upon flexor motor-neurons. *J. Neurophysiol.*, 1965, **28**, 413–422.

Lloyd, D. P. C. The spinal mechanism of the pyramidal system in cats. *J. Neurophysiol.*, 1941, **4**, 525–546.

Lloyd, D. P. C. Reflex action in relation to pattern and peripheral source of afferent stimulation. *J. Neurophysiol.*, 1943a, **6**, 111–120.

Lloyd, D. P. C. Conduction and synaptic transmission of reflex response to stretch in spinal cats. *J. Neurophysiol.*, 1943b, **6**, 317–326.

Lloyd, D. P. C. Post-tetanic potentiation of response in monosynaptic reflex pathways of the spinal cord. *J. gen. Physiol.*, 1949, **33**, 147–170.

Lloyd, D. P. C., & Wilson, V. J. Reflex depression in rhythmically active monosynaptic reflex pathways. *J. gen. Physiol.*, 1957, **40**, 409–426.

Loeffler, J. D. An investigation of auditory responses in insular cortex of cat and dog. M.D. thesis, University of Wisconsin, 1958.

Loewi, O. Über humorale Übertragbarkeit der Herznervenwirkung. *Pflügers Arch. ges. Physiol.*, 1921, **189**, 239–242.

Loomis, A. L., Harvey, E. N., & Hobart, G. Electrical potentials of the human brain. *J. exp. Psychol.*, 1936, **19**, 249–279.

Lorente de Nó, R. Cerebral cortex: Cytoarchitecture. Pp. 274–301 in Fulton, J. F. (Ed.) *Physiology of the nervous system*. New York: Oxford Univ. Press, 1938.

Lorente de Nó, R. A study of nerve physiology. In *Studies from the Rockefeller Institute for Medical Research*, 1947, **131** and **132**, New York.

Loucks, R. B. Preliminary report of a technique for stimulation or destruction of tissues beneath the integument and the establishing of a conditioned reaction with faradization of the cerebral cortex. *J. comp. Psychol.*, 1933, **16**, 439–444.

Loucks, R. B. The experimental delimitation of neural structures essential for learning: the attempt to condition striped muscle responses with faradization of the sigmoid gyri. *J. Psychol.*, 1936, **1**, 5–44.

Loucks, R. B. Studies of neural structures essential for learning. II. The conditioning of salivary and striped muscle responses to faradization of cortical sensory elements, and the action of sleep upon such mechanisms. *J. comp. Psychol.*, 1938, **25**, 315–332.

Loucks, R. B., & Gantt, W. H. The conditioning of striped muscle responses based upon faradic stimulation of dorsal roots and dorsal columns of the spinal cord. *J. comp. Psychol.*, 1938, **25**, 415–426.

Lund, S., & Pompeiano, O. Descending pathways with monosynaptic action on motoneurons. *Experientia*, 1965, **21**, 602.

Lundberg, A. Ascending spinal hindlimb pathways in the cat. Pp. 135–163 in Eccles, J. C., & Schadé, J. P. (Eds.) *Progress in brain research*. Vol. 12, Physiology of spinal neurons. Amsterdam: Elsevier, 1964. (a)

Lundberg, A. Supraspinal control of transmission in reflex paths to motoneurons and primary afferents. Pp. 197–221 in Eccles, J. C., & Schadé, J. P. (Eds.) *Progress in brain research, Vol. 12, Physiology of spinal neurons*. Amsterdam: Elsevier, 1964. (b)

Lundberg, A. Integration in the reflex pathway. In Granit, R. (Ed.) *Nobel Symposium I. Muscular afferents and motor control*. New York: Wiley, 1966.

Lundberg, A., Norrsell, U., & Voorhoeve, P. E. Pyramidal effects on lumbosacral interneurons activated by somatic afferents. *Acta physiol. Scand.*, 1962, **56**, 220–229.

Lundberg, A., & Oscarsson, O. Three ascending spinal pathways in the dorsal part of the lateral funiculus. *Acta physiol. Scand.*, 1961, **51**, 1–16.

Lundberg, A., & Voorhoeve, P. E. Effects from the pyramidal tract on spinal reflex arcs. *Acta physiol. Scand.*, 1962, **56**, 201–219.

Lundberg, A., & Vyklický, L., Brain stem control of reflex paths to primary afferents. *Acta physiol. Scand.* 1963, **59**, Suppl. 213, 91.

Løyning, Y., Oshima, T., & Yokota, T. Site of action of thiamylol sodium on the monosynaptic spinal reflex pathway in cats. *J. Neurophysiol.*, 1964, **27**, 408–428.

Machne, X., Calma, I., & Magoun, H. W. Unit activity of central cephalic brain stem in EEG arousal. *J. Neurophysiol.*, 1955, **18**, 547–558.

Machne, X., & Segundo, J. P. Unitary responses to afferent volleys in amygdaloid complex. *J. Neurophysiol.*, 1956, **19**, 232–240.

MacLean, P. D. Psychosomatic disease and the "visceral brain": recent developments bearing on the Papez theory of emotion. *Psychosom. Med.*, 1949, **11**, 338–353.

MacLean, P. D. Studies on limbic system "visceral brain" and their bearing on psychosomatic problems. Pp. 101–125 in Witthow, E. D., & Cleghorn, R. A. (Eds.) *Recent developments in psychosomatic medicine*, London: Pitman, 1954.

MacLean, P. D., Horwitz, N. H., & Robinson, R. Olfactory-like responses in pyriform area to non-olfactory stimulation. *Yale J. Biol. Med.*, 1952, **25**, 159–172.

MacNichol, E. F. Retinal mechanisms of color vision. *Vision Res.*, 1964, **4**, 119–133.

MacNichol, E. F., & Svaetichin, G. Electric responses from isolated retinas of fishes. *Amer. J. Ophthal.*, 1958, **46**, 26–40.

Madsen, A., & Lennox, M. A. Response to colored light flash from different areas of optic cortex and from retina in anesthetized cat. *J. Neurophysiol.*, 1955, **18**, 574–582.

Maes, J. P. Hypophysectomie et comportement sexuel de la chatte. *Compt. rend. Soc. Biol.*, 1940, **133**, 92–94.

Magnes, J., Moruzzi, G., & Pompeiano, O. Synchronization of the EEG produced by low-frequency electrical stimulation of the solitary tract. *Arch. ital. Biol.*, 1961, **99**, 33–67.

Magoun, H. W. The ascending reticular system and wakefulness. Pp. 1–20 in Delafresnaye, J. F. (Ed.) *Brain mechanisms and consciousness*. Springfield, Ill.: Charles C Thomas, 1954.

Magoun, H. W. Central neural inhibition. Pp. 161–193 in Jones, M. R. (Ed.) *Nebraska symposium on motivation*. Lincoln, Nebraska: Univ. of Nebraska Press, 1963.

Magoun, H. W., Harrison, F., Brobeck, J. R., & Ranson, S. W. Activation of heat loss mechanisms by local heating of the brain. *J. Neurophysiol.*, 1938, **1**, 101–114.

Magoun, H. W., & Ranson, S. W. The afferent path of the light reflex. A review of the literature. *Arch. Ophthal.*, 1935, **13**, 862–874.

Magoun, H. W., & Rhines, R. An inhibitory mechanism in the bulbar reticular formation. *J. Neurophysiol.*, 1946, **9**, 165–171.

Maier, N. R. F., & Schneirla, T. C. *Principles of animal psychology*. New York: McGraw-Hill, 1935.

Malis, L. I., Pribram, K. H., & Kruger, L. Action potentials in motor cortex evoked by peripheral nerve stimulation. *J. Neurophysiol.*, 1953, **16**, 161–167.

Malmo, R. B. Activation: A neuropsychological dimension. *Psychol. Rev.*, 1959, **66**, 367–386.

Mancia, M., Mechelse, K., & Mollica, A. Microelectrode recording from midbrain reticular formation in the decerebrate cat. *Arch. ital. Biol.*, 1957, **95**, 110–119.

Margules, D. L., & Olds, J. Identical "feeding" and "rewarding" systems in the lateral hypothalamus of rats. *Science*, 1962, **135**, 374–375.

Marsh, J. T., McCarthy, D. A., Sheatz, G., & Galambos, R. Amplitude changes in evoked auditory potentials during habituation and conditioning. *Electroencephalog. clin. Neurophysiol.*, 1961, **13**, 224–234.

Marsh, J. T., & Worden, F. G. Auditory potentials during acoustic habituation: Cochlear nucleus, cerebellum and auditory cortex. *Electroencephalog. clin. Neurophysiol.*, 1964, **17**, 685–692.

Marsh, J. T., Worden, F. G., & Hicks, L. Some effects of room acoustics on evoked auditory potentials. *Science*, 1962, **137**, 281–282.

Marshall, W. H. The relation of dehydration of the brain to the spreading depression of Leão. *Electroencephalog. clin. Neurophysiol.*, 1950, **2**, 177–185.

Marshall, W. H. Spreading cortical depression of Leão. *Physiol. Rev.*, 1959, **39**, 239–279.

Marshall, W. H., & Essig, C. F. Relation of air exposure of cortex to spreading depression of Leão. *J. Neurophysiol.*, 1951, **14**, 265–273.

Marshall, W. H., & Talbot, S. A. Recovery cycle of the lateral geniculate of the nembutalized cat. *Amer. J. Physiol.*, 1940, **129**, 417–418.

Marshall, W. H., Talbot, S. A., & Ades, H. W. Cortical responses of the anesthetized cat to gross photic and electrical afferent stimulation. *J. Neurophysiol.*, 1943, **6**, 1–15.

Marshall, W. H., Woolsey, C. N., & Bard, P. Observations on cortical sensory mechanisms of cat and monkey. *J. Neurophysiol.*, 1941, **4**, 1–24.

Masserman, J. H. Is the hypothalamus a center of emotion? *Psychosom. Med.*, 1941, **5**, 3–25.

Massopust, L. C., Jr. Diencephalon of the rat. Pp. 181–202 in Sheer, D. E. (Ed.) *Electrical stimulation of the brain*. Austin, Texas: Univ. of Texas Press, 1961.

Mast, T. Muscular *vs.* cerebral sources for the short-latency human evoked responses to clicks. *Physiologist*, 1963, **6**, 229.

Masterton, R. B., & Diamond, I. T. Effects of auditory cortex ablation on discrimination of small binaural time differences. *J. Neurophysiol.*, 1964, **27**, 15–36.

Matthews, B. H. C. The response of a single end organ. *J. Physiol.*, 1931, **71**, 64–110.

Matthews, B. H. C. Nerve endings in mammalian muscle. *J. Physiol.*, 1933, **78**, 1–53.

Matthews, P. B. C. The differentiation of two types of fusimotor fibers by their effects on the dynamic response of muscle spindle primary endings. *Quart. J. exp. Physiol.*, 1962, **47**, 324–333.

Matthews, P. B. C. Muscle spindles and their motor control. *Physiol. Rev.*, 1964, **44**, 219–288.

Maturana, H. R., Lettvin, J. Y., McCulloch, W. S., & Pitts, W. H. Anatomy and physiology of vision in the frog (*Rana pipiens*). *J. gen. Physiol.*, 1960, **43**, 129–176.

McCleary, R. A. Response specificity in the behavioral effects of limbic system lesions in the cat. *J. comp. physiol. Psychol.*, 1961, **54**, 605–613.

McClung, C. E. (Ed.) *Handbook of microscopal technique*. New York: Hoeber, 1929.

McConnell, J. V. Memory transfer through cannibalism in planarium. *J. Neuropsychiat*, **3**, Suppl. 1, 542–548, 1962.

McConnell, J. V., Jacobson, A. L., & Kimble, D. P. The effects of regeneration upon retention of a conditioned response in the planarian. *J. comp. physiol. Psychol.*, 1959, **52**, 1–5.

McCouch, G. P., Austin, G. M., Liu, C. N., & Liu, C. Y. Sprouting as a cause of spasticity. *J. Neurophysiol.*, 1958, **21**, 205–223.

McGaugh, J. L. Facilitation and impairment of memory storage processes. Pp. 240–291 in Kimble, D. P. (Ed.) *The anatomy of memory*. Palo Alto: Science and Behavior Books, 1965.

McGaugh, J. L. Time-dependent processes in memory storage. *Science*, 1966, **153**, 1351–1358.

McGaugh, J. L., & Petrinovich, L. The effect of strychnine sulfate on maze learning. *Amer. J. Psychol.*, 1959, **72**, 99–102.

McGaugh, J. L., Thompson, C. W., Westbrook, W. H., & Hudspeth, W. J. A further study on learning facilitation with strychnine sulphate. *Psychopharmacologia*, 1962, **3**, 352–360.

McGaugh, J. L., Westbrook, W. H., & Thompson, C. W. Facilitation of maze learning with posttrial injections of 5-7 Diphenyl-1-3-diazadamantan-6-ol (1757 I.S.). *J. comp. physiol. Psychol.*, 1962, **55**, 710–713.

McIlwain, H. *Biochemistry and the central nervous system* (2nd ed.). Boston: Little, Brown, 1959.

McIlwain, H. *Chemotherapy and the central nervous system*. London: Churchill, 1957.

McIlwain, H., & Rodnight, R. *Practical neurochemistry*. Boston: Little, Brown, 1962.

McLennan, H. *Synaptic transmission*. Philadelphia, Pa.: Saunders, 1963.

Meikle, T. H. Role of corpus callosum in transfer of visual discriminations in the cat. *Science*, 1960, **132**, 1496.

Meikle, T. H., & Sechzer, J. A. Interocular transfer of brightness discrimination in "split-brain" cats. *Science*, 1960, **132**, 734–735.

Meikle, T. H., Sechzer, J. A., & Stellar, E. Interhemispheric transfer of tactile conditioned responses in corpus callosum-sectioned cats. *J. Neurophysiol.*, 1962, **25**, 530–543.

Mello, N. K., & Peterson, N. J. Behavioral evidence for color discrimination in cat. *J. Neurophysiol.*, 1964, **27**, 323–333.

Mendell, L. M., & Wall, P. D. Presynaptic hyperpolarization: A role for fine afferent fibers. *J. Physiol.*, 1965, **172**, 274–294.

Mettler, F. A. Extracortical connections of the primate frontal cerebral cortex. *J. comp. Neurol.*, 1947, **86**, 119–166.

Mettler, F. A., Ades, H. W., Lipman, E., & Culler, E. A. The extrapyramidal system. *Arch. neurol. Psychiat.*, 1939, **41**, 984–995.

Meyer, D. R. Some psychological determinants of sparing and loss following damage to the brain. Pp. 173–192 in Harlow, H. F., & Woolsey, C. N. (Eds.) *Biological and biochemical bases of behavior*. Madison, Wisconsin: Univ. of Wisconsin Press, 1958.

Meyer, D. R., Miles, R. C., & Ratoosh, P. Absence of color vision in cat. *J. Neurophysiol.*, 1954, **17**, 289–294.

Meyer, D. R., & Woolsey, C. N. Effects of localized cortical destruction on auditory discriminative conditioning in cat. *J. Neurophysiol.*, 1952, **15**, 149–162.

Meyer, M., & Allison, A. C. An experimental investigation of the connections of the olfactory tracts in the monkey. *J. neurol. neurosurg. Psychiat.*, 1949, **12**, 274–286.

Meyer, P. M., Horel, J. A., & Meyer, D. R. Effects of d,l-amphetamine upon placing responses in neodecorticate cats. *J. comp. physiol. Psychol.*, 1963, **56**, 402–405.

Michael, R. P. Estrogen-sensitive neurons and sexual behavior in female cats. *Science*, 1962, **136**, 322–323.

Mickle, W. A., & Ades, H. W. A composite sensory projection area in the cerebral cortex of the cat. *Am. J. Physiol.*, 1952, **170**, 682–689.

Miles, R. C., & Blomquist, A. J. Frontal lesions and behavioral deficits in monkey. *J. Neurophysiol.*, 1960, **23**, 471–484

Miller, G. A., & Taylor, W. G. The perception of repeated bursts of noise. *J. acoust. Soc. Am.*, 1948, **20**, 171–182.

Miller, N. E. Studies of fear as an acquirable drive. I. Fear as motivation and fear-reduction as reinforcement in the learning of new responses. *J. exp. Psychol.*, 1948, **38**, 89–101.

Miller, N. E. Learning and performance motivated by direct stimulation of the brain. Pp. 387–396 in Sheer, D. E. (Ed.) *Electrical stimulation of the brain*. Austin, Texas: Univ. of Texas Press, 1961.

Miller, N. E., Bailey, C. J., & Stevenson, J. A. F. Decreased "hunger" but increased food intake resulting from hypothalamic lesions. *Science*, 1950, **112**, 256–259.

Miller, N. E., Jensen, D. D., & Myers, A. K. A comparison of the Lilly waveform and the sixty-cycle sine wave. Pp. 64–66 in Sheer, D. E. (Ed.) *Electrical stimulation of the brain*. Austin, Texas: Univ. of Texas Press, 1961.

Milner, B. Intellectual function of the temporal lobes. *Psychol. Bull.*, 1954, **51**, 42–62.

Milner, B. Some effects of frontal lobectomy in man. Pp. 313–334 in Warren, J. M., & Akert, K. (Eds.) *The frontal granular cortex and behavior*. New York: McGraw-Hill, 1964.

Milner, B., & Penfield, W. The effect of hippocampal lesions on recent memory. *Trans. Am. neurol. Ass.*, 1955, **80**, 42–48.

Milstein, V. Contingent alpha blocking: conditioning or sensitization? *Electroencephalog. clin. Neurophysiol.*, 1965, **18**, 272–277.

Minkowski, M. Experimentelle Untersuchungen über die Beziehungen der Grosshirnrinde und der Netzhaut zu den primären optischen Zentren, besonders zum Corpus geniculatum externum. *Erb. hirnanat. Inst. Zürich*, 1913, **7**, 255–362.

Minkowski, M. Über den Verlauf, die Endigung und die zentrale Repräsentation von gekreuzten und ungekreuzten Fasern bei einigen Säugetieren und beim Menschen. *Schweiz. Arch. neurol. Psychiat.*, 1920, **6**, 201–252.

Mirsky, A. F., Rosvold, H. E., & Pribram, K. H. Effects of cingulectomy on social behavior in monkeys. *J. Neurophysiol.*, 1957, **20**, 588–601.

Mishkin, M. Effects of selective ablations of the temporal lobes on the visually guided behavior of monkeys and baboons. Unpublished doctor's thesis, McGill Univ., 1951.

Mishkin, M., & Pribram, K. H. Visual discrimination performance following partial ablations of the temporal lobe: I. Ventral vs. lateral. *J. comp. physiol. Psychol.*, 1954, **47**, 14–20.

Mishkin, M., & Weiskrantz, L. Effects of delaying reward on discrimination performance of monkeys with frontal lesions. *J. comp. physiol. Psychol.*, 1958, **51**, 276–281.

Mishkin, M., & Weiskrantz, L. Effects of delaying rewards on visual-discrimination performance in monkeys with frontal lesions. *J. comp. physiol. Psychol.*, 1958, **51**, 276–281.

Mishkin, M., & Weiskrantz, L. Effects of cortical lesions in monkeys on critical flicker frequency. *J. comp. physiol. Psychol.*, 1959, **52**, 660–666.

Mollica, A., Moruzzi, G., & Naquet, R. Décharges réticulaires induites par la polarisation du cervelet: leurs rapports avec le tonus postural et la réaction d'éveil. *Electroencephalog. clin. Neurophysiol.*, 1953, **5**, 571–584.

Moncrieff, R. W. What is odor? A new theory. *Essent. Oil Rev.*, 1949, **54**, 453–454.

Morgan, C. T. *Physiological psychology.* New York: McGraw-Hill, 1943.

Morgan, C. T., & Stellar, E. *Physiological psychology.* New York: McGraw-Hill, 1950.

Morin, F. A new spinal pathway for cutaneous impulses. *Amer. J. Physiol.*, 1955, **183**, 245–252.

Morison, R. S., & Dempsey, E. W. A study of thalamo-cortical relations. *Am. J. Physiol.*, 1942, **135**, 280–292.

Morrell, F. Lasting changes in synaptic organization produced by continuous neuronal bombardment. Pp. 375–392 in Delafresnaye, J. F. (Ed.) *Brain mechanisms and learning.* Oxford: Blackwell, 1961a.

Morrell, F. Electrophysiological contributions to the neural basis of learning. *Physiol. Rev.*, 1961b, **41**, 443–494.

Morrell, F. Effect of anodal polarization on the firing pattern of single cortical cells. *Ann. N.Y. Acad. Sci.*, 1961c, **92**, 860–876.

Morrell, F., & Jasper, H. H. Electrographic studies of the formation of temporary connections in the brain. *Electroencephalog. clin. Neurophysiol.*, 1956, **8**, 201–215.

Morrell, F. Naquet, R., & Gastaut, H. Evolution of some electrical signs of conditioning. Part I. Normal cat and rabbit. *J. Neurophysiol.*, 1957, **20**, 574–587.

Morrell, F., & Ross, M. Central inhibition in cortical conditioned reflexes. *Arch. Neurol. Psychiat.*, 1953, **70**, 611–616.

Moruzzi, G. General discussion, pp. 392–393 in Wolstenholme, G. E. W., & O'Connor, M. (Eds.) *CIBA Foundation Symposium, The nature of sleep.* London: Churchill, 1961.

Moruzzi, G. Reticular influences on the EEG. *Electroencephalog. clin. Neurophysiol.*, 1964, **16**, 2–17.

Moruzzi, G., & Magoun, H. W. Brain stem reticular formation and activation of the EEG. *Electroencephalog. clin. Neurophysiol.*, 1949, **1**, 455–473.

Motakawa, K. Electroencephalograms of man in the generalization and differentiation of conditioned reflexes. *Tohoku J. Exp. Med.*, 1949, **50**, 225–234.

Moulton, D. G. Electrical activity in the olfactory system of rabbits with indwelling electrodes. Pp. 71–84 in Zotterman, Y. (Ed.) *Olfaction and taste.* New York: Macmillan, 1963.

Mountcastle, V. B. The reflex activity of the spinal cord. Pp. 1014–1052 in Bard, P. (Ed.) *Medical physiology.* St. Louis: Mosby, 1956.

Mountcastle, V. B. Modality and topographic properties of single neurons of cat's somatic sensory cortex. *J. Neurophysiol.*, 1957, **20**, 408–434.

Mountcastle, V. B. Some functional properties of the somatic afferent system. Pp. 403–436 in Rosenblith, W. A. (Ed.) *Sensory communication.* New York: Wiley, 1961.

Mountcastle, V. B., Davies, P. W., & Berman, A. L. Response properties of neurons of cat's somatic sensory cortex to peripheral stimuli. *J. Neurophysiol.*, 1957, **20**, 374–407.

Mountcastle, V. B., & Henneman, E. The representation of tactile sensibility in the thalamus of the monkey. *J. comp. Neurol.*, 1952, **97**, 409–431.

Mountcastle, V. B., Poggio, G. F., & Werner, G. The relation of thalamic cell response to peripheral stimuli varied over an intensive continuum. *J. Neurophysiol.*, 1963, **26**, 807–834.

Mountcastle, V. B., & Powell, T. P. S. Central neural mechanisms subserving position sense and kinesthesis. *Bull. Johns Hopkins Hosp.*, 1959a, **105**, 173–200.

Mountcastle, V. B., & Powell, T. P. S. Neural mechanisms subserving cutaneous sensibility, with special reference to the role of afferent inhibition in sensory perception and discrimination. *Bull. Johns Hopkins Hosp.*, 1959b, **105**, 201–232.

Mouseghian, G., Rupert, A., Marsh, J. J., & Galambos, R. Evoked cortical potentials in absence of middle ear muscles. *Science*, 1961, **133**, 582–583.

Mowrer, O. H. A stimulus-response analysis of anxiety and its role as a reinforcing agent. *Psychol. Rev.*, 1939, **46**, 553–565.

Mowrer, O. H. On the dual nature of learning: A reinterpretation of "conditioning" and "problem-solving." *Harvard Educ. Rev.*, 1947, **17**, 102–148. Reprinted in Mowrer, O. H., *Learning theory and personality dynamics.* New York: Ronald Press, 1950.

Mozell, M. M., & Pfaffmann, C. The afferent neural processes in odor perception. *Ann. N.Y. Acad. Sci.*, 1954, **58**, 96–108.

Muenzinger, K. F. Motivation in learning. I: Electric shock for correct response in the visual discrimination habit. *J. comp. Psychol.*, 1934, **17**, 267–277.

Müller, G. E., & Pilzecker, A. *Experimentelle Beiträge zur Lehre vom Gedächtniss.* Leipzig, 1900.

Myers, R. E. Interocular transfer of pattern discrimination in cats, following section of crossed optic fibers. *J. comp. physiol. Psychol.*, 1955, **48**, 470–473.

Myers, R. E. Function of corpus callosum in interocular transfer. *Brain*, 1956, **79**, 358–363.

Nachmansohn, D. Chapter 10 in Fulton, J. F. (Ed.) *Textbook of physiology.* Philadelphia: Saunders, 1955.

Nakao, H., & Maki, T. Effect of electrical stimulation of the nucleus caudatus upon conditioned avoidance behavior in the cat. *Folia psychiat. neurol. Jap.*, 1958, **12**, 258–264.

Naquet, R., Regis, H., Fischer-Williams, F., & Fernandez-Guardiola, A. Variations in the responses evoked by light along the specific pathways. *Brain*, 1960, **83**, 52–56.

Nauta, W. J. H. Hypothalamic regulation of sleep in rats: an experimental study. *J. Neurophysiol.*, 1946, **9**, 285–316.

Nauta, W. J. H. Hippocampal projections and related neural pathways to the midbrain in the cat. *Brain*, 1958, **81**, 319–340.

Nauta, W. J. H. Neural associations of the amygdaloid complex in the monkey. *Brain*, 1962, **85**, 505–520.

Nauta, W. J. H., & Bucher, V. M. Efferent connections of the striate cortex in the albino rat. *J. comp. Neurol.*, 1954, **100**, 257–286.

Nauta, W. J. H., & Kuypers, G. J. M. Some ascending pathways in the brain stem reticular formation. Pp. 3–30 in Jasper, H. H. (Ed.) *Reticular formation of the brain.* Boston: Little, Brown, 1958.

Neff, W. D. Neural mechanisms of auditory discrimination. Pp. 259–278 in Rosenblith, W. A. (Ed.) *Sensory communication.* New York: Wiley, 1961.

Neff, W. D., & Diamond, I. T. The neural basis of auditory discrimination. Pp. 101–126 in Harlow, H. G., & Woolsey, C. N. (Eds.) *Biological and biochemical bases of behavior.* Madison, Wis.: Univ. of Wisconsin Press, 1958.

Neff, W. D., Fisher, J. F., Diamond, I. T., & Yela, M. Role of auditory cortex in discrimination requiring localization of sound in space. *J. Neurophysiol.*, 1956, **19**, 500–512.

Nesmeianova, T. N. The inhibition of the motor reflex in spinal dogs under conditions of chronic experimentation. *Sechenov physiol. J. USSR*, 1957, **42**, 281–288.

Newell, A., Shaw, J. C., & Simon, H. A. Elements of a theory of human problem solving. *Psychol. Rev.*, 1958, **65**, 151–166.

Nishi, S., & Koketsu, K. Electrical properties and activities of single sympathetic neurons in frogs. *J. cell. comp. Physiol.*, 1960, **55**, 15–30.

Noell, W. K. Studies on the electrophysiology and the metabolism of the retina. *School of Aviation Med. Rep. No. 1*, Randolph Field, Texas, 1953, 1–122.

Norrsell, U. Functional significance of tactile pathways to the cerebral cortex. *XXII Inter. Congr. physiol. Sci.*, Leiden, 1962, **947**.

Norrsell, U. Cerebral sematosensory ablations and a tactile conditioned reflex. *Acta physiol. Scand.*, Abstract, XII Scand. physiol. Congr., 1966.

Norrsell, U. The spinal afferent pathways of conditioned reflexes to cutaneous stimuli in the dog. *Exp. brain Res.*, 1967 (in press).

Norrsell, U., & Voorhoeve, P. Tactile pathways from the hindlimb to the cerebral cortex in cat. *Acta physiol. Scand.*, 1962, **54**, 9–17

Nurnberger, J I. Direct enumeration of cells of the brain. Pp. 193–202 in Windle, W. F. (Ed.), *Biology of neuroglia*. Springfield, Ill.: Charles C Thomas, 1958.

Olds, J. Pleasure centers in the brain. *Scient. Amer.*, 1956, **195**, 105–116.

Olds, J. Self-stimulation of the brain. *Science*, 1958, **127**, 315–323.

Olds, J. Approach-avoidance dissociations in rat brain. *Am. J. Physiol.*, 1960, **199**, 965–968.

Olds, J. Hypothalamic substrates of reward. *Physiol. Rev.*, 1962, **42**, 554–604.

Olds, J., & Milner, P. Positive reinforcement produced by electrical stimulation of septal area and other regions of rat brain. *J. comp. physiol. Psychol.*, 1954, **47**, 419–427.

O'Leary, J. L., & Goldring, S. Changes associated with forebrain excitation process: d.c. potentials of the cerebral cortex. Pp. 315–328 in Field, J., Magoun, H. W., & Hall, V. E. (Eds.) *Handbook of physiology, Neurophysiology*, I. Washington, D.C.: American Physiological Society, 1959.

O'Leary, J. L., & Goldring, S. D-c potentials of the brain. *Physiol. Rev.*, 1964, **44**, 91–125.

Olszewski, J. *The thalamus of Macaca mulatta: An atlas for use with the stereotaxic instrument*. New York: S. Karger, 1952.

Olszewski, J., & Baxter, D. *Cytoarchitecture of the human brain stem*. Philadelphia: Lippincott, 1954.

Orbach, J., & Chow, K. L. Differential effects of resections of somatic areas I and II in monkeys. *J. Neurophysiol.*, 1959, **22**, 195–203.

Ortmann, R. Neurosecretion. Pp. 1039–1065 in Field, J., Magoun, H. W., & Hall, V. E. (Eds.) *Handbook of Physiology, Neurophysiology*, II. Washington, D.C.: American Physiological Society, 1960.

Oscarsson, O., & Rosén, I. Projection to cerebral cortex of large muscle-spindle afferents in forelimb nerves of the cat. *J. Physiol.*, 1963, **169**, 924–945.

Ottoson, D. Analysis of the electrical activity of the olfactory epithelium. *Acta physiol. Scand.*, 1956, **35**, Suppl. 122, 1–82.

Ottoson, D. Comparison of slow potentials evoked in the frog's nasal mucosa and olfactory bulb by natural stimulation. *Acta physiol. Scand.*, 1959, **47**, 149–159.

Ottoson, D. Generation and transmission of signals in the olfactory system. Pp. 35–44 in Zotterman, Y. (Ed.), *Olfaction and taste*. New York: Macmillan, 1963.

Palade, G. E., & Palay, S. L. "Personal communication." 1956, p. 4 in Eccles, J. C. (1957).

Palay, S. L. The morphology of synapses in the central nervous system. *Exp. Cell. Res.*, 1958, **5** Suppl., 275–293.

Palestini, M., Davidovich, A., & Hernández-Peón, R. Functional significance of centrifugal influences upon the retina. *Acta neurol. Lat. Amer.*, 1959, **5**, 113–131.

Palestini, M., Rossi, G. F., & Zanchetti, A. An electrophysiological analysis of pontine reticular regions showing different anatomical organization. *Arch. Ital. Biol.*, 1957, **95**, 97–109.

Papez, J. W. A proposed mechanism of emotion. *Arch. neurol. Psychiat.*, 1937, **38**, 725–743.

Paton, W. D. M. Central and synaptic transmission in the nervous system. *Ann. Rev. Physiol.*, 1958, **20**, 431–470.

Patton, H. D. Special properties of nerve trunks and tracts. Pp. 66–82 in Ruch, T. C., & Fulton, J. F. (Eds.) *Medical physiology and biophysics*. Philadelphia: Saunders, 1960a.

Patton, H. D. Reflex regulation of posture and movement. Pp. 167–198 in Ruch, T. C., & Fulton, J. F. (Eds.) *Medical physiology and biophysics*. Philadelphia: Saunders, 1960b.

Patton, H. D. The autonomic nervous system. Pp. 220–233 in Rich, T. C., & Fulton, J. F. (Eds.) *Medical physiology and biophysics*. Philadelphia: Saunders, 1960c.

Patton, H. D., & Amassian, V. E. Single- and multiple-unit analysis of cortical stage of pyramidal tract activation. *J. Neurophysiol.*, 1954, **17**, 345–363.

Patton, H. D., & Amassian, V. E. The pyramidal tract: Its excitation and functions. Pp. 837–861 in Field, J., Magoun, H. W., & Hall, V. E. (Eds.) *Handbook of Physiology*, *Neurophysiology*. II. Washington, D.C.: American Physiological Society, 1960.

Pavlov, I. *Conditioned reflexes*. New York: Oxford Univ. Press, 1927.

Pearlman, C. A., Sharpless, S. K., & Jarvik, M. E. Retrograde amnesia produced by anesthetic and convulsant agents. *J. comp. physiol. Psychol.*, 1961, **54**, 109–112.

Peele, T. L. *The neuroanatomical basis for clinical neurology*. New York: McGraw-Hill, 1954.

Penfield, W., & Jasper, H. *Epilepsy and the functional anatomy of the human brain*. Boston: Little, Brown, 1954.

Penfield, W., & Rasmussen, T. *The cerebral cortex of man*. New York: Macmillan, 1950.

Penfield, W., & Welch, K. The supplementary motor area of the cerebral cortex, a clinical and experimental study. *Arch. neurol. Psychiat.*, 1951, **66**, 289–317.

Pennington, L. A. The effects of cortical destruction upon responses to tones. *J. comp. Neurol.*, 1941, **74**, 169–191.

Peretz, E. The effects of lesions of the anterior cingulate cortex on the behavior of the rat. *J. comp. physiol. Psychol.*, 1960, **53**, 540–548.

Perl, E. R., & Whitlock, D. G. Potentials evoked in cerebral somatosensory region. *J. Neurophysiol.*, 1955, **18**, 486–501.

Pfaffmann, C. Gustatory nerve impulses in rat, cat and rabbit. *J. Neurophysiol.*, 1955, **18**, 429–440.

Pfaffmann, C. The sense of taste. Pp. 507–534 in Field, J., Magoun, H. W., & Hall, V. E. (Eds.), *Handbook of physiology*, *Neurophysiology*, I. Washington, D.C., American Physiological Society, 1959a.

Pfaffmann, C. The afferent code for sensory quality. *Amer. Psychologist*, 1959b, **14**, 226–232.

Phillips, C. G. Intracellular records from Betz cells in the cat. *Quart. J. exp. Physiol.*, 1956, **41**, 58–69.

Phillips, C. G., & Porter, R. The pyramidal projection to motoneurons of some muscle groups of the baboon's forearm." In Eccles, J. C., & Schadé, J. P. (Eds.) Progress in brain research. Vol. 12, Physiology of spinal neurons. Amsterdam: Elsevier, 1964.

Phillips, D. S., & Michels, K. Selective stimulation and electrophysiological responses of the olfactory bulb of the oppossum. *Percept. mot. Skills*, 1964, **18**, 63–69.

Phoenix, C. H. Hypothalamic regulation of sexual behavior in male guinea pigs. *J. comp. physiol. Psychol.*, 1961, **54**, 72–77.

Phoenix, C. H., Goy, R. W., Gerall, A. A., & Young, W. C. Organizing action of prenatally administered testosterone propionate on the tissues mediating mating behavior in the female guinea pig. *Endocrinology*, 1959, **65**, 369–382.

Plattner, F. Der Nachweiss des Vagusstoffes beim Saugetier. *Pflügers Arch. ges. Physiol.*, 1926, **214**, 112–129.

Pletscher, A., Shore, P. A., & Brodie, B. B. Serotonin as a mediator of reserpine action in brain. *J. Pharmacol.*, 1956, **116**, 84–89.

Poggio, G. F., & Mountcastle, V. B. A study of the functional contributions of the lemniscal and spinothalamic systems to somatic sensibility. Central nervous mechanisms in pain. *Bull. Johns Hopkins Hosp.*, 1960, **106**, 266–316.

Poggio, G. F., & Mountcastle, V. B. The functional properties of ventrobasal thalamic neurons studied in unanesthetized monkeys. *J. Neurophysiol.*, 1963, **26**, 775–806.

Pollock, L. J., & Davis, L. The reflex activities of a decerebrate animal. *J. comp. Neurol.*, 1930, **50**, 377–411.

Polyak, S. An experimental study of the association, callosal and projection fibers of the cerebral cortex of the cat. *J. comp. Neurol.*, 1927, **44**, 197–258.

Polyak, S. *The retina*. Chicago; Univ. of Chicago Press, 1941.

Pompieano, O., & Swett, J. E. EEG and behavioral manifestations of sleep induced by cutaneous nerve stimulation in normal cats. *Arch. Ital. Biol.*, 1962, **100**, 311–342.

Porter, R. W., Cavanaugh, E. B., Critchlow, B. V., & Sawyer, C. H. Localized changes in electrical activity of the hypothalamus in estrous cats following vaginal stimulation. *Am. J. Physiol.*, 1957, **189**, 145–151.

Porter, R. W., Conrad, D. G., & Brady, J. V. Some neural and behavioral correlates of electrical self-stimulation of the limbic system. *J. exp. anal. Behav.*, 1959, **2**, 43–55.

Preston, J. B., & Whitlock, D. G. Intracellular potentials recorded from motoneurons following precentral gyrus stimulation in primate. *J. Neurophysiol.*, 1961, **24**, 91–100.

Pribram, H. B., & Barry, J. Further behavioral analysis of the parieto-temporo-preoccipital cortex. *J. Neurophysiol.*, 1956, **19**, 99–106.

Pribram, K. H. Neocortical functions in behavior. Pp. 151–172 in Harlow, H. F., & Woolsey, C. N. (Eds.) *Biological and Biochemical bases of behavior*. Madison.: Univ. of Wisconsin Press, 1958.

Pribram, K. H. A review of theory in physiological psychology. *Ann. Rev. Psychol.*, 1960a, **11**, 1–40.

Pribram, K. H. The intrinsic systems of the forebrain. Pp. 1323–1344 in Field, J., Magoun, H. W., & Hall, V. E. (Eds) *Handbook of physiology, Neurophysiology*, **II**. Washington, D.C.: American Physiological Society, 1960b.

Pribram, K. H. Limbic system, Pp. 311–320 in Sheer, D. E. (Ed.) *Electrical stimulation of the brain*. Austin, Texas: Univ. of Texas Press, 1961.

Pribram, K. H. Interrelations of psychology and the neurological disciplines. Pp. 119–157 in Koch, S. (Ed.) *Psychology: A study of a science*, vol. 4. New York: McGraw-Hill, 1962.

Pribram, K. H., Ahumada, A., Hartog, J., & Roos, L. A progress report on the neurological processes disturbed by frontal lesions in primates. Pp. 28–55 in Warren, J. M. & Akert, K. (Eds.) *The frontal granular cortex and behavior*. New York: McGraw-Hill, 1964.

Pribram, K. H., & Bagshaw, M. Further analysis of the temporal lobe syndrome utilizing fronto-temporal ablations. *J. comp. Neurol.*, 1953, **99**, 347–375.

Pribram, K. H., & Fulton, J. F. An Experimental critique of the effects of anterior cingulate ablations in monkey. *Brain*, 1954, **77**, 34–44.

Pribram, K. H., & Kruger, L. Functions of the "olfactory brain". *Ann. N. Y. Acad. Sci.*, 1954, **58**, 109–138.

Pribram, K. H., Kruger, L., Robinson, F., & Berman, A. J. The effects of precentral lesions on the behavior of monkeys. *Yale J. biol. Med.*, 1955–1956, **28**, 428–443.

Pribram, K. H., & Mishkin, M. Analysis of the effects of frontal lesions in monkey: III. Object alternation. *J. comp. physiol. Psychol.*, 1956, **49**, 41–45.

Pribram, K. H., Mishkin, M., Rosvold, H. E., & Kaplan, S. J. Effects on delayed-response performance of lesions of dorsolateral and ventromedial cortex of baboons. *J. comp. physiol. Psychol.*, 1952, **45**, 567–575.

Pribram, K. H., & Weiskrantz, L. A comparison of the effects of medial and lateral cerebral resections on conditioned avoidance behavior in monkeys. *J. comp. physiol. Psychol.*, 1957, **50**, 74–80.

Pribram, K. H. Toward a science of neuropsychology (method and data). In Patton, R. A. (Ed.) *Current trends in psychology and the behavioral sciences*. Pittsburgh: Univ. of Pittsburgh Press, 1954.

Pringle, J. W. S. Prologue: the input element. Pp. 1–11 in *Biological receptor mechanisms*, *Symp. soc. exp. Biol.*, vol. 16. New York: Academic Press, 1962.

Prosser, C. L., & Hunter, W. S. The extinction of startle responses and spinal reflexes in the white rat. *Amer. J. Physiol.*, 1936, **117**, 609–618.

Purpura, D. P., & Cohen, B. Intracellular recording from thalamic neurons during recruiting responses. *J. Neurophysiol.*, 1962, **25**, 621–635.

Purpura, D. P., & Grundfest, H. Nature of dentritic potentials and synaptic mechanisms in cerebral cortex of cat. *J. Neurophysiol.*, 1956, **19**, 573–595.

Purpura, D. P., & Housepian, E. M. Alterations in corticospinal neuron activity associated with thalamocortical recruiting responses. *Electroencephalog. clin. Neurophysiol.*, 1961, **13**, 365–381.

Purpura, D. P., & Shofer, R. J. Intracellular recording from thalamic neurons during reticulo-cortical activation. *J. Neurophysiol.*, 1963, **26**, 494–505.

Quilliam, T. A., & Sato, M. The distribution of myelin on nerve fibers from Pacinian corpuscles. *J. Physiol.*, 1955, **129**, 167–176.

Raab, D. H., & Ades, H. W. Cortical and midbrain mediation of a conditioned discrimination of acoustic intensities. *Amer. J. Psychol.*, 1946, **59**, 59–83.

Ramey, E. R., & O'Doherty, D. S. (Eds.) *Electrical studies of the unanesthetized brain.* New York: Hoeber, 1960.

Ramón y Cajal, S. Textura del sistema nervioso del hombre y de los vertebrados, estudios sobre el plan estructural y composición histólogica de los centros nerviosos, adicionados de consideraciones fisiológicas fundadas en los nuevos descubrimientos. 2 vol., Madrid: N. Maya, 1899–1904.

Ramón y Cajal, S. *Histologie du système nerveux de l'homme et des vertébrés.* (Reprinted from the original 1909–1911 ed.) Madrid, Consejo Superior de Investigaciones Científicas, 1952–1955.

Ramón y Cajal, S. Les preuves objectives de l'unité anatomique des cellules nerveuses. *Trob. Lab. Inest. biol. Univ. Madr.*, 1934, **29**, 1–37. (Translation: Purkiss, M. V., & Fox, C. A., Madrid: Instituto "Ramón y Cajal," 1954.)

Randall, W. L. Generalization after frequency discrimination in cats with central nervous system lesions. Pp. 134–153 in Mostofsky, D. I. (Ed.), *Stimulus generalization.* Stanford, Calif.: Stanford Univ. Press, 1965.

Ranson, S. W. Some functions of the hypothalamus. (Harvey Lectures) *Bull. N. Y. Acad. Med.*, 1937, **13**, 241–271.

Ranson, S. W. Somnolence caused by hypothalamic lesions in monkeys. *Arch. Neurol. Psychiat.*, 1939, **41**, 1–23.

Ranson, S. W., & Clark, S. L. *The anatomy of the nervous system.* Philadelphia: Saunders, 1959.

Ranson, S. W., & Magoun, H. W. The hypothalamus. *Ergebn. Physiol.*, 1939, **41**, 56–163.

Rasmussen, G. L. The olivary peduncle and other fiber projections of the superior olivary complex. *J. comp. Neurol.*, 1946, **84**, 141–219.

Rasmussen, G. L. Further observations of the efferent cochlear bundle. *J. comp. Neurol.*, 1953, **99**, 61–74.

Ratner, S. C., & Denny, M. R. *Comparative psychology. Research in animal behavior.* Homewood, Ill.: Dorsey, 1964.

Reichlin, S. Neuroendocrinology. *New Engl. J. Med.*, 1963, **269**, 1182–1191.

Rempel, B., & Gibbs, E. L. The berger rhythm in cats. *Science*, 1936, **84**, 334.

Renshaw, B. Activity in the simplest spinal reflex pathways. *J. Neurophysiol.*, 1940, **3**, 373–387.

Renshaw, B., Forbes, A., & Morison, B. R. Activity of ioscortex and hippocampus: electrical studies with microelectrodes. *J. Neurophysiol.*, 1940, **3**, 74–105.

Reynolds, R. W. Ventromedial hypothalamic lesions without hyperphagia. *Amer. J. Physiol.*, 1963a, **204**, 60–62.

Reynolds, R. W. Radio frequency lesions in the ventrolateral hypothalamic "feeding center." *J. comp. physiol. Psychol.*, 1963b, **56**, 965–967.

Reynolds, R. W. Hypothalamic lesions and disinhibition of feeding. *Science*, 1965, **150**, 1322.

Rheinberger, M., & Jasper, H. H. The electrical activity of the cerebral cortex in the unanesthetized cat. *Amer. J. Physiol.*, 1937, **119**, 186–196.

Richter, D., & Crossland, J. Variations in acetylcholine content of the brain with physiological state. *Amer. J. Physiol.*, 1949, **159**, 247–255.

Riesen, A. H. The development of visual perception in man and chimpanzee. *Science*, 1947, **106**, 107–108.

Riesen, A. H. Stimulations as a requirement for growth and function in behavioral development. Pp. 57–80 in Fiske, D. W. & Maddi, S. R. (Eds.), *Functions of varied experience.* Homewood, Ill.: Dorsey, 1961.

Riggs, L. A., Ratliff, F., Cornsweet, J. C., & Cornsweet, T. N. The disappearance of steadily fixated visual test objects. *J. Opt. Soc. Amer.*, 1953, **43**, 495–501.

Rioch, D. M. Functions of the brainstem in preparations with extensive lesions of the neocortex. *Ass. Res. nerv. Dis. Proc.*, 1942, **21**, 133–149.

Rioch, D. M., & Brenner, C. Experiments on the corpus striatum and rhinencephalon. *J. comp. Neurol.*, 1938, **68**, 491–507.

Riopelle, A. J., & Ades, H. W. Discrimination following deep temporal lesions. *Amer. Psychologist*, 1951, **6**, 261–262.

Riopelle, A. J., Alper, R. G., Strong, P. N., & Ades, H. W. Multiple discrimination and patterned string performance of normal and temporal-lobectomized monkeys. *J. comp. physiol. Psychol.*, 1953, **46**, 145–149.

Riopelle, A. J., & Churukian, G. A. The effect of varying the intertrial interval in discrimination learning by normal and brain-operated monkeys. *J. comp. physiol. Psychol.*, 1958, **51**, 119–125.

Roberts, W. W. Rapid escape learning without avoidance learning motivated by hypothalamic stimulation in cats. *J. comp. physiol. Psychol.*, 1958a, **51**, 391–399.

Roberts, W. W. Both rewarding and punishing effects from stimulation of posterior hypothalamus of cats with same electrode at same intensity. *J. comp. physiol. Psychol.*, 1958b, **51**, 400–407.

Robinson, E. The effect of amygdalectomy on fear-motivated behavior in rats. *J. comp. physiol. Psychol.*, 1963, **56**, 814–820.

Robinson, E., & Gantt, W. H. The orienting reflex (questioning reaction): Cardiac, respiratory, salivary, and motor components. *Bull. Johns Hopkins Hosp.*, 1947, **80**, 231–253.

Rodgers, C. M. Hypothalamic mediation of sex behavior in the male rat. Unpublished doctor's dissertation. New Haven: Yale Univ., 1954, Cited by Beach, F. A., Neural and chemical regulation of behavior. Pp. 263–284 in Harlow, H. F., & Woolsey, C. N. (Eds.) *Biological and biochemical bases of behavior*. Madison, Wis.: Univ. of Wisconsin Press, 1958.

Roger, A., Rossi, G. F., & Zirondoli, A. Le rôle des nerfs craniens dans le maintien de l'état vigile de la preparation "encephale isolé." *Electroencephalog. clin. Neurophysiol.*, 1956, **8**, 1–13.

Roig, J. A., Segundo, J. P., Sommer-Smith, J. A., & Galeano, C. Conditioning of caudate and amygdaloid stimulation effects. *Proc. XXI Int. Cong. Physiol. Sci., Amarrotu, Buenos Aires*, 1959, 234.

Roitbak, A. I. Electrical phenomena in the cerebral cortex during the extinction of orientation and conditioned reflexes. Pp. 91–100 in Jasper, H. H., & Smirnov, G. D. (Eds.) The Moscow Colloquium on electroencephalography of high nervous activity. *Electroencephalog. clin. Neurophysiol.*, 1960, Suppl. 13.

Rose, J. E. The cortical connections of the reticular complex of the thalamus. *Ass. Res. nerv. Dis. Proc.*, 1952, **30**, 454–479.

Rose, J. E., Greenwood, D. D., Goldberg, J. M., & Hind, J. E. Some discharge characteristics of single neurons in the inferior colliculus of the cat. I. Tonotopic organization, relation of spike-counts to tone intensity, and firing patterns of single elements. *J. Neurophysiol.*, 1963, **26**, 294–320.

Rose, J. E., Malis, L. I., & Baker, C. P. Neural growth in the cerebral cortex after lesions produced by monoenergetic deuterons. Pp. 279–301 in Rosenblith, W. A. (Ed.) *Sensory communication*. Cambridge: MIT Press, 1961.

Rose, J. E., & Mountcastle, V. B. Touch and kinesthesis. Pp. 387–429 in Field, J., Magoun, H. W., & Hall, V. E. (Eds.) *Handbook of physiology, Neurophysiology*, I. Washington, D.C.: American Physiological Society, 1959.

Rose, J. E., & Woolsey, C. N. Organization of mammalian thamalus and its relationships to the cerebral cortex. *Electroencephalog. clin. Neurophysiol.*, 1949, **1**, 391–404.

Rose, J. E., & Woolsey, C. N. Cortical connections and functional organization of the thalamic auditory system of the cat. Pp. 127–150 in Harlow, H. F., & Woolsey, C. N. (Eds.) *Biological and biochemical bases of behavior*. Madison, Wis.: Univ. of Wisconsin Press, 1958.

Rosenzweig, M. R. Discrimination of auditory intensities on the cat. *Amer. J. Psychol.*, 1946, **59**, 127–136.

Rosenzweig, M. R. Cortical correlates of auditory localization and of related perceptual phenomena. *J. comp. physiol. Psychol.*, 1954, **47**, 269–276.

Rosenzweig, M. R., Krech, D., & Bennett, E. L. A search for relations between brain chemistry and behavior. *Psychol. Bull.*, 1960, **57**, 476–492.

Rossi, G. F. Sleep inducing mechanisms in the brain stem. Pp. 113–132 in Hernández-Peón, R. (Ed.) The physiological basis of mental activity. *Electroencephalog. clin. Neurophysiol.* 1963, Suppl. 24.

Rossi, G. F., Favale, E., Hara, T., Giussani, A., & Sacco, G. Researches on the nervous mechanisms underlying deep sleep in the cat. *Arch. Ital. Biol.*, 1961, **99**, 270–292.

Rossi, G. F., Minobe, K., & Candia, O. An experimental study of the hypnogenic mechanisms of the brainstem. *Arch. Ital. Biol.*, 1963, **101**, 470–492.

Rossi, G. F., & Zirondoli, A. On the mechanism of the cortical desynchronization elicited by volatile anesthetics. *Electroencephalog. clin. Neurophysiol.*, 1955, **7**, 383–390.

Rosvold, H. E. Physiological psychology. *Ann. Rev. Psychol.*, 1959, **10**, 415–454.

Rosvold, H. E., & Delgado, J. M. R. The effect on delayed alternation test performance of stimulating or destroying electrically structures within the frontal lobes of the monkey's brain. *J. comp. physiol. Psychol.*, 1956, **49**, 365–372.

Rosvold, H. E., Mirsky, A. F., & Pribram, K. H. Influence of amygdalectomy on social behavior in monkeys. *J. comp. physiol. Psychol.*, 1954, **47**, 173–178.

Rosvold, H. E., Mishkin, M., & Szwarcbart, M. K. Effects of subcortical lesions in monkeys on visual-discrimination and single-alternation performance. *J. comp. physiol. Psychol.*, 1958, **51**, 437–444.

Rowsell, E. V. Applied electrical pulses and the ammonia and acetylcholine of isolated cerebral cortex slices. *Biochem. J.*, 1954. **57**, 666–673.

Ruch, T. C. Cortical localization of somatic sensibility. The effect of precentral, postcentral and posterior parietal lesions upon the performance of monkeys trained to discriminate weights. *Ass. Res. nerv. Dis. Proc.* 1935, **15**, 289–330.

Ruch, T. C. The cerebral cortex: its structure and motor functions. Pp. 249–276 in Ruch, T. C., & Fulton, J. F. (Eds.) *Medical physiology and biophysics*. Philadelphia: Saunders, 1960.

Ruch, T. C., & Fulton, J. F. (Eds.) *Medical physiology and biophysics*. Philadelphia: Saunders, 1960.

Ruch, T. C., Fulton, J. F., & German, W. J. Sensory discrimination in the monkey, chimpanzee, and man after lesions of the parietal lobe. *Arch. Neurol. Psychiat.*, 1938, **39**, 919–937.

Rushton, W. A. H. Physical measurement of cone pigments in the living human eye. *Nature*, 1957, **179**, 571–573.

Rushton, W. A. H. The core pigments of the human fovea in colour blind and normal. Pp. 77–106 in *Visual problem of color*. New York: Chemical Publ., 1961.

Rushton, W. A. H. The retinal organization of vision in vertebrates. Pp. 12–31 in *Biological receptor mechanisms*. *Symp. Soc. exp. Biol.*, vol. 16. New York: Academic Press, 1962.

Rusinov, V. S. An electrophysiological analysis of the connecting function in the cerebral cortex in the presence of a dominant area. *Comm. XIX Intern. Physiol. Congr. Montreal*, 1953.

Russell, G. V. Interrelationships within the limbic and centrencephalic systems. Pp. 167–181 in Sheer, D. E. (Ed.) *Electrical stimulation of the brain*. Austin, Texas: Univ. of Texas Press, 1961a.

Russell, G. V. Hypothalamic, preoptic and septal regions of the monkey. Pp. 232–250 in Sheer, D. E. (Ed.) *Electrical stimulation of the brain*. Austin, Texas: Univ. of Texas Press, 1961b.

Russell, W. R., & Nathan, P. W. Traumatic amnesia. *Brain*, 1946, **69**, 280–300.

Santibañez, G., Trouche, E., & Albe-Fessard, D. Étude de l'évolution au cours du temps de l'amplitude des activités corticales et thalamiques évoquées par des stimuli somatiques répétés. *J. Physiol. (Paris)*, 1963, **55**, 335.

Sawyer, C. H. Reproductive behavior. Pp. 1225–1240 in Field, J., Magoun, H. W., & Hall,

V. E. (Eds.) *Handbook of physiology, Neurophysiology,* **II.** Washington, D.C.: American Physiological Society, 1960.

Sawyer, C. H., & Kawakami, M. Characteristics of behavioral and electroencephalographic after-reactions to copulation and vaginal stimulation in the female rabbit. *Endrocrinology,* 1959, **65,** 622–630.

Sawyer, C. H., & Robinson, B. Separate hypothalamic areas controlling pituitary gonadotrophic function and mating behavior in female cats and rabbits. *J. clin. Endocr.,* 1956, **16,** 914–915.

Scheibel, M. E., & Scheibel, A. B. Structural substrates for integrative patterns in the brain stem reticular core. Pp. 31–55 in Jasper, H. H. (Ed.) *Reticular formation of the brain.* Boston: Little, Brown, 1958.

Scheibel, M. E., Scheibel, A. B., Mollica, A., & Moruzzi, G. Convergence and interaction of afferent impulses on single units of reticular formation. *J. Neurophysiol.,* 1955, **18,** 309–331.

Schiller, F. Aphasia studied in patients with missile wounds. *J. Neurol. Neurosurg. Psychiat.,* 1947, **10,** 183–197.

Schmidt, R. F. Pharmacological studies on the primary afferent depolarization of the toad spinal cord, *Pflügers Arch. ges. Physiol.,* 1963, **277,** 325–346.

Schreiner, L. H., & Kling, A. Behavioral changes following rhinencephalic injury in the cat. *J. Neurophysiol.,* 1953, **16,** 643–659.

Schreiner, L. H., Lindsley, D. B., & Magoun, H. W. Role of brain stem facilitory systems in maintenance of spasticity. *J. Neurophysiol.,* 1949, **12,** 207–216.

Schwerin, P., Bessman, S. P., & Wallsch, H. The uptake of glutamic acid and glutamine by brain and other tissues of the rat and mouse. *J. biol. Chem.,* 1950, **184,** 37–44.

Sechzer, J. A. Successful interocular transfer of pattern discrimination in split brain cats with shock avoidance motivation. *J. comp. physiol. Psychol.,* 1964, **58,** 70–83.

Segundo, J. P., Naquet, R. & Buser, P. Effects of cortical stimulation on electrocortical activity in monkeys. *J. Neurophysiol.,* 1955, **18,** 236–245.

Selye, H. *The physiology and pathology of exposure to stress.* Montreal: Acta, Inc., 1950.

Sem-Jacobsen, C. W., & Torkildsen, A. Depth recording and electrical stimulation in the human brain. Pp. 275–287 in Ramey, E. R. & O'Doherty, D. S. (Eds.) *Electrical studies on the unanesthetized brain.* New York: Hoeber, 1960.

Settlage, P. H. The effect of occipital lesions on visually guided behavior in the monkey: II. Loss and recovery of function as studied by performance on patterned string tests. *J. comp. Psychol.,* 1939, **27,** 109–131.

Settlage, P. H., Zable, M., & Harlow, H. F. Problem solution by monkeys following bilateral removal of the prefrontal areas: VI. Performance on tests requiring contradictory reactions to similar and to identical stimuli. *J. exp. Psychol.,* 1948, **38,** 50–65.

Shagass, C., & Johnson, E. P. The course of acquisition of a conditioned response of the occipital alpha rhythm. *J. exp. Psychol.,* 1943, **33,** 201–209.

Sharpless, S. K. Reorganization of function in the nervous system—use and disuse. *Ann. Rev. Physiol.,* 1964, **26,** 357–388.

Sharpless, S., & Jasper, H. H. Habituation of the arousal reaction. *Brain,* 1956, **79,** 655–680.

Shaw, J. A., & Thompson, R. F. Dependence of evoked cortical association responses on behavioral variables. *Psychonom. Sci.,* 1964a, **1,** 153–154.

Shaw, J. A., & Thompson, R. F. Inverse relation between evoked cortical association responses and behavioral orienting to repeated auditory stimuli. *Psychonom. Sci.,* 1964b, **1,** 399–400.

Sheatz, G. C. Electrode holders in chronic preparations: A. Multilead techniques for large and small animals. Pp. 45–50 in Sheer, D. S. (Ed.) *Electrical stimulation of the brain.* Austin, Texas: Univ. of Texas Press, 1961.

Sheer, D. E. (Ed.) *Electrical stimulation of the brain.* Austin, Texas: Univ. of Texas Press, 1961.

Sherrington, C. S. *The integrative action of the nervous system.* (2nd ed.) New Haven, Conn.: Yale Univ. Press, 1947.

Sherrington, C. S. Pp. 1–4 in Laslett, P. (Ed.) *The physical basis of mind.* New York: Macmillan, 1950.

Shimazono, Y., Torii, H., Endo, M., Ihara, S., Harukawa, H., & Matsuda, M. Convergence of thalamic and sensory afferent impulses to single neurons in the cortical association area of cats. *Folia psychiat. neurol. Jap.*, 1963, **17**, 144–155.

Sholl, D. A. *The organisation of the cerebral cortex*. London: Methuen, 1956.

Shore, P. A., Silver, S. L., & Brodie, B. B. Interaction of reserpine, serotonin and lysergic acid diethylamide in brain. *Science*, 1955, **122**, 284–285.

Showers, M. J. C., & Crosby, E. C. Somatic and visceral responses from the cingulate gyrus. *Neurology*, 1958, **8**, 561–565.

Shurrager, P. S., & Culler, E. Conditioning in the spinal dog. *J. exp. Psychol.*, 1940, **26**, 133–159.

Shurrager, P. S., & Shurrager, H. C. Converting a spinal CR into a reflex. *J. exp. Psychol.*, 1941, **29**, 217–224.

Shurrager, P. S., & Shurrager, H. C. The rate of learning measured at a single synapse. *J. exp. Psychol.*, 1946, **36**, 347–354.

Sidowski, J. B. (Ed.) *Experimental methods and instrumentation in psychology*. New York: McGraw-Hill, 1966.

Sindberg, R. M. & Thompson, R. F. Auditory response fields in ventral temporal and insular cortex of cat. *J. Neurophysiol.*, 1962, **25**, 21–28.

Skinner, B. F. *The behavior of organisms: An experimental analysis*. New York: Appleton-Century-Crofts, 1938.

Skinner, B. F. Behaviorism at fifty. *Science*, 1963, **140**, 951–958.

Smith, O. A., Jr. Food intake and hypothalamic stimulation. Pp. 367–370 in Sheer, D. E. (Ed.) *Electrical stimulation of the brain*. Austin, Texas: Univ. of Texas Press, 1961.

Smith, W. K. The frontal eye fields. Pp. 307–342 in Bucy, P. C. (Ed.) *The precentral motor cortex*. Urbana, Illinois: Univ. of Illinois Press, 1949.

Snider, R. S. & Lee, J. C. *A stereotaxic atlas of the monkey brain* (Macaca mulatta). Chicago, Ill.: Univ. of Chicago Press, 1961.

Snider, R. S., & Niemer, W. T. *A stereotaxic atlas of the cat brain*. Chicago, Ill.: Univ. of Chicago Press, 1961.

Snider, R. S., & Stowell, A. Receiving areas of the tactile, auditory and visual systems in the cerebellum. *J. Neurophysiol.*, 1944, **7**, 331–357.

Snyder, M., Hall, W. C., & Diamond, I. T. Vision in tree shrews (*Tupaia glis*) after removal of striate cortex. *Psychonom. Sci.*, 1966, **6**, 243–244.

Sokolov, E. N. Neuronal models of the orienting reflex. P. 187–276 in Brazier, M. A. B. (Ed.), *The central nervous system and behavior*. Trans. 3rd Conf. Josiah Macy, Jr., Found. New York, 1960.

Sokolov, E. N. Higher nervous functions: the orienting reflex. *Ann. Rev. Physiol.*, 1963, **25**, 545–580.

Soulairac, A., & Soulairac, M. L. Effets de lésions hypothalamiques sur le comportement sexuel et le tractus genital du rat male. *Ann. Endocrin. Paris*, 1956, **17**, 731–745.

Sourkes, T. L. *Biochemistry of mental desease*. New York: Hoeber, 1962.

Spaet, T., & Harlow, H. F. Problem solution by monkeys following bilateral removal of the prefrontal areas: II. Delayed reaction problems involving use of the matching-from-sample method. *J. exp. Psychol.*, 1943, **32**, 424–434.

Spence, K. W. *Behavior theory and learning*. Englewood Cliffs, N.J.: Prentice-Hall, 1960.

Spencer, W. A., & Brookhart, J. M. Electrical patterns of augmenting and recruiting waves in depths of sensorimotor cortex of cat. *J. Neurophysiol.*, 1961, **24**, 26–49.

Spencer, W. A., & Wigdor, R. Ultra-late PTP of monosynaptic reflex responses in cat. *Physiologist*, 1965, **8**, 278.

Spencer, W. A., & Kandel, E. R. Electrophysiology of hippocampal neurons. III. Firing level and time constant. *J. Neurophysiol.*, 1961a, **24**, 260–271.

Spencer, W. A., & Kandel, E. R. Hippocampal neuron responses to selective activation of recurrent collaterals of hippocampofugal axons. *Exper. Neurol.*, 1961b, **4**, 149–161.

Spencer, W. A., Thompson, R.. F., & Neilson, D. R. Analysis of polysynaptic response decrement in the acute spinal cat. *Physiologist*, 1964, **7**, 262.

Spencer, W. A., Thompson, R. F., & Neilson, D. R., Jr. Response decrement of flexion reflex in acute spinal cat and transient restoration by strong stimuli. *J. Neurophysiol.*, 1966a, **29**, 221–239.

Spencer, W. A., Thompson, R. F., & Neilson, D. R., Jr. Alterations in responsiveness of ascending and reflex pathways activated by iterated cutaneous afferent volleys. *J. Neurophysiol.*, 1966b, **29**, 240–252.

Spencer, W. A., Thompson, R. F., & Neilson, D. R., Jr. Decrement of ventral root electrotonus and intracellularly recorded post-synaptic potentials produced by iterated cutaneous afferent volleys. *J. Neurophysiol.*, 1966c, **29**, 253–274.

Sperry, R. W., Miner, N., & Myers, R. E. Visual pattern perception following subpial slicing and tantalum wire implantations in the visual cortex. *J. comp. physiol. Psychol.*, 1955, **48**, 50–58.

Sperry, R. W., Stamm, J. S., & Miner, N. Relearning tests for interocular transfer following division of optic chiasma and corpus callosum in cats. *J. comp. physiol. Psychol.*, 1956, **49**, 529–533.

Spinelli, D. N., & Pribram, K. H. Changes in visual recovery function produced by temporal lobe stimulation in monkeys. *Electroencephalog. clin. Neurophysiol.*, 1966, **20**, 44–49.

Spinelli, D. N., Pribram, K. H., & Weingarten, M. Centrifugal optic nerve responses evoked by auditory and somatic stimulation. *Exper. Neurol.*, 1965, **12**, 303–319.

Spong, P., Haider, M. & Lindsley, D. B. Selective attentiveness and cortical evoked responses to visual and auditory stimuli. *Science*, 1965, **148**, 395–397.

Sprague, J. M., & Chambers, W. W. Control of posture by reticular formation and cerebellum in intact anesthetized and unanesthetized, and in decerebrate cat. *Amer. J. Physiol.*, 1954, **176**, 52–64.

Sprague, J. M., Chambers, W. W., & Stellar, E. Attentive, affective and adaptive behavior in the cat. *Science*, 1961, **133**, 165–173.

Stamm, J. S. Retardation and facilitation in learning by stimulation of frontal cortex in monkeys. Pp. 102–125 in Warren, J. M., & Akert, K. (Eds.) *The frontal granular cortex and behavior.* New York: McGraw-Hill, 1964.

Stamm, J. S., & Sperry, R. W. Function of corpus callosum in contralateral transfer of somesthetic discrimination in cats. *J. comp. physiol. Psychol.*, 1957, **50**, 138–143.

Starzl, T. E., & Magoun, H. W. Organization of the diffuse thalamic projection system. *J. Neurophysiol.*, 1951, **14**, 133–146.

Starzl, T. E., Taylor, C. W., & Magoun, H. W. Ascending conduction in reticular activating system, with special reference to the diencephalon. *J. Neurophysiol.*, 1951, **14**, 461–497.

Stellar, E. The physiology of motivation. *Psychol. Rev.*, 1954, **61**, 5–22.

Stepien, I., & Sierpinski, S. The effect of focal lesions of the brain upon auditory and visual recent memory in man. *J. Neurol. Neurosurg. Psychiat.*, 1960, **23**, 334–340.

Stern, J. A., Das, K. C., Anderson, J. M., Biddy, R. L., & Surphlis, W. "Conditioned" alpha desynchronization. *Science.*, 1961, **134**, 388–389.

Stevens, J. R. Electroencephalographic studies of conditional cerebral response in epileptic subjects. *Electroencephalog. clin. Neurophysiol.*, 1960, **12**, 431–444.

Stevens, J. R. Central and peripherical factors in epileptic discharge. *Arch. Neurol.*, 1962, **7**, 330–338.

Stevens, S. S. (Ed.) *Handbook of experimental psychology.* New York: Wiley, 1951.

Stevens, S. S., & Volkmann, J. The relation of pitch to frequency: A revised scale. *Am. J. Psychol.*, 1940, **53**, 329–353.

Stevens, S. S. On the psychophysical law. *Psychol. Rev.*, 1957, **64**, 153–181.

Stevens, S. S. The psychophysics of sensory function. Pp. 1–33 in Rosenblith, W. A. (Ed.) *Sensory communication.* Cambridge: M.I.T. Press, 1961.

Stevens, S. S., & Davis, H. Psychophysiological acoustics: pitch and loudness. *J. acoust. Soc. Amer.*, 1937, **8**, 1–13.

Stevens, S. S., & Davis, H. *Hearing.* New York: Wiley, 1938.

Stevens, S. S., Volkmann, J., & Newman, E. B. A scale for the measurement of the psychological magnitude pitch. *J. acoust. Soc. Amer.*, 1937, **8**, 185–190.

Stiles, W. S. The average colour-matching functions for a large matching field. Pp. 213–252 in *Visual problem of color*, New York: Chemical Publ., 1961.

Stohr, P. E., Goldring, S., & O'Leary, J. L. Patterns of unit discharge associated with direct cortical response in monkey and cat. *Electroencephalog. clin. Neurophysiol.*, 1963, **1**, 882–888.

Stone, W. E. The effects of anaesthetics and of convulsants on the lactic acid content of the brain. *Biochem. J.*, 1938, **32**, 1908–1918.

Stotler, W. A. An experimental study of the cells and connections of the superior olivary complex of the cat. *J. comp. Neurol.*, 1953, **98**, 401–432.

Stratton, L. O., & Petrinovich, L. Post-trial injections of an anti-cholinesterase drug and maze learning in two strains of rats. *Psychopharmacologia*, 1913, **5**, 47–54.

Svaetichin, G. Cone action potential. *Acta physiol. Scand.*, 1953, **29**, Suppl. 106, 565–600.

Svaetichin, G. Spectral response curves from single cones. *Acta physiol. Scand.*, 1956, **39**, Suppl. 134, 19–46.

Svaetichin, G., Laufer, M., Mitarai, G., Fatehchand, R., Vallecalle, E., & Villegas, J. Glial control of neuronal networks and receptors. Pp. 445–456 in Jung, R., & Kornhuber, H. (Eds.) *The visual system: Neurophysiology and psychophysics.* Berlin: Springer, 1961.

Swett, J. E., Bourassa, C. M., & Inoue, S. Effects of cutaneous and muscle sensory nerve volleys in awake cats: a study in perception. *Science*, 1964, **145**, 1071–1073.

Synge, R. L. M. Partial hydrolysis products derived from proteins and their significance for protein structure. *Chem. Revs.*, 1943, **32**, 135–172.

Talbot, S. A., & Marshall, W. H. Physiological studies on neural mechanisms of visual localization and discrimination. *Amer. J. Ophthal.*, 1941, **24**, 1255–1264.

Tasaki, I. *Nervous transmission.* Springfield, Ill.: Charles C Thomas, 1953.

Tasaki, I. Nerve impulses in individual auditory nerve fibers of guinea pig. *J. Neurophysiol.*, 1954, **17**, 97–122.

Tasaki, I., & Chang, J. J. Electric responses of glia cells in cat brain. *Science*, 1958, **128**, 1209–1210.

Tasaki, I., & Davis, H. Electric responses of individual nerve elements in cochlear nucleus to sound stimulation (guinea pig). *J. Neurophysiol.*, 1955, **18**, 151–158.

Taub, E., Bacon, R. C., & Berman, A. J. Acquisition of a trace-conditioned avoidance response after deafferentation of the responding limb. *J. comp. physiol. Psychol.*, 1965, **59**, 275–279.

Tauc, L., & Gerschenfeld, H. M. A cholinergic mechanism of inhibitory synaptic transmission in a molluscan nervous system. *J. Neurophysiol.*, 1962, **25**, 236–262.

Teitelbaum, P. Sensory control of hypothalamic hyperphagia. *J. comp. physiol. Psychol.*, 1955, **48**, 156–163.

Teitelbaum, P. Random and food-directed activity in hyperphagic and normal rats. *J. comp. physiol. Psychol.*, 1957, **50**, 486–490.

Teitelbaum, P. Disturbances of feeding and drinking behavior after hypothalamic lesions. Pp. 39–65 in Jones, M. R. (Ed.) *Nebraska symposium on motivation.* Lincoln, Nebraska: Univ. of Nebraska Press, 1961.

Teitelbaum, P., & Campbell, B. A. Ingestion patterns in hyperphagic and normal rats. *J. comp. physiol. Psychol.*, 1958, **51**, 135–141.

Teitelbaum, P., & Epstein, A. N. The lateral hypothalamic syndrome. *Psychol. Rev.*, 1962, **69**, 74–90.

Teitelbaum, P., & Stellar, E. Recovery from the failure to eat produced by hypothalamic lesions. *Science*, 1954, **120**, 894–895.

Terzuolo, C. A., & Araki, T. An analysis of intra- versus extra-cellular potential changes associated with activity of single spinal motoneurons. *Ann. N.Y. Acad. Sci.*, 1961, **94**, 547–558.

Teuber, H.-L. Perception. Pp. 1595–1668 in Fields, J. Magoun, H. W., & Hall, V.E. (Eds.)

Handbook of physiology, Neurophysiology, **III.** Washington, D.C., American Physiological Society, 1960.

Teuber, H.-L. Brain and behavior. (Summation). Pp. 393–420 in Brazier, M. A. B. (Ed.) *Brain and behavior.* Washington, D.C.: Amer. Inst. biol. Sci., 1961.

Teuber, H.-L. The riddle of frontal function in man. Pp. 410–444 in Warren, J. M., & Akert, K. (Eds.) *The frontal granular cortex and behavior.* New York: McGraw-Hill, 1964.

Thomas, G. J., Moore, R. Y., Harvey, J. A., & Hunt, H. F. Relations between the behavioral syndrome produced by lesions in the septal region of the forebrain and maze learning of the rat. *J. comp. physiol. Psychol.,* 1959, **52,** 527–532.

Thomas, G. J., & Otis, L. S. Effects of rhinencephalic lesions on maze learning in rats. *J. comp. physiol. Psychol.,* 1958, **51,** 161–166.

Thompson, J. M., Woolsey, C. N., & Talbot, S. A. Visual areas I and II of cerebral cortex of rabbit. *J. Neurophysiol.,* 1950, **13,** 277–288.

Thompson, R. The effects of ECS on retention in young and adult rats. *J. comp. physiol. Psychol.,* 1957, **50,** 644–646.

Thompson, R., & McConnell, J. V. Classical conditioning in the planarian, Dugesia dorotocephala. *J. comp. physiol. Psychol.,* 1955, **48,** 65–68.

Thompson, R., & Pennington, D. F. Memory decrement produced by ECS as a function of distribution of original learning. *J. comp. physiol. Psychol.,* 1957, **50,** 401–404.

Thompson, R., & Pryer, R. S. The effect of anoxia on the retention of a discrimination habit. *J. comp. physiol. Psychol.,* 1956, **49,** 297–300.

Thompson, R. F. The effect of training procedure upon auditory frequency discrimination in the cat. *J. comp. physiol. Psychol.,* 1959a, **52,** 186–190.

Thompson, R. F. Effect of acquisition level upon the magnitude of stimulus generalization across sensory modality. *J. comp. physiol. Psychol.,* 1959b, **52,** 183–185.

Thompson, R. F. Function of auditory cortex of cat in frequency discrimination. *J. Neurophysiol.,* 1960, **23,** 321–334.

Thompson, R. F. Role of the cerebral cortex in stimulus generalization. *J. comp. physiol. Psychol.,* 1962, **55,** 279–287.

Thompson, R. F. Role of cortical association fields in auditory frequency discrimination. *J. comp. physiol. Psychol.,* 1964, **57,** 335–339.

Thompson, R. F. The neural basis of stimulus generalization. Pp. 154–178 in Mostofsky, D. J. (Ed.) *Stimulus generalization.* Stanford, Calif.: Stanford Univ. Press, 1965.

Thompson, R. F., Denney, D., & Smith, H. Cortical control of specific and nonspecific sensory projections to the cerebral cortex. *Psychonom. Sci.,* 1966, **4,** 93–94.

Thompson, R. F., & Johnson, R. H. Role of association areas of the cerebral cortex in auditory-visual conditional learning in the cat. *XVIII Int. Cong. Psychol.,* 1966, **1,** 319.

Thompson, R. F., Johnson, R. H., & Hoopes, J. J. Organization of auditory, somatic sensory, and visual projection to association fields of cerebral cortex in the cat. *J. Neurophysiol.,* 1963, **26,** 343–364.

Thompson, R. F., & Kramer, R. F. Role of association cortex in sensory preconditioning. *J. comp. physiol. Psychol.,* 1965, **60,** 186–191.

Thompson, R. F., & Shaw, J. A. Behavioral correlates of evoked activity recorded from association areas of the cerebral cortex. *J. comp. physiol. Psychol.,* 1965, **60,** 329–339.

Thompson, R. F., & Sindberg, R. M. Auditory response fields in association and motor cortex of cat. *J. Neurophysiol.,* 1960, **23,** 87–105.

Thompson, R. F., Smith, H. E., & Bliss, D. Auditory, somatic sensory, and visual response interactions and interrelations in association and primary cortical fields of the cat. *J. Neurophysiol.,* 1963, **26,** 365–378.

Thompson, R. F., & Spencer, W. A. Habituation: A model phenomenon for the study of neuronal substrates of behavior. *Psychol. Rev.,* 1966, **173,** 16–43.

Thompson, R. F., & Welker, W. I. Role of auditory cortex in reflex head orientation by cats to auditory stimuli. *J. comp. physiol. Psychol.,* 1963, **56,** 996–1002.

Tower, D. The neurochemical substrates of cerebral function and activity. Pp. 286–366 in Harlow, H. F., & Woolsey, C. N. (Eds.) *Biological and biochemical bases of behavior*. Madison: Univ. of Wisconsin Press, 1958.

Tower, S. S. The dissociation of cortical excitation from cortical inhibition by pyramid section and the syndrome of that lesion in the cat. *Brain*, 1935, **58**, 238–255.

Tower, S. S. Extrapyramidal action from the cat's cerebral cortex: motor and inhibitory. *Brain*, 1936, **59**, 408–444.

Tower, S. S. Units for sensory reception in cornea; with notes on nerve impulses from sclera, iris and lens. *J. Neurophysiol.*, 1940, **3**, 486–500.

Tracy, W. H., & Harrison, J. M. Aversive behavior following lesions of the septal region of the forebrain in the rat. *Amer. J. Physiol.*, 1956, **69**, 443–447.

Travis, A. M., & Woolsey, C. N. Motor performance of monkeys after bilateral partial and total cerebral decortication. *Amer. J. phys. Med.*, 1956, **35**, 273–310.

Travis, L. E., & Egan, J. P. Conditioning of the electrical response of the cortex. *J. exp. Psych.*, 1938, **22**, 524–531.

Tschirgi, R. D. Protein complexes and the impermeability of the blood-brain barrier to dyes. *Amer. J. Physiol.*, 1950, **163**, 756.

Tschirgi, R. D. Blood-brain barrier, Pp. 34–45 in *The biology of mental health and disease*. New York: Hoeber, 1952.

Tunturi, A. R. Audio-frequency localization in the acoustic cortex of the dog. *Amer. J. Physiol.*, 1944, **141**, 397–403.

Tunturi, A R. Further afferent connections of the acoustic cortex of the dog. *Amer. J. Physiol.*, 1945, **144**, 389–394.

Tunturi, A. R. A difference in the representation of auditory signals for the left and right ears in the iso-frequency contours of the right middle ectosylvian cortex of the dog. *Amer. J. Physiol.*, 1952, **168**, 712–727.

Tunturi, A. R. Anatomy and Physiology of the auditory cortex. Pp. 181–200 in Rasmussen, G. L., & Windle, W. F. (Eds.) *Neutral mechanisms of the auditory and vestibular systems*, Springfield, Ill.: Charles C Thomas, 1960.

Udenfriend, S., Weissbach, H., & Bogdanski, D. F. Increase in tissue serotonin following administration of its precursor 5-hydroxytryptophan. *J. biol. Chem.*, 1957, **224**, 803–810.

Van Deventer, J. M., & Ratner, S. C. Variables affecting the frequency of response of planaria to light. *J. comp. physiol. Psychol.*, 1964, **57**, 407–411.

Vastola, E. F. A direct pathway from lateral geniculate body to association cortex. *J. Neurophysiol.*, 1961, **24**, 469–487.

Vaughan, E., & Fisher, A. E. Male sexual behavior induced by intracranial electrical stimulation. *Science*, 1962, **137**, 758–760.

Velasco, M., & Lindsley, D. B. Role of orbital cortex in regulation of thalamocortical activity. *Science*, 1965, **149**, 1375.

Verney, E. B. The antidiuretic hormone and the factors which determine its release. *Proc. roy. Soc. Series B*, 1947, **135**, 25–106.

Verzeano, M., & Negishi, K. Neuronal activity in wakefulness and sleep. Pp. 108–130 in Wolstenholme, G. E. W. & O'Connor, M. (Eds.) *Ciba Foundation Symposium, The nature of sleep*. London: Churchill, 1961.

Vierck, C. J. Reticular stimulation and generalized drive. *Exper. Neurol.*, 1965, **12**, 109–122.

Vogt, M. The concentration of sympathin in different parts of the central nervous system under normal conditions and after the administration of drugs. *J. Physiol.*, 1954, **123**, 451–481.

Vogt, O., & Vogt, C. Ergebnisse unserer Hirnforschung. *J. Psychol. Neurol., Lpz.*, 1919, **25**, 277–462.

von Békésy, G. The variation of phase along the basilar membrane with sinusoidal vibrations. *J. acoust. Soc. Am.*, 1947, **19**, 452–460.

von Békésy, G. Current status of theories of hearing. *Science*, 1956, **123**, 779–783.

von Békésy, G., & Rosenblith, W. A. The mechanical properties of the ear. Pp. 1075–1115 in Stevens, S. S. (Ed.) *Handbook of experimental psychology.* New York: Wiley, 1951.

von Bonin, G., & Bailey, P. *The neocortex of Macaca mulatta.* Urbana, Ill.: Univ. of Illinois Press, 1947.

von Euler, C. Slow "temperature potentials" in the hypothalamus. *J. cell. comp. Physiol.,* 1950, **36,** 333–350.

von Euler, C., Green, J. D., & Ricci, G. The role of hippocampal dendrites in evoked responses and after-discharges. *Acta physiol Scand.,* 1958. **42,** 87–111.

von Euler, U. S. Autonomic neuroeffector transmission. Pp. 215–237 in Field, J., Magoun, H. W., & Hall, V. E. (Eds) *Handbook of physiology, Neurophysiology.* I. Washington, D.C. American Physiological Society, 1959.

Walberg, F., & Brodal, A. Pyramidal tract fibers from temporal and occipital lobes. *Brain,* 1953, **76,** 491–508.

Wald, G. The photoreceptor process in vision. Pp. 671–692 in Field, J., Magoun, H. W., & Hall, V. E. (Eds) *Handbook of physiology, Neurophysiology.* I. Washington, D.C.: American Physiological Society, 1959.

Wald, G. Retinal chemistry and the physiology of vision. Pp. 15–68 in *Visual problems of color.* New York: Chemical Publ. Co., 1961.

Wald, G., Brown, P. K., & Smith, P. H. Iodopsin. *J. gen. Physiol.,* 1955, **38,** 623–681.

Walker, A. E. *The primate thalamus.* Chicago, Ill.: Univ. of Chicago Press, 1938.

Wall, P. D. Excitability changes in afferent fibre terminations and their relation to slow potentials *J. Physiol.,* 1958, **142,** 1–21.

Walshe, F. M. R. On the mode of representation of movements in motor cortex, with special reference to "convulsions beginning unilaterally." (Jackson). *Brain,* 1943, **66,** 104–139.

Walter, W. G. *The living brain.* New York: Norton, 1953.

Walter, W. G. The electrical activity of the brain. *Scient. Amer.,* 1954, **190,** 54–63.

Walzl, E. M., & Mountcastle, V. Projection of vestibular nerve to cerebral cortex of the cat. *Amer. J. Physiol.,* 1949, **159,** 595.

Wang, G. H. The galvanic skin reflex. A review of old and recent works from a physiologic point of view. Part I. *Amer. J. phys. Med.,* 1957, **36,** 295–320.

Wang, G. H. The galvanic skin reflex. A review of old and recent works from a physiologic point of view. Part II. *Amer. J. phys. Med.,* 1958, **37,** 35–57.

Wang, G. H. *The neural control of sweating.* Madison: Univ. of Wisconsin Press, 1964.

Wang, G. H., & Akert, K. Behavior and reflexes of chronic striatal cats. *Arch. Ital. Biol.,* 1962, **100,** 48–85.

Ward, A. A., Jr. The cingular gyrus: Area 24. *J. Neurophysiol.,* 1948, **11,** 13–23.

Ward, J. W. Motor phenomena elicited in the unanesthetized animal by electrical stimulation of the cerebral cortex. *Ass. Res. nerv. Dis. Proc.* 1950, **30,** 223–237.

Warren, J. M. The behavior of carnivores and primates with lesions in the prefrontal cortex. Pp. 168–191 in Warren, J. M., & Akert, K. (Eds.) *The frontal granular cortex and behavior.* New York: McGraw-Hill, 1964.

Warren, J. M., & Akert, K. (Eds.) *The frontal granular cortex and behavior.* New York: McGraw-Hill, 1964.

Warren, J. M., Leary, R. W., Harlow, H. F., & French, G. M. Function of association cortex in monkeys. *Brit. J. Anim. Behav.,* 1957, **5,** 131–138.

Warren, J. M., Warren, H. B., & Akert, K. *Umweg* learning by cats with lesions in the prestriate cortex. *J. comp. physiol. Psychol.,* 1961, **54,** 629–632.

Webster, W. R., Dunlop, C. W., Simons, L. A., & Aitken, L. M. Auditory habituation: A test of a centrifugal and a peripheral theory. *Science,* 1965, **148,** 654–656.

Weil-Malherbe, H., Axelrod, J. & Tomchick, R. Blood-brain barrier for adrenaline. *Science,* 1959, **129,** 1226–1227.

Weil-Malherbe, H., Whitby, L. G., & Axelrod, J. The uptake of circulating norepinephrine by the pituitary gland and various areas of the brain. *J. Neurochem.,* 1961, **8,** 55–64.

Weinberger, N. M., Velasco, M., & Lindsley, D. B. Differential effects of reinforced and non-reinforced stimuli upon electrocortical recruiting responses. *Psychonom. Sci.*, 1965, **2**, 129–130.

Weiskrantz, L. Behavioral changes associated with ablation of the amygdaloid complex in monkeys. *J. comp. physiol Psychol.*, 1956, **49**, 381–391.

Weiskrantz, L., & Cowey, A. Striate cortex lesions and visual acuity of the rhesus monkey. *J. comp. physiol. Psychol.*, 1963, **56**, 225–231.

Weiskrantz, L., & Wilson, W. A. The effects of reserpine (Serpasil) on emotional behavior of normal brain-operated monkeys. *Ann, N.Y. Acad. Sci.*, 1955, **61**, 36–55.

Weiskrantz, L., & Wilson, W. A. The effect of ventral rhinencephalic lesions on avoidance thresholds in monkeys. *J. comp. physiol. Psychol.*, 1958, **51**, 167–171.

Weiss, B. Morell and Ross's "Central inhibition in cortical conditioned reflexes." *Arch. Neurol. Psychiat.* 1955, **74**, 171–173.

Welker, W. I. An analysis of exploratory and play behavior in animals. Pp. 175–226 in Fiske, D. F., & Maddi, S. R. (Eds.) *Functions of varied experience*. Homewood, Ill.: Dorsey, 1961.

Welker, W. I., Benjamin, R. M., Miles, R. C., & Woolsey, C. N. Motor effects of cortical stimulation in squirrel monkey (*Saimiri sciureus*). *J. Neurophysiol.*, 1957, **20**, 347–364.

Welker, W. I., & Campos, G. B. Physiological significance of sulci in somatic sensory cerebral cortex in mammals of the family *Procyonidae*. *J. comp. Neurol.*, 1963, **120**, 19–36.

Welker, W. I., & Johnson, J. I. Correlation between nuclear morphology and somatotopic organization in ventro-basal complex of the raccoon's thalamus. *J. Anat.*, 1965, **99**, 761–790.

Welker, W. I., Johnson, J. I., & Pubols, B. H. Some morphological and physiological characteristics of the somatic sensory system in raccoons. *Amer. Zool.*, 1964, **4**, 75–94.

Welker, W. I., & Seidenstein, S. Somatic sensory representation in the cerebral cortex of the raccoon (Procyon lotor). *J. comp. Neurol.*, 1959, **111**, 469–502.

Wells, C. E. Modification of alpha-wave responsiveness to light by juxtaposition of auditory stimuli. *Arch. Neurol.*, 1959, **1**, 689–694.

Werner, G. Generation of antidromic activity in motor nerves. *J. Neurophysiol.*, 1960a, **23**, 453–461.

Werner, G. Neuromuscular facilitation and antidromic discharges in motor nerves: their relation to activity in motor nerve terminals. *J. Neurophysiol.*, 1960b, **23**, 171–187.

Wersäll, J. Studies on the structure and innervation of the sensory epithelium of the cristae ampullares in the guinea pig. *Acta oto-laryng.*, 1956, Suppl. 126, 1–85.

West, E. S.. & Todd, W. R. *Textbook of biochemistry*. (3rd ed.) New York: Macmillan, 1961.

Westbrook, W. H., & McGaugh, J. L. Drug facilitation of latent learning. *Psychopharmacologia*, 1963, **5**, 440–446.

Wetzel, A. B., Thompson, V. E., Horel, J. A., & Meyer, P. M. Some consequences of perinatal lesions of the visual cortex in the cat. *Psychonom. Sci.*, 1965, **3**, 381–382.

Wever, E. G. *Theory of hearing*. New York: Wiley, 1949.

Wever, E. G., & Bray, C. W. The nature of acoustic response; the relation between sound frequency and frequency of impulses in the auditory nerve. *J. exp. Psychol.*, 1930, **13**, 373–387.

Whalen, R. E., & Nadler, R. D. Suppression of the development of female mating behavior by estrogen administrated in infancy. *Science.* 1963, **141**, 273–274.

Wheatley, M. D. The hypothalamus and affective behavior in cats: A study of the effects of experimental lesions, with anatomic correlations. *Arch. Neurol. Psychiat.*, 1944, **52**, 296–316.

Whittaker, V. P., & Gray, E. G. The synapse: biology and morphology. *Brit. med. Bull.*, 1962, **18**, 223–228.

Wikler, A. Pharmacologic dissociation of behavior and EEG sleep patterns in dogs: morphine, N-allylmorphine and atropine. *Proc. Soc. exp. Biol.*, 1952, **79**, 261–265,

Williams, D. R., & Teitelbaum, P. Some observations on starvation resulting from lateral hypothalamic lesions. *J. comp. physiol. Psychol.*, 1959, **52**, 458–465.

Wilson, M. Effects of circumscribed cortical lesions upon somesthetic discrimination in the monkey. *J. comp. physiol. Psychol.*, 1957, **50**, 630–635.

Wilson, V. J. Post-tetanic potentiation of polysynaptic reflexes of the spinal cord. *J. gen. Physiol.*, 1955, **39**, 197–206.

Wilson, V. J., & Vernier, V. G. Effect of mephenein on polysynaptic spinal cord reflexes dorsal root potentials, and their potentiation. *Fed. Proc.*, 1955, **14**, 165.

Wing, K. G. The role of the optic cortex of the dog in the retention of learned responses to light: Conditioning with light and shock. *Am. J. Psychol.*, 1946., **59**, 583–612.

Woodbury, J. W. Action potential: properties of excitable membranes. Pp. 26–72 in Ruch, T. C., & Patton, H. P. (Eds.) *Physiology and biophysics.* (19th ed.) Philadelphia: Saunders, 1965.

Woodbury, J. W., & Patton, H. D. Action potential; Cable and excitable properties of the cell membrane. Pp. 32-65 in Ruch, T. C., & Fulton, J.F. (Eds.) *Medical physiology and biophysics.* Philadelphia: Saunders, 1960.

Woodworth, G. S., & Schlosberg, H. *Experimental Psychology.* New York: Holt, 1954.

Woolley, D. W. Participation of serotonin in mental processes. Pp. 176–189 in Rinkel, M., & Denber, H. C. B. (Eds.) *Chemical concepts of psychosis.* New York: McDowell, Obolensky, 1957.

Woolley, D. W., & van der Hoeven, T. Serotonin deficiency in infants as one cause of a mental defect in phenylketonuria. *Science,* 1964a, **144**, 883–884.

Woolley, D. W., & van der Hoeven, T. Prevention of a mental defect of phenylketonuria with serotonin congeners such as melatonin or hydroxytryptophan. *Science,* 1964b, **144**, 1593–1594.

Woolsey, C. N. Patterns of localization in sensory and motor areas of the cerebral cortex. Pp. 193–205 in *The biology of mental health and disease.* Conf. Milbank Memorial Fund. New York: Hoeber, 1952.

Woolsey, C. N. Somatic areas I and II of the cerebral cortex of the chimpanzee. *19th Int. Physiol. Congr., Abst. comm.,* 1953, 902–903.

Woolsey, C. N. Organization of somatic sensory and motor areas of the cerebral cortex. Pp. 63–81 in Harlow, H. F., & Woolsey, C. N. (Eds.) *Biological and biochemical bases of behavior.* Madison, Wis.: Univ. of Wisconsin Press, 1958.

Woolsey, C. N. Organization of cortical auditory system: a review and a synthesis. Pp. 165–180 in Rasmussen, G. L., & Windle, W. F. (Eds.) *Neural mechanisms of the auditory and vestibular systems.* Springfield, Ill.: Charles C Thomas, 1960.

Woolsey, C. N. Organization of cortical auditory system. Pp. 235–258 in Rosenblith, W. A. (Ed.) *Sensory communication.* New York: Wiley, 1961.

Woolsey, C. N. Cortical localization as defined by evoked potential and electrical stimulation methods. Pp. 17–27 in Schaltenbrand, G., & Woolsey, C. N. (Eds.) *Cerebral localization and organization.* Madison: Univ. of Wisconsin Press, 1964.

Woolsey. C. N., & Chang, H. T. Activation of the cerebral cortex by antidromic volleys in the pyramidal tract. *Ass. Res. nerv. Dis. Proc.,* 1948, **27**, 146–161.

Woolsey, C. N., Settlage, P. H., Meyer, D. R., Sencer, W., Hamuy, T. P.,& Travis, A. M. Patterns of localization in precentral and "supplementary" motor areas and their relation to the concept of a premotor area. *Ass. Res. nerv. Dis. Proc.,* 1950a, **30**, 238–264.

Woolsey, C. N., Settlage, P. H., Meyer, D. R., Sencer, W., Hamuy, T. P., & Travis, A. M. Somatotopic organization of " supplementary motor area " of the monkey. *Am. J. Physiol.,* 1950b, **163**, 763.

Woolsey, C. N., Travis, A. M., Barnard, J. W., & Ostinso, R. S. Motor representation in the postcentral gyrus after chronic ablation of precentral and supplementary motor areas. *Fed. Proc.,* 1953, **12**, 160.

Woolsey, C. N., & Walzl, E. M. Topical projection of nerve fibers from local regions of the cochlea to the cerebral cortex of the cat. *Bull. Johns Hopkins Hosp.,* 1942, **71**, 315–344.

Worden, F. G., & Marsh, J. T. Amplitude changes of auditory potentials evoked at cochlear nucleus during acoustic habituation. *Electroencephalog. clin. Neurophysiol.,* 1963, **15**, 866–881.

Wright, R. H., & Michels, K. M. Human processing of olfactory information. In *Bionics symposium*, U.S. Air Force Systems Command, 1963.

Wycoff, R. W. G., & Young, J. Z. The motoneurone surface. *Proc. roy. Soc. Series B*, 1956, **144**, 440–450.

Wyrwicka, W., & Dobrzecka, C. Relationship between feeding and satiation centers of the hypothalamus. *Science*, 1960, **123**, 805–806.

Yasukochi, G. Emotional responses elicited by electrical stimulation of the hypothalamus in cat. *Folia psychiat. neurol. jap.*, 1960, **14**, 260–267.

Yoshii, N., Matsumoto, J., Maeno, S., Hasegawa, Y., Yamagushi, Y., Shimokochi, M., Hori, Y., & Yamazaki, H. Conditioned reflex and electroencephalography. *Med. J. Osaka Univ.*, 1958, **9**, 353–375.

Young, J. Z. Structures of nerve fibres and synapses in some vertebrates. *Cold Spring Harbor Sympos. quant. Biol.*, 1936, **4**, 1–6.

Young, J. Z. Learning and discrimination in the octopus. *Biol. Rev.*, 1961, **36**, 32–96.

Young, W. C. Hormones and mating behavior. Pp. 1173–1239 in Young, W. C., (Ed.) *Sex and internal secretions*, vol. II, Baltimore, Maryland: Williams and Wilkins, 1961.

Young, W. C., Goy, R. W., & Phoenix, C. H. Hormones and sexual behavior. *Science*, 1964, **143**, 212–218.

Zeigler, H. P. Electrical stimulation of the brain and the psychophysiology of learning and motivation. *Psychol. Bull.*, 1957, **54**, 363–382.

Zeigler, H. P. Displacement activity and motivational theory: A case study in the history of ethology. *Psychol. Bull.*, 1964, **61**, 362–376.

Zeman, W., & Innes, J. R. M. *Craigie's Neuroanatomy of the rat.* New York: Academic Press, 1963.

Zimmerman, F. T., Burgemeister, B. B., & Putnam, T. J. Effect of glutamic acid on mental functioning in children and in adolescents. *Arch. Neurol. Psychiat.*, 1946, **56**, 489–506.

Zotterman, Y. (Ed.) *Olfaction and taste.* New York: Macmillan, 1963.

Zubek, J. P. Studies in somethesis. I. Role of the somesthetic cortex in roughness discrimination in the rat. *J. comp. physiol. Psychol.*, 1951, **44**, 339–353.

Zubeck, J. P. Studies in somesthetic. II. Role of somatic sensory areas I and II in roughness discrimination in cat. *J. Neurophysiol.*, 1952, **15**, 401–408.

Zucker, I. Effect of lesions of the septal limbic area on the behavior of cats. *J. comp. physiol. Psychol.*, 1965, **60**, 344–352.

Zwislocki, J. Review of recent mathematical theories of cochlear dynamics. *J. acoust. Soc. Amer.*, 1953, **25**, 743–751.

INDEX